G000154564

—He

Food Lovers'
—Guide to Britain—

1996~1997

BBC BOOKS

The author and publishers would like to thank Food from Britain
for their assistance with this book.

Food from Britain works to promote markets for British food and drink
throughout the world.
In the UK it concentrates on expanding the market for speciality food and drink.
'Speciality' means products which are manufactured using good ingredients, regional or
traditional production skills and imagination – all of which go to produce quality
products with real flavour.
Food from Britain supports a network of regional and county groups whose members
manufacture these products; many of them feature in this book. If you would like further
information on the Speciality Food Programme, please write to:
Food from Britain,
Speciality Food Programme,
London SW1W 9SA

Published by BBC Books, an imprint of BBC Worldwide Publishing,
BBC Worldwide Limited,
Woodlands, 80 Wood Lane,
London W12 OTT

First published in 1993
This revised, updated and expanded version published in 1995
Reprinted 1996
© Henrietta Green 1993, 1995

ISBN 0 563 37092 0

Edited by Lewis Esson
Designed by Ged Lennox
Maps by Eugene Fleury

At the time of going to press all the information given in this book was correct.

All rights reserved. No part of this publication may be reproduced or utilized in any form
or by any means, electronic or mechanical, including photocopy, recording or by any
information storage or retrieval system without permission in writing from the publishers.

Set in Novarese and Frutiger
Printed and bound in England by Clays Ltd., St Ives plc
Cover printed in England by Clays Ltd., St Ives plc

Contents

Foreword

This guide has a very appropriate title. It is for food lovers: people who care about what they eat, who enjoy taste and flavour and who have a deep interest in the way their food is produced. These are the people who have little faith in the technologies that deliver quantity at the expense of quality.

The subtext running through this book needs no underlining by me. The message is simple: intensive factory farming, the use of chemicals in the fields and drugs in the animal sheds are in the short term extremely effective. Things do grow quicker, pigs and chickens mature in half the time, productivity is remarkable. However, treating the production of food as just another industrial activity – like making cars or computers – diminishes it to the level of a commodity. To regard food as a commodity is to deprive it of its traditional cultural and historical role in society. It leads inevitably to thinking of the men and women who produce food as operatives not craftsmen. Farms that were once the foundation of rural communities have become production units and animals mere meat machines.

If you create a fiercely competitive food industry, which is what we have been so successful in doing in Britain, you need not be surprised at the kind of food such an industry turns out. Mass medication of poultry, the use of antibiotics to hasten growth, the feeding of animals on the cheapest possible ingredients and the excesses of mono-culture have created a long-term threat to local and regional food. There is an abundance of food about but it arouses a low level of expectation.

The producers who appear in the pages of this guide have a very different agenda: their activities reflect the growing revolt against uniformity and lack of choice. They are keeping alive the integrity and diversity of food. Much of this food is naturally seasonal; it possesses none of the continuity of supply the supermarkets need to fill their miles of shelves. Much of it is hand-made, hand-reared or hand-grown. In the world of industrial mega-production it may seem anachronistic; but it is not old-fashioned or out-of-date to make fine unpasteurized cheeses that win awards for their flavour or dry-cured bacon that doesn't shrink or splutter in the pan.

Many of the products celebrated in this guide are out of the ordinary but the demand for them suggests there is a hungry market for real and natural food. Ice-creams actually made from cream and free of the emulsifiers and stabilisers we have grown used to; bread baked in wood-fired ovens from properly fermented dough; undyed kippers; meat reared with due regard for animal welfare; hand-raised Melton Mowbray pies; chutneys and preserves without additives – these are the delights which Henrietta has discovered on her second journey of discovery around Britain.

The importance of the food-makers who appear in this book cannot be overestimated; their products have established a benchmark for fine food. Many of them set up their own businesses and learnt how to bake or make cheese by trial and error: a surprisingly large number of them are carrying on old-established firms. All of them are heartening examples of what a refusal to compromise can accomplish in the battle for food worth eating.

Derek Cooper

Introduction

When I wrote the first edition of Food Lovers' Guide to Britain, I hoped that there were Food Lovers who cared enough about the quality of their food to want to read it. I hoped, but I wasn't sure. Well, its success has proved that you do care, so now I offer you the fully revised, updated and – I'm delighted to say – much-enlarged second edition.

Violet, my dog, and I have scoured the country in our search and we have covered thousands of miles discovering new producers and re-visiting established ones. As a born shopper, I cannot begin to tell you how much I enjoy compiling it. Most everyone I met was informative, helpful and welcoming; it makes shopping so much more pleasurable than a trolley dash around the supermarkets' impersonal shelves. Most importantly, though, I was looking for food produced with integrity; by that I mean food with a commitment to taste and texture, made or grown in the 'proper' way with the 'proper' ingredients.

All too often you find farmers, growers or processors who are only too willing to compromise their standards – substituting cheaper alternatives, hurrying along the manufacturing processes – with the result that the eating qualities of their products suffer. These, I hasten to add, are not the producers you will find listed here. What you will find are the producers who instinctively know and care about making the best and the shop-keepers who stock their products. Producing in this way may take more time, as many producers work by hand, in small batches and using the time-honoured methods. They are the crafts-people of the food world and their methods are reflected in their food. They also know that to make good food you must start with good ingredients. For instance, you cannot make good sausages by scrimping and saving on the quantity and the quality of the meat, or bake fruit cakes with poor-grade flour, cheap synthetic fats and hold back on the dried fruit, any more than you can sew a silk purse from a sow's ear.

This year I have also focused on Britain's best bakers, biscuit and cake-makers. As for so many of our foods, in our enthusiasm for the foreign we are in danger of forgetting our own, so I have sought out the traditional bakers who still make the best of our country breads and the myriad baked regional specialities in the way they have been made for generations.

Shopping is the key to good cooking and eating, so I trust you will find this book a mine of information. Use it either in your area, or as you travel around the country-side, or to buy by mail order from the comfort of your home. The treasures I have uncovered exist for your pleasure; to savour and revel in … enjoy them.

All that remains is to thank the farmers, producers and shop-keepers for carrying on making and selling good food, the many kind friends, colleagues and acquain-tances who have pointed me in the direction of new producers and had me (and Violet) to stay in their homes – and above all you, the Food Lovers, for your support, encouragement and suggestions. Please keep them rolling in.

Henrietta Green

How to use this book

Structure

As you can see, I have divided the book first of all into three sections on England, Scotland and Wales. These sections are then further divided by county. Within the counties, there are main entries arranged alphabetically by place-name, boxed entries on certain producers, restaurants, hotels and shops (as well as the occasional recipe) and at the end of each county a 'While You're in the Area' section in which I round up all those other places worthy of mention. London as usual, is the exception as it is arranged by postal district. At the top of each page is a map reference keying it to the appropriate map at the end of the book.

The Maps

These show all the place-names of the entries. The maps are, however, really only meant as a rough guide to location or to help you plan a trip to the various producers within the counties. When on the road I do recommend that they should only be used in conjunction with a good road atlas.

The Entries

At the top of each main entry you will find the full name and address of each producer. Alongside that appear the place-name and products for which I particularly recommend them. You will also see any number of the following symbols alongside the entries:

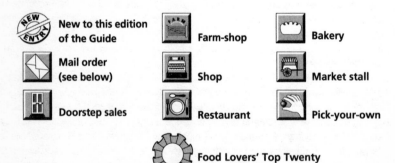

New to this edition of the Guide

Farm-shop

Bakery

Mail order (see below)

Shop

Market stall

Doorstep sales

Restaurant

Pick-your-own

Food Lovers' Top Twenty (see inside front cover)

Mail Order

As so many of the producers are in isolated spots, mail order is a vital part of their business. However, I would like to stress that mail order does not necessarily mean sending food by post, it can mean dispatch by overnight courier or even delivery by their own van: each supplier has their own arrangements. Please also note that not all producers with a mail-order service are prepared to mail order their entire range: when this is the case, I have tried to indicate the available mail-order range at side of the entry.

Stockists

A new feature of this edition is a list of up to five stockists as supplied by the producers themselves – i.e. retail outlets who stock their products. In the margin at the foot of each entry they are listed by county – with national chains listed at the end. If a national chain is listed as a stockist, please remember that not necessarily all branches will carry the products in question. If in doubt, contact their head office or the producer. To find the name and address of the stockists featured, refer to the List of Stockists at the end of the book, which is again arranged by county.

Visiting Suppliers

Where appropriate, I have given opening hours in the main entries. I have gone to great pains to get the latest information in each case, but hours can vary at little or no notice. The same is obviously true of PYO availability, and indeed the seasonality of all fruit and vegetables. Where I have asked you to telephone ahead before visiting, it means that there are no regular and guaranteed opening hours: often there will be someone there, but you should check first to avoid any disappointment.

Indexes

At the end of the book there is a general index listing all the producers mentioned in the book. Following that there is a second more detailed index of the products for which I have recommended each producer – say, for example, you want to scan all the Cheddar-makers, you can find them listed together under cheese. Mail order producers are also clearly indicated in both indexes.

Although I have gone to great lengths to ensure all the information in the book is correct at time of going to press (particularly battling with British Telecom and their seeming constantly changing telephone dialling codes), I do apologize in advance to any reader or producer if there are any inaccuracies, but I cannot accept responsibility for them.

Readers' Reports

If you have any comments – good or bad – on any of the products or services provided by any of the places listed in the book I would love to hear from you. Similarly, if you would like to recommend anyone not listed for inclusion in future editions, please send full details (including the complete name, exact postal address and telephone number with full prefix). Please make your comments as full as possible, to include your opinions of the taste and quality of the product, the service, value for money and the efficiency of the mail-order service, if appropriate, as well as some idea of the date of your purchase. See the inside back cover for the address to which to send your letters. Thank you.

Jekka's Herb Farm

Rose Cottage, Shellards Lane, Alveston, Bristol, Avon BS12 2SY

☎ 01454 418878 **FAX** 01454 418878 **CONTACT** Jekka McVicar – *telephone ahead*

If you go to The Chelsea Flower Show or any of the Royal Horticultural Society's shows in London, you may well have seen Jekka's stand. Her current display looks so appealing – a formal herb garden in miniature, complete with box edging and parterres. If she has not won a gold medal, she jolly well deserves to.

Jekka has been growing herbs commercially since 1984 and now supplies garden centres and nurseries all over the south-west of England, including – further north – Ryton Gardens *see page* 280. You cannot actually visit the nursery (unless by prior arrangement) but you can order from her. Pots of herbs are sent by overnight delivery and they are well enough established to plant straight into the garden.

With the exception of garlic, which she travels to France to collect to be sure of the correct pungency, Jekka propagates all her herbs either from cuttings or from her own seeds and her collection now numbers around 300. Among her particular favourites are cinnamon basil which she uses in stir-fries and lemon basil for scattering in salads. The French tarragon is, she claims, 'an excellent strain with a true flavour' and I was struck by the spicy scent of the caraway thyme's dark green

> — STEWED RHUBARB —
>
> When cooking rhubarb, if you add young angelica leaves you will need less sugar. It is not that the angelica actually sweetens the fruit, but its muscatel flavour cuts through the acidity of the fruit. For every 900 g (2 lb) of rhubarb, add 225 g (8 oz) of angelica stems, the juice and grated rind of 1 orange, 55 g (2 oz) of sugar and about 150 ml (¼ pt) of water and stew until soft. From *Jekka's Complete Herb Book* by Jekka McVicar.

Stockists

Avon: American Museum
- - - - - - - - -
Park Garden Centre

Glos: Bibury Trout Farm

Wilts: Whitehall Garden Centre

leaves; apparently it was once popular in beef dishes. This year she has started growing a range of Japanese culinary herbs and vegetables, including the purple-flowering choi-sum, pak-choi, mizuna and mitzuba.

Published in 1994, her very useful manual *Jekka's Complete Herb Book* gives all the necessary information on propagating, growing and uses, as well as detailed information on the various species.

Mountstevens Ltd
1 *Lower Borough Walls, Bath, Avon* BA1 1QR

☎ 01225 460877 **CONTACT** *Abigail Thomas* **HOURS** Mon-Sat 8.30-17.00
DIRECTIONS *In town centre*

The origins of the Bath bun are a little uncertain. It is thought to have first been served in the Pump Room during the 1670s and it grew in popularity from then on. One theory, no doubt strongly disputed by Sally Lunn's, is that the Bath bun and the Sally Lunn were once one and the same thing, made with the same dough. The Bath bun then acquired its spices and lemon, whereas the latter stayed plain and simple *see below*. To complicate matters even further, there is also a *London* Bath bun; but, as baker Nigel Johns told me, 'on no account is this to be confused with the *Bath* Bath bun. London Bath buns were developed for the Great Exhibition in 1851. They are adaptations, really no more than a fermented rock cake'.

So what is the true Bath bun? Cobb's the bakers in Bath claim the original recipe for 'little cakes the size of a pippin' and, when they were taken over by Mountstevens about five years ago, passed it on. 'In fact, they used margarine and shortening – not very authentic. Those ingredients weren't even around at the time. We have reverted to what we believe to be the right fats – butter and lard – and make it as it should be made'. First yeast, sugar and water are mixed together

Sally Lunn's Refreshment House & Museum, 4 North Parade Passage, BATH BA1 1NX ☎ 01225 461634 fax 01225 469845 *claims to be the oldest house in Bath. You can wander down into the cellars and up to the original bakery, complete with its Georgian range, see the cupboard where the secret recipe for the Sally Lunn bun was 'discovered' or just stop for a cup of tea and one of the eponymous buns.*

Sally Lunn – the bun – is not unlike a brioche and contains butter, eggs, milk, sugar, plain flour and yeast. It has a light fluffy texture that is apparently the result of four provings. As for Sally Lunn, a Huguenot baker, well, who knows for certain whether she ever really existed? It does make for a good story: escaping from religious persecution, she came from France in the late 17th century and started up a bakery in the back streets of Bath.

Even if you hold no truck with the legend, stop and have a bite of history. At the Refreshment House you can eat half a bun served with no end of variations: toasted with Welsh rarebit or Patum Peperium (Gentleman's Relish), or strawberry jam & clotted cream, or brandy butter or even tuna & mayonnaise. If none of the above grabs your fancy, you can always take them home to serve up to your taste.

— BATH BUNS —

An old recipe for Bath buns from *The Observer Guide to British Cookery* by Jane Grigson. Should you want to try them, she does also include a modern – and more practical – version.

'Mix together one quartern of flour and a pound of butter, five eggs and a cup full of yeast and set before the fire to rise. When effected, add quarter pound of sugar mauled fine in an earthern pottle and (add) an ounce of carraways mixed in. Add a little treacle. Make into little cakes the size of a pippen (sic) and place in an iron spider and cover with cloth, to rise. When effected, put on the iron top, cover same with hot ashes and coals and surround with same and bake. These cakes are good with tea. If they are to be sent to a fine gentleman's table, omit the carraways, split and butter and insert berries or fruit and pile same on top.'

---

until it ferments and bubbles 'rather like a liquid slurry'. Then eggs and a little flour are added, and finally the fats, more flour, mixed spices and lemon 'flavouring', which Nigel assures me is 'like the real thing'. Unlike most producers who fiercely guard their recipes as if they were crown secrets, Mountstevens even go as far as to print the 1679 version of the recipe in their shop window.

The true Bath bun is round, relatively wide, decorated with currants and nibbed sugar and baked on top of sugar cubes which soften during baking and are absorbed into the dough. Turn a bun upside down and you can see the neat squares on the bottom; bite into a lump and you get an explosion of crunchy texture. Best eaten when freshly made, they will keep for a couple of days if stored in a cool dry place.

Stockists

Avon: Charlotte's Patisserie
- - - - - - - - -
Mountstevens Ltd

University of Bristol
Department for Continuing Education,
8-10 *Berkeley Square, Bristol* BS8 1HH

BRISTOL
Fungus
Forays

☎ 0117 928 7172   **FAX** 0117 925 4975   **CONTACT** Dr D. J. Hill.

Every autumn, from late September through to the end of October, you can spend a weekend on a fungus foray, courtesy of the Department for Continuing Education at the University of Bristol. These weekends, led by mycologists, are open to anyone at all interested in the subject, be they rank amateur or keen botanist. Each course has a different emphasis, but they all follow more or less the same format of field-work (tramping around the countryside to you and me), lectures and practical identification sessions in a laboratory. The point is to learn how to recognize various fungi and their habitats, with a strong emphasis placed on ecology and conservation. Essential, I would have thought; otherwise we are in serious danger of destroying their very habitats in greedy fevered searches. These are general-interest courses, with edible mushrooms no more than a side-line; but even if you are interested in only collecting ones you can eat, you will find these fascinating weekends.

**CHIPPING
SODBURY**
Bread

Hobbs House Bakery

39 High Street, Chipping Sodbury, Bristol, Avon BS17 6BA

☎ 01454 321629 **FAX** 01454 329757 **CONTACT** *Sam Wells* **HOURS** *Mon-Sat 9.00-17.30* **DIRECTIONS** *In town centre*

Winners of the 1993 Food Lovers' Guide Rosette for Best Baker, Hobbs House Bakery produces bread that is still as good as ever. They have gone from strength to strength, expanding both their range and outlets, but I am delighted to say the quality has not suffered one crumb. Hobbs House has stuck firmly to their bread-making principles of making 'proper' bread in the proper way with slow (and, in some cases, overnight) fermentations, using adventurous recipes and not stinting with the ingredients.

In spite of supplying shops as far away as London, Sam Wells still insists they are no more than country bakers. So you might expect to find the assortment of shapes, sizes and flours of our traditional country breads; and, yes, you will not be disappointed. Every day the shelves of the small high-street shop and the branch shop in the **Yate Shopping Precinct, 2 North Parade** are stocked with bloomers, coburgs, split tins and the like.

However, it is for their 'speciality' breads that I single them out and I am able to report these are just as thrilling. The sun-dried tomato with black olives & pumpkin seeds overflows with thick pieces of the tomato and leaves a lingering savoury-sweet flavour; the black olive, also with pumpkin seeds, has an intense fruity taste, due no doubt to the indulgent amounts of olives and olive oil; and the basil & olive, speckled all over with the herb, has a pleasing open texture and a well-defined taste of basil. There are other favourites: walnut, studded with whole nuts; hazelnut & raisin, moist and plump with its fruits and nuts; and green olive, scattered with sunflower seeds; quern, coarsely milled wholemeal mixed with black treacle; and tiger, fermented overnight and painted with rice-flour paste to give it crunch; and soda bread made, of course, with buttermilk.

New to me is the red onion & Pecorino sardo. Coiled up so it reminds you of a snail's shell, this is a cunning combination of flavours; the sturdiness of the cheese balances the sharpness of the onions – a chunk would go well with a salad of bitter leaves. New to Hobbs House is the pugliese, a large flattish loaf which looks appealingly authentic with its roughly lattice-cut top dusted with flour.

Like any proper Italian bread, it is made with a proportion of semolina and fermented in bulk; the result is an open-textured bread, that tears rather than crumbs, with a lingering deep aroma. Also new are the French baguettes, demi-baguettes and petit pain, made using French flour and techniques; as well as spelt *see Doves Farm Foods page* 21, and mushroom and banana breads.

Hobbs House Bakery is a shining example of a what a small bakery can achieve. Long may they continue to bake.

Mail order

Only sun-dried tomato, Tuscan green olive, red onion & Pecorino sardo, black olive, basil & olive oil, walnut, hazelnut & raisin, and apricot & date breads.

Stockists

Avon: The Fine Cheese Co.

Glos: Gastromania

The Fine Cheese Co.

Wilts: Le Hérisson

Worcs: The Master's Pantry

K. G. Consultants

The Bailiff's Cottage, The Green, Compton Dando,
Pensford, Avon BS18 4LE

☎ 01761 490624 **FAX** 01761 490624 **CONTACT** Keith Goverd – telephone
ahead

Every so often I come across a total enthusiast or – dare I say it – a
fanatic, with whom I could spend several hours learning about his (or
her) passion. Keith Goverd is such a man and he lives, breathes and
drinks apple juices.

Formerly at Long Ashton Research Station, he was made redundant
when the Government 'rationalized' its role – their loss has proved to
be our gain. Now he works as a consultant, advising clients on how to
make ciders, wines, juices and even on restoring orchards or old farm
buildings. His true love, however, is apple juice.

A good apple juice, he sees as, 'as good as a fine wine. First smell
the juice, it should have a whiff of greenness, as fresh as mown grass'.
Then, when first sipping it, there are several characteristics we should
look for. 'The cleanness of the juice is important, otherwise it masks
the flavour; its balance matters – whether it is too sharp or too sweet –
as does its complexity, the build-up of the acidity, aromas and flavour-
notes. Obviously the actual taste is a question of individuality – you
may prefer a light, fresher juice; others go for denser, heavier flavours.
But every juice, every good juice, should have plenty of length of
flavour that lasts in the mouth.'

Keith makes apple juice on a small scale, juicing in a small wooden
press housed in the barn attached to his house. Apples come from
wherever he can find them, 'whenever I walk in an orchard and I see a

---

Steve Downey is a fish specialist and you can find him at **Heritage Fine Foods, Lake-
side, Bridgewater Road, BARROW GURNEY, nr Bristol BS19 1BA** ☎ **01275
474707 fax 01275 474708**. His main business is supplying fish for 'the top boys – the
chefs like Alastair Little, Stephen Bull and Pierre Koffmann', but his mission is to encourage
the public – the likes of you and me – to go for the same quality.

As a nation we are reluctant fish eaters, although a visit to Steve's shop could convince
you otherwise. Prices are reasonable rather than cheap; but the range, quality and freshness is unques-
tionable. With a policy to buy as much as possible direct from the boats, depending on the season you
will see fat scallops from the west coast of Scotland, John Dory, lemon and Dover sole and line-caught
bass caught off Cornwall and Wales. Steve assured me, 'they're literally caught by the rod. One boat
can take about 3 to 4 fisherman each, with 6 to 7 rods. And it's amazing what they can bring back in
a day. The advantages are a better condition, lack of bruising and, of course, peak freshness'.

Behind the shop are tanks full of live native lobsters 'definitely no Canadian', Devon crabs and
freshwater eels from the rivers Itchen and Test. In season you can find wild salmon 'bag-caught, for
minimum stress, from estuaries rather than upstream in the rivers. That's where I believe they're at
their best'. The rest of the year he sells Glenarm salmon, the only fish farmed to conservation-grade
standards.

Steve also sells his 'wild foods'. So at various times of the year look out for samphire, game and a
good selection of wild mushrooms.

variety I fancy, I try to prize it off the owners'. It is not only the actual apple variety that fascinates him, but also where it is grown and the time it is picked: 'Each aspect affects the flavour of the juice: how long you leave the fruit on the tree, the area where it's grown. If you pick a Bramley – which incidentally makes a splendid refreshing breakfast-time juice – early on, it will have a different balance to later in the season. It's due to the degree of oxidization'. To prove his point we sampled two bottles of Falstaff: when juiced the early fruit produces a light green liquid, well-balanced with a tight quiet flavour; on the other hand the well-ripened fruit makes a deeper green juice with an astonishing caramelly raisin-like aftertaste.

According to Keith, any apple can be juiced – some just work better than others. He presses on one day, filters the juice through muslin into a header tank, leaves it overnight to settle then racks it off (bottles it), leaving the sediment behind. All his juices are cloudy, 'I think a clear juice isn't natural. It has to be clarified with a fining agent and then filtered, and is bound to lose some of its intensity'. Of the several that I tried, Allington Pippin is one of which Keith is particularly proud. It has a superb resonance, a deep taste of aniseed, not unlike good old-fashioned peardrops. Alkamene is a new(ish) variety; it is rather dull to eat but drinking its dove-grey juice is another matter. With a full aroma of skins and pips, it is dry to the mouth then opens up to reveal a rich balance of residual sugars. On first sip, Blenheim Orange curiously gave almost an oaty bouquet, but then its taste deepened to a glorious nuttiness. Crimson Bramley, a clearer more golden juice, was tart and sharp with a just a hint of greenness – ideal for a hot summer's day.

Every year the varieties pressed vary and Keith feels he is still experimenting. When I visited he had over 60 different juices, including such glorious names as Cow Apple, Severn Bank and Annie Elizabeth – but if you are a fanatic you are never really satisfied.

Stockists

Avon: The Big Apple

Goodies Delicatessen

Café Fromage

KELSTON
Bath Cheese

Bath Soft Cheese
Park Farm, Kelston, Bath, Avon BA1 9AG

☎ 01225 424139 **FAX** 01225 424139 **CONTACT** *Graham Padfield – telephone ahead*

Until recently Bath cheese was extinct. By that I mean that although locals could tell you about it (some even remembered tasting it), no one was actually making it. Who knows why or how it happened? Perhaps it was because, as a soft creamy cheese, it was difficult to keep; or perhaps it was just another casualty of the conditions imposed on cheese-making by the Milk Marketing Board during the Second World War.

Luckily Graham Padfield was sufficiently curious about the local cheese to do something about it. After researching in the libraries of three agricultural colleges, he found a recipe that works. As a result, for

It beats me how **BATH** *manages to support two flourishing cheese shops when you have a struggle to find even one decent cheese counter in several of our major cities. Here they both are, however, in the centre of town.*

A keen supporter of the small cheese-maker, Ann-Marie Down at **The Fine Cheese Co., 29/31 Walcot Street, BA1 5BN ☎ 01225 483407 fax 01225 483407** *stocks* *at least 100 British cheeses, most of them unpasteurized. One of the first to stock Bath cheese see below, they also sell Mrs Kirkham's Lancashire, the Appleby's Cheshire and several* *more on-farm cheeses. Ann-Marie sees the shop as the place to go for 'informal eating', a one-stop shop for take-aways or picnics; so it is invariably well stocked with meaty pâtés, powerfully flavoured savoury tarts and own-cooked hams carved straight off the bone. Last autumn they spread out into the next-door premises so there is even more space for the olive oils, charcuterie, breads and truffles as big as golf balls made by manager Justin.*

Paxton & Whitfield, 1 John Street BA1 2JL ☎ 01225 466403 *also sells several* *territorial British cheeses. While you are there, pop upstairs to* **Café Fromage ☎ 01225 313525** *on the first floor, which is open six days a week from 9.00 to 17.30. As is only to* *be expected, they specialize in cheese-based dishes. You can try an ever-changing range of soups, warm salads like grilled goats' cheese or blue cheese & avocado, and quiches (broccoli, tomato & Stilton was on the menu the day I visited). During the winter only, they serve a Fondue Neufchâtel with plenty of kirsch. Throughout the year, however, you are certain to find a cheeseboard selection. With as many as seven cheeses from all over Europe, it comes with French bread, pickles and salad.*

the last couple of years he has been making Bath cheese on-farm with the unpasteurized milk from his Friesian herd. How close his is to the original Bath cheese is difficult to estimate. John Arlott in *English Cheese of the South and West* writes, 'it was long popular in the fashionable circles there (Bath) and could be still bought in this century. Originally made nine inches square and an inch deep, its "modern" form was circular, of varying diameters, but still one inch deep. It was a soft cheese, which ripened in a week, white in colour, firm in texture, creamy in grain and its flavour was said to be "piquant" '.

Graham has reverted to the traditional shape and makes his in 10-cm (4-in) squares, but always only 2.5 cm (1-in) deep. He thinks his Bath cheese may be less creamy than the original, as the milk then mostly came from the indigenous breed, the Ayrshire Shorthorn. Unlike Friesians, they are known for their rich milk. His cheeses are ripened for four weeks whereas – contrary to Arlott – Graham thinks the original were kept for three weeks. To add to the confusion John Prince, an agriculturist writing in 1908, said Bath cheeses were only fit to eat, 'when a fine white mould has covered them. (It) will demonstrate its ripeness by spreading on bread as butter does with the aid of a knife'.

Although I find it fascinating digging around for historical comparisons, what is really important is how the cheese tastes. To be honest, the modern version is a little disappointing: springy to the touch and covered in white bloom, its centre is quite compact and its flavour mild, almost bland. I have tried it at least three times and it is inconsistent, so I am inclined to agree with Graham when he admits that 'It isn't quite right – it's not there yet'. As someone who is seriously attempting to revive an extinct food, however, he needs all the encouragement he can get.

Stockists

Avon: The Fine Cheese Co.
- - - - - - - - - -
Paxton & Whitfield

Wilts:
Cheeseboard

TIMSBURY
Cheese

Sleight Farm
Sleight Farm, Timsbury, Bath, Avon BA3 1HN

☎ 01761 470620 **CONTACT** *Mary Holbrook – telephone ahead*

Mary Holbrook is one of my favourite cheese-makers. She farms in the Mendip Hills and from her own unpasteurized goats' and ewes' milk she makes a variety of confident cheeses – each one with a local name. Starting with the goats'-milk cheeses, there is Sleight, a lightly salted, young, creamy and moist cheese with a mild but pronounced flavour in 115-g (4-oz) logs. This is either plain or coated in coarsely ground black pepper, rosemary or crushed garlic and herbs. Ash Pyramid is a more compact creamier cheese, with a flavour described by cheese specialist Juliet Harbutt as 'fermenting fruit'; moulded into 200-g (7-oz) pyramids, it is coated with charcoal. Tymsboro' is a semi-soft, mould-induced round with a hint of sweetness.

Her ewes'-milk cheeses are a soft, crumbly but mild Feta that is matured for up to 6 months; mould-ripened Emlett with a smooth creamy interior that ripens and mellows with age; Little Rydings, a 200-g (7-oz) mould-ripened Coulommiers shape that has a nutty, sweet fullness; and Tyning a superb hard cheese that is matured for 6-12 months. The older this gets, the deeper its rich sweet tangy sheep flavour develops – it is a good cheese that can rival any Pecorino.

Her fans may well have noticed the demise of Mendip, a hard goats' cheese. The bad news is that she has stopped making it for good: the good news is that it is replaced by Tilleys, named after one of her fields. Tilleys has come about partly because Mary was looking for something to do with the spare goats' milk and partly because of a trip to Portugal. Over there a soft ewes'-milk cheese is traditionally made using – and this is the interesting part – the purple stamens from cardoon heads as a starter and coagulator. The idea really excites Mary, 'When I first saw the method, I was so impressed – it's fascinating, so natural. It must be the enzymes in the cardoons that produce the reaction in the milk. The gypsies gather the flower-heads and there are something like 90 different varieties, but they don't necessarily all work. I'm experimenting with some different ones. Theirs is a soft cheese with a crust. When you cut into it, it oozes out, almost as runny as a liquid. And the cardoons also impart a particular flavour. Difficult to describe it's a sort of moderate acidity. But I'm not going to copy the Portuguese exactly, I want to use

Stockists

Avon: The Fine Cheese Co.

London: Jeroboams
Neal's Yard Dairy

Lothian: Iain Mellis

Oxon: The Oxford Cheese Shop

Norwood Farm, Bath Road, NORTON ST PHILIP, *nr* Bath BA3 6LP ☎ 01373 834356 *fax* 01373 834765 *is one of the few approved Rare Breed Survival Trust centres in the country. With 6 rare breeds of pigs, 16 of sheep and 8 of cattle, they offer plenty to look at during the summer months when they are open for visits. The farmshop, where you can buy their meat and sausages, is open all year. Apart from Soay lamb, they tend not to specify the actual breed; a pity, as the different breeds can vary tremendously in texture and taste. 'But', according to owner Catherine Mack, 'most of our visitors are too squeamish to want to know. Anyway a fair amount of our meat is cross-breed'. Stout-hearted customers should ask and she will reveal details.*

my goats' milk instead and, anyway, I don't believe the English would know how to handle a cheese like that'.

At the time of my writing, the cheese may have a name but it does not yet have a definite shape, texture or identity: it is still, very definitely, in the experimental stage. Mary intends to have Tilleys up and running by early autumn, and I find the prospect almost as exciting as she does. It is not often that a new cheese is developed and certainly not one with all the promise that Mary's has to offer.

For a jolly day out, visit **The Kitchen Garden, Oldown Estate TOCKINGTON, nr Bristol BS12 4PG ☎ 01454 413605 fax 01454 413955**. You will find something there for every member of the family. Covering 400 acres of wood and farmland overlooking the river, the Estate offers walks, rides, farm visits, and a 'forest challenge' that boasts 'probably the longest rope slide in the world', as well as the more leisurely activities of picking, shopping or merely eating in their restaurant. In season you can pick-your-own asparagus, runner and broad beans, sugar-snap peas, courgettes, carrots, various lettuces and other salad crops, as well as several varieties of strawberries and raspberries (both main and autumn crops), tayberries, gooseberries, blackcurrants and redcurrants, blackberries, apples and pears.

You can buy ready-picked from their farm-shop, where they also sell jams, jellies, marmalades and chutneys made from their own produce, own-grown potatoes, cakes baked by local ladies, cider, apple juice and sparkling perry from James White see page 248, Cricket Malherbie cream, various cheeses and sausages and Hobbs House bread see page 12 which is delivered on Wednesdays and Saturdays.

While you're in the area...

An old-fashioned butcher, **Bartlett & Son, 10 Green Street, BATH BA1 2JZ ☎ 01225 466731** buy their meat direct from local farms. Expect to find all sorts of bits and pieces, including caul fat, Bath chaps, lamb shanks, cured silverside, kidneys in their suet, ox-tongue and chitterlings (which they no longer make themselves).

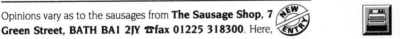

Opinions vary as to the sausages from **The Sausage Shop, 7 Green Street, BATH BA1 2JY ☎fax 01225 318300**. Here, 'a sausage isn't just a sausage – it's an art form'. Everything is made in natural casings on the premises and varieties range from the Champion Aldridge, with pork, egg and nutmeg, to the Vegetarian Waldorf, a mixture of chopped celery, apple and walnut. They also have a shop at **28 The Arcade, Broadmead, BRISTOL ☎ 0117 929309**.

I have heard good reports of the produce from **St Werburghs City Farm, Watercress Road, St Werburghs, BRISTOL BS2 9YJ ☎ 0117 9428241**. In season you can buy a fresh goats'-milk cream cheese, various vegetables (including courgettes, curly kale and garlic), geese, chicken and duck eggs, and lamb, pork and goat.

At harvest-time **Herberts Bakery, 3 Chelsea Road, LOWER WESTON, nr Bath BA1 3DU ☎ 01225 421702** boasts a fetching window display. Throughout the year, you can see the bread baked in the open-plan bakery. Try the creamy overnight-fermented white or the three-seed wholemeal, poppy, sunflower and sesame.

Bedfordshire

**UPPER
STONDON**
Meat

Pure Meat Direct

Rectory Farm, Upper Stondon, Bedfordshire SG16 6LJ

☎ 01462 8515610 **FAX** 01462 8515610 **CONTACT** Bob Birchenall –
telephone ahead

Intensive farming has a lot to answer for. Apart from untold damage to
our environment, the inhumane systems of rearing animals, as well as
the liberal use of chemicals and drugs, the quality of the end-product –
the food on our plate – is often dubious.

Over the last few years there has been a move away from intensive
to extensive and more welfare-friendly meat production. This turnaround is driven by different motives: some people genuinely do not
want animals to suffer unnecessarily – you have only to think of the
outcry and violent demonstrations over crate-reared veal to know this
to be true; others – rightly or wrongly (and I believe rightly, although it
is not quite as simple an issue as it first appears) – believe that a
'happy' animal makes better eating. Yet more people are concerned
about drug-residues in their meat. As a result, various 'alternative'
meat-producing or marketing companies have set up in business. Even
the supermarkets sell meat that is described as 'additive-free', 'traditionally reared' – or whatever marketing descriptions fit. The worry is
that sometimes these marketing claims create an impression of stan-

---

Owner Jennifer Grumbridge of **The Cheese Kitchen, 108 Castle Road,
BEDFORD MK40 3QR** ☎ **01234 217325** *describes her shop as 'a
dairy/vegetarian deli with a few decorative bits and pieces for people who like to
cook'. In the dairy line are several on-farm cheeses, including such staunch favourites as Berkswell see
page 282, Dunsyre Blue, Tornegus see page 262 and Torville. In the deli department are various
fresh dishes, such as vegetable moussaka, 'egg hogs' (a vegetarian Scotch egg made with red lentils,
nuts and herbs) and spinach filo. There are frozen dishes, freshly made salads and excellent focaccia
and olive & sun-dried tomato ciabatta made by a local Italian baker.*

Clophill Fruit Farm, Shefford Road, CLOPHILL MK45 4BT ☎ 01525 861456
fax 01525 861456 *grow the usual range of soft fruit – strawberries, raspberries, red, white
& blackcurrants, gooseberries, tayberries, loganberries and blackberries – for pick-your-own,
ready-picked and picked-to-order. Grower Richard Diss is unusual in that he invariably plants several
different varieties. This year he reckons on about 10 types of strawberries. 'I grow a lot of Elsanta that
are highly efficient. Others for interest and to spread the season. They fluctuate from year to year but
allow picking to potter on through to September'.*

---

dards that, try as you might, you cannot get verified. The standards are
not published, the farms are not open to inspection and you get left
with the slightly nagging fear that all is not quite what it is cracked up
to be.

In its genuine intention to market welfare-friendly meat, Pure Meat
Direct has had a rather chequered history – and that is putting it
mildly. Without wanting to go into all the details, it was launched to
market Conservation-grade meat. This, you should know, is a sort of
halfway house between organic and conventional farming; it sticks to
the principles of lower inputs on the land and better welfare for the
animal but does not insist on land rotation or the banning of pre-
emptive medication.

However, that has all changed. Now Pure Meat Direct has dropped
Conservation-grade meat in favour of the ethically purer Organic (Soil
Association) or Bio-dynamic (Demeter) meat. According to Bob
Birchenall, 'it is the best and purest'. Thus lamb (mainly Suffolk black-
face raised on the edge of Dartmoor) and beef (mainly South Devon-
crossed) both come from selected (and registered) farms in Devon, are
slaughtered in a local abattoir and then sent on to Upper Stondon for
butchering. Pork, on the other hand, is a mixture of Eldon Blue *see page*
122 and organic, and to muddle matters even further all the poultry,
geese, chickens, ducks and turkeys, are reared in Devon to Conservation-grade. Confused? I do not blame you – I am.

To be fair to Bob, I do not think he is deliberately setting out to
muddle us nor does he at any time make any unjustifiable claims for
his meat. However, meat – or rather pure meat – is such an emotive
issue and I do not think it is always made clear what it is we are buying
or why we have to pay a premium price for it. Equally, and I touched on
this earlier, just because an animal has been 'happy' does not necessarily mean it will make you happy when you tuck in. Finishing,
hanging, butchering and storing count here and if he is getting his
meats from different sources, I think it only fair to ask how he maintains a consistency of quality.

Stockists

London: B. & M.
Seafoods

Berkshire

COOKHAM
Traditional
Turkey

Copas Brothers
Lower Mount Farm, Long Lane, Cookham,
Berkshire SL6 9EE

☎ 01628 529595 **FAX** 01628 529512 **CONTACT** Tom Copas – *telephone ahead* **CARDS** *Access, Visa*

Tom Copas is the Chairman of the Traditional Farmfresh Turkey Association and he grows 15,000 birds a year to their rigid standards *see Homewood Partners, page 220* for the Christmas trade. Last year the supermarkets waged a serious turkey price war – some discount stores even charged as little as 25p per pound. Less, dare I admit it, than I sometimes pay for Violet's dog food and about one-tenth of what you have to pay for a TFTA turkey. Even so, do you get value for money?

The point is, do these mass-produced frozen birds have any flavour and texture and how much do a turkey's breed and feed and rearing conditions affect its taste? To find out, on behalf on the *Daily Mail* I conducted a blind tasting with food writer Josceline Dimbleby, Jim Ainsworth, Editor of *The Good Food Guide*, butcher David Lidgate *see page 183* and Caroline Waldegrave, Principal of Leith's School of Food & Wine (where the turkeys were cooked).

And guess what? The overall winner was the TFTA free-range bronze. It came out tops for flavour and texture and looked sensational, with a golden brown, nicely crisp skin and a well-formed breast. As David Lidgate pointed out, 'the test of a true turkey is in the skin as well as the brown and white meat'. It had a deep gamy taste and the skin was superb or as Josceline put it, 'juicy and fatty with great depth of clean flavour'. Next came the barn-reared TFTA white: it was still very moist, if a little milder in flavour. The dark meat came up trumps; gamy and succulent and was pronounced by Caroline as having a 'wonderful and melt-in-the-mouth texture'.

Way down in points came the mass-produced frozen and fresh

birds. At the prices they command there is no denying that they will be intensively reared, pumped with chemicals to counteract stress-related diseases and to make them grow faster, and fed a diet of goodness knows what. They both looked awful, 'Like last Christmas's turkey' remarked Jim.

The frozen one was particularly bad, shrivelled up with a wrinkled, crumpled-up skin that didn't taste very good either. 'Papery with a really horrible bitter aftertaste' said Josceline, which David felt was a sure sign of freezer burn. Obviously one tasting does not necessarily prove the point conclusively, but every time (and I have done it several times over the years) I compare a TFTA turkey – bronze or white – with a conventionally grown, wet-plucked and unhung one, it beats it. Of course, they do cost more, but then for the (supposed) meal of the year, I believe it is worth it. What more can I say?

Tom Copas grows both free-range bronze and barn-reared white birds, ranging from 4-10 kg (9-22 lb). They come oven-ready, with the heart and giblets vacuum-packed, and presented in a box complete with a sprig of rosemary. He takes orders from about September onwards and you can collect from the farm on 23 December, when it is – to put it mildly - 'extremely busy'. He will send by Amtrak all over the country or, failing that, you can contact the Traditional Farmfresh Turkey Association direct on tel 01323 899802 fax 01323 899583 and they will put you in touch with a nearer grower.

Stockists

Berks: Greens Butchers

Bucks: Calves Lane Farm

Glos: Walker

Lancs: Greg Hull

Wilts: Halls Butchers

Doves Farm Foods
Salisbury Road, Hungerford, Berkshire RG17 0RF

HUNGERFORD
Spelt Flour

☎ 01488 684880 **FAX** 01488 685235 **CONTACT** *Clare Marriage* **HOURS** *Mon-Fri 9.00-17.00* **DIRECTIONS** *From Hungerford, take A338 towards Salisbury. Follow the road about 2½ miles. Farm is on the left, about 500 yards after the county sign for Wiltshire.*

Doves Farm call themselves Speciality Flour Millers and they do mill a range of specialist, if not to say unusual, flours. First off is spelt flour; for the uninitiated this is an ancient variety of wheat (*Triticum spelta*) that comes from the same genus as common wheat (*Triticum aestivium*) but has a different genetic structure. Its advantages are a higher protein or

Lurking behind an olde-worlde shop front is the compact **Windrush Wines & Delicatessen, 25 The High Street,** HUNGERFORD RG17 0NF ☎fax 01488 686850. *Open just over a year, Manager Martin Atkins-Byleveld keeps a keen eye out for good British produce and here you will find some of the best of British cheeses – Keen's Cheddar see page 242, Bonchester see page 324 and Mrs Kirkham's Lancashire see page 159. The full range from Innes's see page 246 – both breads and cheeses – is here and among the other British foods are Loch Fyne smoked salmon see page 318, Richard Woodall's bacon see page 62, Duskin's apple juices see page 148 with usually 8 varieties in stock, Fudge's Cheddar Wafers and biscuits for wine see page 92 as well as meaty sausages and locally made filled pastries with fillings of beef in red wine and turkey, ham & mushroom.*

gluten content, a greater concentration of vitamins and minerals, and an intense nutty flavour. With all that going for it, you may wonder why it is not commonly used. One reason is that it's difficult to mill, because of a hard outer husk. With it, however, bread-making is a doddle: you do not even have to knead, rather mix it into a fairly loose dough. It rises miraculously into a light airy loaf with good crumb texture.

Useful for anyone interested in ethnic cookery or following a wheat- or gluten-free diet are gram (chickpea) and brown rice flours. The former, a pale yellow flour, comes from ground chickpeas and is an essential ingredient for onion bhajis and other batters used in Indian and Middle Eastern food. Brown rice flour – not surprisingly a dirty brown in colour – is well known all over the world and is particularly good for certain cakes, biscuits and noodles. Also in the specialist range are maize meal, buckwheat (essential for blinis), rye and malt-house (a blend of wholemeal, soft malted grains and rye) flours and they are all sold in 16-kg (36-lb) sacks or 1-kg (2¼-lb) packs.

The Marriages also both stone-grind and roller-mill organic (to Soil Association standards) and Premium (conventional) flours. These come in a whole assortment of grades, blends and textures; with different 100 per cent organic wholemeals, including a 'strong' from hard wheat for bread-making. Unusually, they also stone-grind unbleached organic white into three grades – strong, plain and self-raising. Clare thinks, however, that whether you choose a stone-ground or roller-milled flour should depend on its end-use as she claims that a roller-milled flour, with its different starch-resistant profile, can actually enhance bread-making. With a total of 19 different types of flour to choose from, any cook should be satisfied.

Stockists

Cornw: Carley & Co.

Leics: Goodness Foods

London: The Health & Diet Centre

Manch: On The Eighth Day

Sussex: Infinity Foods

RISELEY

Spenwood Cheese

Village Maid

The Cottage, Basingstoke Road, Riseley, Reading, Berkshire RG7 1QD

☎ 01734 884564 **FAX** 01734 884564 **CONTACT** Anne Wigmore – *telephone ahead*

Cheese-making is going very well for Anne Wigmore and her husband Andy. For the last year both of them have worked full-time in the dairy, making about 450 kg (1,000 lb) of cheese a week and they even have a couple of part-time helpers 'to turn the cheeses and do the washing-up'.

However, Anne is adamant that only she and Andy make the cheese. She believes it is almost impossible to teach anyone, unless perhaps they spent years with her in the dairy. For, like any craft, you cannot just follow a formula, you have to be aware of the slightest sub-tlest nuances. 'Every day is different. So much can change, the temperature, humidity, the milk itself; and the smallest difference affects the cheese. You've really got to make it yourself or you lose that edge'.

Together they make four cheeses: two are hard, two are soft and

MAP 2   BERKSHIRE   23

There is no doubt that the pies from **The Harrow, West Ilsley,** NEWBURY RG16 0AR ☎ **01635 281260** are home-made. Heather Humphreys rustles them up in her spare time when she is not helping out behind the bar. The latest filling is lamb, apricot, ginger & mint, cooked in Old Speckled Hen, their local strong beer. It makes for a filling meal, with generous chunks of meat and plenty of them, simmered in a rich sauce flavoured with mint and the merest hint of ginger, and covered with a layer of own-made flaky pastry decorated with leaves. Using local game she also cooks hare, wild rabbit, game and venison pies as well as beef & Stilton and steak & mushroom. Baked in foil dishes, they weigh 225 g (8 oz) for one, 675 g (1½ lb) for 2 to 3 portions and 1.25 kg (2½ lb) for 4 greedy guests. Heather will send them anywhere in the country.

As butcher Alan Hayward of **Wm Vicars & Sons, 20 West Street,** READING RG1 1TT ☎ **01734 572904** says, 'if an animal has got it, we sell it', so look out for all the bits and pieces, including cow heel, chitterlings, caul fat, lamb shanks and lambs' and ox tongues (both uncured and cured). Beef – Aberdeen Angus-cross – comes down from Scotland every week, 'it's slaughtered on Thursday, despatched Friday, arrives Sunday. The following week we sell the forequarters and the week after that the better cuts from the hindquarters. And by that time, it's been hung for at least two weeks'. With Mr Hayward a keen shot, game from local shoots is a speciality. In season there is pheasant, woodcock, partridge, hare and pigeon and a chunky game sausage.

they are all from unpasteurized milk. Spenwood, a pressed sheep's-milk cheese is a result of a two-month trip Anne took to Corsica. Lightly pressed and matured for six months, it has that sweet flavour so characteristic of sheep's milk, almost caramelly in its intensity, with a gentle woodiness. Wigmore, also made with sheep's milk, is an unpressed, washed-curd cheese that grows a natural rind. 'It can be very difficult to make, particularly with the fluctuation of temperature and water. If it's too hot, the cheese is too acid and dry. And when it's too cold it takes a while for the starter to get going and the whey won't run enough. The result is a far softer, more moist cheese. It's lovely if we can turn it out quickly, but the shops don't really like handling it'. Nevertheless she perseveres because she really does love her cheeses.

Anne also makes two cows'-milk cheeses. What is particularly interesting about these is that she uses the unpasteurized Guernsey milk from the Duke of Wellington's herd at Stratfield Saye, just down the road. Working with milk with such a high fat content is not easy, in fact a lot of people would say it was well-nigh impossible (it is the dispersing of the fat globules that is the problem) and that there is no such thing as a good Guernsey-milk cheese – that is, until they have tasted Anne's. Wellington, a clear Monet-yellow that Anne insists is natural and is no more than a sign of the milk's richness, is made according to a recipe 'we've messed around with'. Hard-pressed and matured for about 6 months, it is finely textured with a warm buttery afterglow. Waterloo is made on similar lines to Wigmore: it too is curd-washed and matured for 6-8 weeks until it ripens to a mild creamy softness.

All her cheeses are made in her converted dairy next to the house. Wellington is then taken back to Stratfield Saye for maturing in the Duke's cellars; the others Anne keeps in her cheese store. Generally sold in 2.3-kg (5-lb) truckles, Anne also makes them in smaller sizes at Christmas.

Stockists

Avon: The Fine Cheese Co.

Berks: County Delicacies

London: Neal's Yard Dairy

Paxton & Whitfield

Lothian: Iain Mellis

Rock's Country Wines
Loddon Park Farm, Twyford, Berkshire RG10 9RY

☎ 01734 342344 **CONTACT** Hugh Rock **HOURS** Jan to Easter: Mon-Sat 10.00-16.00 Sun 12.00-16.00; *Easter to Christmas:* Mon-Sat 10.00-17.00 Sun 12.00-17.00 **CARDS** *Access, Visa* **DIRECTIONS** *Farm is signposted directly off A4, ¼ mile west of roundabout at junction of A329 and A4.*

Hugh Rock's family has always made country wines and it came to him 'in a blinding flash' one day in 1981 that this was what he wanted to do. 'Until then most country wines were like dessert or fortified wines – very sweet. I thought it would be nice to try to make fruit wines in a similar style to a table wine – lighter, drier and very fruity.' And now he produces around 100,000 bottles a year.

The wine-making takes place during hectic summer months when the fruit is in season. 'Over the years we have built up contacts with fruit growers all over the country. The secret is to choose good fruit in the first place – and use plenty of it.' All his wines are made more or less on the same principle and, as he points out, 'like a grape wine'. First the fruit is crushed and left to macerate in a solution of yeast, sugar-water and grape concentrate 'to get the whole thing going'. As the alcohol content rises, the flavour and colour is drawn out of the fruit and after about 3 weeks, when the ferment has finished, it is ready for maturing in tanks. The length of time varies – lighter wines mature no more than a couple of months, others for a year. At bottling most fruit wine-makers add sugar, and plenty of it. Hugh, aiming for a drier subtler wine, holds back. Sugar not only sweetens but also masks the fruit flavours, the very opposite of what he wants to achieve.

Some wines, such as strawberry and raspberry, are ready to drink within weeks. 'Think of them like a Beaujolais, best drunk when fresh and young. They're not ones that benefit from maturing, with their up-front fruitiness.' Others can change dramatically if kept, 'Plum, made with yellow egg plums that are useless for eating but have a terrific flavour in drink, is best opened after it has matured for a year. So is the gooseberry. We use the bullet-hard green ones that ooze with taste. After keeping, they develop shade and subtleties that I really enjoy'.

What sets Hugh's wines apart is their balance. Elderflower, made with his own flowers, has a pleasant lushness; elderberry, kept back for 3 years, is rather sultry; and blackberry offers a surge of sweet fruit rounded off with a sharpness. If you visit Hugh at his winery, you are welcome to taste his full range.

Stockists

Derbys: Chatsworth Farmshop

Glos: The Organic Shop

Lancs: St Anne's Wine Store

London: Alana Wholefoods

Lothian: Real Foods

While you're in the area...
Friday, Saturday and Sunday between 10.00 and 13.00 locals know to drive to **Brunning Hams at Brunning Ham Farmshop, Heath Ride, FINCHAMPSTEAD, nr Wokingham RG40 3QJ ☎ 01734 733287** for Mrs Brunning's milk loaf plaits, moist honey roast or plain boiled hams and mustard-marinated boned saddle of pork.

Buckinghamshire

Astwood Village Smokery
Swan Cottage, Astwood, Buckinghamshire MK16 9JS

ASTWOOD
Smoked
meats

☎ 01234 391523 **FAX** 01234 391660 **CONTACT** *Christine Basson – telephone ahead*

After 25 years in the food packaging industry, dealing with hi-tech plastic injection moulding, Christine Basson was inspired to start smoking food by an article in *The Times*. At first it was a question of 'seeing what happens', using her favourite restaurant as a guinea pig, then slowly expanding, even 'hocking the Range-Rover' to be able to afford to bring her unit up to scratch and comply with the food regulations. So a career move happened and she was in business.

The way Christine smokes her food is very different from the traditional British method, where either smoke-holes or kilns are used. She uses an American kettle-style smoker that looks like one of those free-standing round-topped waste-bins you often see in shopping centres. A layer of non-carcinogenic charcoal is laid on the bottom and brought to white ash heat, then a pan containing a water-based marinade is suspended above it. The food is stacked on racks over the pan and chunks of hardwood (mainly hickory or apple, although she sometimes uses beech or oak) soaked in water are added to the hot ash.

With no vents to control the heat, the unit is completely enclosed. The marinade heats up and turns into steam and as it rises is soaked up by the food. Density of smoke is all-important, as is temperature – it is 'hot-smoking with a difference, based on the Chinese method. And they've been doing it for 3,000 years'. Anyone who has seen the mouth-watering film '*Eat, Drink, Man, Woman*' should at least recognize the principles. Who could ever forget the father blowing into the duck to inflate it, before a delicate tea-smoking?

The timing varies depending on what ingredient Christine is smoking: a chicken may take about 5 hours, a poussin no more than

3. The flavour depends both on the marinade placed in the smoker and the glaze she paints on the food, and she varies both. The marinade could be water mixed with red wine and herbs or Guinness or white wine; and the glaze could be mandarin, cranberry, redcurrant, rosemary & orange or plain olive oil, although she thinks 'plum is best. It sticks like a blanket and turns the skin a dark red'. Thus the food is assaulted with flavours on two fronts as Christine explains, 'the marinade steams into the meat and causes it to hold its own juices while taking up the marinade's flavours. The glaze is absorbed on the outer surface giving it a sweetness. And the overall result is moist and ultra juicy'.

I tried chicken washed with no more than olive oil and it was remarkably moist, with a lightness and woodiness – far more complex and juicy than conventionally hot-smoked chicken. The duck, smothered in its blanket of plum, had a sweet overlay that complemented rather than battled the meatiness of the duck. To further assault your taste-buds, Christine also stuffs chicken and poussins. Boned chicken, for instance, comes with a choice of fillings: garlic, chestnut purée, herbs & wholemeal breadcrumbs; apple, raisin, chicken liver & wholemeal breadcrumbs; and sage, onion, thyme & wholemeal breadcrumbs. These combined with the marinades and glazes strike me as possible over-kill, but her technique is so different that perhaps I am prepared to give her the benefit of the doubt.

 With 75 *acres of pick-your-own*, **Copas Brothers, Calves Lane Farm, Billet Lane, IVER SL0 0LX ☎ 01753 651175 or 652727 (***recorded information service***)** *have plenty of vegetables and fruit. The season starts in May, with both PYO and ready-picked asparagus, followed by strawberries, gooseberries and broad beans. In July they have a whole range of old-fashioned cherries that span the season, including Early Rivers, Napoleon Bigarreau, Gautier Bigarreau, the dark juicy Bradbourne Blacks, Merton Glory and Merton Bigarreau. Later on, from August through to October, come runner beans, sweetcorn, Opal, Czars, Victoria, Marjorie Seedlings and meaty Giant Prune plums and apples. As both here and Lower Mount Farm in Cookham see page 20 are owned by the same brothers, you can also order and collect a Traditional Farmfresh Turkey for Christmas.*

CHESHAM	**R. Waller**
Aylesbury Duck	Long Grove Wood Farm, 234 Chartridge Lane, Chesham, Buckinghamshire HP5 2SG

☎ 01494 772744 **FAX** 01494 772744 **CONTACT** *Richard Waller – telephone ahead*

It was food writer Michael Raffael who first put me on to Richard Waller, the only remaining commercial producer of the pure-bred Aylesbury duck. The Aylesbury has had a chequered history. Once highly sought-after there were plenty of small-scale 'duckers' in and around the town, keeping them as a side-line and every farm-worker ran a small flock.

> *It is for his cockerels that I seek him out, although, as the company name suggests, Tony Evans of* **Tony Evans Turkeys, Olney Park Farm, OLNEY MK46 5EJ ☎fax 01234 711392** *is better known for his turkeys. He rears about 1,000 Cob cockerels for the Christmas trade, although he sells them frozen during the rest of the year 'until they're all gone – usually some time in June'. Raised in open straw yards, his cockerels are slaughtered at between 12 and 14 weeks old, when they weigh in at around 4.5-5.5 kg (10-12 lb). Hung for between 5 and 6 days, they have a good deep flavour with a surprisingly easy-textured flesh – a welcome relief from the usual dull broiler chicken.*

Then nobody seemed to want them, they were too large for the restaurants, too fatty, or so some people thought, or – worse still – had no meat at all. 'That was the fault of the breeders, the ones who bred them for show', Richard told me, 'Sure they would get points for the shape of the beak and its colour, but you take the feathers off and there was damn all to put on the table'.

The bloodline of Richard's ducks goes back to the 1770s, when the family first kept them, but his ducks – with their well-covered breasts – have obviously never been 'improved'. Now he is delighted to see the fashion has come full circle, the restaurants are crying out for them again. The Bell at Aston Clinton considers a 2.3-2.5-kg (5-5½-lb) bird as a good meal for two.

Richard tends a flock of about 2,000 ducks which produces around 300 ducklings a week that are 'matched, hatched and dispatched within eight weeks'. An Aylesbury duck is easily recognizable by its white feathers, flattened shape and keel, and a beak 'as pink as a lady's thumbnail'. Once the ducklings are hardened off, they live outdoors, although they are shut in at night. Believe it or not, according to Richard, they do not like the wet and go indoors to shelter from the rain. 'They'll swim on a pond all right, but they do not like the wet on their backs. It washes away their waterproofing.'

Fed a specially formulated commercial feed 'with no drugs', Richard insists, 'but with wheat for a light coloured flesh and a firmer fat, and a little barley. Too much and it makes their fat very loose', he slaughters them in the traditional way by wringing their necks. They are dry-plucked, waxed and then hung uneviscerated for 48 hours, although he does admit that, if pushed, they sometimes stay in the chiller for only 24 hours, but never less than that. Sizes vary: some weigh around the 2.3-2.5 kg (5-5½ lb) mark, but more usually they are 2.7-3 kg (6-7 lb) oven-ready, 'enough to feed four people well'.

If you've never had a true Aylesbury, you have a treat in store. They are well-fleshed, with a thin layer of fine-flavoured fat that is hard and solid, 'more like the consistency of beef than pork'. If it is soft, according to Richard, it is not a true Aylesbury. The meat is significantly pale (almost the colour of pork), soft and remarkably tender (with virtually no grain) and a pronounced gamy flavour. As for the cooking, Richard never pricks his skin 'it's crisper that way. And you don't need to, somehow the fat always finds its way out of the pores'.

Stockists

Bucks: Mayo Bros

W. J. Morris & Sons

Herts: Arthur Rickett

Middx: Hilton & Family

Drive through the entrance and park by the front lawn. In front of you, by the house, is the barn where Robert Stevens of **Warrington House Farm,** WAR-RINGTON, *nr* **Olney MK46 4HN** ☎ **01234 711464** *sells own-grown fruit and vegetables. Here you will find ready-picked asparagus bundled into small, medium and large grades; globe artichokes from May right through to the first frosts; ready-picked soft fruit in season (you can, should you want, also pick your own); various vegetables, such as spinach, broad beans, bunched beetroot with their tops, mange-tout peas, sugar-snap peas and courgettes; and, if you ring to warn him, Robert will specially cut baby courgettes with their flowers. He also sells various jams made with their own fruit, turkey meat and sausages from Tony Evans see page 27 and his and other locally reared cockerels, weighing anything from 1.8-6.3 kg (4-14 lb).*

While you're in the area...

Buckingham Nurseries and Garden Centre, Tingewick Road, BUCKINGHAM MK18 4AE ☎ 01280 813556 fax 01280 815491 sell a small selection of old English and cider apple trees. New to them this year is Court Pendu Plat, which they describe as 'valued from Roman times as a dessert apple and decorative tree. Yellow fruit with light-red flush; rich strong fruity pineapple flavour, still intense in February. Excellent late keeper and prolific cropper'.

Sophie Webb of **Sophie's Chocolates, 3/4 The Gatehouse, Elgiva Lane, CHESHAM HP5 2JD ☎ 01494 782999** learnt her trade at Lessiters. Using Belgian couverture, she makes neatly finished chocolates. Café au lait, a foil-wrapped cone piped with a coffee-flavoured milk chocolate had a satisfying coffee intensity. Less successful was the brightly coloured pink champagne truffle, made with a fresh cream ganache, pink champagne and a touch of colouring. Like most of our chocolatiers, Sophie assumes all her customers have a very sweet tooth.

Cambridgeshire

River Farm Smokery

Junction Wilbraham Road & A1303, Bottisham,
Cambridgeshire CB5 9BU

☎ 01223 812577 **FAX** 01223 812319 **CONTACT** David Carter **HOURS**
Mon-Sat 10.30-18.00

River Farm Smokery has smartened up considerably since my last visit.
There is a spanking new shop painted a brilliant white and manned by
David Carter. Followers of the previous edition of this guide may
remember I mentioned that owner Roger Enoch 'admits neither to
liking nor being terribly good at dealing with the public'. Well, I can
assure you that he and David Carter are as alike as chalk and cheese.
David, charming and co-operative, positively blossoms when a customer hoves into sight.

One of the River Farm products that first drew my attention was
smoked pike. I first found it several years ago in Constable country and
was impressed by its gelatinous texture and light meat flavour – but it
is a rare delicacy nowadays and not regularly stocked by David. Equally
sad is the news that most of the Fenland eels that Roger used to
smoke are shipped out live to Holland – presumably because the
Dutch are prepared to pay for them. He does occasionally get a few,
but most of the time has to buy in frozen eels from New Zealand,
which actually work out cheaper. Seems absurd does it not? Absolutely
ridiculous that eel sent halfway round the world still can cost less than
ones caught in your own back-yard.

In the three kilns that he built himself, loosely based on the Torrey
smoker (their advantages are the vented smoke boxes that make the
heat and smoke easy to control), Roger smokes salmon, halibut,
kippers, the occasional yellow-fin tuna, pheasant, chicken, pigeon and
duck breasts. A recent development is the Bottisham ham. Inspired by
the Bruges ham, it is first wet-cured in a cider-based brine, then

Stockists

Cambs: Provender Stores

Essex: D. R. Earey & Son

Great Bardfield Stores

Suffolk: E. W. King & Sons

Fay's Delicatessen

cooked through and finally lightly smoked 'often no more than hung up overnight over the dying embers'. The result is a moist and succulent meat overlaid with a punch of smoke. I was not entirely convinced, but then I am no great addict of smoke flavour. If you are, I can quite see it could become very addictive. They also sell fresh fish and, provided you give them 24 hours' notice, can get anything straight from Lowestoft. In addition there are Cottage Cooking *see page* 109 mustards and sauces, organic herbs from The Herbary Prickwillow in Prickwillow near Ely, Rick's chilli sauce made by a friend's son in Brixton and stone-ground wholemeal flour ground by The Windmill at Swaffham Prior.

ELY
Bread

Pretzels Continental Bakery
Unit 3, Lancaster Way Business Park, Ely, Cambridgeshire CB6 3NW

☎ 01353 669575 **FAX** 01353 669575 **CONTACT** Tina Magdalinski – *telephone ahead*

Pretzels, run by Tina Magdalinski, started as a small bakery on an industrial estate in Cambridge supplying local retailers. Now they occupy a 1,100 sq metre (12,000 sq ft) unit in a business park and supply the likes of Safeway, Waitrose, Tesco and Boots. However, if you ring in advance and warn her you are coming, Tina is still more than happy to sell direct to you.

What makes her bread and rolls different is the imaginative use of ingredients as flavours. As a self-taught baker, Tina is not hide-bound by convention or received knowledge as to what can or cannot work. Sometimes this can be a mixed blessing: some of the more ferocious flights of fancy I have sampled over the years defy description; but never, I had better hastily make clear, at Tina's. What her bread does suffer from, perhaps, is a lack of definite texture; it is still a little too flabby for my liking.

She is forever dreaming up new ideas. On the grounds that, 'everyone makes sweet muffins', she has come up with savoury muffins. Actually I think this is a bit of a misnomer; they are far more like loose aerated baps. The only thing that might faintly remind you that they are muffins is the shape, the top is slightly domed and puffs up (marginally) over the base. The texture is more bread than muffin; in fact they are made from an unkneaded bread mix and if you press them they do squidge down, certainly more a characteristic you would expect from a bap than a muffin. Having dealt with that, they do have a certain charm. The cheese & spinach looks rather inviting, with ribbons of dark green and a positive cheese flavour; the cheese & onion has a pleasant salty tang and the orange-red tomato, herb & olive a thorough pungency. Also new and in a similar choice of flavours are the Baker's Dozen, 13 differently flavoured dinner rolls joined together in a circle and, as Tina puts it, 'aimed at the dinner-party trade'.

Stockists

Boots

Budgen

Safeway

Tesco

Waitrose

MAP 5 CAMBRIDGESHIRE 31

C. E. Brown

Southlawns, Main Street, Shudy Camps,
Cambridgeshire CB1 6RA

SHUDY CAMPS

Game

☎ 01799 584461 **CONTACT** Colin Brown – telephone ahead

Game dealer *par excellence*, Colin Brown is – according to his wife – 'a law unto himself and very fussy with his game'. Dealing from behind his cottage, Colin supplies A. Waller *see below*, some Cambridge colleges and good restaurants in the area. Most of his game comes from local-ish estates. Grouse is a different matter. It is brought halfway by a Yorkshire game-dealer friend and they meet *en route* to do a swap.

The eating quality of game depends on many factors: age, sex and condition of the bird or animal, temperature and length of time hung, and plucking and dressing. Colin picks over everything he is offered and his experience enables him to distinguish immediately between old and young game. Young birds he recommends roasting, whereas older game generally gets sold for casseroles and stews.

As for hanging, it is done to his customers' preferences. Some like a milder bird, but others request it 'so it walks out the door'. Everything is superbly dressed and, in season, Colin sells grouse, pheasants, partridges – young English (grey) or the more common French (red-legged), partridge, woodcock, wood pigeon (either breasts only or whole birds), mallard, widgeon, teal and snipe. Golden plover is a very rare treat but 'we used to have them when it was wetter'. Hares weigh about 3 kg (6½ lb); under that, Colin dismisses them as leverets (immature hares) or just 'very poor hares'. He also has rabbits, venison in a variety of cuts. He also sells own-made juicy game sausages (made from mixed game, eggs and a bit of rusk) and a chunkily cut game pie mixture – again from a selection of mixed game.

Whatever is not sold, Colin freezes while still in prime condition. So out of season he can be relied on to have game birds in his freezers.

Stockists

Cambs: A. Waller & Son

Barker Bros

Caitlin & Sons

Cousins & Sons

Essex: Bretts' Farm Shop

Good old-fashioned butchers are not that easy to find. **A. Waller & Son, 15 Victoria Avenue**, CAMBRIDGE CB4 1EG ☎ **01223 350972** have been established for 75 years and are still going strong. Here you will find a definite emphasis on service; they butcher to order and deliver free in Cambridge and its surrounding area.

No longer slaughtering at the back of the shop, they still buy their meat where there is an emphasis on 'good finishing'. Like all proper butchers, they know that for meat to have flavour it must come from good stock, be well-reared, be properly hung and a have good marbling and 'covering finish of fat'. Breed – of beef in particular – is all-important and they select Hereford crossed with a Continental as a winning combination. Lamb comes from Lincolnshire and is always hung for a minimum of 4 days when it is still spring lamb. As the season progresses they hang for longer 'to relax the meat'. Waller sell own-cooked haslet, a pungent savoury loaf made with pigs' fry and sweetbreads; a range of sausages, including a Royal Cambridge invented in Jubilee Year with a 75 per cent meat content and a 'secret' seasoning; pork & herb for a 'Lincolnshire flavour'; and a juicy long-linked coarse Cumberland with a robust flavour punched with salt; and for Burns' Night (25 January) they make their own well-spiced haggis. Game, once hung and plucked on-site, is now bought in oven-ready from C. E. Brown.

Downfield Windmill
Fordham Road, Soham, Ely, Cambridgeshire CB7 5BG

☎ 01353 720333   **CONTACT** Nigel Moon   **HOURS** Sun 11.00-17.00   **DIRECTIONS** *From Ely, take A142 towards Newmarket. After about 12 miles, at the junction with A1123, take the 3rd exit off the roundabout, signposted Downfield Mill. Mill is about 100 yards on the left.*

'Milling', according to the late Tom Stobart in *The Cooks Encyclopedia*, 'is reducing to a powder or paste. The most primitive method is pounding, and since such creatures as different as otters and vultures have learned to use stones as tools, it is probable that man learned to pound grain even before he could grow it'.

Fast-forward several millennia and you find it was no longer just enough to mill grain; the end-product – the flour – had to be refined. Coarse flour simply would not do. 'Progress in milling', continues Mr Stobart, 'was aimed mainly towards producing a whiter, finer flour. Special bolting cloth was woven for fine sifting, but that only separated the large particles from the small. However, a machine called the purifier, invented in the early years of the 19th century, enabled particles of the same size but different weights to be separated, as was possible by winnowing, on currents of air. It allowed a greater proportion of the husk (the bran) to be taken out of flour in large-scale milling.'

Before that, most milling took place on-farm in mills conveniently placed near the fields where the grain was grown; but these mills did not have the through-put to justify the huge expense of new machinery; a small-scale miller could not afford it. If you wanted refined flour, it had to be sent off to larger mills, invariably situated in the towns. The decline of the small-scale mill was inevitable and one by one they fell out of use. According to Nigel Moon, in the 1850s, Soham – no more than a tiny dot on the map – boasted as many as seven windmills and one water-mill – now only his mill remains in working order.

Of course, fashions do change. Where white flour for white bread was once sought after and commanded a price premium, now, on the grounds that it is nutritionally superior, it is the turn of wholemeal flour. Even better is stone-ground wholemeal flour. This is because if you grind with stones – as opposed to rollers – you grind at a lower temperature and speed and are therefore less likely to destroy the flour's nutritional goodness. I like to think that it is as a direct result of this turnaround that once-derelict mills have been restored to working order. All over the country you can visit them and buy their flour.

Downfield Mill is now bang in the middle of a housing estate, 'although I don't worry too much as I was here first' and he operates it on an irregular basis, milling two to three times a week. From here he produces two ranges of organic (Organic Growers and Farmers registered) flour. One is made with 100 per cent English wheat, the other is a mixture of ⅔ English and ⅓ North American strong wheats. These both come as 100 per cent wholemeal, 85 per cent brown, and 75 per

Stockists

Cambs: Daily Bread

Naturally Yours

Leics: Elliot

Leicester Wholefood Co-op Ltd

Paul's Tofu

Staffs: Innes

cent white. He also produces a 100 per cent conventionally grown wholemeal, organic oatmeal, barley and rye and a non-organic maize.

Although he will send flour by post, it is not very cost-effective.

Naturally Yours
The Horse & Gate, Witcham Toll, Ely, Cambridgeshire CB6 2AB

WITCHAM TOLL
Fresh Meat and Poultry

☎ 01353 778723 **FAX** 01353 778723 **CONTACT** Pam Finn **HOURS** Mon-Fri 8.00-21.00 Sat & Sun 11.00-17.00 – *telephone ahead*

When I wrote about Naturally Yours in the last edition, I expressed certain reservations about their welfare codes. It was not that I questioned how they reared their animals, more a matter that at the time Pam and Roland Finn did not belong to any recognized group, nor did they publish the standards to which they farmed. Since then I am delighted to say that they have applied for Soil Association (full organic) registration. This does not necessarily mean that their meat is any different or better; rather, once they are registered, they will be farming to known standards and will be independently inspected. Then they should have no trouble justifying their claims and you can buy with complete confidence. Incidentally, the other changes are that they have switched to an organic-based feed, have new cutting and preparation rooms, have extended their coldstore and freezer capacity and added a smoke room. Obviously they mean business.

Currently their meat and meat products are sold under the banner 'Additive-free Food Produced Slowly & Carefully for your Health & Enjoyment'. They tend to keep to traditional or rare breeds, apart from lamb 'which is mostly Charolais and not old-fashioned in any shape or form', and Cob chickens, 'the commercial ones'. Theirs, however, are fed 'proper grain', reared outdoors, slaughtered at about 84 days and hung for a week for a deeper fuller flavour. At Christmas-time they have 'hefty big birds with a dressed weight of 10 pounds' and outdoor-reared Norfolk Black turkeys, 'the poults come from Dedham Rare Breed Farm. Dry-plucked by hand, they weigh anything from 8½ to 18 pounds and we also have a few to sell at Easter'. Friend and ex-restaurateur Jack Lang pronounced his 9-kg (20-lb) bird, 'Delicious with a real sort of gamy texture. I had always been led to believe Norfolk Blacks were scrawny little things but mine had a surprisingly deep and full breast'.

Lamb and beef from pure-bred Herefords or British White are reared by local farmers to the Finn's specifications, but about 95 per cent of the pork is home-reared. 'We use a variety of rare breeds – Berkshire, Saddleback, British Lop, Gloucester Old Spot and Middle White, all crossed with our Old Spot boar.' Sold in a variety of cuts, from leg on the bone to belly joint, I have Jack Lang again to thank for pointing out the ham hocks, 'they're a particular bargain. I roast them long and slow as a *hahnschen* in the Bavarian-style. One hock is enough for at least two and, like all their meat, it is excellent quality and well-butchered'.

They also make various sausages and Pam – a former cookery teacher – prepares ready-to-cook dishes ranging from chicken ballotine to faggots with onions & gravy. They also sell a variety of game 'mostly shot overnight by the local farmers' and have started smoking their own bacon as well as pigeon, haddock, cod and kippers. Violet, my Yorkshire terrier, was thrilled with the enlarged Pets' Corner. Mince, with 20 per cent organic 'middlings' (bran and small particles of flour) she had already tried but was avid for marrow bones and – new to her – baked pigs' ears. They also stock most of Downfield Mill's flours *see page 32* and a selection of Rosebud jams *see page 304*.

The Finns will deliver as far afield as Horsham in the south and Grantham in the North, and across the country from Milton Keynes to the sea. 'Most people,' Pam told me, 'like to come and check us out before their first order and we always welcome visitors. After that, they place an order and we're away. And I'm almost always here at the end of the phone to discuss what's what.'

While you're in the area...

Converted from an old piggery, **Chaplin Farm Shop & PYO, off Doggett Lane, FULBOURN CB1 5BZ ☎ 01223 880722** is a father (Adrian) and son (Miles) operation. There is PYO fruit, starting with strawberries in late May closely followed by raspberries, gooseberries and red and blackcurrants. Miles makes small batches of jams from their fruit and Adrian bakes a firm nutty bread on a more or less daily basis, using flour from the Maude Foster Mill in Boston.

Just off Station Road, **Rosemary Dyer, Millfield, WILLING-HAM, ☎ 01954 231257** 'does herbs', supplying pots of the 'usual parsleys, mints, rosemarys' as well as salad burnet, rocket, French tarragon and a few unusual vegetable plants, such as chilli pepper.

Chivers jams are no longer made by the Chivers family, they sold out to Schweppes in the early '60s and concentrated on fruit-growing. A few years ago Caroline Chivers converted an old barn and started **Chivers Farm Shop, IMPINGTON, nr Cambridge, CB4 4PJ ☎ 01223 237799**. *The result is very pleasing, as once again the Chivers family are making jams from their own fruit. They are made off the farm, but, to keep a consistency, each producer makes a particular jam to a recipe laid down by Caroline. These include strawberry, a fruity-fresh raspberry and a dense blackberry. They sell fruit ready-picked, pick-your-own and – throughout the year – frozen. Last year saw the addition of loganberries and tayberries to the collection of the more usual strawberries, raspberries, gooseberries, blackberries, redcurrants and blackcurrants. Look out for Chivers Delight, an apple bred by Caroline's great-grandfather, with a light juicy flavour. You can also buy it as a juice; generally it is blended with Bramley for a well-balanced fresh flavour with good length. They also grow Worcester, Fiesta, Royal Gala (a colour sport of Gala, with a redder skin), Egremont Russet and pears such as Conference, Comice, Williams and a sweet, juicy and grainy Beurré Hardy. There are greengages, damsons and plums, including Victorias and another of great-grandfather's successes, the meaty-fleshed Chivers Seedling.*

They also sell lots of fruit tarts, pies, fudge made by local ladies, who also produce Christmas cakes and puddings. With an accent on East-Anglian products, they also stock Mrs Elizabeth King's pork products see page 212, and Les Fines Herbes' flavoured vinegars and jellies see page 170.

Durig Swiss Patisserie
4 Broomfield Lane, Hale, Altrincham, Cheshire WA15 9AQ

☎ 0161 928 1143 **CONTACT** Mrs Durig **HOURS** Tues-Sat 9.00-17.00
DIRECTIONS *Turn off M56 at Junction 6, signposted Hale. Follow signs into Hale for 2 miles. Where road divides at cenotaph, take left fork into Broomfield Lane. Shop is on the left at the end of the lane.*

More than just a *boulangerie*, Durig follows in the Continental tradition of trebling up as a *chocolatier* and *confiserie* (confectioner). France, Belgium and Switzerland are rich in such shops. The good ones are Aladdin's caves, or the gourmet's equivalent, with every item '*de la maison*'. If any criticism is to be voiced it is for their indulgence in kitsch taste; you know the sort of thing – 'cute' fluffy toys in lurid colours clutching trays of chocolates wreathed in reams of Cellophane. Who, I long to know, actually buys them?

Alas in Britain we have precious few such shops (with or without the kitsch) which makes Durig all the more remarkable. Rumour has it that Mr Durig, fast approaching retirement age, longs to sell up and retire to the mountains of his native Switzerland. Let us hope that when he does his successor keeps up the standards that, under the strict supervision of Mrs Durig, show absolutely no sign of slipping.

Everything here is made on the premises and, incidentally, sold unadorned. There are some very good breads and cakes. Latest additions include a couple of Saturday specials: *pissaladière*, a 25-cm (10-in) olive oil dough round crowned with onions, tomatoes, anchovies and olives; and on the same base, *coca* from Spain, with its mound of onions and red and green peppers. Both can be picked up on a Saturday morning, hot and straight out of the oven. Buttery – if a little bready – croissants are baked daily, as are Linzertorte, Sachertorte and a forest cake of hazelnut sponge with praline and fresh cream.

All their breads are made up at lunch-time and left to prove overnight for a 'light fermentation'. I was intrigued by the fennel bread baked in a gugelhopf mould (a round mould with a hole in the centre). Recommended by Mrs Durig for breakfast, it contains sultanas, ground hazelnuts and fennel seeds 'for an odd explosion in the mouth'. More conventionally there is a very Swiss muesli bread that toasts a treat; walnut bread made from a mixture of wholemeal and rye and walnut quarters; and a sour dough made with mainly rye and a small percentage of wheat flour. At Christmas, the Swiss in Mr Durig gives rise to immense and carefully constructed honey-cake houses; but you will also find own-made Christmas, figgy and ginger puddings.

He also makes traditional hand-made chocolates. I have often felt that with the craze for Belgian, we tend to overlook the merits of Swiss chocolates. With years of experience to hand, Mr Durig makes a point of using only 'the real thing. If kirsch is used, it is kirsch. And the best possible couverture'. The range varies: at Christmas he goes in for 60-cm (2-ft) high moulded Santa Clauses; at Easter there are giant bunnies or named eggs filled with his chocolates. However, you can always expect to find some splendid dark milk and Cognac (made with Cognac and cream) truffles, smooth pralines, and bitter-sweet mint crisps.

The Durigs also produce various frozen cooked dishes and frozen mini vol-au-vent cases, ideal for drinks parties when all you need do is whip up a filling. Ranked above the freezer cabinets are rows of bottles, jars and packets filled with their own preparations. These include various fruit vinegars (damson is the new flavour), vinaigrettes, dried stuffings, a horseradish sauce mix of finely ground breadcrumbs and dried horseradish to blend with cream for a pungent sauce, various chutneys, and flavoured rices made with an American long-grain rice mixed with dried apricots, onion, celery and thyme, or mushroom & bay leaf, or herbs or spiced biryani.

<table>
<tr><td>

TABLEY

Geese and Ducks

</td><td>

Holly Tree Farm Shop
Chester Road, Tabley, Knutsford, Cheshire WA16 OEU

</td></tr>
</table>

☎ 01565 651835   **CONTACT** *Karol Bailey*   **HOURS** *Tues-Sat 9.00-19.00 Sun 10.00-18.00*   **DIRECTIONS** *Turn off M6 at Junction 19, signposted Knutsford/A556. At roundabout, take exit signposted Knutsford. After about 50 yards, farm is signposted on the left.*

Karol Bailey rears around 1,000 Danish hybrid stock geese a year for Michaelmas through to the New Year. Kept out in the fields and grass-fed with a ration of corn, they have a pale flesh, a mild gamy flavour and a moist creamy texture. Once the birds have been hung for between 7 and 10 days, they are hand-plucked, wax-dipped for a clean, smooth finish, dressed with the livers, gizzard, heart and neck and a bag of goose fat stuffed inside the bird's cavity and left unsewn to make stuffing easier.

Using her geese, she prepares a Goose Banquet Roll from a whole

MAP 4 CHESHIRE 37

boned goose rolled around layers of turkey & ham or turkey & pheasant filled with one of her home-made stuffings. A roll can weigh from 3.5 to 6.8 kg (8 to 15 lb). She also brines the breasts and legs in a salt solution mixed with dry sherry, ginger and soy sauce for about 5 days and sends them off to Mooreland *see page* 38 for smoking. Succulent with a chewy texture, the meat has a sweet/sharp resonance, with the merest hint of smoke. Be warned, however, the breasts come with a thick layer of fat that defeated even me, although the flavour of the skin is excellent, buttery and extremely rich. I also liked her smoked goose sausages. Karol mixes the minced goose with pork, herbs and salt, stuffs them into natural skins, hangs them for 1-2 days and sends them off to Mooreland as well. The result is coarse-textured with a full rich taste – excellent for a cassoulet; in spite of how she describes them as a slicing sausage, I think they do need cooking.

Out in her fields she also rears lamb and several sorts of (but mainly Peking-cross) ducks, which are sold weighing 1.8-3.5 kg (4-8 lb), oven-ready or turned into a Duck Banquet Roll. She sells pork reared from 'reputable sources' specially for her and prepares a range of over 18 sausages. Some work better than others. In spite of Karol trying to convince me otherwise, I could not get to grips with turkey & pineapple – the combination was frankly awful, with an acidic sweetness and feeble-flavoured meat. Pork with chopped fresh green & red peppers, on the other hand, proved a cunning combination; if you grill the sausages, the peppers catch and the sausages resound with a glorious charred taste.

No mean cook, Karol prepares stuffings made with fresh ingredients and sold frozen in tubs: there is apricot & parsley, rosemary & orange, thyme & lemon, spicy plum, celery & walnut, and apple (using fruit from her orchard) with celery & almonds. Apart from Christmas-time, most of her produce is frozen; there is some fresh, but not necessarily the complete range. If you let her know you are coming, however, she will do her best to supply you.

Just inside one of **CHESTER'S** main city gates is **The Cheese Shop, 116 Northgate Street**, **CH1 2HT** ☎ **01244 346240** run by Carole Faulkner. A small narrow shop with a cheery blue-and-white striped blind, it has a cellar underneath which gives Carole the advantage of being able to mature cheese. It is a good shop to browse in; every cheese is carefully flagged with a good description of its flavour as well as details of its maker, and tasters are cheerfully given to curious customers. Crammed full with over 100 British cheeses, it has several Welsh cheeses – Penbryn see page 383, Teifi see page 381, Lady Llanover see page 381, Llanboidy see page 383, Tyn Grug see page 392 and Chris Duckett's Caerphilly see page 237 which is actually made in England.

'Up here, they like white cheese', Carole informed me, 'and they're very particular about their Cheshires'. She stocks a buttery 15-month-old Appleby's see page 229 and two pasteurized versions – a crumbly Bournes and a creamy Windsors. There is a fresh goats' cheese with the lightest of tangs made by a lady 'over the other side of the river' and farmhouse butters from Bournes and Appleby's as well as a strong well-salted Welsh version. Mooreland page 38 smoke cheeses for Carole and she makes various chutneys as well as venison and Stilton & walnut pâtés with plenty of bite. Recently Carole has opened a second branch at **1 King's Court, ALTRINCHAM WA14 2RE** ☎ **0161 929 7760**.

> *Cheshire cheese is still made on-farm in the county and the bordering lands of North Shropshire see also Appleby's page 229. Two farms,* **Hares & Son, Millenheath, HIGHER HEATH, nr Whitchurch, Shropshire** *SY13 2HX* ☎ **01948 840288** *specializing in mature Cheshire and* **H. S. Bourne, The Bank, MALPAS SY14 7AL** ☎ **01948 770214,** *can be visited.*
>
>   *Both sell their cheese and blocks of whey butter; but remember to take a cool bag with you as, if left in the warm, whey-butter turns cheesy – some might say rank – very quickly.*

Mail Order

Please note that this service is only available from H. S. Bourne.

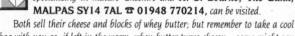

WILMSLOW

Smoked Foods

Mooreland Foods

Vost Farm, Morley Green, Wilmslow, Cheshire SK9 5NU

☎ 01625 548499 **FAX** 01625 548606 **CONTACT** John Ward **HOURS** Mon-Fri 8.30-17.30 Sat 10.00-17.00 **CARDS** Access, Eurocard, Mastercard, Switch, Visa **DIRECTIONS** From Wilmslow, take the A538 towards Altrincham. Turn left at the signpost for Morley Green. The shop is at the Morley Green junction on the right.

Mooreland – curers and smokers of fine foods – is a real family business. John's grandfather started it when, returning from Canada having vainly sought his fortune in the gold rush, he went to work at the Amalgamated Bacon Smokers in Cheetham Hill. Then he moved to Stockport and on to Mellor in the Derbyshire borders, where he set up his own business on-farm until a couple of years ago, when son John and his son Darren moved to the current premises.

Out front is the smokehouse/shop with hams hanging from the beams. It sells the Mooreland range as well as a few well-chosen regional foods, including Womersley Fruit & Herb Vinegars *see page* 312, bread from The Village Bakery *see page* 57 and jams & jellies from Wendy Brandon *see page* 378. Out back are the brand-new processing rooms and the three 6-m (18-ft) high, 2-m (7-ft) deep smoke-holes that look as if they have been in use since Granddad's day. 'They're built to his design. But before you can start using them you have to fire them off. It took us weeks. It's like seasoning a wok, unless it's properly done the food won't cook properly. In an unseasoned chimney, it doesn't get a true smoked flavour and comes out all wishy-washy.'

Apparently Cheshire is 'one big pig area. But the hardest job is selecting the right animal. For bacon we need a bit of cover (fat) and we end up rejecting so much. Most pork is either too lean or too watery or both. We find the right size with the right fatness comes from Large White-Landrace cross'. When they can get them, the Wards also buy rare-breed pigs such as Tamworths, Berkshire and Gloucester Old Spot. 'We do charge a little more for their products and the meat can contain more fat – we say good cover – but you will find the flavour to be excellent and superior to other breeds.'

Whatever the breed, the pork is processed in the same way. Slaughtered off-site, it comes to the unit for butchering. Then the meat is dry-cured in a mixture of salt, sugar and saltpetre. 'Just rubbed in, in the good old-fashioned way, and left to stand. Once cured and hung to dry, there is a weight loss of around 20 per cent of the original weight.' Now most commercial or large-scale curers inject their meat with a brine solution of up to 20 per cent of its original weight, pumping it up with polyphosphates and goodness knows what else. Darren even told me of a manufacturer using potato starch. This solution is absorbed by the meat although, curiously enough, legally they only have to declare 10 per cent added water. 'Of course, it makes it very difficult to compete on price. They only have to declare 10 per cent but, if you think about it, we are actually 40 per cent down. But then our bacon doesn't weep, splutter and shrink in the pan.'

With a range of punchy and firm bacons, all with a good blast of flavour, I particularly liked the gentle sweetness backed with obvious meatiness of the honey-cured rindless back. First it is dry-cured, then soaked in honey and finally lightly smoked. If, however, you prefer yours unadorned then go for the plainer Cheshire dry. I was pleased to find it in chunky blocks of streaky, ideal for cutting up into lardons. The hams are equally impressive: dry-cured bone-in weighing around 8 kg (18 lb), they are cured for about 5 weeks, and matured for around the same length of time. You can order one unsmoked or smoked (which is done over two sessions, each for about 24 hours). There is also York ham, butchered in a long cut that 'traditionally takes in the oyster' and Mooreland ham 'like Granddad used to do. It's dry-cured for 6 to 8 weeks, soaked in honey, molasses and a few spices for about a month, then matured for almost a year. Think of it as an air-dried Bradenham and, with its golden skin, it does look as if it's been smoked – but it is raw. The secret lies in the maturing; temperature and humidity are all-important'. Subtle and sweet with what I can only describe as a meaty clean taste, it had a chewy texture with a good length of flavour and is sold as whole hams or in 225-g (8-oz) and 115-170-g (4-6-oz) packs.

The Wards are also developing a range of sausages or, as they call them, charcuterie. There are various fresh sausages, including pork with coriander & garlic and a robust Cheshire *saucisson sec* made with a chopped coarse pork, garlic and wine, that is filled into natural skins, soaked in brine and air-dried for 8 to 9 weeks. They cure and hot-

Stockists

Ches: Grantham's Grocers

- - - - - - - - -

The Cheese Shop

Derbys: Chatsworth Farmshop

London: Fortnum & Mason

Sussex: The Weald Smokery

A passion for good British food has spurred on Steve Gouldthorpe to start **Gourmet Portfolio**, **Henrwst Smithy**, **HIGHER WYCH**, *nr* **Malpas SY14 7JR ☎ 01948 780379**. *Anyone living within the South Cheshire, North Shropshire, North Wales triangle can expect regular deliveries of meticulously chosen produce. Only the very best qualifies for inclusion: cheeses matured by Neal's Yard Dairy see page 180, honey from Struan Apiaries see page 352, oatmeal from Donald MacDonald see page 342, Wendy Brandon preserves see page 378, fudge from the Toffee Shop see page 58 and cakes from Mrs Gill see page 83 and much more, with prices the same as charged by the producers themselves. At Christmas-time there are hampers imaginatively filled with things everyone really wants to eat as opposed to jars and tins that inevitably end up languishing on the shelves.*

smoke pork loin for a mild kassler; cure topside of beef in red and white wine, bay leaf and cloves for a bresaola that packs a salty punch; and hot-smoke, always over oak chippings mixed with beech, all manner of things, including guinea fowl, duck breasts, turkey and chicken. One smoke-hole is dedicated to fish. Here they leave their salmon for 24 hours, resulting in a juicy, lightly salted and lightly smoked fish, and also produce smoked haddock, trout, eel and tuna.

  At **Tatton Park in KNUTSFORD WA16 6QN** *there is plenty to do. You can wander through the grounds and park, visit Home Farm with its rare-breed pigs, explore the rather severe stone-clad house or simply shop at* **The House-keeper's Store ☎ 01565 654822 fax 01565 650179** *in the converted stable-yards. Unlike several food shops at tourist attractions, this one is worth visiting; it has made a real effort to stock local foods, even selling its own produce.*

Tatton frozen venison from the fallow deer you can see grazing in the Park is always on sale, butchered into steaks, médaillons, and bone-in or boned legs. If you want it fresh or butchered into saddles, haunches or half carcasses, you have to order in advance. They usually sell sliced smoked venison cured in port, juniper berries, orange and herbs to give a sweetish tang, as well as a meaty potted venison also with a sweet aftertaste due, this time no doubt, to the addition of redcurrant jelly .

Bacon and ham from their own rare-breed pigs is cured by Mooreland Foods see page 38 and has a satisfying layer of fat and a pleasant porky flavour. There are plenty of cheeses: Windsors Cheshire, Sandhams Lancashire and Bonchester see page 324, Cheshire Farm ice-cream, preserves by Welsh Mountain Garden see page 395 and a local honey.

While you're in the area...

 With a small rear room for maturing, **The Cheese Hamlet, 706 Wilmslow Road, DIDSBURY M20 2DW ☎ 0161 434 4781** keep Green's Cheddar until 16 months old. There is a good selection of Dale cheeses and also stocks of Mooreland's bacon and sausages *see page 38.*

 Open seven days a week from mid-June to mid-August, **Belle Vue Fruit Farm, GUILDEN SUTTON, nr Chester CH3 7EJ ☎ 01244 300220** sells pick-your-own and ready-picked soft fruit, including various strawberries and raspberries, red, white and blackcurrants, tayberries and Whitesmith gooseberries.

 Haworth's Fruit Farm, Eddisbury Farm, Yeld Lane, KELSALL CW6 0TE ☎ 01829 751188 has several varieties of strawberries and raspberries; various plums, including Early Rivers, Victorias and Damsons; and a good range of apple varieties. They also sell jams and crumbles and pies made with their own fruit.

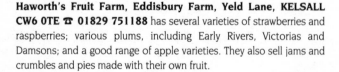 Open for more than two years, **Banarberries Delicatessen, 11 Little Underbank, STOCKPORT SK1 1LA ☎ 0161 4740511** 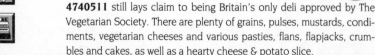 still lays claim to being Britain's only deli approved by The Vegetarian Society. There are plenty of grains, pulses, mustards, condiments, vegetarian cheeses and various pasties, flans, flapjacks, crumbles and cakes, as well as a hearty cheese & potato slice.

Cleveland

Map No. 6

Twizells
Gilly Flatts Farm, Bishopton, Stockton-on-Tees,
Cleveland TS21 1HH

☎ 01740 630111 **CONTACT** *Philip Twizell – telephone ahead*

In an area that can hardly be described as brimming over with small-scale quality food producers, Philip Twizell of Twizells comes as a welcome relief. He runs his own breeding unit of Large White Landrace-cross pigs and every week sends about 100 piglets off to slaughter – and every week about 10 come back to him for processing. It is not, as Philip admits, the easiest of livings, 'Don't get me wrong, I like it and I even make a profit on the processing. It's just that in this area, up here, price is the big thing. People want quality but at a price. And there's no great big market for really good food – not like down South'.

Butchering is done on-farm and he wet-cures the legs for ham for about 3 weeks; middle cuts are dry-cured in salt and demerara sugar for about 2 weeks, hung for about a week and sliced into a gently sweet, firmly textured bacon. The rest – more or less, he sells a little fresh pork – goes into his sausages. These are made in small batches in natural or collagen skins with a medium-coarse texture and a meat content of around 70 per cent. Flavours include Cumberland with 90 per cent meat, farmhouse (a plain chunky pork), leek, apple, spicy with herbs, tomato and garlic.

Stockists

Cleve: Kelsey's Butchers

Dur: Partners

Yorks: Ken Warne

Lewis & Cooper Ltd

Hay's Caterers of Richmond

While you're in the area...
Pop into **Tim Turnbull's Live Lobsters, 5 Dundas Street West, SALTBURN-BY-THE SEA TS12 1BL** ☎ **01287 624834** for live lobsters and crabs, and, in season, wild salmon net-caught in the North Sea. These can weigh anything from 1.5 to 12.2 kg (3½ to 27 lb) but, as Tim Turnbull's is really a wholesaler, expect to clean and gut your fish – it is not a service they offer the public.

BOYTON
Tala Cheese

Heather White
North Beer Farm, Boyton, Launceston, Cornwall PL15 8NR

☎ 01566 785607 **CONTACT** *Heather White – telephone ahead*

Milking sheep and using that milk for cheese was, until recently, a forgotten craft. Apparently it died out in this country about 200 years ago. As Quentin Seddon wrote in a recent edition of *Country Living*, 'Mechanisation of the wool industry at the beginning of the Industrial Revolution, the enclosure movement, then supplies of butter and cheese from New Zealand, all contributed to the disappearance of sheep's cheeses'. I cannot tell you how satisfying I find it that they are now being revived.

Heather White makes Tala with the unpasteurized milk of her small flock of sheep. In a tiny dairy attached to the Cornish farmhouse, she works on a very small scale in a 140-litre (30-gallon) vat. Once the milk has been renneted and started, the curds are cut and washed in warm water. This not only removes the whey and reduces the acidity but also gives the cheese a distinctive – almost caramelly – taste. The cheeses are moulded, pressed for about 20 hours, left to dry for 1 day and finally brined for 1 day. The small 400-g (14-oz) cheeses mature for about 8 weeks; the 2-kg (4½-lb) truckles for about 5 months, until they develop their mild, light, grassy flavour backed up by its sweetness.

Stockists

Devon: Natural Life
- - - - - - - - - -
Ticklemore Cheese

London: Fortnum & Mason
- - - - - - - - - -
Jeroboams

Lothian: Clark's Specialist Foods

Ough's, 10 *Market Street*, LISKEARD PL14 3JJ ☎ 01579 343253 *is under the new management of Robert Creber, ex Crebers of Tavistock. Run by an informal marketing group, United Cornish Producers (Unicorn), it aims to sell as much Cornish produce as possible from its original old wooden counters, shelves and glass-fronted cabinets. Here you will find own-cooked hams, Merrivale charcuterie see page 49, sausages from Tywardreath, Cornish Yarg see page 50, Menallack see page 48 and Tala see page 42 cheeses, saffron cake from the Chapel Bakery in St Keyne, clotted cream and clotted cream butter from Barbara Lake see page 44 and lots more.*

Heather has also just started having the small size smoked over oak, a practice with which I have never had much sympathy as frankly I cannot see the point. Why wreathe a perfectly good cheese in smoke and obscure its flavour? Evidently not everyone shares my opinion and Heather's did win a gold in the smoked class at the 1994 British Cheese Awards.

The Cornish Smoked Fish Company
Charlestown, St Austell, Cornwall PL25 3NY

CHARLESTOWN
Smoked
Mackerel

☎ 01726 72356 **CONTACT** *Martin Pumphrey* **HOURS** *Mon-Fri 8.00-17.00 (Whit to end-Sept also open Sat 10.00-12.00)* **DIRECTIONS** *From St Austell, take A390 towards St Blazey. Follow the road about 1 mile to the third round-about just off the bypass and take the third exit off the roundabout, signposted Charlestown. After about ½ mile, take the first exit off the mini-roundabout and smokery is on the left.*

The Cornish Smoked Fish Company faces out on the old port of Charlestown. Nowadays it is a veritable tourist-trap, although the port was once busy with cargoes of tin, china clay and, of course, fish – mainly mackerel – but no fish is landed here any more. Martin Pumphrey uses some Cornish mackerel for smoking, depending 'on the run (catch) and size of the fish. We need quite large mackerel, between 1½-2 pounds, the ones caught around here are usually much smaller,

---

Stein's Delicatessen, 8 Middle Street, PADSTOW PL28 8AR ☎ **01841 532221 fax 01841 533344** *is compensation for anyone who cannot get a table at – or who cannot afford to go to – **The Seafood Restaurant**. Both are run by the talented (and modest) Rick Stein and his wife Jill. The restaurant is a temple to fish, the deli sells Rick's food-to-go at to-go prices.*

The savouries are cooked in the restaurant's kitchen and you can rest assured they will be good. New this year are beef bourguignonne and navarin of lamb, both sold baked in a crock with a puff pastry top; squid & octopus salad, mackerel escabèche, and salad niçoise. The old favourites are still here: pasties bulging with fillings like pork, apple, onion and sage or cheese & leek; fish with leek dressed in a buttery emulsion with a hint of tarragon; and hearty chunks of steak mixed with peppery potato, onion and swede for the best Cornish filling I have tasted. Also look out for his 'signature' terrine of lemon sole with prawns; gutsy fish soup with a pot of fiery rouille; fish or bubble & squeak cakes; and seafood thermidor – a cunning mixture of white fish, prawns and mustard, dressed in a white wine sauce topped with cheese and breadcrumbs. There are always plenty of fresh salads and cooked meats: slices of rare roast sirloin or topside; a glistening glazed ham; potted ham with lentils; and a vibrant duck liver parfait. After a trip here, you need never cook again.

Breads, cakes and pastries are baked at the back of the shop. Look out for the earthy sour dough, made with a Muscat grape yeast, French unbleached and five-grain flour, or the loaves of walnut, Granary, rye, and crusty white bread. There are all-butter croissants, bread & butter puddings, glazed individual fruit tarts, feather-light millefeuilles, apple crumble tart, pine kernel & ricotta tart, and a glorious Dorset apple cake. Pickles, preserves, pastes, jams and chutneys are own-made and, like every-thing in the shop, bear Rick's inventive stamp. This is an extraordinarily good shop, if only there were more like it in the country.

about 10 ounces. And the oil content must be right; around here in summer they're not oily enough to smoke and, after spawning, their oil content is even lower. You'd never eat a cow after it's calved, neither should you touch a fish'. Martin buys mackerel that fit his specifications, mainly caught off the coast of Scotland, filleted and frozen at sea. He draws off his stock of frozen fish as and when he needs it throughout the year.

He does hot-smoke whole mackerel and fillets, but it is for his cold-smoked mackerel that he excels. Treated exactly as salmon, the fillets are dry-cured in salt for 1½-2 hours, cold-smoked over oak sawdust in his large smoking cabinets for 4-6 hours, and then thinly sliced. Sold in 225-g (8-oz) packets, the finely textured moist pearly-grey slices have a full-bodied meaty flavour lightly cut with salt. They have always cold-smoked salmon but now he also hot-smokes it. This is a process by which the cured salmon is 'cooked', so it turns opaque and looks exactly as if it has been poached or grilled. Theirs has a light salty bite with a warm woodiness and comes as sides or pieces in vacuum packs weighing about 225 g (8 oz).

Stockists

Devon: N. H. Creber Ltd

London: Mr Christians

Somerset: Martin's Stores

COADS GREEN

Clotted Cream and Butter

B. A. Lake

Priors, Coads Green, Launceston, Cornwall PL15 7LT

☎ 01566 782547   **CONTACT** *Barbara Lake – telephone ahead*

Anybody who watched *Rhodes Around Britain*, with chef Gary Rhodes cooking up a storm wherever he went, may well have seen Barbara Lake and her mum. So overcome were they by Gary's visit that they asked him to name one of their Guernsey calves – Cocoa was his choice. Barbara keeps nine Guernsey cows in total – Gloria, Snowdrop, Clover, Rosie, Candy, Mary, Briony, Holly and, of course, Cocoa – as well as a few pigs on their smallholding. As her mother is confined to a chair, every day Barbara singlehandedly milks the cows, separates the milk, clots it into cream and feeds the skimmed milk to the pigs. Using rich Guernsey milk with its higher butterfat content, her clotted cream is made as it has been for generations. Commercially made clotted cream is baked either in the oven or in steam cabinets, but Barbara scorns these, sticking to the old-fashioned way of gently scalding (cooking) it on top of the Rayburn. The cream is poured into enamel pans and placed in a bain-marie. It is then heated, taking great care: if you overdo the heat the cream turns gritty; if you under-do it, it turns out bland. At first nothing seems to happen; then, as the cream slowly condenses, tiny bubbles start breaking to the top, pitting it like the surface of the moon. Suddenly it turns golden and forms a thick honeycomb crust and it has clotted. Left to cool and set overnight, it is ready for potting.

If there is any spare cream, Barbara makes a full-cream butter and, if there is any clotted cream left over at the end of the week, she will turn that – crust and all – into a clotted cream butter. I am fairly sure that Barbara is one of the few people, if not the only one left in the country, who not only makes a clotted cream butter but also makes it by hand. 'Real old-fashioned. Not many do that', she told me. Sadly she is right.

To make the clotted cream butter, first she whips the clotted cream with a hand-held whisk until it goes 'crumbly', then she works it with her hands, squeezing it hard to get rid of as much moisture as possible, washing it with fresh water until it runs clear. She puts a large knob at a time on a round wooden patter (it looks like a darning mushroom) and beats it with a boiled cloth to get yet more water out. Then, twisting the stem so it whizzes round, she works it into a circular pat, 'that can be difficult as, in the hot weather, it gets sticky'. Finally, using a wooden butter stamp carved with a Guernsey cow, she stamps the butter into a perfect round mould. In summer it is a bright, bright yellow; in winter it is paler, but compared to what most of us are used to, it is still a pretty dazzling colour – and, of course, achieved without any artificial aids. As for its taste, it is far richer and far creamier than ordinary butter and has a lingering aftertaste of sweet milkiness. It has to be tried to be believed.

> **Pengoon Farm, NANCEGOLLAN, Helston TR13 0BH ☎ 01326 561219** *milk about 17 Jersey cows. One of the few farms to have a 'green' licence, from the farm gate they sell green-top (unpasteurized) milk, skim the milk for unpasteurized fresh cream, clot that cream in the proper way on top of the stove for clotted cream and, after a few days, churn it into clotted cream butter. A word of advice, never eat clotted cream straight out of the fridge. If it is cold, you lose its full creamy, sweet flavour.*

Stockists

Cornw: Ough's
Philip Warren & Son

The Duchy of Cornwall Oyster Farm
Port Navas, Falmouth, Cornwall TR11 5RJ

PORT NAVAS
Native Oysters

☎FAX 01326 40210   **CONTACT** *Len Hodges*   **HOURS** *Mon-Fri 8.00-16.00 Sat 8.00-12.30*   **DIRECTIONS** *From Falmouth, take road signposted Constantine/Helston. After about 5 miles, turn left, signposted Port Navas. Follow the road about 1 mile into the village and join the private road at the end of the creek. Oyster farm is on the second quay.*

To call this a 'farm' is perhaps a little misleading. The word summons up visions of regimented beds of oysters seeded in regular rows, with tractors ploughing through the mud. Nothing could be further from the truth. When you finally get to the 'farm', all you see is an oyster shed that looks more like an Edwardian boathouse with the river Helford flowing past it tranquilly. The only hint is an oyster dredger moored up alongside.

Len Hodges and his merry band of helpers have the lease for dredging oysters in both the Helford and the Percuil that flows out at St Mawes. A still clean river (graded category A, the top in cleanliness), the Helford is a salt river full of plankton (ideal for oysters) and there have been naturally seeded oyster beds downstream since Roman times. In fact, Len does a little 'farming' by scattering empty shells on the beds to encourage the spats (baby oysters) to settle on them as they grow, and he also relays spats from the river Fal.

Native oysters were nearly wiped out in this country in 1982-3. The problem was *bonamia*, a parasite that feeds off them. Stocks are still lower than they were before the disaster, but they are building up nicely. Although, as Len told me philosophically, 'It's like myxomatosis, it might reoccur any time'. According to him (and most oyster aficionados), Natives are far superior in taste and texture to Pacifics. Generously he opened several for me as we sat chatting by the river bank. A first whiff of sea breezes, and as I tipped one in my mouth chewing gently and swallowing, a burst of biting saltiness mingled with a sweet aftertaste.

Graded into 4 sizes (the smallest ones getting put back), all the oysters are put through ultraviolet purifying tanks for 36 hours. Natives are available from September through to April and – dispelling the myth that you can only eat them when there is an 'r' in the month – Len told me, 'You can eat them any time, they're still plump in May or June, but we have to protect the breeding stock. And they're not too pleasant when spawning as they go milky'. Selling to most of the best restaurants, such as Bentleys, Sweetings and Green's of St James, Len will also send a minimum of 25, packed in seaweed, anywhere in the country. If you go down to visit him, you are welcome to take a picnic of bread, lemon and chilled white wine and sit by the river. Len promises to open as many oysters as you can manage 'as long as you don't hinder us working and don't forget to pay for them!'

Stockists

London:
Ashdowns

PORTREATH
Cornish
Heavy Cake

Portreath Bakery
3 The Square, Portreath, Cornwall TR16 4LA

☎ 01209 842612   **FAX** 01209 843801   **CONTACT** Marion Halling   **HOURS** (July to Aug only Sun 8.00-16.00) Mon-Sat 7.00-18.00   **DIRECTIONS** In town centre.

Unlike several other counties, Cornwall is rich in proper bakers. Many still use the old names for their breads and cakes and, luckily for us, many still bake using the 'right' ingredients, with long overnight fermentations. Carolyn Martin spent several years visiting all the bakers in the county – no easy task – and the fruits of her labour appear in her book *Our Daily Bread*, which gives an interesting insight into the shapes and names of breads as well as the baking practices that still flourish.

Marion Halling is described by Caroline as 'enthusiastic'. Having spent time baking in Germany, you are aware of a certain cross-cultural transference.

> **E. Eddy & Son, Jack Lane, NEWLYN TR18 5HZ ☎ 01736 62535** *still calls his heavy cake 'heavva' in the old-fashioned way. His is made with flour, lard, milk, currants, sultanas, mixed peel, sugar, salt and baking powder, and is as sturdy a slice as you could possibly hope for.*

MAP 1   CORNWALL   **47**

Apart from indigenous breads, you can also sometimes buy a crackled loaf made with cracked wheat, Bavarian with rye, speckle loaf with sunflower seeds or beige – a half white, half brown. In the more traditional line, she also produces good saffron cake, generously filled pasties and heavy cake.

If you have never tried heavy cake, it is an experience. More of a slab than an actual cake, the term 'heavy', I think, refers more to its ingredients of flour, butter, cream, sugar and currants than to its actual texture. Quite why it is called 'heavy', no one seems too sure. One explanation I heard was that look-outs, when posted on the cliffs, saw shoals of mackerel approaching the fishing boats, they would cry 'heavva, heavva'. The sturdy cake they were given to keep them going on the watch then become known as heavva (heavy) cake.

Some old recipes insist on adding clotted cream, some score the top in a criss-cross so it can be pulled apart when cooked, others even add lard or beef dripping, but not Marion. Hers is rich, quite thick and dense – a sort of white fruit cake made with cream and butter and sprinkled with sugar. A fine heavy cake is diet-defyingly good; you should try it at least once.

W. T. Warren & Son

The Top Shop, Market Square, St Just, Penzance, Cornwall TR19 7HD

☎ 01736 788538 **FAX** 01736 788354 **CONTACT** Mrs Mitchell **HOURS** Mon-Sat 9.00-17.00 **CARDS** Access, Eurocard, Mastercard, Visa **DIRECTIONS** In town centre.

More accurately described as a bread or dough cake, saffron cake has become a Cornish peculiarity, although this was not always the case. As Elizabeth David writes in *English Bread and Yeast Cookery*, 'In the 17th and 18th centuries, cakes similar to the modern Cornish version were called simply saffron cakes or perhaps just "an excellent cake"... As is well known, there was once a flourishing English saffron industry. "common or best knowne Saffron groweth plentifully in Cambridge-shire, Saffron Walden and other places thereabout, as corne in the fields" wrote John Gerard in his *Herbal* published in 1597... Gradually, as the cultivation of English saffron declined during the first half of the 19th century, the use of saffron all but died out, surviving in the West Country in saffron buns and the famous saffron cake'.

Bryan Warren believes, however, that the use of saffron in Cornwall dates back to the days when the Phoenician traders exchanged it for tin, but quite how or why it was then made into a cake, he is not too sure. 'Even the Spaniards, who have more saffron than we'll ever see, are amazed by our cake. They've never heard of it before'.

Using a 'family recipe', his cake now contains La Mancha saffron imported from Spain. He makes a rich yeast dough with eggs, various fats and butter, mixes in currants, sultanas and mixed peel and bakes it off in a loaf tin. Quite soft – even squidgy – and welcomingly golden, it is moist and generously fruited with an elegant taste. With Warren branches all over the county, you should have no problem trying Bryan's version.

Stockists
London: Harrods

Both **W. C. Rowe, 22 Victoria Square, TRURO TR1 2SD ☎ 01878 261281** (*with 11 branches in the county*) *and* **Martin's Bakery, 106 Clifden Road, St AUSTELL PL25 4AP ☎ 01726 73681** *have plenty of fans for their saffron cake and both use Spanish saffron and plenty of fruit. Martin's bake a soft moist version, W. C. Rowe's is drier and slightly fruitier.*

 NEW ENTRY

TREVERVA
Cheese

Menallack
Menallack Farm, Treverva, Penryn, Cornwall TR10 9BP

☎FAX 01326 40333 **CONTACT** *Caryl Minson* **HOURS** 10.00-16.00 **DIRECTIONS** *From Falmouth, take unclassified road to Gweek (seal sanctuary). Follow the road through Treverva and, after about ½ mile, farm-shop is signposted on the left.*

John and Caryl Minson run a camping site, riding stables and a farm-shop and still find time to make Menallack cheese. As if this was not enough, they have also taken over the making of Nanterrow from the Cheethams who used to make it near St Ives.

Nanterrow is a Coulommiers-style cheese, made with ewes' milk that the Minsons buy in. First they pasteurize it, then make the soft cheese as it has been done for centuries. The secret of a rich smooth cheese lies in how the curds are handled. Caryl ladles them at a thickness no more than 1 cm (⅜ in) using, of all things, a 25-cm (10-in) Pyrex dish; for her, this works best. Once the 25-cm (10-in) hoops (moulds) are filled to the top, they are turned immediately; and turning carries on for the next 36 hours until they are lightly salted. Sold vacuum-packed in 115-g (4-oz) Brie-shaped wedges cut from the 1.35-kg (3-lb) rounds, Nanterrow comes either as plain or layered with a mixture of fresh garlic, parsley and chives.

Caryl makes Menallack using bought-in unpasteurized milk from a local Hereford herd. The land on which they graze has an underlying granite seam with an acid soil and this, she is sure, contributes to the

---

June Gurd of **Home Stake Farm, BLACKCROSS, Newquay TR8 4LU ☎ 01726 860423** *makes Vashti, a Coulommiers-style cheese, using the unpasteurized milk from her mixed goat herd. Fresh and creamy, it is sold in 8-oz (225-g) rounds, either plain or with mixed herbs. Using her goats' milk, she also makes a hard crumbly cheese, a thick strained yoghurt and invariably has some own-made butter in the fridge. If you have never seen goats'-milk butter, do not be put off by its pure white colour – it may look like lard, but it tastes just like a creamy butter.*

NEW ENTRY

MAP 1 CORNWALL 49

cheese's interesting sharpness and faint lemon tang. Once the milk has been started and renneted, the curds are broken by hand in a method similar to that for Cheshire and she works on them for about 1½ hours until the acidity level is right. Then she 'mills like mad'. Pressed for 3 days, turned daily for 2 weeks, then every 4 to 5 days, the cheese is sold at a minimum of 6 weeks, when it is fresh, quite crumbly and pleasantly sharp. It will mature on; if you try it at 5-6 months it is much stronger and denser. Made into 1.8-kg (4-lb) truckles or 450-g (1-lb) 'babies', they also produce versions flavoured with chives and garlic. They also oak-smoke some cheeses.

All the cheeses are sold from the farm-shop by the gate, together with Vashti *see foot of page* 48 and a goats' cheese made down in the valley that Caryl thinks is best as small balls in a rosemary-flavoured oil. She bakes her own bread and sells various local produce, including Trewithen ice-cream, Merrivale hams *see below*, sausages and pâtés *see below*, lamb 'that's never travelled more than 10 miles in its life' butchered into various joints and frozen, and locally made preserves.

Stockists

Cornw:
Lavender's

Mylor Stores

Stein's
Delicatessen

Devon: Natural
Life

Merrivale Charcuterie
1 Coombes Lane, Truro, Cornwall TR1 2BJ

TRURO
Charcuterie

☎ 01872 222227 **FAX** 01326 377717 **CONTACT** Sally Jones **HOURS** Mon-Fri 9.00-17.00 Sat 9.00-16.30 **DIRECTIONS** In town centre, off Pydar Street.

Since the 1994 edition of this guide, Huw Jones of Merrivale Charcuterie has extended his range of products while Sally, his wife, has extended the range of the shop. Tucked away down a narrow alley off Truro's shopping centre, the uncluttered-looking shop is full of Huw's British- and Continental-style charcuterie, as well as fresh meat and a spanking new cheese counter with a few well-chosen cheeses.

Actual production takes place in a unit a few miles from town. From here Huw prepares everything. He dry-cures bacon and ham, and particularly punchy is the Spingo ham named after a local beer. Once the ham has been dry-cured, it is basted for a month in the beer mixed with molasses and muscovado sugar until it turns a mahogany black, then it is hung and dried for 2-3 weeks. He has been working on his Parma-style ham and, at a recent tasting, I found it much improved – sweeter and more subtle, with a more delicate touch.

Although Huw does make such fresh meaty pork sausages as garlic & herb, Cornish with a touch of nutmeg, coriander & mace, proper faggots and hogs' pudding of pork, thyme, parsley, white pepper and rusk in the Devonian style (stuffed in runners as opposed to the ox middles which are more common in Cornwall), it is for his Continental charcuterie that I think he stands out. There is a German *landjager* sausage made with beef, pork, caraway seed and kirsch. Cornish salami, mellow and meaty, is a mixture of chopped pork, pork back fat and beef, with mixed seasonings, sugar and rum, stuffed in skins and

Two fresh sausage producers have come to my notice, both using free-range pork. Varieties from **Mr Kittow's Famous Sausage Co.**, **1a Church Street, MEVAGISSEY PL26 6SP ☎/fax 01726 842016** include Squire Trelawney, with pork, garlic, herbs and eggs; pork, brandy & walnut; wild boar from Bodmin Moor with apple; and venison & burgundy, all with a minimum of 75 per cent meat content.

 Tywardreath Butchers, 41 Church Street, TYWARDREATH PAR **PL22 2QQ ☎ 01726 812051** won the 1993 Guardian National Sausage Quest with their pork & garlic. They also make Scrumpy pork with cider and apple; beef, mushroom & Guinness; and pork & chilli.

hung to dry for about 5 weeks. Cornish country sausage and Cornish chorizo are both made in the same way. For the former, a mixture of pork, pork back fat, red wine and *quatre épices* is prepared; for the latter, the pork and pork fat is mixed with red wine vinegar, chillies, cayenne, paprika and red and green peppers. This is then stuffed into skins and smoked for about 24 hours and hung for about 10 days. If I have any criticism, it is that Huw vacuum-packs them to stop them drying out. I feel they could do with ageing a little longer as they are perhaps still a little too moist. Cornish country sausage is soft-textured with a gentle meatiness. It can be eaten raw, but intensifies when lightly grilled or pan-fried. However you eat the chorizo, it is always decidedly fiery.

They also sell a good *jambon persillé*, with bags of fresh chopped parsley and juicy meat in a rich jelly; coarse, robust Toulouse sausages flavoured with red wine and garlic; subtler Bratwurst with a hint of lemon; and hot-smoked turkey & ham frankfurters. Even the fresh meat has a Continental bias in its butchering; you will be relieved to see English veal well featured, flattened into wafer-thin escalopes or cut from the loin, boned out, rolled and carefully trimmed into noisettes.

Stockists

Cornw: Ough's

The Good Life

Village Deli

London: Paxton & Whitfield

Selfridges

Lynher Valley Dairy

Netherton Farm, Upton Cross, Liskeard, Cornwall PL14 5BD

UPTON CROSS
Cornish Yarg

☎ 01579 362244 **FAX** 01579 362666 **CONTACT** Michael Horrell **HOURS** *Easter to end Oct: Mon-Sat 10.00-16.00* **DIRECTIONS** *From Liskeard, take B3254 towards Upton Cross. At Upton Cross, turn right signposted Rilla Mill and Cheese Farm. Follow the signs for about 1 mile to the farm.*

Cornish Yarg, a lightly pressed cheese coated with nettles, from its name sounds as if it has been made in the county for years. In fact it was only invented about 15 or so years ago by a Mr and Mrs Gray – and Yarg is their surname spelt backwards. Mike Horrell bought the recipe from them and now makes it on-farm in the Lynher Valley. Incidentally, he is among the first of our producers to have applied for a Protective Designation of Origin, an EU-backed initiative run along similar lines to the French *Appellation Contrôlée d'Origine*. It means that, once approved, no one else will be able to make Yarg, nor can it ever be made out of the area. Some people think this is a bad thing; others, myself

> **Quayside Fish Centre, Harbour Road, PORTHLEVEN, Helston TR13 9JU** ☎ **01326 562008 fax 01326 574386** *comes praised to the sky by food consultant Ann Wilson. 'Run by a former fisherman, John Strike, the fish is always fresh, there's a tremendous selection and the staff are helpful, charming and highly professional. The best kippers I've ever tasted, plump and moist, come from their smokehouse, the smoked haddock is pretty good too. You can see it's not got any colorants added.' Fish is mostly locally caught, so you might find sea bass, grey as well as red mullet, John Dory, sole, plaice, mackerel, lobster and local crab. Recently they have started an overnight delivery of boxes of fresh Cornish fish anywhere in Britain; either choose your selection or they will make it for you up to an agreed price.*
>
>
>
>   *If you are there, Ann also recommends popping over to the other side of the horseshoe-shaped harbour and having a crab sandwich or a plate of mussels at* **The Crabpot, Harbour Road, Porthleven, HELSTON TR13 9JD** ☎ **01326 573355**. *On a sunny day you can sit outside, 'it's an oasis in England'.*

included, can see the advantage. If we are to foster the regional character of our foods, then we must protect them. Think what has happened to Cheddar – once only made using milk from lush West Country pastures and a cheese of startling character, now it is no more than a recipe copied willy-nilly all over the world. At least that can never happen to Cornish Yarg if it acquires PDO status.

Mike makes cheese with the pasteurized milk of his Friesian herd which graze on his land bordering the Cheese Ring, high up on the edge of the Cornish moors. The rounded boulders, stacked one on top of the other on the edge of the quarry, look like huge farmhouse cheeses wrapped in cloth to drain and it was from this very quarry that granite for building the Thames Embankment was taken. Yarg is quite a fast cheese to make, similar to a Caerphilly: the curds are cut and turned and cut and turned again until the acidity level is right. It is then milled, lightly pressed overnight, brined for a few hours and 'nettled'. It is the nettle coating that makes Yarg so distinctive; nettle leaves,

> *In Cornwall, says Ann Muller of* **The Lizard Pasty Shop, Sunny Corners,** THE **LIZARD TR12 7PB** ☎/fax **01326 290889** *'a pasty can be with any ingredient so long as it's baked in pastry'. Recommending one particular pasty-maker is a tricky one, nothing seems to provoke such a heated discussion in the county as the merits of one versus another. None the less, the general consensus is that Ann's pasties are very good. Working from her kitchens and only from Tuesdays through to Fridays (Saturdays will find her rowing in local regattas), she makes her own pastry with lard, margarine and Doves strong white flour see page 22 – or with butter, vegetable margarine and wholemeal flour for the veggies. 'I aim for halfway between puff and shortcrust. Filling should be skirt, with what we in Cornwall call turnips but you call swede, potatoes, onions, salt and black pepper.' A pasty should be generously filled, but never with too much meat, 'It's there more for the flavouring and if I use too much skirt, the juices leak on to the tray'. Vegetarians have the choice of cheese – made, of course, with vegetarian rennet – or just vegetable pasties. Whatever you choose, I do not think you could possibly have any cause to complain.* **An Gegyn,** *(Cornish for the kitchen)* **Fore Street, PORTHLEVEN TR13 9HJ** ☎ **01326 565557** *also make their own pastry for the daily bake of pasties. Theirs come in three sizes: small, medium and large, although I defy anyone to polish off a large one by themselves. Traditional is made with chuck steak and the 'right' vegetables; the other fillings are cheese & vegetable; vegetables; and ox-liver & onions. They also bake various traditional cakes, including heavy, saffron and yeast cakes.*

frozen so they go like limp lettuce for easier handling, are spread all over the cheese and brushed with sterilized water. A deep dark green, they glisten like leaves after a rainstorm. There are precedents for using nettles in cheese; several of our old recipes for cottage or plate cheeses call for nettles and they were widely used in Holland. Teifi cheese *see page* 381 uses them still as a flavouring.

Yarg is kept for a minimum of two weeks, by which time the nettle coating has turned a pale spidery grey. It ages well, at about 4-6 weeks it softens slightly and mellows out to give an almost grassy honey flavour which is when it is at its best. Aware of this and the problems of most wholesalers not wanting to mature it on, Mike thinks there is an argument for selling Yarg in two grades: young at 2-3 weeks and mature at 4-6 weeks, but he has not decided yet. Another reason he is toying with the idea is that he has 'turned the place upside down. I've rebuilt the cheese-making rooms to the satisfaction of *all* known food technologists. Believe me, that is no mean achievement'. Cheeses are now matured in a cheese store under the dairy, the old cheese store is a visitors' centre and you can watch cheese being made without going into the dairy. To round off the improvements, the soft full-fat cream cheeses, Cornish Pepper with its pepper coating and Cornish Herb & Garlic with its herbs, are now made in a separate room. This is obviously a dairy ready to launch itself into the 21st century.

Stockists

Chesh: The Cheese Shop

Cornw: Ough's

London: Harrods
Paxton & Whitfield

Warwicks: Langmans

Tretheague Mill Herbs, STITHIANS TR3 7AF ☎ 01209 861070 grow various culinary herbs, including marjoram, French tarragon, lemon balm and rosemary, and sell them in pots. Deb Fowler also makes herb oils, using sunflower oil – as 'it is the mildest of oils and let's the flavour of the herbs come through'. Sold in 250-g (9-oz) oil-tight plastic bottles, she fills the bottles with several sprigs of either a single herb or a mixture of herbs (with or without own-grown chilli or garlic) and leaves them to infuse. She also makes five differently flavoured marinades, again using own-grown herbs and sunflower oil. These include: fish, made with dill, fennel, lemon juice and white wine; Thai, with coriander leaves and seeds, ginger, chilli, lemon grass, garlic and lemon balm; and French, traditional with red wine, garlic, thyme, rosemary, bay leaf and marjoram.

While you're in the area...

A. & M. Pigott, East Penrest, LEZANT, Launceston PL15 9NR ☎ 01579 370270 make clotted cream from the unpasteurized milk of their Jersey herd, using the proper traditional method of gently 'cooking' it on top of the cooker. Sold in pots, with a knob of the crust in the bottom, then filled with cream and another generous wedge of crust on top, it is rich and very moreish.

Mylor Stores, MYLOR, Falmouth TR11 5NA ☎ 01326 373615 is a proper village shop. They also sell a good selection of the county's produce, including a locally made hogs' pudding, pasties from Phoenix Bakery in Deveran, Merrivale's charcuterie *see page* 49, clotted cream from Trewithen and cheeses from Menallack *see page* 48 and Lynher Valley Dairy *see page* 50.

I have heard that the ice-cream from **S. Jelbert, 9 New Road, NEWLYN, Penzance TR18 5PZ ☎ 01736 66634** is better   than most. Made on a daily basis, using clotted Cornish cream, sugar, ordinary cream, milk, butter, vanilla and vanillin, they only sell one flavour – vanilla. Sold from their shop in cones or tubs, apparently some people treat themselves by smothering it with extra clotted cream. More reports please.

Mail Order

Clotted cream only

Di's Dairy & Pantry, Rock Road, ROCK, Wadebridge PL27 6NW ☎ 01208 863531, with kitchens behind the shop, is a place to go for holiday home catering. They make food-to-go, and you can bring your own dishes, bake pasties, quiches, sausage rolls, superb sticky and delicately spiced treacle tarts, rich fruit cakes in all sorts of shapes and sizes, and cutting loaves such as rich fruit, ginger, banana & walnut for tea-time picnics. They also make fresh egg pasta, pasta sauces and pasta salads, and sell a good selection of local produce, including Trewithan clotted cream and ice-cream, Rodder's clotted cream and Helsett ice-cream, Merrivale sausages *see page* 49 and various cheeses from both Cornwall and Devon.

Mail Order

Tarts and cakes only

Trelay Meat, Trelay, ST GENNY'S, Bude EX23 0NJ ☎ 01840 230378 sell North Devon beef hung for 2-3 weeks, lamb and pork butchered into cuts and joints and own-made sausages from their farm-shop.

Jo Smith of **Trevervan Jams, Trevervan House, TREWARMETT, Tintagel PL34 0ES ☎ 01840 770486** makes a range of fruity jams and marmalades, including pear & cider, pear & apricot and grapefruit marmalade with honey. She also makes a strawberry and a raspberry jam and an orange marmalade, all using Cornish honey.

Stoneybridge Organic Nursery & Farmshop, TYWARDREATH PAR PL24 2TY ☎ 01726 813858 grows several vegetables, herbs and soft fruit to organic (Soil Association) standards. Worth going for are the early potatoes that are ready by mid April and later on in summer, Pink Fir Apple potatoes, ogen melons grown under cover, bunches of fresh herbs and lush sweet strawberries to go with clotted cream.

The Old Smokehouse & Truffles
Brougham Hall, Brougham, Penrith, Cumbria CA10 2DE

☎ 01768 867772 **CONTACT** Rona Newsom **HOURS** *beg March to 24 Dec: 10.00-17.30* **DIRECTIONS** *From Penrith, take A6 towards Shap. Follow the road through Eamont Bridge, then take first left turn at the signpost for Brougham. Shop is ½ mile along on the left.*

Rona Newsom runs two units from the courtyard of Brougham Hall, an old castle that was converted in the 19th century. From one she makes chocolates and from the other, she runs her smokery using an Afos smoker. Dealing with the smokery first, Rona's style is for a light cure and a mild smoke that results in the intrinsic flavour of the ingredient shining through. This comes as welcome relief, as too often the only taste you get from a smoked food is a salty harshness and/or an acrid bitterness and a dried-out product. On the other hand, Rona's smoked local chickens are juicy and the cold-smoked venison moist with a gentle punch of game.

Over the last two years she has developed a couple of local products. Char, similar to the trout in both looks and flavour, was once found in great quantities in nearby Lake Windermere. Indeed, potted char was such a delicacy that it was sent down by the overnight train to Fortnum & Mason. Now it is being farmed outside Wigton from where Rona gets her supplies. She briefly brine-cures the fillets in salt with lemon juice, sugar, garlic and onion. Then she smokes them for no more than about 45 minutes. The result is a smoked fish more moist than trout, with a compact but soft-textured flesh and a subtle taste. Herdwick is the local breed of lamb *see Agnus Quality Meats, page 55* and she takes the rolled shoulder from a shearling and brines it for about 3 days in salt, sugar, pickling spices and garlic. Then she rubs it all over with a fiery oil mixed with pepper, paprika and cayenne and adds sprigs of rosemary. This is cold-smoked for about 5 hours and then hot-

MAP 6 CUMBRIA 55

smoked to cook it through 'until it is done'. Streaked through with a clear-tasting fat, the round slices of meat are slightly pink, tender and juicy, with a marked sweetness of lamb punched with rosemary – but with only the barest hint of smoke. She both smokes a bresaola-style beef, cured by Chris Johnson of the Ramsbottom Victuallers *see page* 158 and does her own cold-smoked

> *If you have never had fresh Morecambe Bay shrimps, you have a treat in store. Tiny, light-brown and sweet as honey, the 'real' ones are caught in and around the bay that sweeps round from Morecambe to Rampside. They have a limited season, from April to the end of November.* **Bob Dickinson, 28A Market Street, FLOOKBURGH LA11 7JU** ☎ **01539 558582** *sells fresh shrimps picked over (peeled). Open at various times in the season, he generally puts a blackboard outside his front door to let you know when he is in.*

beef. Cured for between 3-5 days, this time in a brine flavoured with juniper and bay leaf, it is rubbed in a spiced oil, then hung to dry for about 12 hours. It is finally smoked for about 5 hours – as it is important not to over-smoke it. She prefers to sell it in a piece, then you can slice it as thickly or thinly as you wish. The easiest way is to keep it in the freezer, then you can cut it wafer-thin with a sharp knife.

There has, however, been little change in the chocolate department. Truffles, made using a good-quality couverture, fresh cream, fresh fruit and real alcohol, still have a freshness unsullied by 'essences or flavouring' that mar so many of our British-made ones. The fillings are piped or filled into round shells which are closed with a layer of couverture and the cases are then rolled in yet more couverture and dusted in various powders – mainly cocoa but sometimes even coconut. If you visit, you can pick and choose your selection, I suggest you try at least one Cointreau, with its full fruitiness and strong alcoholic glow, and the strong dark and sophisticatedly dry Coffee. Otherwise Rona will send boxes of mixed truffles weighing 200 or 370 g (7 or 13 oz); remember once opened, they must be kept in the fridge.

Stockists

Chesh: Sandiway Wine Co.

Lancs: Ramsbottom Victuallers

London: Fortnum & Mason

Oxon: Taylors

Agnus Quality Meats

Low Wool Oaks, Calthwaite, Penrith, Cumbria CA11 9RZ

CALTHWAITE
Herdwick
Lamb

☎ 01768 885384 **FAX** 01768 885009 **CONTACT** C. Anthony Head – mail order only

The indigenous breed of sheep in the Cumbrian Mountains is the Herdwick and it is thought to be the hardiest breed in Britain. Living in those climatic conditions, I would have thought it needs to be. There is now a growing interest in its eating quality. It was, I think, initiated by Harry Fellowes of the now-defunct Ashdown Smokers, who revived smoked Herdwick macon (ham). Happily, the tradition continues at The Old Smokehouse *see page* 54. Last year Agnus Quality Meats formed to act as distributors for fresh meat. It is an enterprise I heartily endorse, as it is about time we woke up to the possibility of regional and/or specific breeds with their marked flavours and textures and the

Herdwick does have a distinctive taste. All their Herdwick comes primarily from Borrowdale, Langdale, Wasdale and Eskdale. It grazes in the hills on ling heather and blaeberries and is brought down to the lowlands to be finished on grass. All the animals are pure-bred from registered breeders.

Now, up in the dales the sheep lamb late, not until April to May, so the new season's lamb – with its carcass weight of around 14.5 kg (32 lbs) – is not ready for the table until October, with a season lasting through to May. In the area, however, the best lamb is thought to be the 'shearling', meaning when it has had its first shear or is 12 months old. This is when its meat has its sweeter and more distinctive flavour and has acquired its rich vein of marbling. Understandably, Mr Head is reluctant to stress this as he believes (rightly) that anyone outside of the Lakes will turn up their nose as what is technically mutton. Although you can buy new-season's lamb and it is good, trust me and go for the shearling. Finely grained, it has a deeper, richer and stronger flavour while still being surprisingly lean and juicy. You can also order mutton – proper mutton over 3 years old with all the strength of flavour that implies. All their Herdwick meat is hung for 10 days and comes as whole or half carcasses or in various joints or cuts.

Stockists

Cumbria: A. F. Huddleston

Claytons Butchers

R. Udale

Northumbs:
R. Baty

Suffolk: Denham Estate

GRASMERE
Gingerbread

Sarah Nelson's Grasmere Gingerbread Shop
Grasmere, Cumbria LA22 9SW

☎ 015394 35428 **FAX** 015394 35155 **CONTACT** *Christine Batey* **HOURS** *Mon-Sat 9.30-17.30 Sun 12.30-17.30* **DIRECTIONS** *In town centre.*

Over 140 years ago, Sarah Nelson began baking gingerbread in what was once the old schoolhouse tucked by St Oswald's lych-gate (where none other than William Wordsworth is buried). Such was her reputation that business thrived and Grasmere gingerbread became well-known in and out of the county.

Grasmere is a thriving tourist town and the Gingerbread Shop certainly does capitalize on the tourist trade. However, they have not compromised on the quality of their gingerbread; it still uses the same 'secret' recipe, to which only three families have been privy, and it is superb. Made daily, if you time your visit right you can buy it while still warm and soft. More like a biscuit than a parkin or bread, the thin oblongs harden to a firm chewiness with a texture of melting sand and a glorious afterglow of ginger that fires the throat. Sold wrapped in old-fashioned vegetable parchment in packets of 6, 12 or 24 pieces, the fruity-spiced gingerbread is a deep warm brown. They also make a grainy version, well laced with alcohol rum butter. Let me give you one word of advice. As you hit Grasmere you will notice various shops claiming to sell the 'real' or 'original' item. They are not and do not be taken in. Theirs are no more than poor imitations – thick, floury, bland and looking like low-grade flapjacks – to be avoided at all costs.

Mail Order

Packets of 24 only

Little Salkeld Watermill
Little Salkeld, Penrith, Cumbria CA10 1NN

LITTLE SALKELD
Organic Flour

☎ 01768 881523 **CONTACT** Nick Jones **HOURS** Mill and Tea room (beg March to end Oct): Mon, Tues, Thurs and first Sun of month 10.00-17.00; Mill Shop: Mon-Fri 10.30-17.00 **DIRECTIONS** From Penrith, take the A686 towards Alston. Turn left at Langwathby. After about 2 miles, cross a little bridge and the Mill is immediately on the left.

Little Salkeld Watermill was the 1993 winner of the Organic Food Trophy. The water-powered mill is run by Nick and Anna Jones and they use only organic (to Soil Association standards) English wheat, 'we think it's the most tasty. We buy a load at a time and we don't mix it. Every load is slightly different. We can always say where the flour that we're using comes from'. This single batch approach, Emily Green – food writer in *The Independent* and a keen baker – believes, 'explains the distinctive flavour of the wholewheat flour. The other factor is freshness. Every sack of flour is distributed within a week of being milled'. The flour is sold in packs from 1.5 to 29 kg (3½-64 lb). They also sell oatmeal and flakes, and mix up a dog meal of flaked maize with bran, soya meal, rolled oats, wheat and barley which, incidentally, Violet adores.

Stockists

Cumbria: E. H. Booth & Co

Durham: Molly's Wholefoods

Lancs: Single Step

Lothian: Dam Head Holdings

Northumb: Red Herring

The Village Bakery
Melmerby, Penrith, Cumbria CA10 1HE

MELMERBY
Sour-dough Bread

☎ 01768 881515 **FAX** 01768 881848 **CONTACT** Andrew Whitley **HOURS** Mar to Dec: Mon-Sat 8.30-17.00 Sun 9.30-17.00; Jan and Feb: Mon-Fri 8.30-14.30 Sat 8.30-17.00 Sun 9.30-17.00 **CARDS** Access, Diners, Mastercard, Visa **DIRECTIONS** From Penrith, take A686 towards Alston. At Melmerby, turn left immediately after the sharp left bend in the road at sign for bakery. Bakery is 100 yards along on the right.

Started nearly 20 years ago by Andrew Whitley, a one-time radio producer, The Village Bakery has grown considerably. They even supply Waitrose, Sainsbury and Safeway. Theirs is a success story that is heartening to read, particularly when you realize that it has been achieved without any compromise of Andrew's original intentions of making good proper bread in an ecologically sound environment.

In his wood-fired oven he bakes a variety of breads. His French country bread is naturally leavened (i.e. made without yeast), with a creamy moist interior that tears apart in shards and with a satisfying crusty exterior. Andrew's pride is his sour-dough Russian rye. Made with a Russian starter over 24 hours to give it a chance to develop and mature, it is solid, full of body and tinged with sharpness. Then there are the flavoured breads: tomato; olive; and wild mushroom & garlic, made into a round cob with wild Italian mushrooms and pumpkin

Run by Alan Turnbull, **Ainsworth's Specialist Grocers & Delicatessen, Kentsbank Road, GRANGE-OVER-SANDS LA11 7EY ☎ 01539 532946** is an old-fashioned grocers with plenty of good local produce. Here you will find bread from The Village Bakery see page 57, bacon and ham from Richard Woodall see page 62, cheeses from Thornby Moor Dairy see page 61 and smoked products and chocolates from The Old Smokehouse see page 54. At the back of the shop, Alan also makes his own Turnbull's Cumbrian Mustard. Potted into 255-g (9-oz) jars, it is hot and coarsely grained with a delicate sweetness. Alan particularly recommends it with Cumberland sausage. The shop also sells own-roast hams and occasionally finishes them with a glaze made with their mustard.

seeds. There are also regional specialities, including Borrowdale tea-bread, Cumberland Rum Nicky, shortbread and Westmoreland Parkin.

Recently Andrew, in conjunction with Paul Merry, has launched Leavens Above! one-day or week-end baking courses. These take place in Paul Merry's flagstone floor kitchen, where he has built his own domestic wood-burning oven. The goal of the courses is to learn to make bread with real character and to understand all the aspects of fermentation – so important, as any experienced bread-maker will tell you. To join in you do not need to have ever even baked a single loaf, I went and I was fascinated. Together with two complete strangers we baked away merrily all week-end and when the time came to go home I was clutching several professional-looking – or so I thought – loaves, that could (almost) compete with Andrew's. I had learnt so much about both the principles and practicalities of bread-making that I urge anyone at all interested to go.

Stockists

Cumbria: J. & J. Graham

London: Selfridges

Mersey: Hand To Mouth

Northumb: The Corbridge Larder

Warwicks: Country Bumpkins Delicatessen

PENRITH
Fudge and Toffee

The Toffee Shop
7 Brunswick Road, Penrith, Cumbria CA11 7LU

☎**FAX** 01768 062008   **CONTACT** Mr Boustead **HOURS** Mon-Sat 9.00-17.00 **DIRECTIONS** In town centre.

The Toffee Shop carries on its great tradition of making the best fudge and toffee in Britain. Their fudge is simply glorious. Sold in oblong slabs, it is soft enough to break up into bite-size pieces with your hands. Take a bite through its velvet texture, with the merest hint of grain, and then wait – its clarity of rich butteriness explodes in your mouth. It is the purity that makes their fudge superb. Too many pro-ducers add glucose or glycerine or cheap flavourings or substitute mar-garine for butter and inevitably this detracts from the end-result – it cloys the palate or is sickly sweet. The Toffee Shop make theirs with butter, sugar and milk – and nothing else. They heat it in pan-size batches to make sure it cooks evenly and does not catch, and it is stirred and fussed over as any good product should be. It comes as plain – my favourite as it allows its full glory to shine through – and in two flavours: mint, using the same mint oil as Kendal mint cake; and chocolate, using a dark plain chocolate. A word of warning, do not ask for a mixed box of fudge that includes mint; Mr Boustead will just not send it as the danger is that the mint will overpower the other flavours.

Up until now I have made scant reference to the toffee of The Toffee Shop. I always thought it came a poor second, certainly in terms of popularity. When I stood in the shop, however, I was surprised there were as many customers for the toffee as for the fudge. Made with butter, sugar and – this time – black treacle, it is set in a tray. Mr Boustead is always on hand to break it up with a small hammer and the irregularly sized pieces are then wrapped by hand in paper twisted at the ends. Again there is the lushness of butter, with the sweetness cut by the dark treacle with its hint of spice. It is soft and chewy with an amazing ability to seep through your teeth. Put a bowl on the table and you will discover one piece is just not enough.

Both fudge and toffee can be sent by post anywhere in the country in 225, 450, 675 and 900-g (½, 1, 1½ and 2-lb) boxes.

Stockists

Glos: Gastromania

London: Fortnum & Mason

Shaws

Northumb: The Corbridge Larder

Central Scot: Clive Ramsay

In the spring, people drive up to the Lyth Valley to admire the damson blossom. In the autumn, customers come to **Lyth Valley Farmshop, DAWSON FOLD LA8 8DE ☎ 01539 568248** *to buy the fruit. The damson season starts around the second week of September and 'lasts for perhaps no more than a couple of weeks or maybe right through to the end of October, depending on how heavy the crop', says Christine Walling. Christine also sells pots of her own-made damson jam.*

Slack's
Newlands Farm, Raisbeck, Orton, Penrith, Cumbria CA10 3SG

RAISBECK
Bacon and Sausages

☎ 01539 624667   **CONTACT** Michael Slack – mail order only

Slack's have been producing sausages for several years, but over the last 18 months they have developed a range of bacon and ham. What is particular about these products is the source of the meat. It comes from a pig farmer in Wensleydale, who lives just a few miles from Hawes, one of the centres for Wensleydale cheese. Apparently the farmer collects the whey from the dairy and feeds it to his pigs. Although Michael Slack admits to knowing neither their breed nor the welfare standards to which these pigs are reared, he is certain that their diet is a mixture of whey and soya concentrate and this results in pork with a sweet clean flavour.

He buys in whole carcasses and cures the suitable cuts for bacon and ham. Both are brine-cured in a mixture of salt and saltpetre with, Michael assured me, 'positively no brine injecting'. The bacon is cured for 1 week, hung in the fridge for 2 weeks and then finally air-dried for a further week. Sold as either back, middle or streaky, green or smoked over a mixture of oak and beech, you can order any weight from a 225 g (½ lb) up to a piece weighing around 2.3 kg (5 lb). Hams are treated in much the same way, but obviously cured and matured for longer. Again these can be bought in a joint any size, weighing up to

Stockists

Cumbria: The Barn Shop

London: Harrods

Harvey Nichols

Selfridges

Yorks: Wensleydale Creamery

and over 9 kg (20 lb) for a whole ham on the bone.

Apart from a few that are cured, the shoulders are used up in their sausages. All made in natural skins, these include a coarse-cut Cumberland with salt, pepper and sage in a choice of 93 per cent or 75 per cent meat content; Toulouse, seasoned with ginger, nutmeg, cinnamon and cloves; and chipolatas with a 93 per cent meat content and well flavoured with pepper, coriander, pimento, nutmeg, thyme and cayenne.

STAVELEY
Ice-cream

English Ice Creams

*Gipsy Well, The Banks, Staveley, Kendal,
Cumbria LA8 9NE*

☎ 01539 821562   **CONTACT** *Colin English – telephone ahead*

You may have heard of Colin Cooper English, he wrote *The National Trust Book of Sorbets, Flummeries and Fools* and used to run a restaurant in Hampshire. Well now he lives in Cumbria and makes 'real' sorbets and ice-creams, 'they're what I call chef's ice-cream, they wouldn't do at all in newsagents' and most of them are sold to chefs with just a few private customers coming to his door.

Made on a true cottage-industry scale, Colin's ice-creams are very superior, as near to home-made as you can find. 'I make on a very small scale and to order. I never hold stock, so they're as fresh as possible. If a customer wants a particular flavour, I'll make it. I'll make anything, whatever anyone wants, as I'm small enough to cope but I need 24-48 hours' notice.' His ice-creams are the real thing, made with – and only with – fresh full-cream milk, cream, sugar and fresh eggs 'and a lot of them. For a gallon of vanilla, I use 27 eggs. I crack them in one at a time. And unlike all the old recipes that say only use egg yolks, I use the whole egg as it makes the mix lighter'. As he explains, it is perfectly safe to use fresh rather than pasteurized eggs as 'each time I make a batch up, I have to heat the mix to 79.4°C and hold it for 18 seconds, in effect pasteurizing it. I have to be pretty quick at this point for if the mix rises to 85°C then I have scrambled eggs on my hands'. Sold in 2-litre (3½-pint) tubs, his flavours include vanilla, flavoured with vanilla pods; chocolate; coffee; and nougat. Although, as he says, he will make more or less anything a customer dreams up. I tried his lavender & honey that he claims is based on a Roman combination of flavours. Dense and very creamy, it was slightly perfumed with a heady sweetness and a slight cut of the flower.

Colin also makes sorbets and here his inventiveness knows no bounds. What I like about Colin's sorbets is their freshness and originality. Free of a masking sweetness, my favourite was the sharp and spiced lime & ginger; so light and so true it dazzled with fruitiness. Apple & mint had the texture and taste of fruit, and elderflower all the musky headiness of the flowers. Other stock flavours are blackcurrant,

Stockists

Cumbria: Farrer's Coffee Shop

grapefruit, pink grapefruit, herb, champagne and green apple. If you are in the area, however, just ring Colin and he will make you any flavour that is in season.

James & John Graham, Market Square, PENRITH CA11 7BS ☎ 01768 62281 *with branches at* **26 Fisher Street, CARLISLE** *and* **18 Finkle Street, KENDAL ☎ 01539 720323** *have been in the business since 1793 as grocers, tea dealers, cheesemongers and seedsmen. The original high-ceilinged shop in Penrith is stylishly fitted out with a central counter and shelves around the walls. Here you will find Richard Woodall's ham and bacon see page 62, bread delivered daily from The Village Bakery see page 57, local cheeses, butter from Carron Lodge in Lancashire, lemon curd from Keogh Herb Farm and pork, game and steak & kidney pies by Wm. Brennand who, as butchers, occupied the shop in Kendal that J. & J. Graham have now taken over.*

Thornby Moor Dairy
Crofton Hall, Thursby, Carlisle, Cumbria CA5 6QB

☎FAX 01697 345555 **CONTACT** *Carolyn Fairbairn* **HOURS** *Mon-Fri 9.00-17.00 Sat 10.00-17.00* **DIRECTIONS** *From Carlisle, take the A595 towards Cockermouth. After 8 miles, at the roundabout junction with the A596, continue on the A595 1 mile, then turn right at the stone archway and follow signs to 'cheese farm'. Shop is ¼ mile on.*

Having recently moved a mere mile from her house – where she used to make cheese – to a spanking new dairy with a shop that doubles up as a cheese store, Carolyn Fairbairn is busier than ever with her varied range of unpasteurized cheeses.

Her Cumberland cheese is moist, smooth and mellow, with a pleasant creaminess. Made with the milk from a local herd of Shorthorns, she makes it in a style she describes as 'uncomplicated'. Once the cheese has been started and renneted, it is cut, drained, salted, milled and pressed overnight for the smaller 450- or 900-g (1- or 2-lb) truckles, or left for 2 days for the 9-kg (20-lb) truckles. Then it is matured for either 6-8 or 12-20 weeks, again depending on the size. She makes it either as plain or smoked, or flavoured with a mixture of fresh garlic, fennel seed, dill tips and dried sage. Bewcastle, 'a pure lactic cheese in its simplest form' and finished either in poppy or sesame seeds, is made from the same Shorthorn milk, which Carolyn thinks 'is certainly a great deal better than Friesian milk'.

Using a mixture of about two-thirds of the Shorthorn milk and one-third of milk from her own mixed goat herd, she also produces Crofton, a drained and brine-washed cheese, weighing 1.35-1.8 kg (3-4 lb). This, Carolyn rates as one of her best. Not long ago she changed the recipe so that, after it has been matured for about 1 month, it softens and runs not unlike a Bonchester *see page* 324 and, as she claims, the mixture of milks gives it a good depth and the mildest of tangs. Allerdale and Allerdale Round are both made with goats' milk only. The

---

THURSBY
Cumberland Cheese

Stockists

Cumbria: J. & J. Graham
- - - - - - - - - -
Lucy's

Kent: The Cheese Shop

London: Rippon Cheese Stores

Oxon: Cheese to Please

former is pressed and matured for 6 to 8 weeks, the latter drained in a colander, then rubbed with salt. Both have a smooth, mild and very clean taste of goat. Then there are her Stumpies – Coulommiers-style cheeses sold fresh and suitable for grilling, Logs wrapped in vine leaves and Hedgehogs coated in chopped nuts.

Richard Woodall

Lane End, Waberthwaite, nr Millom, Cumbria LA19 5YJ

WABER-THWAITE
Ham and Bacon

☎ 01229 717237 **FAX** 01229 717007 **CONTACT** *Richard Woodall* **HOURS** *Mon-Fri 8.30-12.15 & 13.15-17.30 Sat 8.30-12.00* **DIRECTIONS** *From Broughton-in-Furness, take A595 towards Ravenglass. Drive through Bootle and follow the road for about 3 miles past the Brown Cow Inn on the right. About 100 yards after the pub, bear left and shop is 200 yards along on the left.*

A seventh-generation Woodall, Richard (Bar to his friends), his wife June and nephew Colin run the bacon, sausage and ham business from the village shop that doubles up as a sub-post office.

Made with a great sense of tradition, their products are without doubt among the best in the country. Most of the meat comes from the pig farm run by Bar's brother. Since 1976, it has been a closed herd (meaning that they do not buy in stock and only breed from within the herd) of Landrace and Large White pigs. Reared on a semi-intensive system, they are fed an antibiotic-free diet of cereal and vegetable proteins. 'Control of the raw material is essential, we aim for a consistency of size and obviously it gives us the great advantage of being able to process when the meat is really fresh'. Their range may be limited, but it is outstanding. Bacon is cured in the old-fashioned way with a dry-cure.

Recently I joined a BBC *Good Food Magazine* blind-tasting of dry-cured bacon from the multiples and a few small producers. Apart from Sainsbury's, every other sample from the supermarkets was a poor imitation – they wept scum (which a proper dry-cure should not), had no flavour, were too dry, too chewy, lacked any distinction or a combination of any of these. Bar's bacon was sneaked in and stood out a mile;

For the best view over the lake and one of the greediest teas imaginable, visit **Sharrow Bay**, ULLSWATER, **near Penrith CA10 2LZ** ☎ **017684 86301 fax 017684 86349**. *The hotel is open from the end of February to the end of November and every day between 16.00 and 16.45 tea is served in the lounge. Anyone can go, you do not need to be a resident, but the teas are so popular you must book. As for the spread, this is proper afternoon tea in all its glory. There are sandwiches, an ever-changing selection of meat, fish, cucumber and egg; toast from their own-made walnut and wholemeal breads; two kinds of scones, plain or walnut & cherry; with various own-made jams from mixed berries in the summer to rhubarb & ginger in the winter; and lashings of whipped cream; cakes in various guises, from a proper Madeira to a light lemon sponge; and biscuits that include such regional favourites as Grasmere gingerbread, shortbread and ginger & almond.*

it had a pronounced sweet meaty flavour, punched with a salty raspiness and, unlike the others, had intra-muscular and outer-layer fat. Like it or not, good bacon must have fat for moistness and flavour – any good butcher will tell you that.

Bar's Cumberland hams, traditionally cured in salt and saltpetre for 1 month, washed and dried and matured for 3 months, has a full-bodiedness. Its texture, similar to a York ham, is resilient with plenty of bite. He supplies them as ham steaks in packs of 2 slices or whole or half hams, bone-in or boned, rolled and vacuum-packed and either smoked or unsmoked. Cumbria Air-dried Ham is a recent invention – ham is dry-cured for 1 month in salt, saltpetre, herbs and a few spices (Bar has always been reticent about the exact ingredients), then air-dried (matured) for 12 months. Cumbria Mature Royal is pickled in beer, treacle, sugar, vinegar and salt for 1 month, then matured for 12 months. Both are sold thinly sliced and eaten like Parma ham, i.e. in their raw state.

Last but by no means least are his sausages, made from shoulder, belly and a few trimmings, 'only good goes in it to get good out' is his motto. His Cumberland, a long continuous link of pure meat, pungently spiced with pepper, is satisfyingly chunky and coarsely ground.

Currently under development is an air-dried beef. I was lucky enough to sample it a while ago and thought that although it was on the way it had not got there yet. It had the punch that I have come to associate with his products, but lacked the usual subtleties. I will keep you posted.

Stockists

Cumbria: Rogers & Tyson

Glos: William's Kitchen Ltd

London: Selfridges

Northumb: The Corbridge Larder

Yorks: The Good Food Shop

While you're in the area...

Cartmel Post Office, Parkgate House, The Square, CARTMEL LA11 6QB ☎ 01539 536201 is well known for its sticky toffee pudding. Sold in 1-2, 3-4, 5-6 and 8-9 portion sizes, the pudding base is a light sponge with chopped dates covered in a rich toffee sauce, made from butter, double cream and sugar. Also on sale are own-made quiches and frozen ready-meals, such as haddock & prawn crumble and Basque chicken.

Irthingspa Dairy, Holme View, GILSLAND CA6 7AJ ☎ 01697 747481 make two semi-hard-pressed cheeses: Irthingspa, made with unpasteurized milk from their own goat herd; and the crumbly but creamy Tynedalespa from unpasteurized cows' milk.

Modelled on the 17th-century chocolate house in Bishopsgate, **The 1657 Chocolate House, 54 Branthwaite Brow, KENDAL LA9 9XX ☎ 01539 740702** sells in both its shop and   restaurant, 'as many forms of chocolate as you can possibly imagine'. These take the form of chocolates to eat, chocolate to drink, ice-cream, chocolate cakes and even chocolate pancakes.

If you have been lucky enough to fly Concorde recently and sampled the on-board chocolates, you may be interested to know that they are made by the brother and sister partnership of Alison and David Kennedy of **Kennedy's Fine Chocolates, Silver Yard, Orton, PENRITH CA10 3RQ ☎ 01539 624781**. They make 60 plus varieties, including a Scotch Whisky Selection, various truffles, crunches and clusters, made up in 115, 170, 225, 350 and 450-g (4, 6, 8 and 12-oz and 1-lb) boxes. If you call at the factory, you can choose your own selection.

With almost everything cooked to order 'because of the lack of bits and pieces in our pies', Tim Burbush of **Burbush's, Unit 3 & 4, Gilwilly Industrial Estate, PENRITH CA11 9BQ ☎ 01768 863841** needs 24 hours' notice to avoid disappointment. Using local game, he makes a good selection of open pies topped with fruit, weighing 500 g, and 1, 2 or 3 kg (1 lb 2 oz and 2¼, 4½ or 6½ lb) , as well as some interesting fairly coarse pâtés, including pheasant & brandy, game liver with the livers first soaked in milk to stop them from being too pungent, duckling and Calvados & apple.

Visit **The Barn Shop at Low Sizergh Farm, SIZERGH, Kendal LA8 8AE ☎ 01539 560426** for a good range of local produce, including Richard Woodall's hams and bacons *see page 62*, breads from The Village Bakery *see page 57*, tea loaves from Bentham Home Bakery, pickles from Ancient Recipes and locally-reared Mansergh lamb in various cuts. From the new cheese shop within the shop they sell on-farm cheeses, including Thornby Moor Dairy *see page 61*, Loch Arthur *see page 331* and Mrs Kirkham's *see page 159* cheeses. Also during the season, there are pick-your-own strawberries and own-made strawberry jam from the fruit.

Ullswater Trout, Sockbridge Mill, TIRRIL, nr Penrith CA10 2JT ☎ 01768 65338 operates from an old converted flax mill. The original mill stream is still put to good use channelling the water from the river Eamont. Here you can fish-your-own for farmed rainbow and the odd brown trout escaped into the river, or buy fresh rainbow trout at any weight up to 4.5 kg (10 lb). They also sell oak-smoked trout and tubs and blocks of various pâtés, including devilled trout pâté made with lemon and horseradish.

Mail Order
Smoked trout only

Derbyshire

Bloomer's Original Bakewell Puddings

Tannery Bakery, Matlock Street, Bakewell, Derbyshire DE45 1EE

☎ 01629 813724 **CONTACT** John Bloomer **HOURS** April to Sept: 10.00-17.00; Oct to March: Mon-Sat 10.00-16.00 **DIRECTIONS** In town centre.

According to the local legend, Bakewell Pudding came about as the consequence of a 'mistake' by a cook at a local inn. Instead of putting a layer of jam over the custard filling, she spread it straight on the pastry and then poured the filling on top and thus the new pudding was born.

Bakewell Pudding is not, in fact, what we now call a pudding; rather it is an open tart. Bloomer's Original Bakewell Puddings are made with a puff pastry base which is usually own-made; although in the summer, at the height of the season, they are sometimes forced to buy it in. The jam is either strawberry or raspberry ('we put a good blob on the pastry and spread it with a spoon') and it comes as a relatively thick layer. Their custard is made with pasteurized liquid egg yolk, sugar, butter, ground almonds and a drop of almond essence – as, apparently, 'people say that without it, it isn't almondy enough'. Made on a daily basis, sometimes as many as three batches a day, it is pleasant enough but no great sensation. There are two sizes: small for 1 person; or large that 'cuts comfortably into 6 portions'. Best eaten warm, to 'bring the puff back', they recommend gently heating it, unless you are lucky enough to catch one as it cools down straight from the oven.

Stockists

Derbys:
Chatsworth Farmshop
- - - - - - - - - - -
Connoisseurs

BUXTON mineral water is sold bottled – either still or carbonated – throughout Britain. Are you aware, though, that in Buxton you can get it for free from the stone fountain at **St Ann's Well** in The Crescent right in the centre of Buxton? It spews water out at the rate of 7,000 litres (1,232 pints) an hour – all day and night. Canny locals know to come laden with bottles for filling.

Holdsworth Chocolates
Station Road, Bakewell, Derbyshire DE4 1GE

☎ 01629 813573 **FAX** 01629 813850 **CONTACT** Barbara Holdsworth
HOURS Mon-Sat 9.00-17.00 **DIRECTIONS** From Bakewell, take A619 towards
Chesterfield. On the outskirts of the town, bear right off the main road immediately after the old bridge. Follow signs for Holdsworth to the industrial estate at
the top of the road.

Barbara Holdsworth has gone from strength to strength with her hand-
made chocolates. Her range develops nicely and she has avoided the
usual pitfalls of most British chocolate-makers of using inferior-quality
ingredients and over-sweet fillings.

Her latest addition are Carrés, squares of bitter chocolate with a
minimum of 60 per cent cocoa solids in orange or mocha coffee
flavours, or mint and extra bitter with 70 per cent cocoa solids. Usually
I find the higher the cocoa solids, the better the chocolate; in this case
I preferred the coffee, with its dry tang that creeps up on you, and the
satisfyingly bitter-sweet orange. All the Carrés are neatly finished and
embossed with the initial 'H'. Barbara is obviously highly competent at
raised chocolates as it is she who produces the bitter-mints with the
Duchess of Devonshire's personal crest – one of my favourite finds at
Chatsworth Farmshop *see page 67.*

Stockists

Derbys:
Chatsworth Farm-
shop

Hants: Wiltons

London: Harvey
Nichols

Strath: The
Chocolate Box

All her chocolates are made with a good Belgian couverture containing a minimum of 60 per cent cocoa solids, unsalted butter, and
'proper' spirits and liqueurs, fruit purées and essences as flavourings.
Her pralines are worth singling out; these are made with a ganache of
chocolate, butter and cream mixed with a nut paste. They have a
markedly smooth texture and a good depth to them; you certainly
know you have eaten chocolate after biting into one of them, although
I must admit it is not always easy to tell exactly which nut it is. I also
liked her orange cream, with its loose – almost runny – centre of

---

**Pugsons of Buxton, Cliff House, Terrace Road, BUXTON SK17 6DR ☎ 01298
77696** *is the eponymous domain of Peter Pugson. To staunch the flow away from his shop
to the supermarkets, he has perked up his own-made range and has introduced several new
mousses. These include a rich smoked salmon mousse made with lemon juice, sherry, horseradish, sweet paprika and cream, wrapped in large slices of Goldstein's smoked salmon, on
the grounds that 'there's nothing like the smoker who's kosher'. Try his punchy potted ham,
made with ham from Maynard Davies see page 230, brandy and spices, 'but no butter
inside, only on top to seal the mixture', or any one of his open fruit tarts – all made with a
rich buttery pâte brisée as the base and a generous helping of fresh fruits laid on a layer of
crème pâtissière or apples cooked down to a thick purée and mixed with vine fruits and brandy and
finished with an apricot glaze – or the special order hams baked off, generously washed in a marmalade
glaze and carved off the bone. There is also a good selection of cheeses, including a local creamy and
smooth-textured fresh goats' cheese from Jumble Farm, Deaville's Staffordshire Organic see page
244 and Buxton Blue, and to eat with them, Derbyshire oatcakes see page 67. If you are feeling
thirsty while shopping, Peter always keeps a supply of chilled Buxton water in a cooler and you just
help yourself.*

MAP 4 DERBYSHIRE 67

chocolate, butter and orange purée; it was clean-tasting and, in spite of its obvious richness, refreshing and surprisingly sharp. Her range of truffles, filled chocolates and cream centres are all well-finished and smack of a good honest *chocolatier* at work.

Holmfield Bakery

Holmfield, Burbage, Buxton, Derbyshire SK17 9DF

BURBAGE
Derbyshire Oatcakes

☎ 01298 23543 **FAX** 01298 74441 **CONTACT** Peter Higgins **HOURS** Mon-Fri 7.00-15.30 Sat 7.00-12.00 **DIRECTIONS** *From Buxton, take the A53 towards Leek. Pass through Burbage. After the traffic lights, go through a cross-roads with a church on the right. Take the first left. The Bakery is immediately on the right.*

Peter Higgins has been churning out Derbyshire oatcakes for the last 48 years. Little has changed since he first started, 'the recipe is exactly as it was. The only difference is once I deposited the mixture on the hot plate with a scoop, now I use a mechanical 3-across depositer'.

You could easily be forgiven for thinking that Derbyshire and Staffordshire *see page* 245 oatcakes are one and the same thing. An unfamiliar palate would be hard pushed to tell them apart. Mr Higgins thinks otherwise, 'They are distinct. Derbyshire oatcakes are thicker and larger. And although the ingredients – oatmeal, flour, water, sugar, yeast and salt – are the same, the proportions vary'.

I like them with no more than a little butter, as it is the best way to allow their slightly sour but nutty flavour to come through.

Mr Higgins also makes pikelets, which he describes as 'crumpets without the rings'. Made with a crumpet mix of flour, yeast, water, salt and sugar, they are dropped directly on the hot plate. 'As they have no ring to hold them in and up, they don't rise. Instead they spread up to about 5 inches across.'

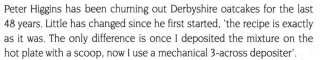

Stockists

Derbys: Pugsons of Buxton
- - - - - - - - - - -
Edwin Wild
- - - - - - - - - - -
Fletchers Butchers
Lomas Foods
- - - - - - - - - - -
Mettricks

Chatsworth Farm Shop,

Stud Farm, Pilsley, Bakewell, Derbyshire DE45 1UF

PILSLEY
Sausages and Cheese

☎ 01246 583392 **FAX** 01246 583464 **CONTACT** Sandy Boyd **HOURS** Apr to Oct: Mon-Sat 9.00-17.30 Sun 11.00-17.00; Nov to Mar: Mon-Sat 9.00-17.00 Sun 11.00-17.00 **CARDS** Amex, Switch, Visa **DIRECTIONS** *From Junction 29 on the M1, follow the signs to Chatsworth House. Drive through Baslow and turn left at the roundabout on to B6012, signposted Edensor. After about 1 mile, turn right, signposted Pilsley. Farm-shop is on the left after about ¼ mile.*

Chatsworth Farm Shop, on the Duke of Devonshire's estate, is primarily a fresh food shop. Sandy Boyd's first intention is 'to source from the farm, either Chatsworth itself or tenant or local farms. Then I buy elsewhere, with an emphasis on quality British foods'. Sold from the butcher's counter at the far end is meat mainly from the estate. There is the Duchess's Jacob lamb, on-farm beef hung for 14 days, and ducks from the Hereford Duck Company *see page* 133, free-range geese and turkeys for Christmas and a splendid range of meaty sausages – including the Duke's favourite, a robust 90 per cent pork with pork liver to give it a greater intensity. Only British cheeses are on sale here and with over 80 to choose from, you can expect most of the on-farm favourites. One very local, from near-by Beeley, is a rich and creamy soft goats' cheese made by Mrs Clark. Made one day and drained overnight, it is sold as a lactic cheese with a tinge of sharpness and the merest trace of goat.

Then there are the pâtés and prepared foods made by the busy chef André, who used to cook at the House but now is gainfully employed in the shop's kitchen. New this year is the rabbit & gin terrine; it is chunky and succulent with a good flavour of game. He also is in charge of all the baking, which includes a rich game pie generously filled with game from the estate; various other pies, terrines, cakes and biscuits and, at Christmas, a rich dark and generously fruited Christmas pudding.

Expect to find on the attractive pine-pedimented shelves such specialities as Duskin's apple juice *see page* 148, heather honey from the moors above the House, vinegars from Les Fines Herbes *see page* 170 and jams from Stonham Hedgerow *see page* 250.

What is also interesting are their own jams or preserves, 'We used to make them, then they were made for us under the Duchess's own label. Now we've come full circle and once again they come from our very own kitchens'. Under the supervision of André, they produce a limited-edition range using produce in season, 'after all, the world does have seasons. So why not reflect them?' says Sandy. This means that not everything is in stock all year round. According to Sandy, however, that is part of the excitement. Last autumn – and hopefully the same will be true this – there was a thick, richly fruited proper damson cheese, quince and some crab apple jams, all made with fruit from the estate. This spring saw a sharp rhubarb preserve made with the best Yorkshire rhubarb. Whatever time of year you visit, I can guarantee that you will not be disappointed.

George Stafford

130 Belper Road, Stanley Common, Derbyshire DE7 6FQ

STANLEY COMMON
Black Pudding

☎ 0115 9325751 **CONTACT** *Janice Greaves* **HOURS** *Tues-Fri 8.00-13.00 14.00-17.30 (-13.00 Wed) Sat 7.30-13.30* **DIRECTIONS** *From Ilkeston, take A609 into the centre of Stanley Common. Shop is on the right, just opposite the recreation ground.*

I am pleased to hear that George Stafford who is – to put it bluntly – way past retirement age, still gets up every morning at 4.00 am to make

> I *have also heard that pork butchers* **Jerry Howarth, 7 King Street,** BELPER DE5 6PW ☎ **01773 822557** *make good black puddings based on their grandfather's recipe. More reports please.*

his black puddings. Using a 'secret' recipe which came to him after years of making what he considered to be unsatisfactory ones, he has since won six gold, four silver and two bronze medals at the annual French black pudding championships at Mortagne-au-Perche.

Frankly I find some black puddings far too overpowering: too harsh, too strident and too obviously piggy in flavour – but not George's. His are milder and more subtle than what I have come to expect from a British version; in fact, they are much more like the French *boudin de Paris*, with their light creamy texture. How he achieves this he is far too canny to tell, but I suspect that he cuts down on the copious amount of starch – either oatmeal, barley or flour – that British butchers tend to use, and possibly even adds a little milk or cream. Who knows? George certainly is not letting on.

While you're in the area...

Gingerbread has been made in **ASHBOURNE** since the 1820s by **William Spencer & Son, 35-39 Market Place, DE6 1EU** ☎ **01335 342284**. Unlike the gingerbreads of the North that are dark, sticky and made with black treacle, theirs is pale and firm and contains chopped candied mixed peel.

With an owner who has an Italian for a mother-in-law, expect to find a good selection of Italian food at **St James Delicatessen, 9-11 St James Street, DERBY DE1 1QT** ☎ **01332 331255**. Ken Davis also keeps a good selection of British on-farm cheeses, so look out for Isle of Mull Cheddar *see page* 321 and Little Derby made by Mrs Fowler *see page* 283.

Stockists

Avon: The Sausage Shop

Derbys: Hollingsworth Butchers

Michael's Delicatessen

Wayne Spiers

London: Simply Sausages

ASHPRINGTON
Sharpham
Cheese

Sharpham Creamery
Sharpham House, Ashprington, Totnes, Devon TQ9 7UT

☎ 01803 732203 **FAX** 01803 732037 **CONTACT** *Mark Sharman* **HOURS**
Easter to end Sept: Mon-Fri 14.00-17.00 **DIRECTIONS** *From Totnes, take*
A381 towards Kingsbridge. After about 1 mile, turn left signposted Ashprington.
Follow the road about 2½ miles into village centre. At the war memorial, turn left
uphill into dead-end road. Follow the road 1 mile on to the estate and follow signs
to Sharpham Vineyard.

Set in the stunning valley of the river Dart, the Sharpham estate covers
500 acres of mixed farmland that includes pastures for the dairy herd,
vineyards from which an English table wine is produced, orchards,
woodlands and gardens. In the 17th-century cobblestone courtyard
behind the house, one of the stone buildings has been converted into
a dairy.

Here cheese-maker Debbie Mumford works making Sharpham, a
Coulommiers-style cheese made using the milk from the estate's Jersey
herd. The milk is thermized (flash-heated), a less stringent treatment
than pasteurization. (To explain the difference briefly: for straightfor-

---

Country Cheeses, Market Road, TAVISTOCK PL19 0BW ☎ 01822
615035 fax 01837 840510 *has recently opened behind the main Pannier*
Market. With the exception of Stilton, every one of the 50-odd cheeses sold in the
shop come from the South-West. Apart from such favourites as Beenleigh Blue see page 85,
Devon Garland see page 79, Keen's Cheddar see page 242 and Sharpham see above,
you can expect to find some very unusual ones made on a small scale. There is Vashti a soft
goats' cheese see page 48; Campscott a sweet, well-matured hard ewes'-milk cheese; and the full
range of Colespark cheeses, including their Wensleydale and soft goats'-milk rounds plain or flavoured
and wrapped in vine leaves. Owner Elise Jungheim also sells a farmhouse clotted cream, whey butter
from Quickes see page 86, biscuits from Fudges Bakery see page 92 and Crosse Farm Bakery olive
and walnut breads see page 74.

ward pasteurization the milk is heated to 72°C/161°F and kept at that heat for 15 seconds; whereas for thermization the temperature of the milk does not go above 65°C/149°F.)

Either a 1-kg (2¼-lb) round or a 250-g (8½-oz) square, Sharpham is made over 4 days. The curds are cut, moulded, brined and drained, then left at a comparatively warm temperature (9-10°C/48-50°C) for about 4 weeks to allow its white mould to develop and the cheese to ripen. With a creamy richness underlayed with a salty-sweet grassiness, over the past couple of years there has been a marked improvement in its consistency. It ripens far more evenly and fully so that while you can still cut it with a knife you can spread it too.

Stockists

Chesh: The Cheese Shop

Devon: Ticklemore Cheese

Lancs: Ramsbottom Victuallers

London: Cheeseboard

Surrey: Vivian's

Dittisham Fruit Farm
Capton, Dartmouth, Devon TQ6 0JE

CAPTON
Vegetables and Salads

☎ 01803 712452   **CONTACT** Edward Kain   **HOURS** Mar to end Oct: 10.00-17.00   **DIRECTIONS** *From Dartmouth, take A3122 towards Halwell. After about 2½ miles, follow signs for the Prehistoric Hill Settlement Museum (part of the farm), which start at The Sportsman's Arms.*

One of the best pick-your-own in the country, each season Dittisham Fruit Farm adds to its interesting and unusual choice of vegetables, salad leaves, herbs and edible flowers. Here everything is grown with flavour in mind and they supply several local restaurants, including the *doyenne* of the area, Joyce Molyneux *see below*.

> Joyce Molyneux at **The Carved Angel, 2 South Embankment**, DARTMOUTH TQ6 **9BH ☎ 01803 832465** *is known for only buying the best possible local ingredients. If you hit on one of her suppliers, then they must be good. Eating at her restaurant is one of life's great treats; but if neither time nor budget runs to it, she sells pots of her own-made pickles, jams or marmalades, made with 'whatever I feel like, with whatever's in season'. At Christmas there are her rich, fruit-laden puddings for sale.*

Introduced this year are Greek cress (a new one to me); American or land cress with its dark green, shiny leaves and its hot flavour, similar to watercress; Linzer Delicatesse and Belle de Fontenay potatoes which, with their firm waxy texture, are perfect for salads. Mitsuba, described by Joy Larkcom in her excellent *Salad Garden* as 'hardy, ever-green … also known as Japanese parsley or honewort. The stems and leaves are used raw in salads: their delicate flavour could be described as a blend between parsley, celery and angelica'; and planted this spring for picking summer 1996, canes of autumn-fruiting lush golden raspberries.

These will join the existing herbs and salad leaves, such as flat-leaf parsley, various basils, sorrel and rocket (in more-or-less continuous supply as they have 12 sowings a year), mizuna, gold and green purslane; edible flowers like courgettes, from late June to the end of August, chives, borage, pinks, marigolds and nasturtium; lettuces, including red Continuity, pinky-red frilly Rossa fruillana, oak leaf in both red and green, Tom Thumb and Little Gem; and baby vegetables, like leeks the size of a Biro, ping-pong ball (or smaller) turnips and beetroots, mange-tout that measure no more than 2.5 cm (1 in), Yellow Currant tomatoes the size of a large pea with a piercingly sweet flavour, nutty patty pans, baby broad and runner beans, and the most minute peas. In the potato line, there are Pink Fir Apple and La Ratte, an early waxy salad potato; two unusually coloured potatoes – Purple Congo with blue flesh and Pentland blue with a blue skin. They also grow a good range of soft fruit from which they make fruit liqueurs and they also make a Dittisham plum liqueur using the famous local fruit *see below*.

When you go, do not be put off if half the crops mentioned do not appear on their list. Mr Kain is probably far too busy planting, picking or brewing to write everything down. So if you cannot find what you are looking for, just ask.

Mail Order

Liqueurs only

Stockists

Devon:
Dartington Farm
Foods

Dartmouth:
Vintners
- - - - - - - - - -
Killerton House
- - - - - - - - - -
N. H. Creber Ltd

Victoria Wine Co.

Dittisham, pronounced 'ditsum' by those in the know, is a charming village on the sweeping banks of the river Dart. It is famous for two things – sailing and Dittisham plums. The Dittisham plum is, so the locals claim, a species of plum grown on its own root stock that is propagated by planting its suckers and can only be grown in Dittisham's micro-climate. Similar in shape to the damson but bigger, its skin is a deep pink merging into a yellow blush and its flesh a golden yellow. In taste it is not unlike a Victoria, although altogether fruitier and richer. With a very short season around the second and third week of August, usually it crops well, except last summer which was a disastrous year for all plums. One local orchard that can be relied on for about 100 tons each year, only produced a dismal 10 pounds. **Dittisham Post Office & Village Stores, DITTISHAM, Dartmouth TQ6 0ES ☎ 01803 722214** *sells them, collected from three orchards. Some orchards around the village also sell direct from the gate.*

CHAGFORD

Lamb and Mutton

Express Mail Order Meat

Lingcombe Farm, Chagford, Newton Abbot,
Devon TQ13 8EF

☎ 01647 433300   **CONTACT** Stuart Baker – telephone ahead

Stuart Baker has worked with sheep for over 40 years and there is probably very little he does not know about them. He tends two flocks on his farm right up against the Common – local-speak for Dartmoor. Even though he does have extensive grazing rights up on Dartmoor, he does not keep his lambs there, 'the grass it just not good enough to produce the quality I want'. So they graze either on his land or on 'grass-keep' rented out by dairy farmers in South Devon in winter and he makes a point of banning unnecessary chemicals, including organophosphate sheep dips.

After years working with different breeds, he has settled for Suffolk ewes and White-faced Dartmoor ewes, 'a strange breed, one most people have never heard of. But native to here. They're quite small and easy to handle, rather important when you get to my age'. Both ewes are crossed with a Charolais ram, 'but a proper one – wedge-shaped. Broad and tall on the rear end and diminishing towards the shoulder. So the right quality is at the right end', meaning the legs are broader than the shoulders.

For the Suffolk Charolais-cross, lambing starts in January with the meat ready for the table in April through to June. Their finish and quality – with maximum conformation (shape) and minimum fat cover – is first class, as several of the local hotels (including Giddleigh Park) will testify. The White-faced Dartmoor lamb later in the year during April, with the lambs ready for slaughter by July. They put on more fat and tend to a richer meat. Both are hung from 7-10 days, depending on their age, the weather and how advanced the season is. Although certain chefs ask for 14-day-hung lamb, he thinks it is 'excessive'.

Mutton comes from the White-faced Dartmoor, 'Suffolks just wouldn't do', but what you or I think of as mutton – that is to say a 2- or 3-year-old sheep, is but a pale imitation as far Stuart is concerned. 'Mutton to me is when it's got to the far end of its life. It's fulfilled its use – lost its teeth or can't lamb any longer. Then it's proper mutton. Anything from 6 to 10 years old. And it must be hung for at least 14 days, sometimes it can go up to a month'. Because, as he admits, his White-faced can run to fat, he sells haunch (leg and chump) or loin joints; the rest of the meat he gets stripped and turned into mutton mince. His mutton is excellent: tender, finely grained, not too fat, with a deep lingering taste that is certainly different from lamb and without a hint of the rankness that you usually associate with mutton. As Stuart says, 'Good mutton only comes from a ewe, I'd never sell anyone a ram'.

Wild Beef
Hillhead Farm, Chagford, Devon TQ13 8DY

CHAGFORD
South Devon Beef

☎**FAX** 01647 433433 **CONTACT** *Richard Vines – telephone ahead*

What, you may ask, is 'wild beef'? I imagined huge horned beasts roaming the moors waiting to be rounded up, *Rawhide*-mode, with a lasso. That was before I went to see Richard Vines at his farm on the edge of Dartmoor. His wild beef are British native breeds, either Welsh Blacks or South Devons, and they seem the most tranquil of creatures.

Now you should know about the great divide when it comes to Devonian cattle. South Devons are huge, copper-coloured and were traditionally dual-purpose: cows were milked and bullocks, usually castrated at about 2 months, reared for meat. Devons (the correct breed book name, although they are also called North Devons, Red Devons or Ruby Reds) are smaller and richly red. The A30, which meanders its way through the county, is the acknowledged dividing line: to its north graze the Devons, to its south, the South Devons. 'Native breeds', says Richard, 'are like wines, they have their differences. For flavour, their life-style also matters; how they're reared, what they feed on and – for muscle-tone – how much they walk, is just as important'.

Although he owns only 20 acres and rents another 200 acres of grass, Richard's cattle are kept wild in the sense that they are run at about a head per 5 acres. He can manage this as he has common rights to the Moor. 'It's an age-old tradition. You live on the Moor, you breed on the Moor and you rent grass keep'. His Welsh Blacks, a far hardier breed, stay on the Moor most of their life, whereas the South Devons he brings down in their second year to finish either in the yard or in the richer meadows around the South Hams.

All his meat is steer beef 'heifers have another destiny' and is slaughtered – depending on required finish – at any age between 2-3½ years. Taken to a tiny abattoir, no more than two in a lorry, they are slaughtered within 30 minutes of arrival to avoid stress. Hung for 3-4 weeks, butchering is 'bespoke' and he tends not to differentiate between the breeds. You can order rib on the bone, rolled rib, fillet, sirloin steak, rolled sirloin, rump, top rump, topside, etc., in whatever quantities you want.

For our simple lunch – he has rather primitive cooking facilities on the farm – we had a joint of rolled brisket, pot-roasted over onions. The fat had been stripped out and it looked like a piece of silverside, although it ate like a prime cut, with its buttery texture and grassy flavour. Martin Lam, chef/patron of Ransome's Dock restaurant in London, is one of Richard's keenest customers. He prefers the braising cuts for his kitchen, as 'they stand up so well to long slow cooking, they're never stringy nor fibrous. They're rich in flavour, gelatinous, surprisingly lean and meltingly tender. And, if I'm honest, they have more flavour than the prime roasting cuts'. Richard makes regular trips up to London and surrounding areas and will deliver to your door.

CHERITON BISHOP

Breads and Pâtisserie

Crosse Farm Bakery
Cheriton Bishop, Exeter, Devon EX6 6JD

☎ 01647 24442 **FAX** 01647 24442 **CONTACT** Harriet Helliwell – telephone ahead

In the leaflet describing her range, Harriet Helliwell starts off with two columns. One headed 'We Do Use' runs as follows: 'butter; French pâtisserie flour; chocolate; fresh fruit; fresh dairy cream; all-butter pastry; free-range eggs'. The other, the 'We Don't Use' column, lists 'margarine; cheap flour; chocolate substitutes; tinned fruit or essences; UHT cream; bought-in pastry; battery eggs'. Harriet, as you have probably gathered, is a firm believer that to make good cakes, pastries, puddings and breads, you need good ingredients, 'I place a lot of emphasis on the quality of my raw ingredients – if you don't, it just doesn't work'.

From her bakery, converted from an out-building on the family

MAP 1 DEVON 75

farm, Harriet bakes an exceptionally well-finished and professional range. Stuck, as she is, in the middle of the country, there is no such thing as a passing trade; consequently everything is cooked to order and sold fresh, so ideally she likes about 48 hours notice.

Depending on the time of year, her range varies. In summer you can expect luscious summer puddings, plenty of cream-filled open fruit tarts and refreshing key lime pies. Her chocolate truffle tart is a triumph: a base of chocolate sponge made with ground almonds is soaked with rum and then covered with a deep layer of truffle, using a 60 per cent bitter chocolate beaten with cream and yet more rum. Lightly textured and satisfyingly smooth, it had a deep resonance and a lingering bitter-sweet taste. Her lemon tart is as sharp and fruity as you could hope for: the shortbread crust is crisp and buttery and the filling of double cream, eggs, lemon juice and lemon zest is light and airy. I also tried the American-style baked cheesecake: it has no base as such, but is a whole cake made with double cream mixed with lemon juice and sour cream. Again it had a velvety smoothness and, when served with one of Harriet's fresh fruit coulis, is a well-balanced combination of flavours. She also makes French apple tarts glazed with apricot preserve; a 60-cm (2-ft) high *croquembouche* of choux buns filled with a praline cream and crowned in caramel; and delicate lemon & almond crisps or nutty and gooey chocolate florentines.

Although she is not really set up to makes breads as such, she does produce a glorious focaccia. Made with lashings of olive oil and hand-kneaded by her mother 'who's very good at it, as she trained as a weaver', it is one of the best I have ever tried. Possibly an Italian might disagree, dismissing it as too thick or too bread-like, but I could not stop tearing away at it. Crisply textured, Harriet first makes a slack dough, which she leaves to rise twice so the texture of the bread opens up to absorb the copious quantities of olive oil while baking. She flavours it with pumpkin and sunflower seeds, sun-dried tomatoes, fresh rosemary and black olives, garlic or possibly a mixture of any of these. As soon as it comes out of the oven even more olive oil is poured over it. She produces it in a smallish size, enough for 4, and for parties or barbecues an impressive 60-cm (2-ft) round. If you are in the area, this is one bakery that is worth the detour.

Mail Order
Christmas cakes and puddings only

Bollhayes Cider
Bollhayes Park, Clayhidon, Devon EX15 3PN

CLAYHIDON
Champagne Cider

☎ 01823 680230 **FAX** 01823 680807 **CONTACT** Alex Hill – *telephone ahead* **CARDS** Access, Visa

By and large, cider has a seedy reputation as a rustic, unrefined drink, only good for getting well and truly smashed – or that is how some people see it. It was not ever thus, as Alex Hill points out. 'As long ago as the 17th century, landed gentlemen in Herefordshire and the West

Country put much time and effort into the production of cider. The best still Herefordshire cider, matured in the cask for 2 or 3 years, sold for a higher price than any French wine'. There were even unsuccessful attempts to make sparkling cider, with a second fermentation in the bottle, but in those days no one had discovered how to get rid of the sediment while still keeping the fizz.

Alex makes his bottle-fermented Devon cider in exactly the same way as the French make their champagne. It is a very labour-intensive process which I shall attempt to describe as briefly as possible. Alex collects cider apples from within a 5-mile radius (it is a source of constant disappointment to him that he only owns 1 acre of orchard), the apples are pressed and the juice is left to ferment in vats until spring. When he feels and smells it is ready, he racks it off into barrels, adds sugar and champagne yeast and then bottles it for the secondary fermentation that takes about a year. The bottles are then placed horizontally in a sloping oak *pupitre* (rack) and carefully turned no more than a quarter-turn each day, while gradually upending the bottle. This process of riddling causes all the sediment to settle in the neck of the bottle. This is then frozen – and there is an extraordinary-looking machine for that – the cap is flipped off and the internal pressure of the bottle causes the solid mass of sediment to blow out. The bottle is then corked and wired and is ready to be laid down.

Alex only started making his bottle-fermented Devon cider in 1992, with the first bottles released last year. The craft of *méthode champenoise* cider was revived by James Lane of Gospel Green *see page* 270 and, as with champagne, each maker produces a drink of different character. Alex's, a lively straw-gold liquid, is austere, dry and 'flutey', with a cider nose. He admits that, as for any vintage wine, it will vary from year to year and that he may be completely mad to even attempt making it, but then – why not?

Stockists

Derbys: Chatsworth Farmshop

Devon: The National Trust Shop

London: The Beer Shop

Somerset: The County Stores

Sussex: The English Farm Cider Centre

CULLOMPTON
Meat

Pipers Farm
Cullompton, Exeter, Devon EX15 1SD

☎ 01392 881380 **FAX** 01392 881600 **CONTACT** Peter Grieg **HOURS** *Farm: Mon-Fri 9.00-17.00 Sat 9.00-12.30 or telephone ahead; Shop: Mon-Tues & Thurs-Fri 8.30-17.00 Wed & Sat 8.30-12.30* **CARDS** *Access, Switch, Visa* **DIRECTIONS** *From Cullompton, take the B3181 towards Broadclyst. After about 3 miles and opposite Fagin's Antiques, take the second left turn, signposted Clyst Hydon and Plymtree. Pipers Farm is 1¼ miles along on the right. Do not take the first left at the Merry Harrier Pub, also signposted Clyst Hydon and Plymtree.*

Peter and Henrietta Greig favour traditional breeds. Beef is from pure-breed (North) Devon, which is single-suckled until 6 months, reared on Exmoor then brought down to be finished at Pipers Farm. 'Here we have a grade-1 permanent pasture and we use minimal fertilizers. It's rich in clover, rib grass and meadow grass, it's so deep-rooted that

MAP 1   DEVON   **77**

when they feed they pull up all the minerals. And you can tell by their flavour. Slaughtered at approximately 2½ years, they are remarkable for their marbled meat. Lamb is Suffolk-crossed North of England mule as Peter thinks 'it gives a good meat-to-bone ratio and a good balance of meat and fat'. Pork comes from a mixture of traditional and rare English breeds – Gloucester Old Spot, Large Black, Welsh and a few Saddlebacks – which are kept in small groups both indoors and out. There is no denying that all their animals are reared and finished to high standards. What is also striking is the standard of butchery, described by Peter himself as 'a full range of traditional cuts, plus our own style of Continental cuts'. 'Our own style' tells a story; completely inexperienced, he taught himself to butcher by taking carcasses apart, muscle by muscle, throwing them in the pan and seeing how they ate and contracted. 'After several weeks', he told me ruefully, 'I realized that lamb and beef were exactly the same butchery-wise. I could have saved myself a lot of time'.

Hanging also plays an essential part, 'first the animals have to be unstressed at the time of slaughtering; we use a small abattoir not far from here. Then it's no good sloshing the carcass down with mains water as they so often do. By washing them down, you remove the thin membrane of protection and provide the perfect medium for

---

Albert Beer, secretary of the Devon Cattle Breeders' Society, lives at **Barn Lane Farm, STOKE RIVERS, Barnstaple EX32 7LD ☎ 01598 710836**. From there he runs **Devon Friendly Butchers**. Devon, in this case, stands for Devon or North (as opposed to South) Devon cattle, also known as Red Devons or Ruby Reds. When it comes to buying beef, some butchers in these parts think 'It's Angus for conformation, but Devon for taste'. With its rich veins of intra-muscular fat and fine-textured grain, it can be very good indeed. Albert produces a leaflet listing the Friendly Butchers in the South-West who usually stock the breed. These include Pipers Farm see left Heal Farm Meats see page 78, F. Heard, Nelson Road, Westward Ho! and several others. If you are interested in trying it, contact Albert direct.

Magdalen Road on the edge of **EXETER** is a good street for food shopping. Pipers Farm have a shop at **27, EX2 4TA ☎ 01392 74504**. **Bon Goût Delicatessen** is just a few shops away at **45 Magdalen Road, EX2 4TA ☎ 01392 435521** and sell cheese, own-made quiches, pâtés and salads, as well as some good local produce. Further down the road and on the other side are fishmongers **Gibson's Plaice at 38, Magdalen Road, EX2 4TD ☎ 01392 495344**. A marble slab laid out with – among other fish – dab, bass, brill, crab and skate wings from Brixham market.

---

bacteria. The skin must be dry'. Beef is hung for 4 weeks, lamb for 2-2½ weeks, mutton for 3-4 weeks, pork for 10 days, chickens for 1-2 weeks and their bronze turkeys at Christmas 3 weeks. I went into the chilled storage and there were the carcasses, dry as a bone, solid to touch and as clean as could be.

Apart from the various cuts, Pipers Farm also produces oven-ready stuffed cuts: there is boneless leg or topside of lamb, butchered in Peter's inimitable way (and I could not begin to describe how he does it) and stuffed with a pencil of apricot, peach hazelnuts, fresh mint & cumin, coriander & garlic, pesto or rosemary & garlic; or their gigot (boneless thigh) of chicken with pesto & brown breadcrumbs, and apricots, hazelnuts & fresh herbs. The quality of whatever I tried was first-rate: chicken, so often insipid, had a true clean lingering flavour with a close texture; lamb was sweet and flowery; sirloin of beef succulent, with depth of flavour and firm texture, had plenty of bite – but, as Peter says, 'proper meat shouldn't just melt in your mouth. It should have plenty of bite and then you should get your taste reward'. Whether you buy from Pipers Farm itself or their new shop at 27 Magdalen Road, Exeter EX2 4TA ☎ 01392 74504, you will get your 'taste reward'.

KINGS NYMPTON
Rare-breed Meat

Heal Farm Meats
Kings Nympton, Umberleigh, Devon EX37 9TB

☎ 01769 574341 **FAX** 01769 572839 **CONTACT** Anne Petch **HOURS** Mon-Fri 9.00-17.00 Sat 10.00-16.00 **CARDS** Access, Mastercard, Visa **DIRECTIONS** *From South Molton, follow the road signposted George Nympton. Follow the road out of George Nympton and take the first turning on the right, signposted Sampson Barton Guesthouse. Follow the road straight over Sampson Cross and take the first turning right at Sletchcott Cross, signposted Heal/Yeotown. Farm is signposted on the left.*

From running the first business selling rare-breed meats (Heal Farm is a breeding centre approved by the Rare Breed Survival Trust) to launching recipe dishes, there seems to be no end to Anne Petch's inventiveness. She started by rearing rare-breed pigs – Gloucester Old Spot, Middle White, russet-red Tamworth, Berkshire, Large Black, Saddleback with their distinctive stripe, and British Lop the rarest of the rare breeds – and sending them straight off to the abattoir. However, the price they fetched did not even cover the feed bill. The obvious and necessary course of action was to process herself and so she began retailing the meat. Just like Topsy, the business grew and grew.

Now all this was several years ago. Anne still keeps her pigs 'my first love' and farms according to her own principles, 'based on humane animal husbandry'. The retailing side, however, is increasingly important. Butchery and processing is done on-farm, in a well-equipped butchery. Pork, from her own pigs, comes as legs on the bone weighing from 1.25 kg (2½ lb) up to 7.2 kg (15 lb) – a hefty size, or off the bone 900 g-5.85 kg (2-13 lb); bone-in or boned loin, tenderloin, belly and she even sells 225 or 450-g (½ or

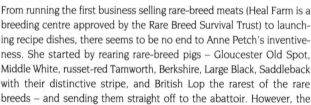

Treloar's, 38 High Street, CREDITON EX17 3JP ☎ 01363 772332 sells a small but well chosen range of groceries: jams, mustards, local cheeses, various cakes and biscuits baked by a troupe of local ladies, herbs from owner Guy Treloar Garrett's garden, various specialist vegetables in season and even – in Autumn – locally picked wild mushrooms. The kitchen at the back of the shop has always produced pizzas, pasties, quiches, pâtés, salads and pies – ideal for a picnic if you are travelling about. This year they have expanded and gone for an interesting and well-cooked range of oven-ready meals that only need heating up when you get back home. These include Devon pork & apple, a casserole of pork with apples in a cider and onion sauce; Cod Mauritius, cod steaks with fennel baked in a fresh tomato and coriander sauce; and for the vegetarians a ratatouille bake of various vegetables, including courgettes and pepper with garlic and herbs covered in a layer of potatoes and cheese. They also make their own pesto with fresh basil, Parmesan, pine nuts and virgin olive oil with fennel. There is also a whole range of two-bite-size puff pastry cases stuffed full of all sorts of fillings, including chicken & tarragon, ham & mushroom, and salmon & shallot.

MAP 1   DEVON   79

1-lb) tubs of fresh lard. Her hams are superb, some even say the best in Europe, with their deep succulence and pungent meatiness. Brine-cured in salt, saltpetre and water, 'because the flavour of the meat is so outstanding that this is the best way to bring it out', they are hung for 3-4 weeks to age. A whole ham weighs 3.5-5.5 kg (8-12 lb), halves 1.8-2.7 kg (4-6 lb) and you can order them unsmoked or smoked, uncooked, plainly cooked or cooked in cider. Bacon, with a good length of meaty flavour and layer of rich fat, is cured similarly and is available as back or streaky, unsmoked or smoked over oak, beech and apple-wood. Coarsely ground sausages, with a meat content of 85 per cent, are made from shoulder meat, hard back fat (and occasionally belly) in natural casings. They also have a good punchiness, and flavours include plain, pork with herbs, pork with garlic, tomato & chilli and a boiling sausage of smoked garlic with pork.

Her latest developments are the recipe dishes that won the 1994 Gold Medal in the West Country Food Awards. However, I am not totally convinced. Anne sees them as '... providing busy people with good home-cooked food without the bother of shopping and time-consuming preparation, in fact just the kind of things they would make themselves if they just had the time'. I tried the Provençal beef & wine casserole and I certainly would not quibble with the quality of the ingredients or the end-result. As they are meant to save us time, though, I was somewhat taken aback to find that 3 hours of cooking time was involved. Admittedly, I did not have to do much other than drain and heat the marinade, brown the pork rinds, bacon, beef and vegetables then add the heated marinade (about 15 minutes), then shove the whole lot in the oven and wait 2½-3 hours for it to cook, checking it every so often to make sure it did not dry out. Other dishes include Roman lamb, pork with lemon & ginger, coq au vin, Sussex steak with Guinness, and venison in port. They come with all the ingredients, easy-to-follow cooking instructions and in portions from 2 to 8.

Anne also sells North Devon 'Ruby Red' beef hung for 3 weeks, conventional and primitive rare-breed lamb, and – at Christmas – turkeys, geese and ducks all reared to her specifications. She also packs original hampers with the best of local produce.

Stockists

Avon: Chewton Cheese

Devon: Mole Valley Farmers

Snows Delicatessen

Somerset: Laurel Bank Dairy Co.

White Hall Delicatessen

Peverstone Cheese Company
Peverstone, Mutterton, Cullompton, Devon EX15 1RW

PEVERSTONE
Devon
Garland
Cheese

☎ 01884 35292 **FAX** 01884 35041 **CONTACT** Jeremy Frankpitt – *telephone ahead*

Several years ago there used to be a delicate creamy cheese called Devon Garland, made by Hilary Charnley. Hilary talked evocatively about it, describing how in the spring it was as yellow as the cowslips waving in the fields and, as the days lengthened and the cows relished their grass, the cheese would deepen in colour and flavour. Then sud-

If you are at **HATHERLEIGH Market** on Tuesday mornings, **SOUTH MOLTON Market** on Thursday mornings or **BARNSTAPLE Market** on Friday mornings, look out for **Eileen Toon's Cheese Stall** as she specializes in West Country cheeses. She has a fine selection, including a new one to me – Campscott, a tangy hard ewes'-milk cheese, made in Lee near Ilfracombe.

denly there was no more Devon Garland, she had ceased production. The good news is that once again there is Devon Garland, only this time it is made by Jeremy Frankpitt. He has bought the recipe from Hilary along with some of her expertise to help him.

When I visited him last summer in his state-of-the-art dairy, he was still a little uneasy as he thought he had not quite mastered the technique. Local gossip had it otherwise. Hilary was said to have pronounced his is as good as hers ever was, but she was not letting on in case he got over-confident – you will just have to judge for yourself. If you have never tried Devon Garland, either now or in the days when Hilary was making it, please do as it is glorious.

Jeremy makes his with the unpasteurized milk from the Friesian herd (Hilary originally used Jersey milk, but for the last 6 months of making, she too was using Friesian milk). He uses the morning milk and it goes straight into the 800-litre (176-gallon) vat. Starter is added and left for about 45 minutes, for a slow acid build up. Then rennet goes in and the milk is top-stirred so the cream does not rise to the surface as the curds form. 'After a while the curds drop like stones' to the bottom of the vat and then the whey is slowly drawn off. Next comes the cutting and blocking, a technique similar to cheddaring. The curds are then salted and ready for moulding.

Now Devon Garland is a distinctive-looking cheese, easily recognizable by its necklace of green herbs – made from finely chopped spring onions, thyme and oregano – strung through it. Jeremy packs each 3.5 kg (8 lb) mould about half full, spreads the herbs mixed together with a little curd on top, then fills the mould right up to the top with plain

---

There are two working stone-ground mills in the county particularly worth a visit for their flour, bakeries and a good cup of tea. **Crowdy Mill, Bow Road, HARBERTONFORD, nr Totnes TQ9 7HU ☎ 01803 732340** uses two varieties of wheat: Flanders 'that makes wonderful white flour' and Maris Widgeon for its nutty flavour. They mill a 100 per cent wholemeal, plain or self-raising flour; 85 per cent brown, plain or self-raising; and an unbleached white with the bran and middlings (the coarser elements of the flour) removed, also in plain or self-raising. They also mill organic rye and malted grain, a Granary flour made with wheat, rye and malted wheat flakes. At the mill, you can either eat in the café or take away the various own-baked scones, breads and cakes, including cheese & onion, sour dough, seeded wholemeal and spiced fruit loaf, carrot, sponge and fruit – all made from their flour.

Otterton Mill, OTTERTON, nr Budleigh Salterton EX9 7HG ☎ 01395 568521 also mill from English wheat. They produce a 100 per cent wholemeal and an unbleached white. Both flours are particularly finely ground so that they are suitable for both bread and cakes. At the bakery they sell a 100 per cent wholemeal, Granary, white bread and rye breads, as well as various cakes, including walnut & raisin and a sticky-topped moist gingerbread made with black treacle, golden syrup, ginger and eggs; honey flapjacks, shortbread and chocolate coconut squares; again you can either take them away or try them in the café.

curd. 'I want the green to blend in with the cheese, a soft haze rather than a definite line' is the look he is after. Everyone has their fond memories and Jeremy has been mightily surprised about 'what a lot of old women' there are around – all telling him he ought or ought not blend his herbs to get the right texture and balance of flavour.

The cheese is lightly pressed for 1 hour, re-moulded and pressed overnight, then covered with vegetable lard to keep the moisture in. It is turned daily for about 4 days, then left on the racks for about 3 weeks, turning it occasionally. Even here there is some dispute about the age at which it is best eaten: Sarie Cooper of Ticklemore Cheese *see page 85* likes it comparatively young at 3 weeks; others go for 4 to 5. I tried a 3-week piece in the dairy and thought it was too young. Later on in South Molton market, I tried it at 5 weeks and it had all the honey grassiness that I remembered from the original, the same mellow fruitiness, springiness and delicacy that makes it one of our great on-farm British cheeses.

Stockists

Avon: The Fine Cheese Co.

Devon: Natural Life

Lancs: Ramsbottom Victuallers

London: Neal's Yard Dairy

Yorks: Arcimboldos

Most food lovers like to buy locally wherever they are. Unfortunately, to find good quality this can mean hurtling around the countryside for miles. So imagine my excitement when I came across **Holne Producers Co-op**. It is such a good idea I cannot imagine why other villages have not thought of it before. The Holne Co-op has six members who live in or around the village and all farm or grow and process food. This spring they opened up at **Village Farm, HOLNE TQ13 7SL ☎ 01364 631532** which doubles as a butchering unit for the meat and game and a showcase for the members. Here you can buy Deer Force 10's park venison, butchered into various cuts or transformed into pâtés, pies and sausages; organic (to Soil Association standards) lamb from Village Farm; Pat & Charles Hill Smith's shiitake mushrooms, fresh herbs, lamb and beef; luscious clotted cream from Tony and Sue Colwill; and a creamy goats'-milk yoghurt, a fresh delicate cheese, various soft fruit in season and vegetables from Mrs Henderson who also runs a comfy B&B. If only there were more co-ops like this, we would all be able to eat much better.

Melchior Chocolates
Tinto House, Station Yard, South Molton, Devon EX36 3LL

SOUTH MOLTON
Chocolates

☎ 01769 574442 **CONTACT** Carlo Melchior **HOURS** Mon-Fri 9.00 -17.00; week-end – telephone ahead **CARDS** Access, Mastercard, Visa **DIRECTIONS** From Tiverton, take the A361 towards Barnstaple. At the South Molton junction, leave the A361 and drive 500 yards to the next junction, then turn right into Station Road. After 500 yards, Melchior is the first house on the left.

Since our last edition, Carlo Melchior has been on the move, no more than a few miles from Chittlehampton to South Molton. As far as I can taste, this has not affected his chocolate-making one jot. They are still as intense, clear and fresh as they ever have been – Carlo is a firm believer that chocolates should 'leave the palate fresh'. As you would expect from a Swiss, he uses Swiss couverture with 60 per cent cocoa solids, but his cream he assures me is local. He makes nuttily intense pralines – using nut oil extract instead of the more usual nut paste or nut butter for a cleaner and better defined taste – as well as liquid liqueurs that burst in your mouth with brio. For me, however, his real speciality is his luscious truffles in white, milk or dark chocolate. Adding this year to the existing range, he has come up with a 10-year-old single malt whisky truffle. Carlo still has not 'settled on a particular one. It's Glenfiddich sometimes, I've even tried Bushmills. As long as it's a good 10-year-old and a single malt – it works' … and work it does, it is a sensation. Made with his creamy butter-free ganache, it packs a powerful punch that warms and reverberates in the mouth, lingering with a silky smoothness.

Also new are his mini Christmas chocolate logs. Like all Carlo's chocolates, they are deftly finished with well-defined detail; the logs are draped with white chocolate 'snow' and decorated with a mini green marzipan leaf. They come in two flavours: milk chocolate with a ganache rum centre that is dense and coolly sweet; and the drier, darker in flavour as well as in colour, dark chocolate log with a chocolate ganache.

Stockists

Avon: Chandos Deli

Cumbria: The 1657 Chocolate House

Lancs: Ramsbottom Victuallers

London: Coco

Fortnum & Mason

TIVERTON

Mustards

Highfield Preserves

Highfield Vineyard, Longdrag Hill, Tiverton, Devon EX16 5NF

☎ 01884 256362 **FAX** 01884 253729 **CONTACT** *Jennifer Fraser* **HOURS** *Apr to end Dec: Mon-Sat 10.00-18.00* **CARDS** *Access, Mastercard, Visa* **DIRECTIONS** *From Tiverton, take B3137 towards Nomansland. Follow the road up Longdrag Hill and vineyard is on the right.*

While husband Ian Fraser tends the vineyards of over 6,000 vines of Seyval Blanc, Siegerrebe, Madeleine Angevine and Kernling grapes, his wife, Jennifer, and their son, Donald, make mustards with their own wine or cider.

Using a blend of yellow and brown whole seeds and yellow mustard powder, with quantities varying according to which mustard she is making, Jennifer tends to grind the seeds quite fine, 'the danger is', she told me, 'if you soak whole seeds in alcohol, they swell up and it ends up like eating tapioca'. Most of her mustards are relatively smooth, although sometimes she does mix in a few whole grains 'to give detail'.

On the edge of the market square, **Snows of Devon**, 2 King Street, **SOUTH MOLTON EX36 3BL** ☎ **01769 572447** *doubles up as a delicatessen, with a couple of tables for coffee, teas and light lunches. There is a well-chosen range of local produce, including honey from Exmoor, creamy Greek-style yoghurt from Stapleton Farm, sausages from Bangers, Heal Farm smoked ham see page 78, a superb rich and thick clotted cream that comes straight from a nearby farm in its enamel bowl and is scooped up into 225 or 450-g (½ or 1-lb) tubs, and local cheeses such as Devon Garland see page 79, Beenleigh Blue see page 85, and Sharpham page 70. From the kitchen at the back, proprietor Lizzie Stocks makes salads, pâtés, quiches, homity pies, various tarts and puddings and, at Christmas time, dark cakes and puddings rich in brandy. She also has her own range of chutneys, including a spicy pear and a sweet well-textured tomato & red pepper.*

NEW ENTRY

Her range has expanded and she now makes about 10 different flavours, including a dill, lime, garlic & gherkin, hot and fiery green peppercorn, a relatively mild white wine using their Madeleine Angevine and a mellower red wine.

They also make various chutneys, jellies and herb-flavoured oils. Jennifer's sister runs a herb farm in Gloucestershire, so good supplies of fresh herbs can be relied on. New this year are a satisfyingly sparse traditional horseradish made from the grated root mixed with vinegar, mustard, sugar and spices, and a prune & walnut conserve. Based on a French recipe, the prunes are soaked for 24 hours, then slowly cooked down to a thick purée with muscovado sugar. Chopped walnuts are added as late as possible, otherwise 'if they're in the pot too long, they loose their flavour and identity'. Rich, meaty and very dense with a good crunch of nut (but do watch out for the rogue piece of shell), some people do eat it with cold meat but it is equally good spread on a slice of coarse country bread.

Stockists

Avon: Masons of the Mall

Devon: County Stores

The National Trust Shop

London: Hamish Johnston Marketing Ltd

Selfridges

Mrs Gill's Country Cakes
Unit 5, Link House, Leat Street, Tiverton, Devon EX16 5LG

TIVERTON
Fruit Cakes

☎ 01884 242744 **FAX** 01884 257440 **CONTACT** Jacqueline Gill – telephone ahead

Recipes are extraordinary: no matter how carefully the ingredients are listed and how meticulously the methods are explained, no two people ever end up cooking an identical dish. When it comes to cakes, the difference can be even more apparent. Let's face it, some people are born to bake others are not – and however hard they try, they never make it.

Jacqueline Gill is a born baker. She hit on a recipe 'from a friend in Canada, via Scotland' for a rich dark fruit cake and has stuck with it ever since. She may have scaled up her throughput, but in essence hers is still a home-scale bakery. She still mixes in small batches, will not compromise on the quality of the ingredients and the results are still as fresh and as polished as ever. Her cakes are very old-fashioned, rich and dark with just a smidgen of spice. The ingredients are all of the best quality: equal quantities of plump currants, raisins and sultanas, juicy mixed peel, dark muscovado sugar, black treacle, unbleached white flour, butter, fresh eggs, fat glossy undyed black-red morello cherries, and brandy, whisky or sherry drizzled over the cakes as they come out of the oven. Matured for at least 2 months, Jacqueline's cakes come either plain or neatly decorated with circles of nuts and cherries in 12.5, 15 and 17.5-cm (5, 6 and 7-in) rounds. She also ices them for Christmas.

Stockists

Hants: Whites

Lancs: Ramsbottom Victuallers

London: Fortnum & Mason

Selfridges

Waitrose

New this year is her Dundee cake, with ground almonds and sherry, and a light moist almond cake. With a glorious crunchy texture, due no doubt to the addition of ground and nibbed almonds in the mixture, it has running through its centre a layer of own-made marzipan that was clear and pure and delicately almondy. It does show that using real almonds – as opposed to a cheap essence – makes the world of difference. Jacqueline, you may rest assured, would never use anything but the best.

TORQUAY
Ice-cream

Rocombe Farm Fresh Ice-cream Ltd
123 Union Street, Castle Circus, Torquay, Devon TQ1 3DW

☎ 01803 293996 **FAX** 01626 873645 **CONTACT** *Peter Redstone* **HOURS** *Sep to end Jun: Mon-Sat 10.00-17.30 Sun 14.00-17.30; July to end Aug: Mon-Sat 10.00-17.30 & 19.00-23.00 Sun 14.00-17.30 & 19.00-23.00* **CARDS** *Access,* Visa **DIRECTIONS** *In town centre, near the town hall.*

Readers of the last edition may remember how I raved about the quality of Rocombe Farm Ice-cream, describing it as, 'rich, luscious, creamy, pure and infinitely moreish, this is ice-cream at its most magnificent'. Well nothing has changed; it is still as good as it ever was. It still contains the best – and only the best – ingredients, with a basic mix made with organic (to Soil Association standards) full-cream Jersey milk, double cream, unrefined cane sugar and organic free-range eggs. In other words, everything you would hope for in an ice-cream.

However, I would like to raise a serious issue here (and by doing so I am in no way casting aspersions on Rocombe). Several food lovers have made the point that Rocombe Farm's ice-cream is very expensive. Well of course it is, it is a luxury ice-cream. How could it not be with all those prime ingredients? But is it, and I think this is equally relevant, value for money, particularly when you realize that ice-cream is the only product that is legally sold by volume rather than weight? Now all ice-cream needs a certain amount of added air (the technical term is over-run), otherwise it would set rock-hard. The question is how much is acceptable? Some companies add as much as 120 per cent, whereas Rocombe Farm adds on average a mere 35 per cent. If you were to take two tubs, one of theirs and a cheaper competitor's, you might find that that Rocombe Farm's would weigh almost twice as much. It goes without saying the more air you add to an ice-cream, the cheaper the costs to the manufacturer. So, although one tub may look like a bargain on the shelves, what you may be buying is no more than a small amount of actual ice-cream fluffed up by air.

Curiously the manufacturer does not even have to declare the amount of over-run on his label; nor is there much supervision as to how the selling (as opposed to the ingredients) label is written. I have seen ice-cream proudly claiming 'made with real double cream'. Yet when I made further enquiries, I discovered it contained only 1 per cent double cream. It is just not good enough. I also dislike the wholesale use by most manufacturers of emulsifiers and stabilizers as, apart from the fact that I really do try and avoid all additives, they leave a nasty

Mail Order

For details of home delivery in London ring Swaddles Green Farm ☎ 01460 234387 or Home Farm Foods ☎ 01380 722254. Overnight delivery a possibility: ☎ 01626 872291 for details taste in the mouth. Rocombe Farm do not use them, 'They are put in to hold the mix together, to trap the molecules of air and to give the ice-cream texture and shelf-life', Peter Redstone told me, 'but if you have as high a fat content (and for the right texture it must be cream) and use eggs as we do, you don't need them. Because they aren't there, not only does it make ours a purer product but it also means it has that cleaner, clearer, fresher flavour'.

Rocombe Farm has grown considerably since it first started about 8 years ago. All their ice-cream for their wholesale range is made on-farm and this includes: Farmhouse Original, with its clear creamy taste; Bananas 'n' Cream, which is just like sucking on a rich lush banana milk-shake; Crunchies 'n' Cream, with its explosion of honeycomb that pops in your mouth; and, still my favourite, Lemon Meringue, a sharp lemon base softened with melting meringue; as well as lots more. At the shop they 'invent' a new flavour every day. Some are seriously good – apple with blackcurrant and Somerset Cider Brandy, or Thunder & Lightning (treacle & clotted cream). Others prove to be a little over the top, but you can never argue with the quality.

Ticklemore Cheese

1 Ticklemore St, Totnes, Devon TQ9 5EJ

☎ 01803 865926 **CONTACT** Sarie Cooper **HOURS** Mon-Fri 9.00-17.30 Sat 9.00-16.45 **DIRECTIONS** In town centre.

Ticklemore Cheese, with its impressive selection of on-farm British cheeses, is actually a cheese shop tucked away down an alley off Fore Street. It is also the headquarters for the manufacture of Robin Congdon's incomparable cheeses – Beenleigh Blue from ewes' milk, Harbourne Blue from goats' milk, and Devon Blue from Ayrshire cows' milk – although the making takes place a few miles up the road, deep in the countryside.

Robin's cheeses are exceptionally good. He started 14 years ago with Beenleigh Blue, then came Harbourne Blue and finally he added Devon Blue to the range about 4 years ago. He buys in all his milk and makes his 3 cheeses in more or less the same way. The milk is flash-heated, started, renneted and a mould *penicillium roquefortii* is added. At this point Robin deviates from the norm, 'as I cut the curds early – that's how the French do it. And I stir frequently for the feel of the curd'. His is the French style of making: our blue cheeses, Stilton for example, are matured first to allow a hard crust to form, then spiked to encourage the blueing; the French spike after a matter of days, leave them to blue, then wrap them in foil to stop the rind. These subtle but important differences in technique result in very differently textured cheeses: Stilton is softer, more paste-like than the crumblier French blue cheeses, such as Roquefort.

Last autumn at the Specialist Cheesemakers Association annual

Stockists

Devon: Ticklemore Cheese Shop

London: Harrods

Selfridges

The Real Food Store

Oxon: The Wine Shop

Beenleigh Blue

conference, I tasted Robin's blues with his partner Sarie Cooper – here are my notes. 'Beenleigh Blue – matured for 6 months, crumbly creamy texture, salty sharp with good immediate tang, opens out to full richness with marked echoes of sheep, superbly balanced. Devon Blue – matured for 5 months, light yellow in colour, quite dry crumble, milder with slight sharpness and hint of lemon honey, less complex than Beenleigh [Sarie did say that it could have done with a bit more age, how long it is matured depends on what time of year it is made]. Harbourne – matured 4 months, pale creamy-white, strong sharpness that dies away quite quickly, nice edge of blue tempered with slight sweetness'.

I also sampled his hard pressed, dry-salted Ticklemore. Made with goats' milk, it has a distinctive ridge shape and a creamy, mildly acid flavour. Ticorino is the ewes'-milk version and the sample I had, matured for 6 months, was at first bite sweet – almost caramelly – that dies away down the throat with a warm fullness. Robin, it has to be said, is one of our great cheese-makers.

Stockists

Avon: The Fine Cheese Co.

Devon: Natural Life

London: Neal's Yard Dairy

Lothian: Iain Mellis

Surrey: East Side Cheese Company

While you're in the area...

The address to contact Anne Tarrant of **Heaven Scent Herbs** is **Pound Cottage, Pound Lane, BRIDFORD EX6 7HR ☎ 01647 252782**, although she actually makes her mustards in the former station in Crediton. Here she produces 22 flavoured mustards, with black and white mustard seeds, cider vinegar and olive oil as their base. Some – herb & honey, lime & thyme, and green peppercorn – are relatively mild; others – chilli, mint & onion, and horseradish – are unashamedly hot. Recently introduced is the spiced cranberry, with chopped berries and cinnamon, to go with the Christmas bird.

Quickes Traditional, at **Home Farm, NEWTON ST CYRES, Exeter EX5 5AY ☎ 01392 851222 fax 01392 851382**, make Cheddar and various other cheeses on a large scale. You can visit the dairy shop and buy their range. Look out for well-matured unpasteurized Cheddar and their salted or unsalted creamy whey butter.

Thanks to Mr Dugdale of Exeter who wrote in response to the last edition of the Guide recommending the 'amazing' chicken & mushroom pies at butchers **Moores of Heavitree, 5 North Street, EXETER EX1 2RH ☎ 01392 73243**. 'Like a number of others I thought they needed a touch of salt, but were otherwise perfect. I bought five of the next batch and confirmed that they froze well.' More reports please.

Rachel Stephens, Stockbeare Farm, JACOBSTOWE, Okehampton EX20 3PZ ☎01837 810587 makes Curworthy, a mild and pleasant cows'-milk cheese. She also matures it on for about 5 months for a deeper, crisper flavour and sells it under the name of Devon Oke.

River Exe Shellfish Farms, Oak Farm, KENTON, Exeter **EX6 8EZ ☎ 01626 890133 fax 01626 891789** sell pacific oysters farmed in the estuary of the River Exe and they will deliver anywhere in mainland Britain within 24 hours. Sold in dozens, packed in waxed boxes surrounded by seaweed, they weigh around 'the 100 gram plus mark'. In season, they sometimes have freshly picked samphire.

Salcombe Smokers, 54 Fore Street, KINGSBRIDGE TQ7 1NY ☎ 01548 852006 sell a good range of wet fish, bought mainly from Looe and Plymouth. They also sell pacific oysters and mussels farmed in the river Avon, dressed crab and – in season – samphire. What they are possibly best known for are Salcombe Smokies, hot-smoked mackerel with a firmer than usual texture and a powerful punch of salt. They also smoke farmed salmon from Scotland, trout, cod's roe, haddock and halibut.

Langage Farm, PLYMPTON, nr Plymouth PL7 5AW ☎ 01752 337723 fax 01752 339712 will send 115 and 225-g (¼ and ½-lb) tubs of clotted cream by post. From the shop, you can also buy a thick sharp sour cream that tastes just like crème fraîche.

Stop off for tea with one of the best views of the Salcombe Estuary at **The Wardroom, 19 Fore Street, SALCOMBE TQ8 8B ☎ 01548 842620**. All the delicious cakes are own-made on the premises and served in generous portions. At lunchtime, try the Salcombe crab, fresh from the crabbing boats, or home-made soup.

Food writer Josceline Dimbleby uses **Riverford Farm Shop, RIVERFORD, Staverton, Totnes TQ9 6AF ☎ 01803 762523** regularly when she is staying at her holiday cottage in the area. 'It's very enterprising, full of all sorts of different things – some own-made or own-grown, such as the vegetables. The pork comes from the farm, the bread is baked in their bakery and there's lots of good local cheeses and other products from local producers'. Among her favourites are the 'chewy and warm-flavoured' port-cured ham sold in thin slices, leek & pork sausages that she considers, 'the best of an exciting range' and the chunky, generously filled game pies.

The smoked trout from **Head Mill Trout Farm, Head Mill, UMBERLEIGH EX37 9HA ☎ 01769 580862 fax 01769 580950** are so good that they find their way to the dining tables of the Connaught Hotel in London. You can buy them straight from the farm, as either whole trout or 170-200-g (6-7-oz) fillets. They also sell freshly caught trout, weighing anything from 285 g (10 oz) up to 450 g (1 lb).

Bridfish
Unit 1, Sea Road North, Bridport, Dorset DT6 3BD

☎ .01308 456306 **FAX** 01308 456306 **CONTACT** *Patrick Gibb* **HOURS**
Mon-Fri 9.00-17.00 Sat 9.00-16.00 **CARDS** *Access, Visa* **DIRECTIONS** *On
the outskirts of Bridport, on the A3066 Beaminster road.*

Stockists

Devon: Joshua's
Harvest Store
- - - - - - - - -
Provisioner
- - - - - - - - -
Watty's
Delicatessen

Somerset:
Bonners N. L.
(Butchers)
- - - - - - - - -
Loders Country
Fayre

Bridfish is on the outskirts of town on the Old Laundry Estate. They sell
some fresh and frozen fish but what they are best known for is their
smoking. All the preparation, curing and smoking is done behind the
shop's counter in a processing area suitably clad in white tiles, where
they use a modern Afos kiln fuelled with oak sawdust. Local silver eels
are hot-smoked for a mild juicy meatiness, and are sold whole weighing
a minimum of 350 g (12 oz) or as skinned fillets in 225 and 450-g (½ and
1-lb) packs. Hot-smoked Scottish mackerel, sold whole or as plain or
peppered fillets, has long been a favourite. Recently they have introduced a cold-smoked mackerel for a more delicate, drier fish that
comes in slices as thin as paper.

    Their salmon is farmed on the West coast of Scotland and I remem-
ber their smoked salmon as having a soft pliant texture with a pleasant
juiciness. New this year are their hot-smoked fillets which are lightly
cured then hot-smoked so they are cooked through; with a texture
similar to plain grilled salmon, they have the added flavour of a salty

R. J. Balson & Son, 9 West Allington, BRIDPORT DT6 5BJ ☎ 01308
422638 *are the oldest butchers in Britain. Trading started in 1535 at the shambles
(market stalls) under Bridport's town hall and they came to rest at the current shop
in 1880. Unlike several shops with such pretensions, their claim can actually be substantiated; a local
historian did the necessary research and traced an unbroken family line right back. Nowadays they
trade in a modern way, with some own-made traditional products such as faggots, black puddings, Bath
chaps and a fiery hogs' pudding. Meat is locally bought and, during the game season, it is worth visiting the shop just to see the abundant display of local game in fur or feather hung up outside the shop.*

NEW ENTRY

smoke. With a strong smoke and a good cut of salt is the rich punchy cods' roe imported from Iceland. These are dry-cured, cooked first and then smoked at 49°C (120°F). They also smoke kippers using herrings from Scotland, trout, prawns, haddock (with a markedly yellow colour that they assured me is natural), cod, pollack, chickens and duck breasts. They even prepare a gravad trout (sweet-cured with dill as gravad lax, only using trout). They will smoke customers' fish for them and, when they can get supplies, wild salmon.

Denhay Farms
Broadoak, Bridport, Dorset DT6 5NP

☎ 01308 422770 **FAX** 01308 424846 **CONTACT** Amanda Streatfeild **HOURS** Mon & Thurs 9.00-17.00 **CARDS** Access, Visa **DIRECTIONS** From Bridport, take the B3162 towards Chard. After about 2 miles, turn left at sign for Broadoak. Drive through the village and turn left at sign for Denhay only, on to a farm track.

BRIDPORT
Cheddar Cheese, Butter, Ham and Bacon

Marshwood Vale, Thomas Hardy's 'vale of small dairies', was once littered with small dairy farms. Most farmers owned no more than 5 or 6 cows and they would skim the milk for butter, make Blue Vinney cheese *see page* 94 with the skimmed milk and sell these along with their eggs at the markets from Axminster to Bridport. Now the only cheese-producing farm left in the Vale is Denhay. They make Cheddar using pasteurized milk from their own Friesian herd in block, traditional cloth-bound 5.5-kg (56-lb) rinded wheels or Dorset Drums, a 2-kg (4½-lb) truckle. They do, however, carry on the butter-making tradition and produce a cheery yellow, mildly cheesy, salted whey cream butter.

The Streatfeilds, a husband and wife team of George and Amanda, have always kept pigs. This was also a traditional and economically sound practice on dairy farms as the pigs could be fed the whey, a by-product of cheese- and butter-making. The Streatfeilds, however, have gone one stage further and process or 'add value' to their pigs, producing Denhay air-dried ham and, new this year, dry-cured bacon and Denhay cured sausages. 'I'm fanatical about feeding the whey to our pigs' George told me, 'it's crucial to our product. Not only does it produce a more succulent meat but – and it's been scientifically proved – its composition changes. There's a difference in the ratio of saturated to unsaturated fats, the balance is better.'

Their pigs are sent off to slaughter and they buy the long-cut legs (leg and chump) for the hams and the short middles (from the chump to the shoulder) for the bacon. The hams are made by curing the legs in a brine flavoured with Dorset apple juice, honey and herbs, then lightly smoking them over oak chippings before finally air-drying them for several months. The result, a cross between an Italian Parma and a German Westphalian ham, is more resilient in texture than Parma, 'We have reduced the salt and refined and improved our techniques since

Stockists

Avon: The Fine Cheese Co.

Devon: Ticklemore Cheese

Dorset: Pamphill Farm Shop

London: Hamish Johnston

Surrey: Secretts of Milford

we first made it in 1990'; the taste, I am delighted to say, has much improved over the past years and it now has a fuller sweetness, a greater depth and richness. The short backs are dry-cured in salt, nitrite and vitamin C for about 10-14 days; some are smoked 'not for very long – just a matter of hours', others are left green but both types are then cooled down almost to freezing point and sliced immediately. It is sold as smoked or unsmoked back and smoked streaky in 225-g (8-oz) or 900-g (2-lb) packs. Using cured pork, off-cuts from the air-dried ham, extra fat, and various herbs, they also produce a cured sausage. Disarmingly, however, George is not confident about it yet, 'I'm still working on it'; so let's save it for the next edition.

FERRY BRIDGE Oysters

Abbotsbury Oysters
Ferry Bridge, Weymouth, Dorset DT4 9YU

☎ 01305 788867 **FAX** 01305 760661 **CONTACT** *Matthew Rodwell* **HOURS** *Easter to end Sept: Mon-Sat 9.00-17.00 Sun 12.00-15.00; Oct to Easter: Mon-Fri 9.00-17.00* **CARDS** *Access, Visa* **DIRECTIONS** *From Weymouth, take A353 towards Portland. The oyster farm is on the right, just before the causeway.*

Abbotsbury oysters are grown in the Fleet Lagoon, a natural estuary that runs from the Island of Portland as far up as the village of Abbotsbury. In *Moonfleet*, J. Meade-Falkner mentions the Lagoon (or lake, as it is known locally) as 'good for nothing except sea-fowl, herons and oysters'. Today it is a nature reserve – the Swannery at nearby Abbotsbury is enchanting – with clean, mineral- and plankton-rich waters, essential elements for oysters.

Although they do farm a few natives, the bulk of the 1 million oysters a year are pacifics. Graded and sold by weight – 80, 90, 100 and 110 g (3, 3½, 4 and 4½ oz) – they are markedly salty with plenty of meat and a firm texture. As they are so meaty, they are also very good for cooking. Abbotsbury purify their oysters in UV tanks for about 48 hours, and keep them in aerated holding tanks until sold. This, they claim, is necessary 'to maintain public confidence in the quality of our

Right in the centre of **CORFE CASTLE,** *an 'olde-worlde' National Trust bequest village complete with ruined castle, is* **Dragons Village Bakery, The Square BH20 5EZ** ☎ **01929 480400.** *Baker Nigel Dragon spent 2 years on a bakery scholarship in Germany; and although he does produce a traditional white cottage and a tin loaf with a long (8-hour) fermentation and 2 provings, it is for his German-style breads that he stands out. These he makes from bought-in German pre-mixes that, unlike ours, are of good quality. One of the reasons that other bakers do not use them is that they do not understand how to handle the dough. It is far stickier and sloppier and has to be proved in lined baskets then baked off on trays. He produces a good firm 100 per cent rye that, as he points out, any good German will tell you is better the next day when the rye has had a chance to mature. For a lighter rye, there is a 60 per cent with 30 per cent white flour mix; 6-grain, a mixture of rye, barley, wheat, millet and corn; and 12-herbs, that has in it such curious things as club moss, nettle and hawthorn leaves and camomile flowers – but for all that tastes light and grassy.*

oysters' even though they are grown in such pure waters. Are we really that fastidious a nation?

Sold from the farm off the causeway that links the Isle of Portland to the mainland, you can either take away (they will pack them for your journey) or sit by the Lagoon and be served them ready-opened with French bread and a glass of wine. Prices are kept very low as the policy is 'to encourage everyone to try'.

James Trehane & Sons
Stapehill Road, Hampreston, Wimborne, Dorset BH21 7ND

**HAMPRESTON
Blueberries**

☎FAX 01202 873490 **CONTACT** Jeremy Trehane **HOURS** mid Aug to early Sept: Mon-Fri 10.00-17.00 **DIRECTIONS** From Wimborne, take A31 towards Ringwood. Turn right into Ham Lane (B3073) and first left into Stapehill Road. Nursery is signposted on the right.

To the north of Bournemouth, around Ferndown, the land is heath-land. The sandy soil with a high acid level of pH4.5 to 5.5 makes ideal growing conditions for blueberries, cranberries and camellias. Under the new management of Jeremy Trehane, there are both blueberry groves where you can pick the fruit and a nursery where you can buy plants. Quite how and why blueberries ever came to be grown here is a long story dating back to 1949. Since those early days, the business has developed into one of the largest growers in the country, with 3 planted hectares.

The pick-your-own season starts around mid August (you should ring to check exactly when, it depends on to the weather) as they like to wait until there are whole clusters of ripe fruit, otherwise picking can be very tedious. Picking the fruit is easy enough; the blueberries are ripe when the whole fruit is blue – pick an unripe red fruit and you will find it is tart and bitter. Gently grasp the berry between your fingers, you do not want to squeeze it, and roll it over to avoid spoiling the bloom.

On the other hand you may want to try growing-your-own. Few gardens in Britain have the right soil for blueberries, but you can always grow them in large well-drained tubs using pure moss peat. Two differ-ent varieties, each in their own tub, will ensure pollination and it works best if you stagger their seasons; running through the varieties in order of ripening there are Bluetta, Patriot, Bluecrop, Berkley and Coville. Advice is on hand as to which are best. Delivery or collection is any time between late September and April, and all plants come with culti-vation sheets. Good luck!

Mail Order
Plants only
Stockists
Marks and Spencer

Two organic (to Soil Association standards) farms that grow both fruit and vegetables have farm-shops, run box schemes see Alan Schofield page 158 and come highly recom-mended are **Gold Hill Farm, CHILDE OKEFORD, Blandford DT11 8HB ☎ 01258 860293** and **Longmeadow Organic Vegetables, Longmeadow, GODMAN-STONE, Dorchester DT2 7AE ☎ 01300 341779**. More reports please.

Fudges Bakery

Bridge Bakery, Leigh, Sherborne, Dorset DT9 6HJ

☎ 01935 872253 **FAX** 01935 873397 **CONTACT** *Stephen Fudge* **HOURS** *Mon-Fri 8.30-12.30* **DIRECTIONS** *From Sherbourne, take the A352 towards Dorchester. After about 2 miles, turn right at sign for Leigh. Follow the road into the village. Bakery is on the right.*

For a small bakery based in the tiny village of Leigh, Fudges has done remarkably well. They still have a tiny shop attached to their bakery and they still bake some bread, but it is for their biscuits and cakes that they have built a reputation. Although they will no longer do mail order, several of their products already have national distribution – appearing in the 'right' shops - so the chances are you can buy them around the country.

Dorset Cheddar wafers were one of the first biscuits Stephen Fudge 'invented' when he joined the family business. I praised them to the skies in the last edition as 'crisp, light and airy, with a lingering deep intense cheesiness, they are so moreish I ate an entire packet in one go' and see no reason to revise my opinion.

New this year are the thin hexagonal butter biscuits for cheese and the wine-tasting biscuits. In fact I prefer the latter, with wine or with cheese; they are dead plain, made only with flour, butter, water, sugar, salt and sodium bicarbonate. Pleasurably crisp and clean to the palate, I find them a far better foil to cheese than the butter biscuits, with their intrusive additions of herbs and spices. There is also a cunningly simple and slightly sweetened savoury digestive. All these biscuits are markedly pure and come as a welcome relief from their mass-manufac-tured poor relations, where goodness-knows-what has been added.

Another addition is the ginger kringle cake, inspired by the Christin-gle ceremony. The 10-cm (4-in) chestnut-brown cake contains fruit and masses of it, fresh orange and lemon juice and zest, raisins, sultanas, almonds, walnuts, stem ginger and demerara sugar. It is a delight, well-spiced and as you take a bite you find a little pocket of stem ginger that warms the palate. More traditional fare comes in the form of the cocktail-size (2 bites) butter & brandy mince pies. Sold loose or in packs of 12, generously filled with a rich mincemeat, they are covered in a buttery, crumbly pastry. There are excellent florentines, with a good dark chocolate and masses of peel; *'weihnacht'* stollen (traditional Christmas bread) – a moist fruity bread enriched with butter and fruit is wrapped round a generous cylinder of marzipan with an obvious taste of bitter-sweet almonds – are but another two of my favourites from their large(ish) range.

What singles Fudges Bakery out is the obvious quality and care that goes into their products. They do not skimp on ingredients. If a recipe calls for butter they use butter, and when the 'proper' ingredients are used and used carefully the results are bound to be good. Although they have expanded rapidly, what a relief to find the products are still as good as ever.

Stockists

Cambs: W. Eaden Lilley & Co. Ltd

Derbys: Chatsworth Farmshop

Devon: N. H. Creber Ltd

London: Harvey Nichols

Northumb: Holly Avenue Delicatessen

MAP 2   DORSET   93

Whistley Crayfish
Whistley Waters, Milton-on-Stour, Gillingham, Dorset SP8 5PT

☎/**FAX** 01747 840666 **CONTACT** *Christopher Campbell – telephone ahead*

Although there are about 80 producers of signal crayfish *see below* in Britain, very few are open to the public on a regular basis. Christopher Campbell is one and I have had several encouraging letters from food lovers, all saying how much they have enjoyed their visit. If, however, you want details of a rancher near you, I suggest you contact Mo Richards, British Crayfish Marketing Association, Riversdale Farm, Stour Provost ☎ 01747 85495 fax 01747 51474. All the members ranch and pack to the Associations standards.

Only in season between May and October as they hibernate in winter when the water is cold, signal crayfish take about 3 years to reach 'restaurant size – 4-5 inches long, weighing around 2 oz, so you get between 8-10 to the pound' and about one-third of their weight is succulent flesh; the rest is shell that can go into a soup.

Christopher sends his crayfish live – you should never, ever even think of cooking a dead one. Kept cool and damp, packed in boxes, they should stay alive for about 2 weeks. If you call in season, he usually has some in stock, suitably starved and ready for sale, but it is advisable to ring first – just in case.

S. Moores
The Biscuit Bakery, Morcombelake, Bridport, Dorset DT6 6ES

☎ 01297 489253 **FAX** 01297 489753 **CONTACT** *David Winship* **HOURS** *Mon-Fri 9.00-17.00* **DIRECTIONS** *From Bridport, take A35 towards Honiton. After about 4 miles the bakery is on the left.*

In the 18th century, there was a small but thriving cottage industry in Dorset making buttons: one of the most popular buttons was the hand-sewn Dorset knob and, apparently, it is after these that the Dorset knob biscuit is named. Once eaten by farm-workers for break-fast, even an alleged favourite of Thomas Hardy when taken with a slice of Blue Vinney, they are curiously old-fashioned, with their dry-as-a-bone texture and faintly sweet flavour.

For all the years that I have slavishly bought them, I had never seen them made. Until this year, that is, when I hit on the bakery at exactly the right time. It is not that there is any season as such for making Dorset knobs, rather that S. Moores are so busy with their other bis-cuits that knobs have been relegated to a brief period of production between January and March.

At one time most of the local bakers made them at the end of the day in the dying embers of the wood-fired oven with any left-over dough. Now S. Moores are their only producers and they mix up a

Every country that produces cider has their own version of cider cake but, as far as I can see, they are no more than subtle variations on a theme. Mary Stewart of **Lower Farmhouse, SANDFORD ORCAS, Sherbourne DT9 4RP ☎ 01963 220363** *follows a rather unconventional recipe for her cider fruitcake; she adds mixed dried fruit and a 'touch' of her own-made marmalade to her basic mix of flour, margarine, sugar, eggs and her son's dry cider made in Somerset. Pale in colour, moist and with a light apple flavour, she bakes them in 15-cm (6-in) rounds.*

special dough with flour, sugar, yeast, a tiny amount of fat (margarine) but no salt. The dough is knocked back twice and then is ready for rolling out by hand, which – I can tell you, as I tried it myself – takes a lot of practise. Dough is rolled into a sausage with the left hand and using your right, you break off a small amount. There is no measuring, but everyone in the bakery is so adept they can judge the correct amount by eye. Then you press down with the palm of your right hand, cup it and roll up the dough to form the round, dome-shaped knob. Everyone was working at break-neck speed and in one session about 5 or 6 bakers roll out 1,600 in 1¼ hours – everyone except me. I took about 5 minutes just to get one correctly shaped. The knobs are proved for 1 hour, baked off at a very high temperature for about 15 minutes, turned over and baked for a further 10 minutes. Then they are separated by hand – by this time they have joined together at the base – and finally put back in the cool oven and left to dry for 3-4 hours.

I really like them; they are a particularly good with a salty cheese and best of all with a soft salty cheese, when their crunchy crisp texture acts as a good contrast. They also have good keeping qualities, well they would wouldn't they after all that baking and drying out? A packet in an airtight tin stays fresh for well over a year, provided you have not eaten them first.

Stockists

Dorset:
Cranberrys
- - - - - - - - - -
Something
Different

Somerset: The
County Stores

Surrey: Secretts
of Milford

Sussex: Tully's
Farm Shop

STOCK
GAYLARD
**Blue Vinney
Cheese**

Dorset Blue Vinney Cheese

Woodbridge Farm, Stock Gaylard, Sturminster Newton, Dorset DT10 2BD

☎ 01963 23216 **CONTACT** *Michael Davies – telephone ahead*

In the days when there were hundreds of small dairy farms in Dorset, each supporting perhaps six cows at the most, every farmer's wife would make Blue Vinney cheese. The milk, usually from Shorthorns, was skimmed, the cream was churned for butter and the leftover milk – with a fat content of about 1.8 per cent – was turned into a very-low fat hard cheese. The word 'Vinney' comes from *vinew*, an old English word which meant mould. It was in common use all over the country until the 16th century when it became confined to the dialect of the South-West and was, in particular, associated with the Dorset cheese.

Vinney was traditionally a blue cheese, 'But' explained Michael Davies, the only existing maker of a farmhouse Blue Vinney, 'a skimmed milk cheese is difficult to blue. With so little fat in the milk, there's very little medium for the moulds to work with. So it often was a

MAP 2　　　　　　　　　　DORSET　　　　　　　　　95

hit-and-miss affair'. Cheeses would spoil, turn as hard as cartwheels, with a wastage rate often as high as three in four. Moreover, in the days when blueing was a natural phenomenon (before controlled mould spores were added to milk), there was no guarantee that they would ever develop their blue veins. That is why rumours were legion of cheese-makers dipping old horse harnesses into the vats – or storing the cheese on damp flagstones covered with hessian bags or next to mouldy boots – to encourage the growth of the moulds.

Michael Davies, you will be relieved to hear, resorts to none of these practices. He still makes his cheese in the time-honoured way although, since my last visit, he has 'juggled with his recipe'.

*Run by Simon Harvell, **The Butchers Shop**, IWERNE MINSTER, nr Blandford DT11 8NA ☎ 01747 811229 is tucked on to the end of a row of cottages and has the thickest oak door imaginable. Beef, normally Hereford, is bought off local farms, is hung for a minimum of 14 days and – for the best possible flavour – Mr Harvell favours heifers. Extensively reared pork, hung for at least 5 days, comes from the rare-breed centre at Milton Abbas; bacon and ham is from Richard Woodall see page 62 and Sandridge Farm see page 284. Game and poultry are also well-hung and at Christmas there are locally reared geese, Bronze and Norfolk black turkeys and Mark Chilcott's 'heavy chickens' that can weigh up to 5.5 kg (12 lb). With a brine 'on the go', they usually have pickled brisket and tongue and you can rely on finding 'bits and pieces', such as trotters and caul fat.*

The morning's milk from his Friesian herd comes into the parlour by about 7.00 am and is now left to stand for a couple of hours, then it is skimmed to reduce its fat content to about 3 per cent, 'That's lower than was traditional, but makes a cheese more suited to our modern tastes'.

It takes about 24 hours to make. Starter is added to the unpasteurized skimmed milk, then vegetarian rennet and a penicillin mould (to ensure blueing). Once the milk has coagulated, it is cut into 'small pieces the size of walnuts' and left to settle overnight. The following morning, the whey is drained off and the curds are cut into blocks, milled, salted and packed into moulds. They stay in the moulds in the warm dairy – to encourage blueing – for 5 days and are turned regularly. When taken out, they are coated with a paste of flour and blue mould, and then stored in the ripening rooms for anything from 2½ to 5 months. After about 1 month, they are pierced so the mould can develop and spread through the cheese. After this they are carefully monitored and may be spiked a couple more times, 'but it's very exciting, they're quite unpredictable and sometimes we don't need to spike them at all'.

From the farm, Michael sells only whole cheese, weighing 1.35-2.3 or 5.5-6.5 kg (3-5 or 12-14 lb). A good Blue Vinney, although unpressed, is quite a hard crumbly cheese. Paler, with lighter, finer veins than a Stilton, it is also drier and tighter, with a rounded sharpness and a positive taste of blue.

I have heard tell – but cannot possibly vouch for its truthfulness – of a dubious practice of passing off second-class Stiltons as Blue Vinney; but each cheese has such an individual character, I can only wonder at it. Equally, if you have tried a good Blue Vinney, you will not forget it.

Stockists

Dorset:
Fordingbridge
Dairy Shop
- - - - - - - -
Sabins

Somerset:
Martin's Stores

Surrey: Garson
Farm Shop
- - - - - - - -
Priory Farm Shop

Just outside **POOLE** centre, by the docks, is fishmonger **Frank Greenslade, Fish Market, New Quay Road, POOLE BH15 4AF ☎ 01202 672199.**
Display is not their strong point, but everything is exceptionally fresh and mostly locally caught in and around the bay of Bournemouth. There is mackerel in summer, sprats from October to February, the odd John Dory, plaice, slip soles, grey mullet, brill, chicken turbot that was dazzlingly fresh, brown live crabs and lobsters kept in viviers, winkles from September to May, whelks all year round and scallops dived from around Lulworth. The quay at Poole was apparently built on oyster shells and both natives and pacifics are farmed in Poole Harbour, but you need to give a day's notice.

While you're in the area...

Keynston Mill Shop, Keynston Mill, TARRANT KEYNSTON DT11 9HZ ☎ 01258 452596, a farm-shop and pick-your-own much admired in the last edition is under new management. More reports please as to whether the high standards are being maintained.

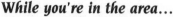

Groves Nurseries, West Bay Road, BRIDPORT DT6 4BA ☎ 01308 422654 fax 01308 420888 have a varied selection of fruit trees and soft fruit bushes, canes and one of the most extensive collections of violets. Keen confectioners will know the only violets scented strongly enough for candying or flavouring sugars, ice-creams and sorbets are Parma violets. Groves stock 3 varieties: Duchesse de Parme, Swanley White and Marie Louise.

Trencherman's, The Old Dairy, COMPTON PARK, Sherborne DT9 4QU ☎fax 01935 32857 sells a good selection of local cheeses, including Dorset Blue Vinney *see page 94*, Fudges Bakery biscuits *see page 92*, local cream, clotted cream, and butter; own-cooked ham and game, including hare, pheasants, partridges and wild duck from local shoots – with fallow deer from Sherborne Castle.

Pass the sailing boats and keep on walking as far as you can go – you might think you are going straight into the sea, but just before you will find the kiosk where **J. M. & V. Batchelor & Son, The Fresh Fish Stall, Mudeford Quay, CHRISTCHURCH BH23 4AB ☎ 01425 275389 fax 01425 274828** sell fish. Generally there is a good selection, including sea bass, skate and lobsters caught locally. The day I went I saw the hugest one ever, it weighed 2.6 kg (5 lb 12 oz)

Saporito, Bere Marsh Farm, SHILLINGSTONE, Blandford DT11 0QY ☎ 01258 860284 is run by very English Fiona Idda, married to an Italian. Here you can find piercingly fresh fruit ices (sorbets) in melon, lemon, orange, strawberry and raspberry flavours as well as ice-creams, including vanilla, coffee and cappuccino and ice-cream cakes.

For a good selection of cut culinary herbs, visit **Coach House Herbs, Lewell Lodge, WEST KNIGHTON DT2 8NT ☎ 01305 853779** from where Noelle Campbell supplies several of the top kitchens in London.

Durham

The Teesdale Trencherman
Startforth Hall, Barnard Castle, Durham DL12 9RA

☎ 01833 638370 **FAX** 01833 631218 **CONTACT** Johnny Cooke-Hurle – *telephone ahead*

BARNARD CASTLE

Smoked Grouse

Johnny Cooke-Hurle is a traditional smoker. From his smoke-holes, using oak chips and sawdust from Yorkshire furniture makers, he smokes grouse shot on his local moors. First they are brined in a plain salt solution, then cold-smoked to give them a smoke flavour, and finally hot-smoked to cook them through. Sold as whole breasts, they are lightly gamy, tinged with a woody smoke and remarkable for their moist succulence. He also cold- and hot-smokes whole chickens and pheasants which are sold as either a pair of breasts or whole birds, and cold-smokes wild boar hams from the nearby Wensleydale Wild Boar Breeders.

You may remember, and possibly have even tried, the products from Ashdown Smokers run by Harry Fellows, another traditional smoker in Cumbria. Last year he ceased trading and the business has been taken over by Johnny, 'His style of smoking was almost exactly the same. In fact, so much so that when I went there, I felt totally at home'. Johnny is now in the throes of producing his first smoked macon (mutton ham) but where Harry used Herdwick – his local breed of fell-ranging sheep – Johnny is using Swaledale, his local breed. The hams are dry-cured in a blend of salt and spices for about 3 weeks, cold-smoked over oak mixed with juniper wood for about 4 weeks, then hung to mature for about 8 months. I wait with interest to see how they turn out. The first hams will not be fully matured until late summer and I long to know whether there will be any obvious differences, particularly as I have always thought Johnny to have lighter, more 'easy-going' style than Harry's, which was markedly strong – at times almost overpowering.

Following Harry's recipes, Johnny is also brining and cold-smoking

Stockists
Durham: Partners
Yorks: The Wine Shop & Delicatessen

loin of pork and fillet of Aberdeen Angus, producing dry-cured smoked and green bacon and smoking the 'odd' cheese. He has also started mail-ordering various imported sauces, oils and pastes from Leatham's Larder in London.

EGGLESTON
Fruit Cakes

H. D. & R. *Bainbridge*

The Post Office & Stores, 1 Greenbank, Eggleston, Barnard Castle, Durham DL12 0BQ

☎ 01833 650250 **CONTACT** *Rhona Bainbridge* **HOURS** *Mon-Fri 9.00-17.30 (-13.00 Thurs and Sat)* **DIRECTIONS** *From Barnard Castle, take B6278 towards Eggleston. In village, turn left opposite the Methodist chapel. Post office is 100 yards on left.*

The more Violet and I drive around in what seems to have become a never-ending search for really good food, the more I am struck by wasted opportunities. Take rural post offices; so many are under threat of closure as they do not turn over enough to justify their continued existence. Yet they perform a valuable service to the community, many of whom are unable to travel to the nearest town. When you come to Eggleston Post Office & Stores you see a possible solution. Like the many farmers who have been forced to 'add value' or diversify, they have built up a successful business making cakes.

The Post Office & Stores is opposite the sleepy village green. Inside it looks like any other village store, that is until you notice Rhona Bainbridge's cakes. Good old-fashioned tea loaves properly made with the fruit soaked overnight in tea to plump it up; sticky gingerbreads made with flour, eggs, milk and lots of syrup; and fruit cakes, her speciality. There are stacks of them, either out in the shop or in her specially constructed maturing cupboards in the corridor by the kitchen. No fruit cake is ever sold younger than 3 months to ensure its flavour melds and its gentle spiciness comes through. Deep dark, rich brown, completely unadorned, in perfect circles or precision squares, her cakes range in size from 15 to 32.5 cm (6 to 13 in).

What started with two cakes for a church bazaar has now become a full-time occupation and she has stuck – more or less – to the same recipe for the last 31 years. Made with 'all the best stuff – butter but no brandy as I try to keep the price realistic' she modestly describes her cakes as 'just as you would make yourself in your own kitchen'. In fact, the post office industry

Stockists

Durham:
Greenwells
Partners
Philberts

Yorks: Country Bake
J. & M. Reah

Jenkins & Hustwit Farmhouse Fruit Cakes, Low Grewburn Farm, Quarry Lane, BUTTERKNOWLE, Bishop Auckland DL13 5LN ☎ 01388 605005 also make good cakes. Their rich fruit cake, moist and fruity but perhaps lacking in spiciness, is made with rum, matured for 1 month and can be ordered as round, square, heart-shaped or hexagonal shapes and in 15 cm (6 in) (weighing 1.4 kg/3 lb), 20 cm (8 in) (2.2 kg/4¾ lb) 25 cm (10 in) (4 kg/9 lb) or 30 cm (12 in) (5.5 kg/12 lb) sizes. They also make a richer celebration cake with more glacé fruit and this time a liqueur, which one they were not prepared to tell; as well as 450-g (1-lb) cherry and granny (fat-free) cakes and Christmas puddings with vegetarian suet.

MAP 6   DURHAM   99

is highly professional. The kitchen houses one of those professional cake-mixing machines; but she still keeps her batches to a small but manageable size and the fruit is still picked over and sorted by hand. Rhona makes two grades of fruit cake: farmhouse and wedding/celebration, 'Although', she cheerfully admits, 'there's not that much difference – just more of everything, more cherries and more ground almonds'. Her cakes are much appreciated by cake-icers for their straight sides and level tops and she often sells them in sets for tiered wedding cakes.

> **Zissler & Sons, 104 Bondgate, DARLINGTON DL7 3LB ☎ 01325 462590** *is a proper pork shop. Established in 1871, the current Mr Zissler is the great-grandson of the original and nothing much has changed since. As well as fresh pork, they sell own-made pork pies, sausage rolls, pasties, black puddings, polony, haslet, ham & egg pies, brawn from the minced pickings off the bones, and ham stock. There is also savoury duck and minced cooked meats mixed with rusk, herbs and spices, rolled into a ball and roasted. Their chipolatas and pork & tomato sausages have a meat content of 70 per cent plus, while the coarser-cut farmhouse sausages contain 80 per cent pork. Each day they roast pork, ham, skin for scrappings (crackling) and cheek on the bone, and boil up feet (trotters), shanks, and tails – which are apparently very sweet and tender. They also have their own pease pudding, pork dripping and Twizells dry-cure bacon see page 41.*

Cotherstone Cheese
Quarry House, Marwood, Barnard Castle, Durham DL12 9QL

☎ 01833 650351   **CONTACT** Joan Cross – *telephone ahead*

Joan Cross is not entirely convinced that the Cotherstone she now makes bears any resemblance to what was known as Cotherstone at the turn of the century. The cheese is named after a village in Teesdale and in those days virtually every farmer's wife in the Dale made cheese for the family. No doubt each one was slightly different. In a true cautious Dales spirit, Joan remains reluctant to give details about how she makes hers, other than to say it is made with the unpasteurized milk from her Friesian herd, pressed for about 12 hours, dry-salted and sold in 450-g, 900-g and 2.7-kg (1, 2, and 6-lb) flattish rounds. She prefers it fairly young at about 2-3 weeks – when it has a mild acidity similar to crème fraîche – with a tangy saltiness and an open crumbliness, although Neal's Yard Dairy *see page* 180 mature it on very successfully.

MARWOOD
Cotherstone Cheese

Stockists
Durham:
Cotherstone Post Office
- - - - - - - - - -
Greenwells
- - - - - - - - - -
Partners

London: Neal's Yard Dairy

Northumb: The Corbridge Larder

> **Partners, 26 Horsemarket, BARNARD CASTLE, Durham DL12 8LZ ☎ 01833 638072 Fax 01833 631245** *is right in the centre of town. On the ground floor of this department store is the food hall, which has a good balance of fresh and packaged foods.* *Cheeses are well chosen, with the accent on locally made on-farm cheeses and they include Cumberland Farmhouse Cheese from Thornby Moor Dairy see page 61 and Bonchester see page 324. The Dales are well represented, so here you will find a choice of Wensleydales from Wensleydale Creamery see page 309, Richard III see page 309 and Redesdale Dairy see page 208, Swaledale see page 310, Ribblesdale see page 310 and Cotherstone see above. They keep the shelves of cakes from Eggleston Post Office & Stores see opposite well stocked up and there is smoked fish and chicken from The Teesdale Trencherman see page 97, bacon from Richard Woodall see page 62 and Twizells see page 41 and well-filled and nicely seasoned pies from Pepper Arden.*

Mail Order

Cheese and cakes only

Essex

Map No. 3

Crapes Fruit Farm

Rectory Road, Aldham, Colchester, Essex CO6 3RR

☎ 01206 212375 **CONTACT** *Andrew Tann* **HOURS** *Mon-Sat 8.00-17.00*
DIRECTIONS *From Colchester, take A12 towards Chelmsford. Turn off at signpost
for Marks Tey. At roundabout, take A120, direction Puckeridge. At next roundabout, follow the sign to Aldham Village. After about 1 mile, turn left on to
Rectory Road and orchard is on the left.*

With over 70 years of apple-growing spread over 3 generations to back
him up, Andrew Tann has an unparalleled collection of varieties. To call
him a commercial grower is perhaps to stretch a point. Of the 150 different apples only about 15 to 18 are grown in commercial quantities.
The rest are measured in pounds, coming from one or two trees with a
few 'with no more than a branch grafted on to a tree bearing 15 apples
a season'. This is a true apple fanatic speaking.

   If you can, go and see him during the picking season. There are
always apples to taste and buy, as well as bottles of juice blended from
his apples. The aroma of well-ripened apples in his sheds is a joy. Of
course, you will never find the entire range ripe at the same time –
apples have their seasons too. For those too far away, Andrew has
rationalized the mail-order list and divided up the main apples seasonally. They are sent well-protected in either 2.3 or 4.5-kg (5 or 10-lb)
boxes, that contain 20-25 or 40-45 apples respectively, and you can
order in advance.

   Box A brings the early summer varieties: it contains (and let me
stress here that this is no more than a guide – if one variety is unavail-
able, another will be substituted) sharp but juicy Crimson Beauty of
Bath; crisp, red and sweet Discovery; and a few equally early varieties
both old and new. Box B is for late summer apples from late August to
late September and includes St Edmund's russet, the first russet of
good flavour that, alas, is a poor keeper; Laxton's Fortune, with its

MAP 3   ESSEX   **101**

smooth green skin with a flush or stripes of red; and Worcester Pearmain. Autumn, from mid September to late October, has Box C: with Red Ellison, with its stunning scent and taste of aniseed; Michaelmas Red, which Andrew recommends as 'good for toffee apples and bobbing'; and Cox's for those 'who prefer them hard and not so sweet'. Box D has the winter's apples and it includes Cox's now at its best; Ribston Pippin, with its taste of pear drops; the finely russetted Kidd's Orange Red; and Orlean's

> *Christopher Kerrison* at **Colchester Oyster Fishery Limited, Pyefleet Quay, North Farm, EAST MERSEA, Colchester CO5 8UN ☎ 01206 384141 Fax 01206 383758** *used to farm Colchester oysters until the disease* bonamia *decimated stocks. The good news is that once again he can supply them. His Colchesters are wild stock dredged by fishermen from disease-free waters and held in the Pyefleet Channel. Christopher purifies and grades them into sizes 1, 2 and 3 (1 is the largest) and then sends them out. He can also supply pacific oysters from Ireland.*

Reinette 'an apple to enjoy with cheese by the fire and at its best in December'.

Of course he grows several more varieties and one that is particularly worth mentioning is D'Arcy Spice. A local variety, the first tree was found in the late 18th century in a garden in Essex – it is juicy, sharp and fruity, with a hot spicy taste.

Remfresh

Mansards, Harts Lane, Ardleigh, Colchester, Essex CO7 7QH

ARDLEIGH
Baby
Vegetables

☎/**FAX** 01206 230144 **CONTACT** *Ron Smith – telephone ahead (April to Oct only).*

Ron Smith used to grow what he describes as 'ordinary' vegetables and sell them at market. While there he would buy in – at a price – French baby vegetables for supplying a few local restaurants. That set him thinking – of course, he could grow them himself – and so with true entrepreneurial spirit, he set about it.

Now he has around 15 acres under cultivation, with about 2 acres of poly-tunnels or under glass and, during the busy season, 10 people helping out in the fields or packing. Scrupulous about how his vegetables are packed, 'chefs, my main customers, can be very fussy', his vegetables are 'graded to size, in perfect condition and without a trace of mud'. One of the tricks of growing baby vegetables is finding the right varieties that give the required size while offering good colour, shape and 'most important of all – flavour'. Ron makes a point of taking time and trouble choosing his seeds, even going to France to see 'what's what' and he is keen to respond to chef's requests or the latest fashions.

Depending on the season, he has round green courgettes, finger-thin courgettes *en fleur*; baby turnips 'the size of radishes – golf balls are too big for my customers'; golf-ball-sized kohlrabi; cauliflowers with tight white curds; romanesco, with its pea-green peaks; canary-yellow patty pans; pousse (tiny sweet spinach leaves); and leeks straight and almost as thin as an arrow. There are plenty of herbs, lettuces and edible flowers: rocket; sorrel; curly and flat-leaf parsley; all sort of lettuces, such as lollo rosso and biondo, radicchio, and crisp red pablo that 'hearts up like an iceberg, but soon loses its colour', violas and nasturtiums. He also assured me, 'I only spray when I have to'.

BOXTED
Chickens

Munson's Poultry
Emdon, Straight Road, Boxted, Colchester, Essex CO4 5QX

☎ 01206 272637 **FAX** 01206 272962 **CONTACT** *John Munson – telephone ahead* **CARDS** *Mastercard*

John Munson specializes in poultry, with a variety of birds and breeds. Some are reared on-farm, others contracted out in the neighbourhood. Now, it is worth remembering that outside appearances can be deceptive. I have called on the sprucest farms imaginable only to find that the produce has no taste whatsoever. Munson's, on the other hand, looks a pretty ramshackle sort of a place – not what you could call, by any stretch of the imagination, a tidy farm with well-kept outbuildings. If the proof of the pudding is in the eating, however, then he is a good bet; as his poultry is highly regarded by several food writers, including Delia Smith.

Bought in as day-olds, the breeds of chickens he currently rears are Cobbs or Rosses, although he has plans for Indian game crosses. The current chickens are both perfectly ordinary commercial breeds and, important though the breed may be, John Munson says it is how you rear and feed your birds and whether they are full-grown that makes the real difference in taste. He rears to feather indoors (kept in until strong and well-covered enough to go outdoors), they then have constant access to the outdoors and are fed a commercial feed free of growth-promoters and supplemented with soaked corn. The bulk of his chickens are slaughtered at around 13 weeks and he will supply any weight from 1.5 to 5.5 kg (3½ to 12 lb) oven-ready. Occasionally he has cockerels weighing 6.8 kg (15 lb), but 'I charge the earth for them'. Dry-plucked and hung for 2 days in the summer and as long as a week in the winter, his chicken has a creamy-textured flesh with plenty of body, and a far more pronounced and deeper gaminess than usual, with a good length of flavour. If you detect that I may sound a little hesitant, it is purely because I never actually saw the birds, they are reared in nearby Bradfield and I do like to see for myself – and, as John never stopped talking, I was never able to ask him, let alone get him to answer my questions.

However, I did see the turkeys and these he lets out in the fields from October to fatten nicely for Thanksgiving and Christmas.

MAP 3   ESSEX   103

Although not a member of the TFTA *see Homewood Partners, page* 220 he uses their feed, making sure they also have plenty of stone 'to develop their crop', grass and natural vegetation. Killed between 22-27 weeks, they are stunned and bled 'although my grandfather would turn in his grave – he thought an unbled bird best'. He dry plucks them and hangs them uneviscerated for at least 7 days. He grows a mixture of breeds, Kelly's Bronzes, own-bred Norfolk Blacks and Websters, which make a larger, darker-fleshed bird with some as heavy as 18 kg (40 lb). He keeps a few geese and ducks. Again in a mixture of breeds they are fed and reared very much on the same lines.

Stockists

Chesh:
Mooreland Foods

Derbys: P. Phillips
Butchers

Lancs: Walmsleys
Butchers

London: Harvey
Nichols
- - - - - - - - -
Randall & Aubin

Leigh Old Town is divided in two by a concrete slip-road; on one side are the rows of old fishermen's houses clinging to the High Street, on the other the wooden cockle-sheds looking out over the Estuary. The cockle industry still more or less thrives and the town is still a favourite spot with day trippers for their 'fix' of cockles, jellied eels or packets of shrimps. **Estuary Fish Merchants, 8 Cockle Row, LEIGH OLD TOWN, ☎ 01702 470741** *is just one of the many sheds from where you can buy fresh juicy cockles lightly boiled in salt water. In season from June to December, they are now dredged and brought back for cleaning and boiling (apparently it contravenes hygiene laws to sell them uncooked).*

Kelly Turkey Farms
Springate Farm, Bicknacre Road, Danbury, Chelmsford,
Essex CM3 4EP

DANBURY
Turkeys

☎ 01245 223581 **FAX** 01245 226124 **CONTACT** Paul Kelly **HOURS** Mon-Fri 8.00-17.00 **DIRECTIONS** *From Chelmsford, take A12 towards Colchester. Turn off at A414, direction Maldon. After about 1½ miles at The Bell Pub, turn right on to Well Lane. Follow the road for about ½ mile, turn left at T-junction. After about 1 mile at the Bicknacre parish boundary sign, farm is signposted on left.*

It has taken Derek Kelly and his son Paul eight years to breed the Kelly Bronze to 'perfection', from a mixture of 'Norfolk Black, Cambridge Bronze salted with Rolstead white'. This, in turn, was improved by selecting from the best birds and now they are confident they have a bird with everything going for it – a full-flavoured, densely textured meat, a good fat cover (essential for moist meat), ample 'breast mass' and a slow maturer (for optimum flavour). It also matures to a range of sizes, meaning that even if you order a smaller bird, it will have been grown for the same amount of time as a larger one and will have the same deep flavour. I tried one last Christmas and it truly was the Rolls-Royce of birds. Finely textured, with a deep lingering gamy flavour and crisp juicy skin, it was a triumph. It also ate well when served cold on Boxing Day which, as Paul told me, 'is the true test of turkey'.

Although up until now they kept it a dark secret, they do have a small number of Norfolk Blacks 'purely because everyone keeps asking for them, although I'm not sure why'. Pure-bred, they have been improved 'barely' over the years by the slow process of weeding out the poorer specimens and breeding from the better. At first, Paul reckons they were unacceptable because of their mean breasts, but now he thinks their meat-to-bone ratio is comparable to a goose. 'For flavour, I honestly can't find a difference between the Bronze and Black, although the Black's meat is finer with a closer-grained texture'. The Blacks also come smaller – a hen weighs 3.5-4.5 kg (8-10 lb), a stag 6.5-6.8 kg (14-15 lb) – and the proportion of breast is about 20 per cent as compared to the Bronze's 32 per cent.

The Kellys grow to Traditional Farm-fresh Turkey Association standards *see Homewood Partners, page* 220, so all their birds will be dry-plucked and hung for a minimum of 7 days. Weighing from 3.5-13.5 kg (8-30 lb), they are available fresh for Christmas and Easter. During the rest of the year you can get frozen birds from the freezer cabinet in their office. They also run an information service to deal with enquiries for Kelly Bronzes all over the country and if they cannot supply you with a Bronze bird, they will put you in touch with a grower who can.

Stockists

Herts: Eastwood Butchers

Kent: Scotch Meat Shop

London: C. Lidgate Ltd

Lothian: A. Crombie & Son

Oxon: M. Newitt & Sons

FINGRINGHOE
Quinces

Clay Barn Orchard
Clay Barn, Fingringhoe, Colchester, Essex CO5 7AR

☎ 01206 735405 **CONTACT** *Charles Trollope* **HOURS** *Aug to Jan: dawn-dusk* **DIRECTIONS** *From Colchester, take B1025 towards Mersea. After about 5 miles, at The Langenhoe Lion, turn left on to Fingringhoe Road. Follow the road to T-junction, turn left and after about 1 mile orchard is signposted on the right.*

Native to such romantic-sounding lands as Turkistan, Transcaucasia and Anatolia, quinces can have problems here. The trees can be far too easily seduced by the promise of an early spring. As Charles Trollope explains, 'Last year we had an early winter and when the snow finished by February, they thought "gosh spring is here" and away they went. But there was still a month of frost left. And what growth wasn't already damaged was then taken away by a seriously late frost in May'. Usually in late September, just before picking starts, the trees are laden with their green-turning-to-golden globes, like a fir tree dressed up for Christmas. Last year, when I walked the orchards it was one of the bleakest sights imaginable; the odd fruit hidden behind the leaves, dark green with a layer of grey-green felt underneath – virtually nothing to pick. If I felt sad, you can imagine how near to despair the Trollopes were.

Downy-skinned, quinces are hard and astringent when raw but, when cooked, transform into the most glorious of fruits, with a deep-pink, lush and honey-scented flesh with a slightly grained texture. Glorious baked with cream and butter, spiced as a jelly or in a pie or tart with or without apples, their heavy perfume makes them a fruit to savour. All we can do is to keep our fingers crossed and hope for a generous crop this year. If there are any, the Trollopes will sell them from a table by the front door of their house. Remember, though, that big is not necessarily best. 'It's perfectly understandable, but it's wrong. As quinces are so hard, if they are large they are a nightmare to cut'. To prepare them, first you must wash off the grey down that covers the skin. As soon as you have cut, peeled and cored them, drop the pieces in lemon juice to stop them from discolouring.

ChinaVeg Ltd
Sunray Nurseries, Great Horkesley, Colchester, Essex CO6 4AL

GREAT HORKESLEY
Chinese Vegetables

☎/**FAX** 01787 377928   **CONTACT** *Alan Holyoake – telephone ahead*

Alan Holyoake is a one-off character. Two years ago he took over 5 acres of glass that had lain derelict for a couple of years, renovated them, fitted out underfloor heating and a sophisticated spraying system and set up in business growing Oriental vegetables for the Chinese market. In summer about 80 per cent of his crops go straight to London; in winter the percentage drops as he is unable to grow the full range and, anyway, 'the Spanish come in'.

When I went to Alan's glasshouse, it was like stepping into another world: acre upon acre of curious vegetables, some growing flat on the ground, others tumbling and twisting down canes to create scratchy thickets. In winter it looks pretty dull, but in summer the place comes into its own and the range and diversity is extraordinary. There is choi (meaning vegetable) and sum (stem); a tricky one to grow as, as Alan explains, 'The Chinese want it in flower, that's the delicate part. But it bolts and grows tall very quickly. If it's too tall and you cut too late, the flower stem will be too fibrous and inedible – too tough. If you cut too early, it's tooyoung. Get the timing just right and it's sharp and clean and stays green'. Pak-choi is probably more familiar, with its juicy leaves and bland flavour 'that's good with sauce' but I had never before seen kai-lan, which reminded me of kohlrabi. He also grows chi-kwa, a hairy melon from which the Chinese make a summer soup. Its ideal size is 900 g (2 lb), but he grows some as big as 11.3 kg (25 lb) for

---

Marney Meats are sold from **Layer Marney Tower, LAYER MARNEY, Colchester CO5 9US** ☎/*fax 01206 330784. Layer Marney Tower, decorated with ornate Italianate terracotta, is a superb example of a Tudor house, with an 24-m (80-ft) gate tower – the highest in England. Both the house and surrounding parkland – which is home to various rare breeds and farmed deer – are open to the public and there is a small farm-shop where you can buy their produce. From here they sell eggs, venison farmed to the British Deer Farmers Association standards see pages 337 and 339, hung for 7-10 days and butchered on site in a variety of cuts, including saddle, boned and rolled saddle, medallions, haunch and haunch steak, cold-smoked saddle and haunch and burgers, sausages, and pâtés. They also sell pure- and cross-bred ('accidents do happen') rare-breed meat, including Soay, Portland, Lincoln Longwools and Norfolk Horns lamb; beef, hung for 3 weeks from Red Poll and the miniature Dexters; and pork from Saddlebacks, as well as dry-cured bacon and own-cured hams.*

their seed. Incidentally, cutting them is a skilled job as if you touch one with your hands, the acid in your fingers will stain it; so first you have to wrap the fruit in a leaf. Fu-kwa is the knobbly bitter melon used for soups and stir-fries; wo-loo-kwa, the bottle gourd, also has the same uses, but a perfectly shaped one will also be hung outside the house to suck in the bad spirits. Dow-koc are yard-long beans as thick as a bootlace – sweet and tender, they are white or a pale eau-de-nil in colour. Chinese cucumbers were a real find; rounder, chubbier and more like a ridged gherkin than ours, they are far sweeter and less watery than ours. In the 'trial area' for next year's crops were ong-choi or water spinach, with both its leaves and stems eaten; gow-choi, Chinese chives, that were just showing their flower heads before opening; and ce-kwa, an amazing loofah gourd. Alan will sell to the uninitiated, but only in 2.3-kg (5-lb) boxes; otherwise ferret around London's Chinatown to find his vegetables.

WEST MERSEA
Pastries

Indulgence Patisserie

Unit 4, Rushmere Close, West Mersea, Colchester, Essex CO5 8QQ

☎ 01206 383397   **FAX** 01206 385689   **CONTACT** Stuart Allan – *telephone ahead*

Stuart Allan always wanted to be a chef, even when he was 6 years old. At 16, he went to catering college and by the tender age of 20 had started his own business making pâtisserie. This is serious pâtisserie in the Continental mould. Glossy and gleaming, the pastries are finished with the meticulousness of a professional chef. They are, in fact, aimed at the restaurant trade, but any member of the public can buy direct from his unit's door, provided they give at least 24 hours' notice as everything is freshly made to order.

Flushed with a recent success – Stuart won the 1993 British baking industry's equivalent to an Oscar – his range seems to be constantly expanding. Everything, he is adamant, is made with good ingredients – Belgian couverture for chocolate, butter and fresh cream (and he gets

---

Butcher Paul Earey of **D. R. Earey & Son, 97 Swan Street, SIBLE HED-INGHAM, Halstead CO9 3HP** ☎ **01787 460278** *specializes in a Suffolk-type cure that 'can't be called Suffolk proper as we're in Essex'. He cures whole hams and middles for streaky bacon first in a Wiltshire-cure for 3 weeks, then for a further 3 weeks in a sweet cure of black treacle and stout. Finally, he cold-smokes them for about ½ a day over oak chips in the smoker he built himself. Sold all year round in the shop, sliced off the bone, he sells whole hams on the bone only at Christmas-time. The meat is close-textured with a sweet dark flavour that does not really percolate further than the fat. The streaky bacon, however, has a sharp sweet flavour running right the way through. Paul also brine-cures silverside for slices of soft pink beef laced with fat and a good salty punch, and makes a coarse brawn and a selection of sausages, including Essex with nutmeg and pepper. He can also be relied on for supplies of ham hocks, trotters and chitterlings.*

through about 530 litres/140 gallons a week). Most everything is own-made; the only concessions are concentrated fruit purées and a pre-mix for making up his sponge bases. He has an interesting selection of bavarois, a cold dessert made with a flavoured base of egg custard stiffened with gelatine and set in a mould. Actually that description does not do the glories of the bavarois justice; when made well, they can be meltingly smooth and forcefully flavoured. I tried the layered chocolate & hazelnut and its construction is as follows – a base of sponge covered with a mixture of chocolate ganache deepened with chocolate and lightened with whipped cream, covered with a hazelnut cream and finished with a final layer of cream. No one could say it is not rich, but it is light, silky smooth and offers a good contrast of rich nuts and deep chocolate.

The Priory Farm Shop
Priory Farm, Wrabness, Manningtree, Essex CO11 2UG

WRABNESS
Fruit Cakes

☎ 01255 880338 **CONTACT** Edmund Swift **HOURS** Mon-Sat 9.00-17.30 Sun 10.00-13.00 *(closed bank holidays)* **DIRECTIONS** *From Manningtree, take B1352 towards Harwich. After about 5 miles, farm-shop is on left.*

At first glance, the Priory Farm Shop looks just like any other good farm-shop. There are baskets of own-grown vegetables, bottles of James White apple juice *see page* 248, jars of this and sacks of that. Look again, though, and tucked away in the corner is a wooden-framed contraption, a sort of shop within a shop, and it is here you must go as it houses Claire Swift's excellent fruit cakes. Using a recipe that has been in the family for years, she bakes them in her farmhouse just across the road.

Production is currently rather small-scale, running to no more than 'a couple of thousand a year' and she bakes 3 days a week in an exceptionally painstaking way. Each cake contains Californian raisins, Australian sultanas and currants, unbleached self-raising white flour milled in Essex, unrefined demerara sugar, slightly salted butter, fresh eggs, mixed peel, glacé cherries, rum and spices. Claire makes up batches of 1.8-kg (4-lb) mixes in the morning – larger than that would be difficult to handle. 'I cream using the mixer, but I stir the fruit in by hand as I think the machine crushes it. The bowls stand all day and in the evening, I tin up. I like to leave them standing as it firms the mixture and gives the rum a chance to filter through'. Next comes the neat decoration on top – serried ranks of nuts, sorted by hand to make sure they match. 'And if you decorate before baking, it will stay perfect'. The cakes are left overnight and the following day finished with an egg wash and baked.

Aged for a couple of months or up to 9 months, 'after that the top goes dull and they seem to lose their glossiness', they weigh 900 g or 1.8 kg (2 and 4 lb) and come plain or decorated, with a choice of round or square in the larger size only. Loose-textured and with a good crumb, Claire's cakes are generously endowed with fruit and are note-worthy for what I can best describe as a honey aftertaste. She does also make a Special Rich Fruit Cake, which is richer and darker and this also has chopped walnuts, muscovado sugar and more rum. It is excel-lent, sweeter, more moist, and with a nutty flavour and a crunch of nuts in the crumb.

Her husband Edmund's domain is ginger cakes, flapjacks, craggy rock cakes, various tea breads with the vine fruits soaked in tea, and a simple richly buttery shortbread. 'I use unsalted butter, caster sugar and flour – I hate a long list of ingredients' and he bakes when Claire is not making her cakes. A good team, they both bake with lavish care and good ingredients, it makes all the difference.

Mail Order

Fruit cakes only

The Company Shed, 129 Coast Road, WEST MERSEA CO5 8PA ☎ 01206 382700 *is just my sort of place. Run by the redoubtable Heather Haward, whose collection of fish earrings has to be admired, it doubles as a fish shop and an unlicensed shellfish bar. A sure sign of freshness when it comes to fish is a queue of Chinese or Japanese customers as they really know a thing or two – and there they were, come from as far afield as the Suffolk border, so Heather told me. Together with her husband Richard, they buy direct from boats that land in Wivenhoe, Brightlingsea, Harwich or Mersea, and you can expect to find skate wings, slip soles still covered with their protective slime, red gurnard, grey mullet, sea bass, mackerel, plaice and pouting. Cockles from Leigh or Holland and salmon are bought in, there are herrings caught in drift nets, eels from the Fens and a friend smokes eels, salmon and herrings for kippers, bloaters and buckling. Richard farms oysters, he gets the spats from Scotland and fattens them locally, and they are on sale along with locally caught lobsters and crabs, all kept in viviers. Heather will dress or cook or open them to order. In the freezer, she also keeps tubs of fish stock made from trimmings; crab soup; fish stew packs made up with 'whiting, pouting, a bit of cod, a few prawns and whatever else is going'; and fish cakes made of a mixture of cod and whiting. Heather only serves shellfish to eat in the simple shop, with a few tables dotted about and a view of the sailing clubs. You can, of course, also take away; either way you are sure of finding wonderfully fresh fish.*

While you're in the area...

Recently opened, **Procter's Speciality Sausages, Red Lion Yard, COLCHESTER CO1 1DX ☎ 01206 579100** is attract- ing quite a following with their range of sausages, including Hog & Hop (pork and real ale), pork, red cabbage & walnut, and Suffolk Orchard (pork and local cider). More reports please.

Hillside Dairy Farm, GREAT WIGBOROUGH, Colchester CO5 7RZ ☎ 01206 735232 run a Jersey herd. During day-light hours you can call at the farm to buy their unpasteurized full-fat milk which is as good as drinking cream and, for an even richer experi-ence, 150 and 300-ml (5 and 10-fl oz) pots of their thick unpasteurized cream.

For a really interesting selection of seeds for unusual vegetables, salads and herbs, send for the catalogue from **Suffolk Herbs, Monks**

Farm, Pantlings Lane, KELVEDON CO5 9PG ☎ 01376 572456 fax 01576 571189. Just reading about the varieties will make you want to rush out into the garden.

If you like to buy food 'by appointment', **Hepburns of Mountnessing, 269 Roman Road, MOUNTNESSING, Brentwood CM15 0UH ☎ 01277 353289 fax 01277 355589** is one of the sources for Highgrove organic lamb and beef, reared on Prince Charles's estate in Gloucestershire. Some of their beef is own-reared and they also buy in meat from local sources. They sell poultry and game, and cure hams – an excellent brine-cured bacon finished in maple syrup – tongue and silverside. They make sausages, sweet and savoury pies, pâtés, brawn and ready-cooked dishes. At Christmas they bake Dundee cakes and have fresh suet for your Christmas pudding.

Fuller's Dairy, Brickwall Farm, SIBLE HEADINGHAM, Halstead CO9 3RH ☎fax 01787 460329 run a pedigree Jersey herd. They process about one-third of their own milk and – from the farm-shop – sell unpasteurized double, single and whipped cream, a full-cream Greek-style yoghurt, and plain or flavoured gold-top and low-fat yoghurts. They also make a soft curd cheese, cheesecakes, various ice-creams with a 12 per cent dairy fat content and pack a lightly salted full-cream butter made in bulk for the Quality Milk Producers.

From an old-fashioned converted shop **Lay & Robson, 150 Swan Street, SIBLE HEADINGHAM, Halstead CO9 3PP ☎ 01787 462617 fax 01787 277924** deal in game, make sausages, pork and game pies in any size up to 1.8 kg (4 lb), various pâtés and terrines, and smoke game, fish, bacon and poultry, including a mild chicken.

Margaret Thomas, 25 Tyrone Road, SOUTHEND-ON-SEA SS1 3HE ☎ 01702 588534 keeps her beehives in the Crouch Valley by Burnham-on-Crouch. Her bees make honey mainly from the pollen collected from the swathes of sea lavender growing on the marshes and mudflats. Sea lavender flowers in August and Margaret's honey is mild in flavour and pale-gold, setting to a white – quite unusual for a summer honey.

Allison Horne of **Cottage Cooking, Oldhouse Farm, WAKES COLNE, Colchester CO6 2DR ☎ 01787 222250 fax 01787 222484** makes honey-based mustard relishes in various flavours, including horseradish, coriander & lemon, and red wine. She also makes a range of dressings, flavoured mayonnaises and stir-fry marinades.

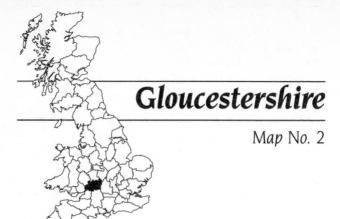

Gloucestershire

Smart's Gloucester Cheeses

Old Ley Court, Chapel Lane, Churcham, Gloucestershire GL2 8AR

☎ 01452 750225 **CONTACT** Diana Smart **HOURS** Mon-Thurs 8.30-18.30
DIRECTIONS From Gloucester, take A40 towards Ross-on-Wye. Drive about 6 miles to Birdwood. Turn left into Chapel Lane immediately before Mobil garage. Drive ½ mile and farm is signposted on the left.

As long ago as the 18th century, there were two distinct Gloucester cheeses – Single and Double. Both were made with the milk from the Gloucester, the native breed of the county whose milk was particularly suitable for cheese-making, as it contained a good percentage of fat of small-globule size. Although there are all sorts of theories as to why or how the cheeses were so named (one being because Double was always made in larger moulds than Single), the essential difference between the two cheeses is that Double is a full-milk cheese made with either the cream from the overnight milk added to the whole morning milk, or the whole of the overnight milk ripened to start the whole morning milk when added to it. Single, on the other hand, is made from skimmed overnight milk mixed in with the morning's milk.

Diana Smart makes each cheese once a week. She uses her own unpasteurized milk from a 45-strong herd of mainly Holsteins, although she is introducing Brown Swiss, as their milk is similar in composition to the Gloucester. Single Gloucester is a slower and more difficult cheese to make: the curds are scalded to a lower temperature, then cut and turned three times to make tiny pieces before they are finally milled. Traditionally Double has always been coloured a pale orange (now using anatto) and it is made on similar lines to a Cheshire: the curds are cut into wedges and piled one on top of the other and then turned. Both cheeses are pressed for 36 hours, during which period they are turned once. They are made in 3.2-3.5 and 1.35-1.5-kg

MAP 2   GLOUCESTERSHIRE   **111**

(7-8 and 3-3½-lb) truckles, with a small 675-900-g (1½-2-lb) truckle for Single Gloucester only.

Single is eaten far younger, at anything from 3 to 12 weeks, and it has always been thought of as a poorer cheese. Even Evan Jones in his *Book of Cheese* dismisses it as 'require(ing) only half the milk and much less ageing'. I do not necessarily agree. Recently I tasted both Gloucesters with Eurwen Richards, a well-respected cheese consultant, and we were both struck by the 5-week Single. A pale ivory cream, it was charmingly buttery and rich in the mouth. Certainly it was mild and very delicate, but it had a well-formed – if gentle – character. The 5-month Double was far more obviously aggressive, it made a more positive statement, but it was perhaps a little pasty and a little too acid. We both agreed it would have improved with more ageing.

On Tuesday and Thursday you can watch Diana making her cheeses. This is a slow all-day process, so it is best to avoid lunch-time – between 11.00-12.30 – when nothing much happens. She also makes unpasteurized double cream and yoghurt, and raises whey-fed Tamworth/Gloucestershire Old-Spot cross pigs cured for bacon and hams *see Farmhouse Fresh Foods above*.

> ***Farmhouse Fresh Foods*, 61 Northgate Street, GLOUCESTER GL1 2AG ☎ 01452 521784** *cure for bacon Diana Smart's whey-fed Tamworth/Gloucestershire Old-Spot-cross pigs in a mixture of salt, brown sugar and herbs. The result is a succulent meaty and – because of the breed – particularly fatty bacon that is rich in flavour. They also sell own-made Bath chaps, faggots and brawn, and cure their own hams.*

Stockists

Glos: Birdwood House Farm Shop

Gwent: Irma Fingal-Rock Food

London: Neal's Yard Dairy

Lothian: Iain Mellis

Surrey: Vivian's

The Cotswold Gourmet
PO Box 26, Cirencester, Gloucestershire GL7 5TJ

CIRENCESTER
Rare-breed Meat

☎/**FAX** 01285 860229 **CONTACT** *Richard Lutwyche – mail order only*
CARDS *Access, Visa*

The Cotswold Gourmet deals in pure-bred rare-breed meat. Richard Lutwyche finds the range of succulence, flavours and textures in rare-breed meat is enormous, 'With lamb, it's far more obvious. There's a huge range from the earthy to smoky to sweet. With pork, the differences are subtler'. To this end I tried his Cotswold, Manx Loughtan and Shetland Lamb – and, yes, each one was distinct. A boned loin of Shetland had a tight grain and was superbly tender, with a lingering flavour of earthy peat; Manx Loughtan, again finely grained, was succulent with a deep nuttiness and a dash of honey. Cotswold, I must admit, was by

> *Just off the ring road,* **Chesterton Farm Shop, Chesterton Lane, CIRENCESTER GL7 8JP ☎ 01285 642160** *is run by Gary Wallace. He was the first butcher to be nominated to sell pure rare and traditional breeds by the Rare Breed Survival Trust under their new scheme known as the Traditional Meat Foundation. As a result he has regular supplies of Gloucestershire Old Spot and Tamworth pigs in various cuts and joints, made up into sausages and cured for bacon, as well as lamb from breeds similar to The Cotswold Gourmet, and mutton.*

comparison surprisingly dull.

Richard can supply – in half carcasses or various cuts and joints – pork from British Saddleback, Gloucester Old Spot, various sausages including 100 per cent Gloucestershire Old Spot meat that were rather too peppery and consequently drowned the meat's intrinsic flavour; lamb from Cotswold, Ryeland, Grey-faced Dartmoor, Norfolk Horn; and primitive shearling from Shetland, Soay and Manx Loughtan and Old Gloucester beef. Everything is well-butchered, with primitive lamb hung for 2 weeks and downland lamb for 10 days.

FILKINS
Smoked
Salmon

Minola Smoked Products
Kencot Hill Farmhouse, Filkins, Lechlade,
Gloucestershire GL7 3QY

☎ 01367 860391 **FAX** 01367 860544 **CONTACT** *Hugh Forestier-Walker* **HOURS** *Mon-Fri 8.00-17.30 Sat 9.30-17.30 Sun 10.00-12.00* **CARDS** *Access, Mastercard, Visa* **DIRECTIONS** *From Burford, take A361 towards Lechlade. After 3½ miles, turn left at the blue plastic bag, signposted Minola, on to a track. Follow the track about ¼ mile to the airfield. Cross the airfield and smokery is on the right.*

Having written that I harboured 'a sneaking suspicion that Hugh Forestier-Walker will smoke anything – provided it stays still long enough', I was somewhat surprised to hear from him that he would 'like to smoke fewer items'. There is, you can rest assured, no immediate sign of his cutting down the range, which includes smoked butter, smoked cashew nuts, smoked foie gras and even this year smoked aubergines. Admittedly these are 'funnies smoked for chefs by special request', although he will take on commissions for anyone. This year he cured and smoked a leg of lamb for one customer for about 16 weeks.

The mainstays of his business are the more conventional products – moist chicken cold-smoked for 24 hours then hot-smoked for 30 minutes to cook it through; cheeses; game; bloaters, buckling, kippers, and a masterly firm-textured smoked salmon that is dry-cured in Cheshire salt – and only salt – for 1 hour to every 450 g (1 lb) of salmon, then cold-smoked for between 2-3 days. The point of smoking, according to Hugh, 'is for the flavour of the smoke to go right through, while still retaining the inherent taste of the product'. To this end he smokes in small wooden smoke-houses with iron smoke-pots, holding whole oak logs. Hugh considers 'sawdust too impure, particularly if it's from pine, as the oil gets into it and can taint the food. Hugh is adamant that, in spite of fridges, chilled cabinets and freezers, the keeping quality of smoked food is still important. Using whole logs also means you can achieve a steady low temperature and this gives Hugh the ability to cold-smoke for a long time; the result is all his products are marked by an obvious overlay of smoke.

Stockists

Bucks: Good Food Shop

Glos: Maylam's

London: Le Pont de la Tour

Oxford: The Delicattesserie

His smoked bacon is particularly successful, it bursts with a meaty woody flavour. Other products I personally find a little too pungent but, with several top chefs buying from him, he certainly has a following.

Workman & Meadows
Stall 40, Eastgate Market, Gloucester, Gloucestershire GL1 1PL

☎ 01452 522257   **CONTACT** Tim Meadows   **HOURS** Mon-Thurs 8.30-17.00 Fri-Sat 8.00-17.00   **DIRECTIONS** *In covered market in centre of town.*

The life cycle of the eel is a bit of a mystery. Its spawning ground is the Sargasso Sea and the silver (mature) eels return there heading off in autumn. Every spring come the babies – the elvers – tiny, worm-like creatures no more than 6-8 cm (2¼-3¼ in) long and 2-3 mm (½-⅛ in) thick. Carried by the currents over the Atlantic Ocean, in England they are attracted by the huge outpourings of freshwater from the Severn and Parrot rivers into the Bristol Channel, and they wait off the coast to be carried up these rivers by the spring tides in huge shoals known locally as an 'eel-fare'.

Workman & Meadows sell elvers, either live or frozen, along with a range of other fish from their stall in Gloucester Market. Elvers are in season from about the end of February until the end of May. In order to secure a supply last year, orders had to be placed before the end of February, with the warning 'not to expect any until the nearest tide to Easter weekend'. To be sure for this year, I suggest you ring up as early as possible.

> — TO COOK ELVERS —
> The Gloucester method for cooking elvers is to fry them in the fat of home-cured Gloucester Old Spot bacon and then to scramble an egg in with them. Serve with the bacon.
> *(Supplied by Workman & Meadows.)*

The Flour Bag
Burford Street, Lechlade, Gloucestershire GL7 3AP

☎ 01367 252322   **CONTACT** Maurice Chaplais   **HOURS** Mon-Sat 8.00-18.00   **DIRECTIONS** *In town centre.*

Maurice Chaplais is keen that I should tell you that he runs 'not just a bakery' but a shop selling various cheeses, oils, preserves, olives and charcuterie. It is, however, for his breads, tarts and cakes that I think he shines.

Bread is, as only to be expected, baked on a daily basis and, working as a one-man baker, his shelves only start filling up at 9.00 am and you may have to wait until midday if you are after a particular loaf. He is the sort of baker who starts from scratch; not for him any pre-mixes and he likes to experiment, developing new flavours and textures. His two white breads, made with untreated flour, are splendid proper crusty country loaves. Old-fashioned takes 16 hours to make; it has bulk rising and then a second rising in the tin. Extra Old-fashioned is left to rise for 4 days in bulk, then rises again on the tray for 8 hours. To aid fermentation, the dough is made up with a small proportion of the previous batch's dough. Both breads have that splendid deep yeasty flavour and open but firm texture that only comes with a slow rising.

New this year is Irish bread 'my concoction and it has no connection with the Irish apart from Mackeson'. It is made with white flour, malt flour, oatmeal and oat-flakes, a minimal amount of yeast and generous quantities of Mackeson, 'but', he insists, 'no other liquid whatsoever'. Again there is a long overnight fermentation and the result is a dense loaf, dark treacle brown in colour, with a rich nutty flavour that sweetens considerably when warmed. Inspired by the French *pain au lard*, he has come up with a bacon bread. Using dry-cured oak-smoked back bacon chopped into fairly small pieces, he mixes the bacon into a well-fermented white dough, leaves it to rise and bakes it off so the flavours intermingle. A slice studded with bacon not only looks interesting but has a rich meaty taste pervaded with the mildest hint of smoke.

Maurice also makes Provençal bread which he developed after tasting just about every ciabatta he could find in the supermarkets. 'Mine is different, lighter-textured, with 10 per cent as compared the more normal 2 per cent of extra-virgin olive oil. It has sun-dried tomatoes and a mixture of green and black olives.' With all that oil, it has a green grassy flavour and a crisp open texture that melts away, leaving a bright warm flavour. He still makes his seed bread from a mixture of poppy, sesame, sunflower and millet seeds, malted oats, wheat flakes and four malt flours. He also makes his own interpretation of *challah*, a Jewish bread, only his is rich in butter and eggs and far more like a feathery brioche.

His baking is a good mixture of novel and traditional. So expect to find own-made doughnuts oozing with raspberry jam and a truly glorious lardy cake – studded with currants, made with a rich lard-based dough and spread with apricot jam – that is succulent, light and flaky but clean-tasting, an almost impossible combination to achieve.

He also makes mini treacle, Bakewell and pecan tarts, French apple flans, pear frangipanes, apple and raisin Danish, and individual crème brûlées, nestling in cases of buttery pastry.

---

*Why more country restaurants do not follow the example of **The Marsh Goose, High Street**, MORETON-IN-MARSH GL56 0AX ☎ 01608 52111 fax 01608 652403 and open shops selling their food, I cannot imagine. It seems such a sensible idea, particularly when you hear how so many restaurants are struggling. Using the same restaurant kitchen and cooking to the same high standards, the shop is kept constantly supplied with terrines, pâtés, quiches and breads. Provided you give them enough notice, they will cook almost anything to order.*

Shipton Mill
Long Newnton, Tetbury, Gloucestershire GL8 8RP

LONG NEWNTON
Flours

☎ 01666 505050 **FAX** 01666 504666 **CONTACT** John Lister – *telephone ahead* 9.00-17.00

If you want to make really good bread, the secret of success is to match the flour with that bread. 'Most large millers,' says John Lister of Shipton Mill, 'grind their flour to match the demands of the Chorley-Wood process of baking. They mill wheat very hard to crack open the starch molecules so it absorbs and keeps a lot of water and lowers its ability to ferment.' Apparently that is what is required for the quick turnaround, mass-produced and fully automated process of making sliced bread. As you can imagine, it does not do much for the bread's flavour and texture.

John mills his flour according to very different principles. Talk to him and he will keep you for hours explaining about the nature of protein in wheat and how strong flours need to be worked to develop (soften) the gluten otherwise they will not rise. He is also adamant that for really good bread you first need to ferment the dough to make the gluten digestible and to allow subtler more complex tastes to develop. Sadly this process of an overnight sponge that bubbles and buzzes away – with the enzymes working on the carbohydrates digesting the sugars – is all but dying out in most small bakeries: 'It takes anything from 8 to 24 hours, in a couple of hours nothing happens. Some bakers always used to keep back some of the day's dough for the following day's batch. Few work like that now'. Interestingly, he told me that if a dough has been properly fermented, the proving is more a function of what we want the bread to look like rather than developing its texture.

---

*The quiet town of Nailsworth is not exactly where you might expect to find a first-rate food hall, so **William's Kitchen, 3 Fountain Street**, NAILSWORTH GL6 0BL ☎ 01453 835507 fax 01453 835950 comes as a bit of a surprise. What is also encouraging is that they have been trading for several years and there is no sign at all of standards slipping. As you enter the long narrow shop, the first thing you notice is the huge marble slab filled with fish as fresh as you could hope to find. It may look a little empty on a Monday or Tuesday but, as William says, 'this is Nailsworth and hours might go by without anyone even passing by'. By Thursday, however, the slab fills up as shoppers anticipate the weekend. Expect to find red mullet, sea bass, Dover sole, chicken halibut, crabs, oysters, cockles, mussels, salmon, undyed kippers and langoustine. You can order take-away made-up plateaux de fruits de mer. They also make a huge range of food-to-go, such as breast of chicken stuffed with cheese and mustard, a light and well-seasoned terrine of salmon and monkfish, pork cassoulet, various salads freshly made each day, and soups including a nicely balanced carrot & coriander. Ever-expanding, they now bake their own focaccia with sun-dried tomatoes, black olives & rosemary or purée of fresh garlic & basil, as well as various fruit flans, cheesecakes and roulades. They have also enlarged their choice of fruit and vegetables, adding locally picked soft fruit or wild mushrooms from Scotland to their list. In the grocery line, there are various jams, oils etc., as well as bags of Cotswold Homemade Meringues in shells and nests of different sizes that are made with fresh eggs a couple of miles down the road.*

In his quest to match the right flour to the right bread, he mills an enormous range of over 15 sorts of wholemeal, sunflower, maize, malthouse, country brown, oat, soda bread and white flours, with some from organic grains. For a 'proper' sour-dough with a long fermentation, there is his Fifty/Fifty 100 per cent Wholemeal, made up of half strong Canadian and half English wheat. This gives the best of both worlds, with the strength of the Canadian to withstand a long fermentation with the weaker English stopping the fermentation from roaring away – resulting in a 'spent' dough long before it is ready for baking. Try his ciabatta flour; here the problem was to develop a mixture of flours that would be strong enough to develop a mildly sour flavour, be active enough to develop holes to give the 'right' texture and at the same time absorb quantities of olive oil. Rye flours are a subject near to his heart; now rye is notoriously difficult to work as it contains little or no gluten. 'There's a knack to making a rye. You have to work quickly. Most British bakers don't understand, they add far too high a level of yeast, bake in far too hot an oven that instantly fires everything. And out comes a pillar of salt.' In Europe bakers buy their rye flour (and indeed all their flours) according to its ash content, a reflection of the amount of fibre in the flour. Without wanting to be too technical, ours is far higher and suffers a different starch damage that ultimately affects the quality of the bread.

Any keen baker – domestic or commercial – should visit Shipton Mill; but be warned, they are primarily set up for commercial bakers. They will supply anybody, but you should order ahead as not all the flours are always in stock. Although their flours are sold in 32-kg (70-lb) sacks, if you give them warning for certain flours they will bag up in 2.5-kg (5-lb) weights.

Stockists

Avon: Wild Oats Wholefoods

Glos: The Stow Wholefood Shop

London:
Mortimer & Bennett
- - - - - - - - - -
Neal's Yard
- - - - - - - - - -
Villandry

MINSTERWORTH

Smoked Salmon

Severn & Wye Smokery
Walmore Hill, Minsterworth, Gloucestershire GL2 8LA

☎ 01452 750777 **FAX** 01452 750776 **CONTACT** *Richard Cook – telephone ahead*

As far as I know, Severn & Wye Smokery is the only company to smoke Glenarm salmon. Farmed to Conservation grade in Ireland, the fish are kept in larger enclosures with lower stocking densities, in cages sited in the open seas. The result is fitter, leaner, healthier fish that are forced to swim against the tides and – because they are not so crowded – are not prone to stress-related diseases. Severn & Wye Smokery do also smoke wild and conventionally farmed fish, but it is for their Glenarm salmon that I single them out. All their salmon is dry-cured and smoked over oak chips in modern Maurer kilns. Conventionally farmed and Glenarm salmon are always cured and smoked fresh; wild salmon, caught mainly by rod-and-line fishermen from rivers in the south of England, is smoked fresh in season (during the rest of the year they use frozen stock).

Glenarm has a firm texture, neither too dry nor too oily, with a pleasant succulence of mild fish. Wild was also well-textured, although slightly drier. In comparison, the conventionally farmed was far less interesting, a little flabby, too 'melt-in-the-mouth' or lacking in any bite and with only the mildest flavour of fish. Severn & Wye also smoke kippers, trout, haddock, mackerel fillets – either plain or coated in various pastes – and hot-smoke succulent wild eels with a rich woody finish, chicken and duck breasts.

Ruskin Mill
Old Bristol Road, Nailsworth, Gloucestershire GL6 0LA

☎ 01453 832571 **FAX** 01453 835029 **CONTACT** *Aonghus Gordon* **HOURS** *Wed 9.00-17.00 Thurs 9.00-20.00* **DIRECTIONS** *From Stroud, take A46 towards Nailsworth. Go through Nailsworth and take the Horsley road on right. Ruskin Mill is about ½ mile along on the left.*

I discovered Ruskin Mill purely by chance on one of last summer's shimmeringly sunny hot days. Even if it had been pouring with rain I could not have failed to be impressed. More than just a glorious old mill surrounded by running streams and well-tended gardens, it is a registered charity with a serious purpose and a point. Its philosophy, or if you like *raison d'être*, is to help the disenfranchised young. They may be educationally sub-normal, in trouble with the law or have serious behavioural difficulties and they are sent here in the hope of acquiring a skill or craft so they may in time engage in society by learning more about themselves and their environment.

To this end they are taught such traditional craft skills as tanning leather for shoes or making paper or willow-work, as well as working on the land. The land, farmed to Biodynamic standards, is part woodland, part farm with livestock, a newly acquired trout farm still under development and a market garden. It was here that I went to see the crops, down the narrow windy path running alongside the stream, with Violet trotting behind me. On the steep banks behind they keep hives for honey and are planning terraces of nut and fruit trees. In the market garden itself they grow a huge range of vegetables, salads, herbs and edible flowers in open beds or under polytunnels. They make salad mixtures that, depending on the time of year, may have as many as 15 different leaves, including mizuna, sorrel, rocket, salad bowl, basil, chives, fennel, nasturtium leaves and lollo rosso. They grow more or less everything that a good market garden should: root crops

Way off the beaten track at **Newark Farm**, OZLEWORTH, **Wotten-under-Edge GL12 7PZ** ☎ **01453 842144**, Sue Limb tends a small organic flock of unusual breeds of hens such as Cream Legbar, with its blueish eggs, or Welbar, known for its deep brown – sometimes speckly – eggs. With over 200 acres to peck at, hers are free-range eggs in the true sense of the word. They are sold in boxes of mixed colours, from pure white to deep dark, almost chocolate brown. As the farm is miles from anywhere, it is far easier to buy them at Ruskin Mill see above.

Stockists

Avon: Chandos Deli

Glam: Shelley's Delicatessen

Glos: Cavendish House

London:
Jeffersons
Selfridges

NAILSWORTH
Vegetables and Salads

such as beetroot, parsnips, potatoes, celery, celeriac and carrots; leaf crops such as spinach; baby peas and beans, and courgettes. The list goes on for ever. I tried a piercingly sweet and scarlet-ripe cherry tomato, while Violet – much to her indignation – was given a well-meaning but unappreciated hosing to cool her down.

There is a small farm shop and here you can buy their produce: excellent fresh vegetables grown to good condition, honey, meat and sausages, all from their farms, as well as local apple juice and eggs. The point about Ruskin Mill, as far as food lovers are concerned, is that you can buy their produce and at the same time you are supporting a valuable community project from which ultimately we will all benefit.

**NORTH
CERNEY
Goats'
Cheese**

Cerney Cheese

*Cerney House, North Cerney, Cirencester,
Gloucestershire GL7 7BX*

☎ 01285 831300 **FAX** 01285 831676 **CONTACT** Lady Angus **HOURS** *Easter to Oct: Tues, Wed & Fri 14.00-18.00 (otherwise telephone ahead)* **DIRECTIONS** *From Cirencester, take A435 towards Cheltenham. After about 3½ miles, in North Cerney, turn left opposite Bathurst Arms pub. Drive past church up the hill and turn right at Cerney House gates.*

Lady Angus, ably abetted by Marian Conisbee-Smith, has been commercially making an unpasteurized semi-soft goat's-milk cheese for 7 years. Some of the milk comes from her own mixed herd of British Saanen, Anglo-Nubian and Golden Guernsey goats and the rest is bought in. The cheese, based on a Valençay recipe Lady Angus learnt to make while living in France, is made every day and takes 5 days to complete.

Full-cream milk is started and renneted and left to stand for 24 hours. Then the milk is ladled into cheesecloths and left to drain freely for another 24 hours. The curd is scooped into pyramids, lightly pressed down to shape it, and left to drain for a further 24 hours. Next it is sprinkled with a mixture of salt and oak ash from France (giving it a speckly stubbled coating) and left to stand for 24 hours. As the cheese absorbs the salt, it gives out more moisture. Finally it is turned out of the moulds, the remaining sides are lightly coated and it is put in the fridge to mature.

Sold in 225-g (8-oz) very-French-looking pyramids, if eaten at 5 days the cheese is young and very fresh, with the merest hint of goat. As it matures, it develops a deeper fuller taste. Possibly it is at its best when matured for between 1 and 2 weeks, when it is still moistly creamy and quite smooth, but with a more obvious flavour.

Stockists

Glos: Barnetts

The Flour Bag

Jessie Smiths

Oxon: The Oxford Cheese Shop

Warwicks: Paxton & Whitfield

The Fine Cheese Company *in Bath see page 15 has just opened a sister shop at* **5 Regent Street, CHELTENHAM GL50 1HE** ☎/**fax 01242 255022** *where you can find a similar supply of on-farm British cheeses, all in prime condition.*

While you're in the area...

Birdwood House Farm Shop, BIRDWOOD, Huntley GL19 3EJ ☎ 01452 750248 sells locally made cakes, bread, dry-cured bacon, poultry, various sausages, pies and own-cooked ham. There is a small but well-chosen selection of British cheeses with a preference for unpasteurized milk, the notable exceptions are Charles Martell's Hereford Hops, a hard cheese coated with – and matured – in hops, and the perry-washed Stinking Bishop.

For well-hung game in season from local estates, various sausages, Bath chaps from Sandridge Farm *see page* 284 and poultry, as well as wet and cured fish, visit **Charles Barnett, I Market Place, CIRENCESTER GL7 2NL ☎ 01285 652418**.

Since my visit, I hear **Gastromania, 3 The Market Place, CIRENCESTER GL7 2PE ☎ 01285 644611 fax 01285 644101** have expanded, with a 'never cook again' section offering the service of a French traiteur. They still sell Hobbs House Bakery breads *see page 12*, Rocombe Farm ice-cream *page 84* and various cheeses.

Drury's Butchers and Delicatessen, 17 High Street, MORETON-IN-MARSH GL56 0AF ☎ 016086 50318 are best known for their generously filled own-made meat pies that many a reader has told me are a 'must' for a picnic in the Cotswolds.

The Bottle Green Drinks Company, Frogmarsh Mills, SOUTH WOODCHESTER, Stroud GL5 5ET ☎ 01453 872882 fax 01453 872188 is already well-known for its elderflower cordial which is made from the fresh flowers steeped in a sugar syrup, then lightly crushed, pressed and filtered, as well as the ready-mixed with water Elderflower pressé. New last summer is their Elderflower Spritzer, a blend of white wine, sparkling spring water and the cordial. It is remarkably refreshing and has an alcohol content of only 3 per cent.

The Organic Shop, The Square, STOW-ON-THE-WOLD GL54 IAB ☎ 01451 831004 sells almost exclusively certified organic produce. There is a good choice of flours, breads, meats, pies, pasties, a few cheeses, eggs, the entire range of Rachel's Dairy products *see page* 380 and various vegetables, salads and herbs.

Right in the centre of town is the **House of Cheese, 13 Church Street, TETBURY GL8 8JG ☎/fax 01666 502865** stocking a good range of British cheeses, including Charles Martell's Single Gloucester and Stinking Bishop.

Tetbury Traditional Meat, 31 Church Street, TETBURY GL8 8JG ☎ 01666 502892 are good butchers. Meat comes well-hung and neatly trimmed. There are always some interesting coarsely cut sausages, including pork & cheese, apple & cider and a chunky French-style Toulouse. They also makes good pies, and cure their own bacons and hams.

Hampshire

Map No. 2

The Blackmoor Nurseries & Apple Shop
Blackmoor Estate, Blackmoor, Liss, Hampshire GU33 6BS

☎ nursery: 01420 473576; shop: 01420 473782 **FAX** 01420 487813
CONTACT Mrs Hudson **HOURS** (*nursery*) Nov to Mar: Sat 9.00-12.30; (*shop*)
Oct to Dec 24: Mon-Sat 9.00-16.30 *all year*: Sun 10.00-16.00 **DIRECTIONS**
From Greatham, take A325 towards Farnham. After about 1 mile, turn left, sign-posted Blackmoor. Follow Blackmoor Apple Shop signs for about 1 mile to the estate.

The Blackmoor estate is home to Lord Selbourne. A leading light in the agricultural world, he is also Chairman of the Brogdale Horticultural Trust *see page 146*, so you would expect his fruit to be of the very best quality.

The nurseries are thought to be among the finest in the country, they supply fruit trees to commercial growers, nurserymen, garden centres and – on Saturday mornings only – to amateur growers, the likes of you and me. Lord Selbourne is a serious apple enthusiast and his private collection has some rare treasures. So as well as the modern commercial varieties, you would hope to find some fine old varieties in his nursery. You will not be disappointed as, listed in the catalogue under the apt heading of 'Connoisseur's Choice', are some very choice trees.

There is my favourite, Pitmaston Pine Apple, with its tiny golden

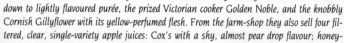

Hill Farm Orchards, Droxford Road, SWANMORE SO32 2PY ☎fax
01489 878616 *grow around 30 varieties of apples, including some quite unusual ones, such as the astringent Exeter Cross, Crawley Beauty which cooks down to lightly flavoured purée, the prized Victorian cooker Golden Noble, and the knobbly Cornish Gillyflower with its yellow-perfumed flesh. From the farm-shop they also sell four filtered, clear, single-variety apple juices: Cox's with a shy, almost pear drop flavour; honey-sweet Russet; crisp Bramley; Discovery; a blended apple juice, and ready-picked soft fruit in season.*

bell-shaped fruit endowed with the aroma of pineapple; Court Pendu Plat, first described in 1613 and thought to be one of the oldest apples in cultivation, it has a curious flattened shape and a sweet luscious flavour; Devonshire Quarrenden, an 18th-century apple that is crisp to eat; Peasgood Nonsuch, raised by Mrs Peasgood in 1858 in Stamford, where the original tree is apparently still growing, is described as 'flesh tender, yellowish, of pleasant flavour and cooks frothily'; and the richly flavoured Cornish Gillyflower Aromatic. As Blackmoor Nurseries grow both root stock and bud trees, you can usually order the size to suit your garden – from dwarf to half-standard. They also have trained trees (espaliers, or fan-shaped, for growing against a wall) or family trees (one tree with different varieties grafted on). With so much choice, it is probably best to ring first to discuss your order.

Apart from apples, they have a good selection of pears, including the buttery Beurré Hardy, Glou Morceau, Louise Bonne of Jersey which boasts beautiful blossom and the meltingly fleshed Nouveau Poiteau. Plums are not forgotten with, amongst others, Cambridge Gage and Shropshire Prune Damson, described as 'blue/black and rich flavour'. There are cherry, cob nut, fig, peach, apricot and nectarine trees as well. They also have a good selection of soft fruit bushes and I was pleased to find the gooseberry Whinham's Industry, with its large dark-red hairy berries that overflow with fruitiness.

From the shop, they sell about 20 – mostly commercial modern – varieties, including Jupiter, Gala, Discovery, Katy, Jonagold, Cox's and Russet. Lord Selbourne is also one of the largest apple growers, indeed many of the apples that find their way on to the supermarket shelves are grown at Blackmoor. They also sell pears and quinces (in season in October) as well as a selection of own-made cakes and jams from their fruit. Every year, either on the second or third Sunday in October, there is a huge apple day when you can taste the different apples. It makes for a fun day out.

West Lea Farm Shop
Borough Bridge, Itchen Stoke, Alresford, Hampshire SO24 0QP

BOROUGH BRIDGE
Watercress

☎ 01962 732476 **FAX** 01962 732710 **CONTACT** John Curtis **HOURS** *Mon-Fri 10.00-16.30 Sat 10.00-16.00;* **DIRECTIONS** *From Alresford, take B3047 towards Winchester. After about ½ mile, turn right, signposted Itchen Stoke. Shop on the right.*

Perched on the end of a little wooden pier built out over watercress beds is West Lea Farm Shop, converted from an original bunching shed. From here you can buy bunches of freshly picked watercress straight from the West Lea Farm beds. The main growing areas for watercress follow the chalk belt from Dorset and Wiltshire through Hampshire and up to the Home Counties, with Hampshire having the biggest production.

Jenny Woodham runs the shop and is constantly trying to develop new products using watercress. Apart from fresh bunches, she also sells cartons of her watercress soup. Using a simple recipe of milk, chicken stock, onion, flour, margarine and, of course, masses of watercress, she makes it at home and freezes it in 200, 350, and 500-g (7 and 12-oz and 1 lb 2-oz) tubs. A delicate green and well puréed, it has that gentle pepperiness you expect from watercress. There are fishcakes made from locally farmed trout, potatoes and watercress that come into the shop as fresh and are frozen at the end of the day. Generously studded with watercress, they are a good buy. Helen Sutherland *see below* makes special watercress & pork sausages. They also sell freshly picked fruit from Durleighmarsh Farm *see page* 125, Blackburn & Haynes ice-cream and various cakes, fruit pies and biscuits by local ladies, as well as bottles of Hazeley Down, the local spring water.

Stockists

Cornw: The Good Life

Hants: Dean Farm Shop

Evans

Whites

Whites, The Square, WINCHESTER SO23 9EX ☎ 01962 840805 fax 01962 841924 *is a new delicatessen run by Geoffrey White. I arrived on a hot day and outside the attractive double-fronted shop was a thoughtfully placed dog bowl filled with water – thirsty dogs take note. It won Violet's eternal thanks and after that, I admit, it was jolly difficult to look around with a totally unbiased view. On the other hand, if you are going to open a small speciality shop in competition with well-stocked supermarkets, service is one thing you have to offer. Another is a good range of speciality foods from small producers – and here they score. There were plenty of my favourites: ham from Richard Woodall see page 62, Fudges Bakery breads and biscuits see page 92 as well as some good locally baked bread, Mrs Gill's cakes see page 83, chocolates from Melchior see page 81, Rocombe Farm ice-cream see page 84, S. Moores Dorset knobs see page 93, Joyce Molyneux's Christmas puddings see page 71, Shipton Mill flour see page 115, cartons of soup from West Lea Farm Shop see page 121, and bacon from Sutherlands of Eldon see below, some carefully chosen cheeses and a good selection of quiches and salads in a well-laid-out deli counter.*

KING'S SOMBORNE

Wild Blue Pork

Sutherlands of Eldon

Upper Eldon Farm, King's Somborne, Hampshire SO20 6QN

☎ 01794 368158 **FAX** 01794 368158 **CONTACT** Helen Sutherland – telephone ahead

Developed by Helen Sutherland in conjunction with her partner Sam Olive, the Eldon Wild Blue pig has been bred to produce excellent meat. The sows farrow about twice a year and the piglets are weaned at 8 weeks and slaughtered at about 12 months. Their aim is 'to produce meat to a quality, not down to a price'. The pork is generally hung for 7 days. It can go for longer, up to 14 days, when it acquires a deeper lingering resonance. 'The only disadvantage', Helen told me, 'is that the skin becomes very leathery and is no good for crackling at all.' It is sold as whole legs weighing about 6.8 kg (15 lb) or half legs at 3.2 kg (7 lb); boned whole legs at 5.9 kg (13 lb) or half at 2.7 kg (6 lb); bone-in or boned loin joints or chops, loin steaks (eye of loin), tenderloin, belly, casserole meat (from the shoulder), and boned and rolled whole shoul-

MAP 2　　　　　　　　　　　HAMPSHIRE　　　**123**

der. Shoulder is the cut Helen likes above all for roasting as 'it's particularly sweet and succulent with good intra-muscular fat'. With food writer Susan Campbell, I tried a small piece of boned leg. The crackling was superb, chewy but crisp, the actual flesh was strangely disappointing. With a closer-grained texture than pork, it was a little tough and dry – not nearly so good as I have had in the past and we both agreed that perhaps it needed either more hanging or less time in the oven.

Helen also sells Eldon Wild Blue Ham. I loved the hard, tough, rasping flavour, its dryness and sheer meatiness. On the other hand, Susan – who prefers her ham soft, sweet, pink and fatty – was left unmoved.

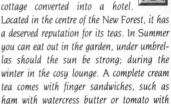

The Thatched Cottage Hotel, 16 Brookley Road, BROCK-ENHURST, Hampshire SO42 7RR ☎ 01590 23090 FAX 01590 23479 is a real thatched cottage converted into a hotel. Located in the centre of the New Forest, it has a deserved reputation for its teas. In Summer you can eat out in the garden, under umbrellas should the sun be strong; during the winter in the cosy lounge. A complete cream tea comes with finger sandwiches, such as ham with watercress butter or tomato with cream cheese, three homemade plain, fruited and wholemeal & walnut baby scones served with clotted cream, jam and butter and various cakes and pastries.

Recently developed is an air-dried ham which is cured in salt, peppercorns, coriander seeds and juniper berries, then soaked in molasses and hung to mature for 8 months. Both Susan and I felt that perhaps a little adjustment is needed to the method, the salt was overwhelming. A pity that, as we both felt the underlaying taste of meat was complex and interesting.

Helen processes Wild Blue into sausages with a 90 per cent meat content. These come as salt & pepper, green peppercorn, honey & mustard, tomato & fennel, garlic, and 100 per cent meat. All the mixes are made up individually and she is more than happy to create a personal recipe for you with your favourite ingredients, provided you order a minimum of 9 kg (20 lb).

Stockists

Hants: Barlows
W. Stares Ltd
- - - - - - - -
Whites

London: The
House of Albert
Roux
- - - - - - - -
Harvey Nichols

Mrs Tee's Wild Mushrooms

LYMINGTON
Mushrooms

Gorse Meadow, Sway Road, Lymington, Hampshire SO41 8LR

☎ 01590 673354 **FAX** 01590 673336 **CONTACT** Brigitte Tee-Hillman – telephone ahead

There are those who think 'Mrs Tee is Mrs Mushroom'. Even Roger Phillips, mycologist *par excellence* and author of *Mushrooms* has been heard to say that Brigitte Tee knows more about the ingestible (edible) mushroom than anyone else in the country.

Mrs Tee has been collecting in the New Forest since 1978. True to form, mushroom pickers are a very secretive lot and she will not reveal exactly where. What started as a hobby, however, has 'mushroomed' into a business. She now supplies several top restaurants with own-picked ceps, chicken o' the woods, wild oyster mushrooms, pieds de moutons, chanterelles grises, blewetts, trompettes de mort and

This year Alex Aitken chef/proprietor of **Le Poussin, The Courtyard, Brookley Road, BROCKENHURST SO42 7RB ☎ 01590 623063 fax 01590 622912** *won a well-deserved Michelin star. What is less well known is that he runs a larder service from the rear of the kitchen that keeps to his restaurant hours. You can buy British cheeses in prime condition, as well as foods-to-go made to the same impeccable standards. On the list are chicken & wild mushroom and seafood sausages, squab pigeon in pastry, various terrines, millefeuilles and lemon tart. If you give him warning, he will prepare 'more or less anything' from the menu.*

girolles in season. She also has imported fungi from all over the world during the rest of the year.

Picking mushrooms can be skilled work; 'You need good powers of observation – some people see them, others don't. You must learn to identify the mushrooms, know about its growing habits, where it likes, or where it doesn't and when. Then you won't waste time. There's no point in looking in the wrong woods or at the wrong time. And you must learn to pick carefully. Not to destroy the woods, not to tear at the stem and the right depth to cut'. Mrs Tee, a German, believes only Continentals have a real instinctive feel for picking, although I know an awful lot of British pickers who would take issue with her about that.

Stockists

London:
Mortimer & Bennett

Panzer Delicatessen

Selfridges

She specializes in boxes weighing from 450 g to 2.3 kg (1 to 5 lb) of mushroom mixtures; each box is divided into paper compartments and the mushrooms are separated by variety, 'as this helps for correct cooking times'. What you get will depend on the time of the year, but she is happy to discuss an order. This autumn, Mrs Tee plans to run mushroom forays and throughout the year you can book in for B&B – at nights she cooks a full mushroom meal.

The Game Centre, 1 Petersfield Road, GREATHAM, Liss GU33 6AA ☎/fax 01420 538162 *is expanding and last year won a county award for exporting to Europe. You can buy oven-ready game all year round from them as they keep frozen supplies out of season. Expect to find pheasant, partridge, woodcock, whole pigeons or just the breasts, various wild ducks including teal and mallard, and saddle or haunch of hare. They also sell a game pie mix, and make sausages from venison and, using the breast meat only, pheasant – both with a meat content of 80 per cent.*

SHIRLEY
Clams

Pirouet Seafoods

3 Redcar Street, Shirley, Southampton, Hampshire SO15 5LL

☎ 01703 788139 **FAX** 01703 322263 **CONTACT** David Pirouet **HOURS** Tues-Sat 9.00-17.00 **DIRECTIONS** *From Southampton, take Commercial Road towards Shirley, signposted. Follow the road about ¼ mile to Shirley High Street. Shop is on the right, in the shopping precinct.*

Fishmonger David Pirouet, who sells hard-shell clams – kept under ice to stay moist and cool – from his well-stocked shop, is vague about their source. If anyone can help me track them down please do. 'They're wild and dredged in the harbour' was the best lead I could get. They come about the size of 'a lady's fist' and are juicy-fleshed, with a chewy texture and a sweet clear and mildly salty flavour. Notoriously difficult to open, the solution is to pop them in the freezer for 10-15 minutes and thaw them quickly. They will then be in no condition to resist the onslaught of your knife and will willingly give way. He also sells *amandes de mer* (dog cockles) and *palourdes* (carpet shell clams) imported from France, winkles and whelks, along with a good selection of white fish and lobsters kept live in his vivier.

Food writer Susan Campbell, who lives nearby, buys her bread at **Marks Bakery, 5 St Thomas Street, LYMINGTON SO41 9NA ☎ 01590 672467**. Mr and Mrs Marks have run the shop for 22 years and everything is baked on the premises 'starting from scratch'. White bread is made exactly as it used to be, using a proportion of one day's dough to start off the next day's bread and leaving the dough to ferment for the rest of that day and overnight. The result is a creamy dense interior crumb with a slight sharpness and a good crust. They still use the old brick-floor ovens that are now gas-fired 'for convenience' and, using the old-fashioned wooden slips or peels, most of their bread goes straight on the oven floor. They make a good range of breads, crisp doughnuts, a yeasty Danish ring and a bready lardy cake that was sweet but not sticky.

Durleighmarsh Farm, Rogate Road, PETERSFIELD GU31 5AX ☎ 01730 821626 has a good selection of pick-your-own and ready-picked fruit and vegetables. The season starts with asparagus and takes in new potatoes, soft fruit including red and white currants, gooseberries, tayberries, cherries, plums including Czars and Victorias, several varieties of strawberries, broad beans, an American white variety of sweetcorn, and spinach. You can even pick-your-own bunches of culinary herbs. Everything both in the fields and in the shop is well-labelled, so you can tell exactly what is what and whether it is own-grown or bought-in. In the barn of a shop there is some good local produce: Hill Farm cloudy apple juice, bacon from Old Spot Farm see page 273, Rumbolds cheese see page 273, ice-cream from Blackburn & Haynes, and plenty of cakes and pies baked by two local ladies, as well as their chutneys and jams. The light fresh raspberry jam sharpened with a touch of lemon juice is well worth seeking out.

While you're in the area...

Olivia Mills of Brebilait Products, Wield Wood, ALRESFORD SO24 9RU ☎ 01420 563151 fax 01420 561018 makes Walda cheese from her flock of Friesland and Friesland-cross sheep between April and November. Similar in texture to an Emmental, it has a sweet, mildly toffee flavour and is sold as whole cheeses weighing about 2 kg (4½ lb), or in pieces cut to size.

M. & A. McCutcheon, 44 West Street, ALRESFORD SO24 9AU ☎ 01962 732569 are a good high-street bakers. They bake a variety of flavoured breads, including cheese & onion, tomato made with both tomato purée and fresh tomatoes, and a well-textured oatmeal. Their crisp round cheese biscuits have plenty of cheesy punch and the lardy cake – sticky, full of lard and very heavy – is about as authentic as you can buy.

A. & M. Johnson, Grasmead Dean, BISHOPS WALTHAM SO32 1FY ☎ 01489 892390 make five different mustards, including a pale honey mustard with a lingering sweetness and a medium kick. Mustard seeds are ground quite finely for a pleasing smoothness, with crushed seeds added to break up the texture. They also sell honey and own-made marmalade using their honey.

Chawton Park Farm, CHAWTON, Alton GU34 1SW ☎ 01420 83300 farm Red deer. Hung for 7-10 days, butchered into various cuts, including saddle on or off the bone, whole or half-boned and rolled haunch or haunch steaks. Unless you pre-order, however, the meat is frozen. They also sell chiffon-thin slices of smoked haunch, prepared for them by Minola Smoked Products *see page* 112, with a sweet after-taste and the merest hint of venison.

Kimbridge Farm Shop, KIMBRIDGE, Romsey SO51 0LE ☎ 01794 340777 fax 01794 341295 sell own-farmed fresh trout in packets as hot- or cold-smoked. They also sell various British cheeses, locally made cakes and biscuits, and fresh egg & watercress pasta made by chef Mauro Bregoli of Old Manor House.

If you are catching the ferry to the Isle of Wight, pop into **Earth Monkey, The Cottage, Walhampton Lodge, LYMINGTON SO41 5SB ☎ 01590 671049 fax 01590 676364** just before you reach the terminal. Here you can buy all sorts of edible herbs, including the gelatinous and peppery Sedum Acre (wall pepper), sweet rocket with hairy leaves and Bramble Bank Bee honey. They also have a stall in Lymington market on Saturdays.

Lymington Larder, 13 High Street, LYMINGTON SO41 9AA ☎/fax 01590 676740 is a cheery enough shop, although it is generally thought that the owner is perhaps a little unfriendly. Per-severe and you will find a good selection of local foods, including Denhay cheese and butter *see page* 89, Rocombe Farm ice-cream *see page* 84, and The New Forest Sausage Co.'s sausages *see below*. In the summer they make pies, quiches, and slices of a version of salmon coulibiac with brioche pancakes, spinach, cheese and pistachio.

Locals recommend the meat and game from butcher **S. W. Pickles & Son, 3 Fernhill Lane, NEW MILTON BH25 5JN ☎ 01425 614577**. Beef, hand-picked on the hoof, is hung for a minimum of 2 weeks and Dorset lamb for about 10 days. Everything is well-butchered. Venison is mostly fallow deer from the New Forest and comes nicely barded with pork fat. They also cure salt beef and bacon.

The New Forest Sausage Company, Station Road, SWAY SO41 6AA ☎ 01590 682302 are Hampshire Champions and national award winners. How good this makes their farmhouse, or pork, apple & sage, or pork & mixed herbs, or pork & garlic, or pork & Thumper ale sausages, who can tell?

Herefordshire

Map No. 2

September Dairy Products
Newhouse Farm, Almeley, Kington, Herefordshire HR3 6LJ

☎ 01544 327561 **CONTACT** *Carey Glyn-Jones* **HOURS** 9.00-19.00 **DIRECTIONS** *From Kington, take A4111 towards Eardisley. After about 3 miles, turn left at sign for Almeley. Follow signs for farm-shop for ¾ mile. Shop is on the right.*

Just because a product is 'made on the farm' does not necessarily mean than it is any better than if it had been made in a factory. All too often the phrase is bandied about, being used to project an image of purity and freshness that can be miles from the truth. *Where* it is made is not important, what it *contains* and *how* it is made *is*. This was what was going through my mind as I called on Carey Glyn-Jones at her farm to sample the ice-creams.

The setting could hardly be bettered, a square farmhouse standing proud deep in Herefordshire's rolling hills. A small farm-shop by the farmyard operates on a degree of trust rarely seen nowadays: Carey can be summoned by a bell, but most customers help themselves and leave the money. Here you can buy green-top (unpasteurized) milk from their Friesian herd; a buttery unpasteurized double cream; own free-range eggs; and, sporadically, pork and bacon (cured by a butcher in Cinderford) from their whey-fed pigs; and of course, the ice-creams.

These are among the few ice-creams that deserve to be called 'farmhouse'. From a 'farmhouse' ice-cream, I want the 'real thing': a mix made with the farmer's own milk, with 'real' flavours made up as and when they are needed. I do not want stabilizers and emulsifiers to hold a mixture together; nor do I want flavours from a tin bought in from a flavour-house, that is what I expect from a commercial brand.

Using their own milk, and making in small batches, Carey's ice-cream has a fat content of 10-11 per cent and an over-run (added air) of about 50 per cent; to stabilize the mixture she uses fresh eggs. It may shorten its shelf-life but that, Carey feels, is a small price to pay for a 'pure' ice-cream.

The basic mix was clear, with a clean restrained milky flavour, quite sweet but not overly so, and to this she adds various flavours. Vanilla was, perhaps, a little disappointing, Carey uses an essence and I have never been that keen on its overtly sweet masking aftertaste; coffee, simply made with an instant brew, was dry and invigorating; honey & ginger made with just that – a runny honey and diced stem ginger – was nicely sweet and spiced; brown bread was crunchy with its caramelized breadcrumbs; and both tayberry and strawberry were packed with fresh fruit picked from a local fruit farm. If I am going to be really picky, I did not enjoy the chocolate range – Choc Orange, Choc Mint and Choc Ginger – but then I like my chocolate dark, dry and very bitter (and probably very expensive); Carey, with an eye on her market, uses cocoa as her base. Sold in individual 1 and 4-litre (1¾ and 7-pint) tubs, September ice-cream is a good 'farmhouse' ice-cream and worth seeking out in the county.

Stockists

Heref: Orleton Farmshop

Harvest store

Nant-or Nurseries

Organic Options

Salop: Monkton Farmshop

HEREFORD
Cider Apple Trees

H. P. *Bulmer* Ltd

The Cider Mills, Plough Lane, Hereford, Herefordshire HR4 0LE

☎ 01432 352855 **FAX** 01432 345722 **CONTACT** Chris Fairs – *telephone ahead*

The name Bulmer is synonymous with cider; what is less well-known is that they run an advisory service for anyone who already has started – or would like to start – a cider-apple orchard, or just plant a few trees. Strictly speaking it is for potential customers or suppliers of Bulmer, but Christopher Fairs – who rejoices in the title of 'Growers Advisory Manager, Orcharding Department' – will stretch a point and help anyone.

The sort of information he needs to know is where is the (projected) orchard, what is the soil like, its type, depth and pH, details of the rainfall and drainage, what other apples or fruit are grown in the surrounding area, what was grown before on the land, and what you intend to do with the fruit. If you are planning an orchard, you might be interested to know that the planting rate is 200-300 bush trees an acre for a dedicated orchard; 120 half standard trees for a more traditional orchard that allows room for sheep to graze around the trees; and 40 standard trees an acre gives 'space for all classes of livestock – except giraffes'. The best time for planting is between December and March, which is conveniently when trees are available.

Cider apple varieties always have such old-fashioned convoluted names and the ones on Bulmer's list are no exception. There is Harry Masters Jersey, or Broxwood Foxwhelp, Tom Putt, Ellis Bitter and Bulmers Norman, to name but a few of those that make up the 25-odd on this year's list. They also have some perry pear trees; and, if you give Christopher plenty of notice ('sometimes it may be as long as 2 years'), he will do all he can to graft a rare or local cider apple variety for you.

Little Marcle Organic Partnership
Lilly Hall Farm, Ledbury, Herefordshire HR8 2ID

☎FAX 01531 632892   **CONTACT** Ray Hunter – delivery only

Little Marcle Organic Partnership runs a vegetable box scheme. For the uninitiated, a vegetable box scheme works like this – and here I quote from Local Food Links by Judy Steele – 'At its simplest ... the grower packs a box of whatever seasonal vegetables he or she has available and delivers it to the customer. The customer pays a standard price for a box and accepts whatever is inside. It sounds too simple. One would expect customers to complain because they haven't got a choice. This doesn't seem to be a problem. People seem to accept what they get and are often relieved because they don't have to decide what to buy'.

So what are the advantages of buying vegetables in this way? The vegetables are bound to be fresh as most box-schemers will pick on the delivery day. The quality is as good – if not better – than you would buy in the shops and the prices competitive. If a schemer grows to Soil Association standards – and most do – you know that you are buying organic vegetables. Choice is not a problem and, believe it or not, most customers like the element of surprise that comes with never knowing exactly what is in a box; they also say it puts them back in touch with seasonality.

Ray Hunter is one of the more successful schemers. His box was the overall winner of the 1994 organic food awards judged at the BBC Good Food Show. Unlike some, he packs his boxes with produce from other growers and imports as well as what he grows himself. 'We undertake to supply at least 8 different vegetables or fruits every week. But the choice is ours.' He actually grows about 18 different vegetables throughout the year and, supplemented with his co-op members, has about 50-odd vegetables to call on, with some grown under glass or in poly-tunnels. Ray delivers to 7 collection points within a radius of about 4 miles from his farm; from there the boxes are collected by the subscribers. Most of the schemers I talked to, Ray included, make up boxes to a size rather than a weight, for convenience and ease of packing. Ray currently sells a £5.00 box that contains, on average, 4.5 kg (10 lb) of vegetables 'more than enough for two' and a £7.00,

The Mousetrap Cheese Shop *has two branches in the county, one at* **1 Bewell Square, Hereford HR4 0BB** ☎ **01432 353423** *the other at* **3 School Lane,** LEOMIN-STER HR6 8AA ☎ **01568 615512**. *Both make a point of selling on-farm British cheeses, so you will find such local examples as Charles Martell's Stinking Bishop, Old Worcester see page 299, Diana Smart's Single and Double Gloucester see page 110 and a good selection of Welsh cheeses. New this year are the olive oil breads, with walnuts or sun-dried tomatoes & olives made by restaurateur Jacqui Gilleland of The March at Eyton. Karen Hindle, who runs the shops with her husband Mark, has just started making cheese. Still at the experimental stage, she is producing a Little Hereford and has plans for a Shropshire Sage. If anyone has a good recipe she would love them to get in touch.*

with 6.4 kg (14 lb) of vegetables 'for a whole family'.

It is a good idea and is, not surprisingly, catching on fast. Should you be interested in finding out about a box scheme in your area, Ray suggests ringing Geoff Mutton of The Organic Marketing Company on 01531 640819 and he will put you in touch with a source of supply.

PEMBRIDGE
Cider and Perry

Dunkertons Cider Company

Hays Head, Luntley, Pembridge, Leominster, Herefordshire HR6 9ED

☎ 01544 388653 **CONTACT** Susie Dunkerton **HOURS** Mon-Sat 10.00-18.00 **DIRECTIONS** From Leominster, take A44 towards Kington. After about 7 miles, turn left in the centre of Pembridge at The New Inn, signposted to cider mill. Follow the road for about 1 mile and farm is signposted on the left.

Susie and Ivor Dunkerton make their still cider and perry with the same care and attention to detail as wine-makers make their wine. All the fruit is unsprayed and, like wine growers who constantly tend their vines, they have been busy re-planting their orchards with such rare and curiously named cider apples as Bloody Turk and Sheeps Nose or Moorcroft and Thorne perry pears.

Most of their cider is a blend of several well-known cider apples, such as the sharp Foxwhelp, the bittersweet Knotted Kernel that is high in tannin and sugar, the Brown Snout, Yarlington Mill, Roi de Pomme and Strawberry Norman. However – and this is what makes their cider special – each variety of apple is pressed and fermented separately. Blending takes place later, continuing throughout the year, into 4,542-litre (1,200-gallon) oak vats. Each blend varies according to the degree of tannin, sharpness and fermentation of the individual varieties. It is sold as 'crisp and unsweetened' traditional dry, 'rounded and mellow' medium-dry, 'sweeter and fruity' medium-sweet, and 'rich and full-bodied' sweet, in draught gallons and corked 1-litre and ½-litre bottles.

They also discovered while blending that, while most cider apples are too acid, too bitter or too sweet to be bottled singly, certain ones do have sufficient body, depth of character and flavour to stand up on their own. So they have developed Single Variety ciders made with Breakwells Seedling, fresh, fruity and medium-dry; Court Royal medium-dry, with a smoky tinge; Kingston Black, a dry, strong old-fashioned no-nonsense cider; and, new this year, Princess Pippin, with an almost lemony flavour.

Just released are their low-alcohol ciders, with an alcohol level of 5.5 per cent as opposed to their norm of 7-8 per cent. This they achieve by adding less sugar at fermentation stage. As Susie explains, 'Once the apples are pressed we use a hydrometer to measure the natural sugars in the juice. There's a scale that works out how much sugar to add to give it the right percentage of alcohol. By cutting down on the sugar, the yeast has less to feed on so the fermentation will not

Stockists

Chesh: Demeter Wholefoods

Derbys: Chatsworth Farmshop

London: Fortnum & Mason
- - - - - - - - - -
Selfridges

Yorks: York Beer Shop

MAP 2   HEREFORDSHIRE   **131**

be so strong'. Blended to the same principles as their other ciders, they are lighter and fruitier with less depth 'more of a lunch-time drink' and come as medium-dry and medium-sweet.

The Dunkertons also make a fruity medium-dry perry which really tastes of pears from a blend of traditional varieties, such as Redhorse, Merrylegs and Painted Lady, and sold in corked 1-litre and 0.75-litre bottles. The Dunkertons have a deserved reputation; last edition I described their ciders and perrys as 'finely tuned, old-fashioned, with a long, lingering throaty taste to remind you of how they must have been when they were properly made by our forefathers' and I see no reason to change my mind.

> *The Cider House* at Dunkertons is open all day for coffee, lunch and teas. The Dunkertons have re-erected two 400-year-old half-timbered barns for a pretty café with French windows that open out on to a terrace. In summer you can sit outside, sipping draught cider or perry, while looking out over the fields and beyond. The accent is on serving local and – whenever possible – organic produce; a plate of organic cheeses from Wales comes with generous chunks of home-made bread, and home-made scones are served with local cream. As you might expect, they are always experimenting with cider in cooking, so there is fruit cake steeped in cider, or apple, hazelnut & cider cake or chocolate cake with a perry & chocolate icing.

R. J. Moxley
1 Winchester Avenue, Tupsley, Hereford, Herefordshire HR1 1QJ

TUPSLEY
Hereford Beef

☎ 01432 265351   **HOURS** Mon & Sat 8.30-13.00 Tues-Fri 8.30-13.00 14.15-17.30   **DIRECTIONS** In Tupsley centre.

It was Rudolf Steiner who first pointed out that one cannot improve upon a breed of animal bred in its area. So you might be forgiven for thinking that in the county of Hereford, buying pure-bred Hereford beef would be a doddle. Well, think again. According to butcher Dick 'I've been in the trade 61 years' Moxley, 'pure-breds are bred for breeding, not for eating'.

The eating characteristics of pure-bred Hereford are well known. Butcher David Lidgate *see page 183* says that top-quality Hereford wins hands-down over any other breed, with the very highest grade Aberdeen Angus finished in Scotland as the only possible exception. Hereford has a particularly good conformation and its meat is well marbled, with an inimitable flavour in the true tradition of 'the roast beef of England'.

All is not well, though, even with the pedigree Hereford blood-line. As Prue Coats wrote in *The Field* in March 1993, 'The Hereford is the world's largest beef breed and for this reason it has been subject to more commercial pressure than any other. Its hallmark is its colour marking, which is a dominant characteristic. This is its greatest strength, because any crosses can be easily identified, but it is also its greatest weakness as it has enabled the unscrupulous to introduce foreign breeds without any record in the pedigree'. These 'foreign breeds' were more often than not, so-called 'improved' Herefords introduced from abroad and thus the decline of the purity of the breed's blood-line commenced. All is not lost, as Michael Symonds – 'concerned at the diversity of colour and markings, loss of conformation and, more important, the lack of ability to flesh off forage' – runs one of the very few herds (if not the only herd) based on selection within pure-bred lines without any outside interference. Thus one of our native breeds is being preserved. So even if you can buy pure-bred Hereford, it might not even be to its original and historical conformation.

R. J. Moxley will sell pure-bred 'when and if we can get them' and Dick, who buys in the open ring (market), has the reputation for buying any good ones around. Mostly they are steers, at anything from 20 months to 2½ years and will be hung 'for 14 days plus'. More likely, what they sell will be Hereford crossed with a Continental breed as this is what we apparently want. The result is a leaner animal, with the heavier hind-quarters that butchers prefer, and it matures earlier, which is what the farmers prefer. It will have less of the glorious marbling which gives Hereford beef its richness and flavour and a comparatively coarser-textured and less tender flesh. Furthermore 'a cross will not hang as well, it deteriorates'. Moxley with a branch at 100 Grandstand Road, Westfields, Hereford HR4 9NR ☎ 01432 266074 tend not to identify whether their Herefords are pure- or cross-bred. In their defence I should say that whatever beef I have had from there, has been excellent.

As I have never done a comparative tasting, I cannot honestly say for a fact that the differences are discernible; none the less I find this is yet another worrying example of how we allow our food heritage – our native breeds or varieties – to be corrupted for the sake of commercialism.

The Dairy House
Whitehill Park, Weobley, Herefordshire HR4 8QE

☎ 01544 318815 **CONTACT** *Pru Lloyd* **HOURS** *Mon-Fri 8.30-16.00 Sat 9.00-13.00* **DIRECTIONS** *From Leominster, take A44 (becomes A4112) towards Sarnesfield. After about 7 miles, turn left on to B4230, signposted Weobley. After 100 yards, turn left into the estate, signposted Whitehill Park.*

Before calling on The Dairy House, do take a few minutes to walk around the village of Weobley. It is a superb unfussy example of half-timbered black-and-white village in the local style. On its outskirts is the dairy run by Pru Lloyd and Jackie Bowen, who modestly considers herself as 'general dogsbody'. They have opted for the modern approach, by running the operation from a unit on a small industrial estate.

From here they produce a range of excellent dairy products, processing the milk from a local Friesian herd delivered on a daily basis. Although Pru does make low-fat yoghurts, either plain or flavoured, I was rather surprised when she told me that that her customers had 'gone off low-fat'. It goes against all predictions of dietary trends but, as she knowingly added, 'a bit of fat does add flavour'. For the best of all flavours, you should try her Greek-style yoghurt. Made with full-cream milk, extra cream for extra richness and a lactic culture, it come with a thick crust that bubbles up to the top. This is because, as Pru explained, unlike most yoghurts, hers is made with unhomogenized milk, so the fat globules are not broken down and evenly distributed in the milk – hence the glorious crust. Dig down through it and you will find a clear, clean and very unctuous cream, tinged with the sharpness of lemon. Also rich with a good tang and plenty of body is the crème fraîche, and she makes sour, whipping and double cream.

She also makes soft curd cheeses, with the curds hung up in cloths to drain and then shaped by hand into rounds. These come as the infinitely preferable creamy medium-fat with 13 per cent fat content or the bleaker low-fat with 2 per cent fat. It is fair to say that both cheeses do taste fresh and delicate, with a smooth texture. There is a fromage frais with a 6 per cent fat content and for this she blends the curd cheese with milk for a runnier texture.

Then there is the butter. Once supplies were a bit irregular, but it has proved so popular that Pru has been persuaded to make it on a regular basis. Using double cream left to ripen overnight with a lactic culture, she first chills it 'You can't make good butter if you use warm cream', then churns it in a motor-driven wooden butter churn. It is thoroughly washed and lightly salted 'about two 5 ml spoons of salt to every 2 gallons of cream' and then patted by hand into 225-g (½-lb) primrose-yellow blocks. Good full-cream butter is a rarity and Pru's reminded me of what a joy it is. Clear, clean and untainted are the first characteristics you must look for, but these must be backed up with flavour. Hers had a delicacy and a pert freshness, a gentle creaminess and a full, rounded richness that makes it a welcome treat.

Hereford Duck Company
Trelough House, Wormbridge, Herefordshire HR2 9DH

WORMBRIDGE
Ducks

☎ 01981 570767 **FAX** 01981 570577 **CONTACT** Barry Clark – *telephone ahead*

Not content with developing a strain of duck – the Trelough – Barry Clark now has his sights on producing a welfare-friendly English foie gras; 'it may be just wishful thinking' he ruefully admits 'but I'm determined to have a go'. The Trelough duck was bred by Barry for flavour, texture, (comparative) leanness, a good meat-to-bone ratio and a quick maturity; it takes about 10-14 weeks to mature, when it weighs 1.8-2.3 kg (4-5 lb) with some as heavy as 2.7 kg (6 lb). Other advantages are its good-sized breast – about 225 g (8 oz) a side and just what chefs want for a magret – and the fact that there is no difference in the size and conformation between the male and female.

It does have an interesting flavour, the meat has a deep fruity resonance and a compact but pliable texture. With production reaching 24,000 birds a year, the ducks are fed an own-formulation mix of various grains – including wheat, barley and maize – reared and slaughtered humanely, hung upside down for between 24-48 hours (but never bled, 'as this diminishes the flavour'), then dry-plucked and wax-dipped by machine. Ducks are sold oven-ready with giblets, or the plump breasts and surprisingly meaty legs are sold separately.

New this year are duck sausages, made with breast and leg meat, thyme, marjoram, oregano, shallots, seasoning and pork back fat, stuffed into natural hog casings. They were meaty, quite compactly textured and did have an interesting flavour although I have to confess that neither my fellow taster or I could have said categorically they tasted of duck. Barry also sells ducks' eggs, ducks' livers (useful for salads or pâtés), jars of well-clarified duck fat and lightly oak-smoked breasts. He also makes a confit with legs salted in rock salt with rosemary, then cooked and packed in fat, and a terrine of ducks' livers.

Stockists

Derbys: Chatsworth Farmshop

Devon: Heal Farm Meats

Glos: Organic Shop

Northants: K. Johnson, Oundle

Powys: Graig Farm

While you're in the area...

Food writer Rosemary Moon recommends **Hay Wholefoods and Delicatessen, 1 Lion Street, HAY-ON-WYE HR3 5AA** ☎ **01497 820708** for its 'Welsh specialist produce and excellent range of shelf stock'. More reports please.

Woonton Court, Leysters, LEOMINSTER HR6 0HL ☎ **01568 750232** sells straight from the farmhouse door a full-cream green-top (unpasteurized) milk and a rich buttery yellow unpasteurized double cream from the milk of their Guernsey herd.

Muriel's Homemade Jams, Forge House, ST OWENS CROSS HR2 8LG ☎ **01989 730653** are sold from a converted wash-house. You can buy a good range of jams, jellies and marmalades, including Seville and lime, lemon & grapefruit; as well as pickles, chutneys and lemon curd. Everything is made on a small scale in 4.5-kg (10-lb) batches, using fruit fresh in season or frozen during the rest of the year.

Although primarily wholesalers, **Micarelli's Fresh Roman Pasta, The Firs, SUGWAS POOL HR4 7QD** ☎ **01981 590259 fax 01981 590407** will sell you pasta, provided you ring up 48 hours ahead as everything is made to order. Using 'proper' durum wheat semolina and fresh eggs, they make a wide range of shapes, including flat ribbons of fettuccine, even wider pappardelle, and tagliolini, described as 'thin bootlace noodles'. All the pasta comes in five different colours for five different flavours: yellow with egg, pale green with frozen spinach, a pale red with tomato powder, grey-yellow with garlic powder and black with squid ink. They also make various filled pasta, including tortelloni with ricotta and spinach.

Hertfordshire

Map No. 3

Ashwell Delicatessen

Farrowby Farm, New Inn Road, Hinxworth,
Hertfordshire SG7 5EY

HINXWORTH
**Hams and
Bacon**

☎ 01462 733700 **FAX** 01462 733302 **CONTACT** Nicholas Tracey-Williams
HOURS Mon-Sat 9.00-18.00 **CARDS** Access, Visa **DIRECTIONS** From
Baldock, take A1 towards Biggleswade. After about 2 miles, turn right, signposted
Hinxworth. Farm is signposted immediately on the right.

Breed, feed and age of the pig are just some of the variables that affect
the eating quality of a ham. Then, as Dorothy Hartley wrote in *Food in
England*, 'the methods of curing and salting varied locally – some districts dry-salting and some brine-salting, some using sugar and treacle
(the old replacements of the original honey), some juniper berries, and
others ale and sundry herbs'. Hertfordshire, as far as my research
reveals, has no particular connection with pigs – or the consequent
ham or bacon – and as such, reveals no particular variation on a local
cure.

In fact Nicholas Tracey-Williams's pigs, although reared in Hertfordshire, end up in Suffolk for curing, via Northamptonshire where they
are slaughtered. Therefore, it seems perfectly logical that they should
be brine-cured in a sweet-cure made up with molasses, this being
similar to a Suffolk-cure. As Nicholas was unwilling, or perhaps unable,
to furnish any great details about times, techniques, etc., there is little
more that I can usefully add other than I found his ham densely textured with a well-rounded flavour. Interestingly, the sugar accentuates
the flavour of the meat rather than providing a sweetness in its own
right.

What is useful to know is that he has cured two ranges of ham and
bacon – Norfolk and Farrowby Farm. The former are conventionally
reared pigs which he buys in, the latter are his own free-range herd
reared to Conservation-grade standards, although they are unable to

be sold as such as they are not slaughtered in a Conservation-grade-approved slaughterhouse. His pigs live outdoors in arks, running at 10 to the acre, are fed Conservation-grade feed and slaughtered at about 7 months. On average, the Farrowby Farm pigs are slightly smaller and cost around 25 per cent more per half kg (pound) than the Norfolk. Both hams are sold as boned half and whole hams, in graded weights from 1.8-5.5 kg (4-12 lb), with a whole leg on the bone for the Norfolk only. Given the difference in welfare standards and price, I would honestly like to be able to say that the Farrowby Farm was better. Hand on heart, however, I failed to notice any discernible difference. A pity, as I believe that most of us want a better-reared pig to taste better; but then as Dorothy Hartley wrote (and here I paraphrase), taste is as much a question of the character of the animal as it is the character of the cure.

From the recently expanded farm-shop, which also now stocks locally grown vegetables, they also sell a sweet-cure bacon and, from the Farrowby Farm range only, sausages with a 70 per cent meat content.

Bowmans
Coursers Road, London Colney, St Albans, Hertfordshire AL2 1BB

☎ 01727 822106 **FAX** 01727 826406 **CONTACT** *Bruce Luffman* **HOURS** *9.00-17.30* **DIRECTIONS** *Turn off M25 at Junction 22 and follow signs for Open Farm for about ½ mile.*

With their 380 Friesian cows kept in 3 dairy herds, Bowmans are the biggest milk producer in Hertfordshire. Everything they do seems to be large-scale: their outdoor pig unit houses 250 sows – visitors can walk through its farrowing paddocks to see the sows and their piglets – and their busy farm-shop and restaurant covers an area of 4,129 sq. m (4,000 sq. ft).

For once, the scale of the operations seems not to have affected the quality of the produce. From their milk they make a range of yoghurts, both low- and full-fat in plain and fruit flavours. They claim to be the largest producer in this country of Greek-style yoghurt. Unlike several producers who stabilize their yoghurt to make it thicker, Bowmans use the traditional method of first leaving it to set in buckets once the *Bulgaricus* culture has been added, then straining it through Roquefort cheese bags to remove the whey 'for as long as needed for the right thickness'. The advantages are that it makes for a clearer flavoured yoghurt that will not fall apart or loosen up and turn watery when you add it in with other ingredients. With a fat content of 8 per cent, theirs is delightfully creamy, with just the slightest hint of acidity that catches in the throat.

New this year is a low-fat drinking yoghurt. Using a low-fat yoghurt,

MAP 3 HERTFORDSHIRE **137**

'the curds are broken up and a small amount of water is put back in to make the right consistency'. Flavours – strawberry, and banana – are added and it is packed in a 250-ml (8 fl-oz) plastic bottle with a ring-pull cap for, as Bruce Luffman endearingly told me, 'a macho image when you pull the cap off'. Currently under discussion with a health-food store is developing an evening primrose oil version.

Bowmans also make a satisfactory ice-cream. With a high fat content of 18.5 per cent and an over-run of 40 per cent, Bruce adds

The Silver Palate, 3 Vaughan Road, HARPENDEN AL5 4HU ☎ 01582 713722 has also just opened up at 18 Christopher Place, ST ALBANS AL3 5DQ ☎ 01727 868494. The new shop has an in-store bakery and it produces salt ciabatta and walnut bread made with a mixture of white and brown flour; as well as the dome-shaped Famagusta, studded with olives; and Coriada, stuffed with Spanish and spring onions. They offer a good selection of on-farm British cheeses, including Wigmore see Village Maid, page 22 and Isle of Mull Cheddar page 321, own-made pasta with various sauces, ready-meals and a huge olive bar with olives from all over the Mediterranean, as well as a good selection of Mediterranean produce.

to his basic mix eggs, double cream, 'about one-third of its weight is double cream. That means every third lick is cream' and, as a stabilizer, sodium alginate. Edwardian Vanilla, rich and creamy and – as a welcome change – restrainedly sweet, is his best-selling line. Next comes Velvet Chocolate, which also has a rich smoothness but lacks full vibrancy, perhaps because it is made up with Dutch cocoa. Other flavours are a milky Plantation coffee, Meadow strawberry, Colonial rum & raisin, Autumn hazelnut, Fruits of the Forest and a seasonal Christmas pudding. The farm-shop also has its own butchers. From there they also sell own-pork, hams, sausages and pies, lamb from Wales and pure Aberdeen Angus beef imported from Scotland.

Stockists

Herts: A10 Farm Shop

Battlers Green Farm Shop

Kitts End Farm Dairy Ltd

Willian Farm Shop

Surrey: Vivian's

While you're in the area...

Gedi, Plumridge Farm, Stagg Hill, BARNET EN4 0PX ☎ 0181 499 0695 fax 0181 449 1528 make five different soft cheeses from pasteurized goats' milk, such as Velde dusted in charcoal, mould-ripened Chavannes and creamy log-shaped Roubliac. Distributed widely throughout the South-East, you can buy them direct from the farm.

For boxes of freshly picked watercress and bunches of ungraded asparagus, visit **Nine Wells Watercress Farm, WHITWELL, Hitchin SD4 8JP ☎ 01438 871232**. The watercress is grown in natural spring water that bubbles up in the nine wells or bore-holes. They germinate their own seeds and the watercress takes about 6 weeks to grow from seedlings once it is planted out in the fields. There are two harvests a year, from February to June and September to December, although if the climate is exceptionally mild they can keep it going throughout the year. At the start of each harvest, the watercress – with its dark-green succulent leaves – is mild in flavour. As the season progresses, however, its pepperiness intensifies.

GRIMSBY
Smoked Fish

Alfred Enderby Ltd

Maclure Street, Fish Docks, Grimsby,
Humberside DN31 3NE

☎ 01472 342984 **FAX** 01472 342984 **CONTACT** *George Enderby* **HOURS** Mon-Fri 9.00-16.00

It was food writer Arabella Boxer who kindly introduced me to Alfred Enderby Ltd. She discovered it when researching for an article 'The Smoking of Fish', published in *Convivium*. 'In the mid-1950s this (Grimsby) was our largest fishing port, with a fleet of 279 fishing boats. Now it stands about tenth, with only 100 small boats while Peterhead stands in first place. The drop in Grimsby's fishing trade reflects, sadly, the story of our fishing industry as a whole. Between 1955 and 1985 the number of registered fishermen in the UK fell from more than 22,000 to less than 16,000. There were three main reasons: the cod wars with Iceland, the extension of the 200-mile fishing zone, and our entry into the Common Market.'

As you drive down through the docks, the smokehouse looks like it has been invaded by Darth Vader. Six huge black-hooded chimneys cling to the roof, twisting and turning in the wind, beacons of bleakness on top of a brick warehouse. Inside there are six traditional smokehouses, with two sets of huge doors opening on the two storeys and fitted out with ledges running up the side walls. The fish is suspended over speats (metal rods); each kiln holds 42 speats and they are handed up from one man to another in the chimneys.

Once the fish is in place – salmon on ground level, haddock and cod further up – the fire is lit in the square pit, using softwood sawdust with a little oak, and left to smoulder overnight. Farmed salmon is chosen for plumpness and good colour 'but not too red as people are used to a deep pink'. Then it is dry-salted for about 12 hours, given a long cool 16-20-hour smoke in its separate smoke-hole and it emerges with a light cutting texture and a mellow hint of fish. Haddock fillet

Mail Order

Smoked salmon only

Stockists

Glos: J. W. Rigby

London: Fish & Fowl

Mersey: Dial a Deli

Norfolk: J. & J. Shellfish

Oxon: Banbury Fisheries

'mostly undyed now as popular demand has changed' is given the merest soak in brine, no more than 10 minutes, then smoked for 14 hours or often overnight; cod is given pretty much the same treatment.

Everything is judged by eye or feel: the condition of the fish for how it takes

> Just around the corner is **Superior Seafoods**, **2 Riby Street**, **GRIMSBY DN31 3HF** ☎ **01472 362881** fax **01472 242134**. They are really fish merchants, buying at Grimsby's daily fish auctions, but they have a small shop selling to the public and here you can expect 'more or less anything' in the fish line.
>
>

a cure; how the smoke is running, if it is slow the ventilation doors are opened and the fish are moved up and down the chimneys. The weather plays its part 'the hotter it is, the quicker it is'. To watch the men at work is to see the craft of smoking at its best.

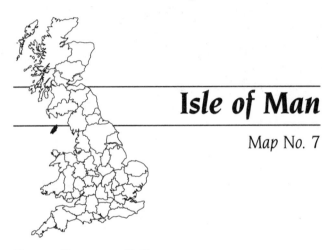

Isle of Man

Map No. 7

George Devereau & Son
33 Castle Street, Douglas, Isle of Man IM1 2EX

DOUGLAS
Kippers

Stockists

Lancs: C & G Neve
J. Sykes and Son Ltd

Yorks: M. H. Taylor & Son Ltd

London: J. Bennett Jnr London Ltd

Mersey: Henry Welsh & Sons

☎ 01624 673257 **FAX** 01624 843405 **CONTACT** Peter Canipa **HOURS** Mon-Sat 8.00-17.30 (8.30-17.00 1 Oct to 1 May) **DIRECTIONS** In town centre.

Peter Canipa, you will be reassured to know, only buys in fresh herring from his local waters. Other kipper curers may use frozen herring and cure throughout the year, but he prefers to work with fresh fish and freeze them as cured for the rest of the year. 'They will keep in peak condition as they are so rich in high-quality oil' is his reasoning. Out of season he sells them vacuum-packed and defrosted and they last up to 10 days in a fridge. During the herring season he only sells them fresh and you can buy them from their shop or straight from the 'factory' in Mill Road any time, night or day. He buys every morning at 6.00 am from the fish market or straight from the breakwater in Peel.

The herrings are first split on a machine, at the height of the season they may deal with as many as 100,000 a day. Then they are brined for about 20 minutes. Although Peter employs a total of 48 staff, he still insists on smoking himself: 'I've been doing it for 40 years and it's only me doing it'. Rather reticent to pass on chapter and verse of how he smokes – how long and at what temperature, etc. – he did explain that every fish can be different. It depends on its age, its condition, how it is broken down by the smoke, even the outside temperature will affect it.

 John Curtis, Manx Cold Storage Building, Mill Road, PEEL IM5 1TA ☎ **01624 842715** *fax 01624 843316 cures for a more robust kipper. Unlike George Devereau, he will supply fillets as well as whole pairs, but only in quantities of 3.2 kg (7 lb) or over.*

With a 'cure for the palate rather than the eye', it goes without saying that he uses no dyes or colourings. This time around I tried them fresh and in season. A pair weighs 225-285 g (8-10 oz) and they were gorgeous, mildly fish with plenty of body. Mellow, juicy, mildly sweet, they had a delicate flavour that hinted of kipper.

Isle of Wight

Map No. 2

COWES
Bembridge
Prawns

Phillips Fine Foods

Units 1 & 2, 290 Newport Road, Cowes,
Isle of Wight PO31 8PE

☎ 01983 282200 **FAX** 01983 281768 **CONTACT** Jeff Dove **HOURS** Mon-Fri 9.00-17.00 Sat 9.00-13.00 **CARDS** Eurocard, Mastercard, Visa

The difference between a prawn and a shrimp is, according to Victor Gordon in *Prawnography*, merely one of size. 'There are hundreds of different species of prawns *Decapoda natantia*, most of them too small for human consumption, too rare or too hard to extract from their deep sea retreats. However, some 340 species are reckoned by the Food and Agriculture Organisation to have commercial potential ... Edible *Decapoda natantia* range in length from under one inch to over one foot. The smallest, those up to, say, three inches long, are called shrimps in England ... For culinary purposes, prawns can be divided into three categories – small (shrimps), medium and large. This is puerile taxonomy but practical gastronomy.'

Morecambe Bay apart *see page* 157, for some reason it is rather difficult to buy fresh – let alone raw shrimps in this country. Yet I know they are out there swimming (or whatever it is shrimps do) in the sea. Whenever I ask, I am fobbed off with the usual 'there's no call for them' or 'there's no money in them, it's not worth the trouble' – another example of us not valuing our local produce. Visit Cherbourg or any of its surrounding towns in La Manche and you will see crowds jostling at the fish shops for les baies roses – wriggling live shrimps, a delicate dusty grey with the sweetest of nutty flavours and a prized local and seasonal delicacy.

Phillips Fine Foods do sell Bembridge prawns, caught off the coast – presumably near Bembridge. Apparently they have two seasons: a short one in early spring, just for a few weeks when they are really very small; then later on in the summer around June and July, when they are fatter, juicier

> **Puffin Fisheries, Saltern Wood Quay, YARMOUTH PO30 0SE ☎ 01983 760090 fax 01983 531722** *are mainly wholesalers who buy whole catches from the fishing boats and then sell on to fishmongers. They will sell direct to the public provided you are prepared to drive down the bumpy track through the caravan park to their unit decorated with scallop shells. Here you will find in their viviers live lobsters caught mainly off the Needles, and crabs from the Solent. If you ask, they will boil them for you in sea water. Fish obviously depends on the catch of the day but when I visited there were some fine-looking sea bass, plaice, dabs, tiny dabs, skate and brill. They usually have stock of farmed oysters and mussels from Poole Harbour and occasionally and only in summer, prawns caught off Bembridge.*

and sweeter. Sadly, they are all cooked on arrival, so although you can rest assured you are buying a local shrimp, it still does not solve the problem of buying them raw. Having moved to new and bigger premises, they sell various fresh and frozen shellfish and smoke in an Afos kiln, using hardwoods from the island such as oak and ash. Herrings, either from Scotland or Norway, are briefly brined then given a low slow smoke for about 12 hours for kippers. Keen sailors might be interested to know that they are the very same served for breakfast at the Royal Yacht Squadron. They also smoke bloaters, salmon farmed in the west coast of Scotland for a mild, quite salty finish, brisling that are meaty sprats and Island 'smokies' from whole hot-smoked pollack (which were sadly out of stock the day I called). They also prepare mackerel and herring fillets by brining them briefly, then rolling them up, securing them with a skewer and smoking them.

Kingcob Garlic
Mersley Farm, Newchurch, Sandown, Isle of Wight PO36 0NR

NEWCHURCH
Garlic

☎ 01983 865229 **FAX** 01983 862294 **CONTACT** *Colin Boswell* **HOURS** *Mon-Fri 9.00-17.00 Sat 10.00-16.00 Sun 10.00-13.00* **DIRECTIONS** *From Newport, take B3052 towards Sandown. After about 4 miles, turn left at The Fighting Cock pub crossroads, signposted Newchurch. Go through Newchurch and farm-shop is about 400 yards on the left, named Langbridge Farm.*

Colin Boswell is Britain's largest grower (and importer) of garlic. He planted his first bulbs in 1976 and now cultivates 30 acres, producing about 100 tons a year. I was surprised to find that he is able to grow garlic with any pungency under our dreary summer skies, but he put me right. 'It's partly a question of variety. I grow *ail rose*, a French mountain garlic with creamy white flesh and a silvery pale pink skin. At first, just after it's harvested, the garlic is quite mild. But as it dries out, its strength increases, so by November it is quite strong'. He also claims that, surrounded by sea, his land benefits from a micro-climate that gives good growing conditions. Harvesting takes place on and around 5 July, when the heads are lifted up and either laid in the fields or taken to a huge greenhouse to dry. With plump heads about 4-6 cm (1½-2½ in) round and about 12-15 cloves to the head, it has good keeping qualities, a balanced but not overpowering strength and is well-juiced.

Like so many of our younger, more ambitious farmers or growers, he has started to add value to his crop. As a result, not only can you buy garlic loose or neatly tied into plaits with 5, 10, 15 or 30 heads from the farm-shop but they are also available as whole oak-smoked heads, jars of smoked peeled cloves or minced cloves, or plain purées or cloves in oil.

Helen Lowe of Island Mustard, Pelham House, 9 Bath Road, COWES, ☎/fax 01983 291115 makes 8 different flavoured mustards, grinding a mixture of white and brown seeds as the base. Using an old family recipe which originally came from Bedale in Yorkshire, she also makes Island Hunt Sauce – a blend of vinegar, soy sauce, mushroom ketchup, shallots, mustard seeds and 'various spices'. Left to steep in a vat for several months, 'giving it an occasional stir', it is then strained and bottled for a sauce similar in flavour to (dare I mention?) Lea & Perrins.

He also sells Island potatoes, own-grown asparagus, and yellow, white and American Bicolor sweetcorn. The latter is an unusual variety in that its grains are both yellow and white on the cob. They also have a thinner than normal pericarp (outer skin), which means that when you bite into it, the skin is not automatically pulled out and gets left behind – what a relief, no annoying bits of skin stuck between your teeth. Another advantage is its sugar-to-water-to-solids ratio, so when you take a bite there is a vivid burst of sugar in the mouth.

While you're in the area...

Benedict's Delicatessen, 128 Holyrood Street, NEWPORT, PO30 5AU ☎ 01983 529596 fax 01983 826868 sells various cheeses, including Colston Bassett Stilton *see page* 211 and Wensleydale from Wensleydale Creamery *see page* 309. They also make various quiches and savoury puffs and a well-fleshed crab pâté, as well as selling a selection of the island's products, including Isle of Wight-shaped shortbread made by Island Biscuits.

Calbourne Classics, Three Gates Farm, SHALFLEET PO30 4NA ☎fax 01983 531204 make clotted cream in the modern method – in a humidity oven. They also make ice-cream to which they add their clotted cream and the result is a pleasant, fresh-tasting base with an 11 per cent fat content. To this they add such flavours as rum-soaked raisins, various fruit purées and Irish whiskey. These can be bought directly from the unit or at various shops on the island.

Kent

Map No. 3

Appledore Salads
Park Hill, Appledore, Ashford, Kent TN26 2BJ

☎ 01233 758201 **CONTACT** *Frances Smith – telephone ahead*

Frances Smith is a grower extraordinary, with a particular passion for salads. When grown by Frances, however, these are not just leaves, glorious though those may be. They encompass a whole brave new world of roots, shoots, tendrils, pods and flowers.

New this year are pea shoots: cut in spring at about 5 cm (2 in), just as they are emerging from the ground 'and the rabbits are getting interested'. They are either bright green or blanched for a bright yellow colour with an intense pea flavour. Another addition to Frances's list is Snow Bell or Three-cornered garlic, *Allium triquetrum*. Milder than the more common wild garlic or ramsons A. *ursinum*, which Frances describes as 'a coarse brute', Three-cornered garlic has a broad fleshy leaf not unlike a blade of grass and white star flowers. Its flavour reminds Frances of a Chinese garlic chive 'only milder' and when I found some in a salad at Caroline Brett's newly opened Union Café in London, I loved its texture.

Frances works on the principle of 'get me the seeds and I'll grow anything'. To this end she is growing bison grass for a gentleman who wants to use it to flavour his vodka and is keen to experiment with its other possible culinary uses. Then there is agretti, you may have seen it on sale in Italy in bunches of needle-shaped fleshy leaves; Frances tries to keep it going from April through to June from packets of seeds brought back by a keen friend, although it does not always germinate.

In touch with – and, indeed, supplying – several of the more adventurous chefs, Frances predicts that in 1995 flavours of the year will be onion and garlic. 'The cycle has come round from dainty to *terroir* to rustic. Soon everyone will be sick of huge mounds of puréed this or that and bowls of parsnip chips and there'll be a return of the baby veg'. With her own prophesy ringing in her ears, she is currently plough-ing up an enormous field to plant baby veg. Thus she too is completing a full circle, as baby veg is where she started her growing career.

What else can you find under her eight poly-tunnels, one shade tunnel and open beds? Winter squashes 'I'm expanding my range this year'; cresses such as land and mega, with its larger peppery leaf; the hotter-tasting plain and curly American salad mustards; rocket; mizuna; green and gold summer purslane, with its hint of sorrel; curly-leaf celery, 'a cracker of a plant with its powerful flavour'; baby spinach; mooli pods; shungiku (garland chrysanthemum), 'for a certain some-thing'; all sorts of Italian chicory, including the bitter pink and white-spotted Castelfranco; a tiny and very juicy frisée; and strawberry spinach, a member of the Chenopodium family which has tiny heart-shaped toothed leaves that taste like spinach and bear small sweet nutty berries.

Be warned, Frances never sends lists of her varieties 'as they're always changing'. Most of what she grows, she sells direct to chefs. She will, however, make up boxes or bags of salad leaves for us mere home-cooks – even mixed bags according to our choice, provided we give her plenty of warning and make arrangements to collect them. All you will then need for the salad of a lifetime is to mix in a couple of little gem lettuces, a few drops of a good nut oil and a sprinkling of sea salt.

Stockists

London:
Mortimer & Bennett

- - - - - - - - - -

Villandry

BIDDENDEN

Double Cream

S. E. Lane

White House Farm, Three Chimneys, Biddenden, Kent TN27 8LN

☎ 01580 291289 **CONTACT** Michael Sargent **HOURS** Mon-Sat 8.00-18.00 **DIRECTIONS** *From Biddenden, take A262 towards Tunbridge Wells. After about 1½ miles, turn right at The Three Chimneys Pub. Farm is about ¼ mile on the left.*

Like several other dairy farmers, the Sargents started 'adding value' to their milk about seven years ago and now they keep back about 60 per cent of the milk from their 95 Jersey cows to turn into cream, ice-cream, yoghurt and green-top (unpasteurized) full-cream milk which is rich and buttery, with a hint of earthiness.

Their unpasteurized cream is gorgeous; thick and unctuous, it glis-tens in all its buff yellow glory and tastes fresh and true with a honey floweriness. Now, why one cream can be so superior to another is best explained by Edward Behr in his excellent quarterly letter *The Art of Eating* which comes winging its way from Peacham, Vermont. First there is the question of pasture, which gives the cream its character. The breed of cow will affect the taste, particularly if – as in the case of the Sargents – it is a Jersey herd, with their high-butterfat-content milk. 'The taste of cream is mostly the taste of fat. Generally, the more fat in milk or cream the better it tastes. … Fat not only gives flavour but viscous texture. The more fat, the thicker the cream'.

Finally, there is the question of pasteurization. As far as I am concerned, there never has been any doubt that pasteurizing results in a flavour loss – a muddying of the clarity, at times an alteration that must follow once it has been 'cooked'. Edward Behr backs this up, '... to me pasteurized cream tastes stronger and simpler than raw cream, being mostly hints of caramel and custard rather than the subtly sweet fresh flavours that I think of as "flowery" though they aren't musky at all'.

In their small farm-shop attached to the house, they also sell their own sweet cream butter; a rich ice-cream with a butterfat content of about 14 per cent, which is sadly marred by the addition of over-sweet synthetic flavours; own creamy stirred yoghurts; as well as soft fruit; the odd vegetables; field mushrooms as big as saucers in season; local honey; eggs; fudge; and Duskin Farm's apple juice *see page* 148.

Stockists

Kent: Badgers Hill Farmshop

The Barn Shop

Downing Bury Farmshop

Ide Hill Stores

London: Neal's Yard Dairy

Crowhurst Farm
Crowhurst Farm, Crowhurst Lane, Borough Green, Kent TN15 8PE

BOROUGH GREEN
Cherries

☎ 01732 882905 **CONTACT** *Martin Leat* **HOURS** *mid-June to July: 9.30-20.00; Aug to Oct: 9.30-17.00* **DIRECTIONS** *From Wrotham Heath, take A25 into Borough Green. Turn left at the main village crossroads, signposted Crowhurst Farm. At roundabout, take the first exit signposted Crowhurst Farm. Drive up the hill and go straight over the crossroads. Farm is on the left, 1¼ miles from Borough Green.*

It is rare nowadays to see anywhere in England old-fashioned cherry orchards with widely spaced tall bushy trees. Due to foreign imports, the cherry industry has taken a bit of a dive and several orchards have been grubbed up. Those who do still grow have planted trees grown on smaller root-stock, which makes picking far more convenient and netting against plagues of starlings far easier.

Crowhurst Farm planted their 9-acre cherry orchard in 1948 and have over 300 trees on the farm. Picking from them can be hard work. If you arrive late in the day the largest clusters of cherries are tantalizingly at the top of the trees; but ladders or picking poles, buckets and plastic bags are provided. You can nip up the ladder, from where I am

---

Farming World, Nash Court, BOUGHTON, Faversham ME13 9SW ☎ 01227 751224 *is one of the largest commercial cherry growers, but you can buy ready-picked from the farm-gate when cherries are in season, from the end of June to the end of July. Apart from the small deep-coloured Bradbourne Black, the varieties are mostly the larger firmer juicier modern ones.*
Henry Bryant, The Bounds, HERNHILL, Faversham ME13 9TX ☎ 01227 751261 *also sells ready-picked cherries in 5 kg (12 lb) boxes or 1.8-2.3 kg (4-5 lb) chips (punnets). He grows about 6 modern varieties and 4 old-fashioned ones which, although much smaller by comparison, cannot be beaten for flavour. Try his soft but superb white Merton Glory; or hard and small Noir de Gubon, with a piercing sweetness; or the deep red and juicy Gaucher.*

assured you get a stunning view over Kent (I never dare, I rather weedily suffer from vertigo). Otherwise, with your feet firmly planted on *terra firma*, you lift the long pole with hooks and bag attached up to the tree, give it a sharp tug and the cherries simply fall into the bag.

The cherry orchard is a grassy-green leafy area and it is a delight to wander through. The Leats are, however, not too strong on what varieties they grow – nor are the trees marked – but nobody seems to mind if you 'sample' a few different ones before you decide which tree to pick from. Depending on the weather, the season starts around mid-June, with Early Rivers and the large pointy Merton Glory, then continues with the juicy Gaucher, Heart, Noir de Guben, and finishes early in July with just a few fruit-bearing tress of White (really yellow flushed with red) Napoleon and Florence. The rest of the summer they grow the usual range of pick-your-own vegetables and soft fruit.

Brogdale Horticultural Trust
Brogdale Road, Faversham, Kent ME13 8XZ

☎ 01795 535286 **FAX** 01795 531710 **CONTACT** *Joy Wade* **HOURS** *Easter to Dec: 9.30-17.00; Jan to Easter: Sat and Sun 10.00-16.00* **CARDS** *Access, Visa* **DIRECTIONS** *Turn off M2 at Junction 6, signposted Faversham. At roundabout, turn left down to T-junction. Turn left and, after about 500 yards, turn left into Brogdale Road. Follow the road over the motorway and farm is signposted on the left after about ½ mile.*

Brogdale boasts what is probably the world's largest collection of temperate fruits with a current purpose 'to conserve the diversity of temperate fruits, to evaluate, develop and improve new varieties and to reintroduce the most appropriate varieties for today's commercial world'.

What this means to you and me is that we can go and wander through orchard after orchard to see the astonishing diversity of varieties. Here you will find 2,500 distinct apple varieties, 550 pears, 8 quinces and a few medlars, 350 plums, 220 cherries, 350 bush fruit (currants gooseberries and blueberries), 42 cobnuts, 150 strawberries and 50 cane fruit (raspberries, blackberries and hybrid berries). From walking through at blossom time – when the trees and bushes are at their showy best – to harvest time when the fruit is ripening on the

Two excellent nurseries in the county will supply a wide range of unusual fruit trees, specializing in older varieties. Both will propagate to order, so you should be able to buy almost any tree you want. Both send out bare-rooted trees from late November through to March and both have impeccable botanical pedigrees. Jack Ingram of **Copton Ash Garden, 105 Ashford Road, FAVERSHAM ME13 8XW** ☎ **01795 535919** *was Director of the National Fruit Trials (now Brogdale) and Mr Cook of* **Keepers Nursery & Fruit Garden Designs, 446 Wateringbury Road, EAST MALLING, ME19 6JJ** ☎ **01622 813008** *used to be at East Malling Research Station.*

MAP 3   KENT   **147**

boughs, this is the place for anyone even remotely interested in fruit. You can walk alone or take a guided tour, buy fruit from the shop, attend a grafting or pruning demonstration or any number of the special events organized by the Trust.

On certain days they run a 'Graft While U Wait' scheme where trees are grafted especially for you, or if you prefer you can buy them from their nursery. There are identification days, when you can bring fruit along for the experts to give it its correct name. There is a Strawberry Fayre in Summer and an Apple Day in Autumn. In fact, there is something going on practically every weekend. There are plans afoot to extend its visitor centre with 12 gardens showing the history of fruit cultivation from medieval times to the present day; a further Garden of Fruit Diversity to illustrate how our great range of domestic fruits have evolved from their wild ancestors; a model nursery that will show how fruit trees are budded, grafted and trained; and another area with the full range of fruit tree shapes and sizes.

If I have made Brogdale sound dry and uninteresting, nothing could be further from the truth. I cannot begin to tell you how fascinating a trip can be. There are always experts on hand to answer any questions, discuss the merits of particular varieties and – if you hit the right time of year – samples to taste and buy from the shop. It is a must for anybody who likes fruit, cares about our culinary history or is just looking for different flavours. Brogdale needs your help too, they rely on public donations to carry on their diverse work. For a mere £15.00 a year you can join as a 'friend', receive details of all the events and an interesting newsletter. It is one of my favourite places to visit.

Meg Game
Oldbury Farmhouse, Ightham, Kent TN15 9DE

IGHTHAM
Kentish
Cobnuts

☎ 01732 882397 **CONTACT** Meg Game **HOURS** *Depending on season, but usually last week Aug to early Oct: Sun 10.00-17.00 – telephone ahead for availability* **DIRECTIONS** *From Borough Green, take A25 towards Sevenoaks. After about 1½ miles, turn right at The Cobtree Pub into Oldbury Lane. Follow the road for about ¼ mile to the top off the road, then turn a sharp right down a steep hill. House is on right at bottom of the hill.*

To quote the informative Kentish Cobnuts Association's factsheet, 'A Kentish cobnut is a cultivated type of hazelnut, just as a Bramley is a type of apple'. Up until a century ago, cobnut plantations or 'plats' were a great feature of the Kentish countryside, extending over 7,000 acres. Now only 250 acres remain, centred on the stony soil of the parishes of Ightham, Plaxtol and Maidstone.

Unlike other nuts, cobnuts are eaten fresh, never dried. Their season starts towards the end of August – traditionally on St Philiberts Day, 22 August – and lasts through to about the first week of October. For the first few weeks the husks and shells are still green and the kernel (nut) white and crunchy. This is when I like to eat them, as they are fresh, rich and juicy and quite superb dipped into sea salt. On the other hand, Meg prefers them harvested later on in the season, when they have brown shells and husks and the full nutty flavour of the kernel has developed. Unshelled nuts can be kept in the fridge for a week or two at the beginning of the season in a loosely-fastened plastic bag. Nuts harvested later on should last through to Christmas if they are kept cool. Apparently a little salt shaken into the bag helps to lengthen their life.

Stockists

London:
G. Walton

  Cobnut trees are largely self-sterile, meaning the pollen from one variety cannot pollinate the female flowers of the same variety, whether on the same or a different tree. **J. I. B. Cannon & Son, Roughway Farm, Roughway Lane, TONBRIDGE TN11 9SN ☎ 01732 810260** *sells cobnut trees and will happily advise you about compatible varieties to plant in your garden. Trees can be bought from November to February – the right time for planting – and are either one or two years old. You will not have to wait long as John Cannon assures me that, depending of growing conditions, they will start cropping by the time they are four.*

Meg, in charge of the Kentish Cobnuts Association's publicity, keeps two varieties in her 2-acre orchard: the Kentish Cob, with its long kernel; and the smaller, sweeter White Filbert. A place of great charm and natural beauty – in spring the bluebells mass under the trees – she makes a point of never spraying her trees. The season starts usually during the last week of August and from then until early October, she is open every Sunday for picking. At the start of the season, nuts have to be picked off the trees, hence the Kentish question, 'Are the nuts shaking?' – meaning are they ripe. As the season progresses, they can be shaken off the trees and collected from the ground.

 Meg Game's is possibly the most atmospheric orchard, but it is only open on Sundays. Several other growers will sell their nuts either as pick-your-own or ready-picked during the week, but it is wise to telephone ahead to check. **Hampton Nurseries, Pillar Box Lane, HADLOW, Tonbridge TN11 9SS ☎ 01732 810633** *sells both pick-your-own and ready-picked as does* **Silverhill Barn, DUNKS GREEN, Tonbridge TN11 5SD ☎ 01732 810745** *and* **Allens Farm, Allens Lane, PLAXTOL, Sevenoaks TN15 0QZ ☎ 01732 822904.** **Merrimans, Sandy Lane, Ivy Hatch, IGHTHAM TN15 0PB ☎ 01732 810884** *only sells ready-picked from the gate. For further information and membership details for* **The Kentish Cobnut Association**, *you should contact* **Vivien Coleman, Clakkers House, CROUCH, Sevenoaks TN15 8PY ☎ 01732 780038.**

KINGSTON
Apple Juice

Duskin Farm

The Ruffett, Duskin Farm, Covet Lane, Kingston, Canterbury, Kent CT4 6JS

☎ 01227 830194 **FAX** 01227 830194 **CONTACT** Andrew Helbling – telephone ahead

 Andrew Helbling of Duskin was amongst the first to sell apple juice as pressed from a single variety rather than as a blend. What is important is to be able to extract the character and flavour of the apple in order to make a juice with definite character and personality. Andrew

Owlet Apple Juice, Owl House Fruit Farm, **LAMBERHURST TN3 8LY ☎ 01892 890553** *won the first prize at the 1993 Marden British Apple Juice Competition. They make a sweeter than normal Cox/Bramley blend with plenty of apple depth, and – as single varieties – a soft mellow Cox, a light and airy Worcester, Russett and Jonagold. They will also press anybody's apples for them, provided you can deliver them there. Minimum quantity for a press is 600 pounds or 16 bushels, the approximate weight of the crop from a tree. They will bottle and label the juice for you.*

achieves this by his method of pressing. Using a slow labour-intensive method of macerating and cloth-pressing the apples in a cider press, making a 'cheese' along similar lines to a cider-maker, 'bashing the living daylights out of the apples to extract the juices'. He does 'as much as I can, when I can, when the apples are ripe', the rest of the year he draws on apples kept in store. Some are grown by him, others he buys in. Once juiced, the unfiltered apple juice is bottled in 1 litre bottles and subjected to a low-temperature pasteurization. The results are densely flavoured juices with a good length and a particular flavour.

As a guide, Andrew divides his entire range into: sweet (Russett, Worcester, Spartan); medium sweet (Ellison, Gala, Golden Delicious, Gloster, Ida Red); medium (Cox, Fiesta, Jonagold, Laxton Superb, Melrose); medium sharp (Crispin, Discovery, Granny Smith, James Grieve); sharp (Bramley, Lord Derby and, new this year, Suntan, a variety raised by Tydeman in 1956, with a sharp but aromatic flavour).

When talking about apple juices, it is only fair to mention the dreaded word patulin, particularly as one of Andrew's juices was found to contain it. As Andrew explains, 'I obviously take extreme care. I do not juice apples with moulds as, apart from any off-flavours, patulin comes from certain moulds. It is erratic and of those moulds that do produce patulin, some don't always do it. The fact is the Government have adopted an "extreme caution situation". I calculated that with their permissible level of 50 parts to the billion, you could drink 135 litres a day to get an effect. If you were to drink my Bramley – where patulin was found, to a marginally higher level – you would still need to drink 50 litres a day before any possibility of harm'. None the less, and in spite of what he regards as over-reaction, 'on the Continent noone cares', he has taken to spraying his late-store Bramleys – a variety particularly prone to the mould – with chlorinated water to eliminate any possible danger.

Huffkins are an East Kent tea-bread. 'All over England', writes Florence White in Good Things in England, 'there are to be bought small traditional tea-breads similar in type but differing more or less in varying districts. Huffkins are simply thick flat oval cakes of light bread: with a hole in the middle'. Tony Cook of **The Bakers Oven, 10 King Street, SANDWICH CT13 9BY ☎ 01304 613323** *remembers when he was a boy in the 1950s, 'every baker made them – now, as far as I know, I'm the only one'. Traditionally huffkins were enriched with lard and fresh milk, but he uses emulsified vegetable fat and milk powder; and, although Florence White refers to a 'hole in the middle', Tony's huffkins dip in the centre, 'We push them back to stop them from "blowing", so a huffkin is recognized by its dimple'.*

MARDEN
Hopshoots

H. E. Hall & Sons
Little Mill Farm, Underlyn Lane, Marden, Kent TN12 9AT

☎ 01622 831448 **FAX** 01622 831376 **CONTACT** Peter Hall – *telephone ahead (early April to early May)*

Peter Hall is a hop farmer who sells hopshoots, but only between April and May. His hops come from the 2½ acres of the hop garden, where the hops are grown organically (to Soil Association standards), so you can be certain that the shoots are unsprayed. As these hopshoots are grown outdoors in broad daylight, they tend to be tougher, hairier, more bitter and have a more pronounced flavour than those grown in darkness – it reminds me of bitter-sweet celery. This toughness can be got round by blanching the outdoor shoots; a simmer in plain water for a good 10-15 minutes will soften their flavour. Peter picks hopshoots to order only – they go limp quite quickly and have quite a short shelf-life – so do ring him first. Try them, they are a novel experience. From his gate he also sells asparagus and various top fruit, all grown to either conservation or organic standards.

WHITSTABLE
Oysters

Seasalter Shellfish
The Harbour, Whitstable, Kent CT5 1AB

☎ 01227 272003 **FAX** 01227 264829 **CONTACT** Elaine Kirkaldie **HOURS** Mon-Fri 9.00-17.00 **CARDS** Access, Visa **DIRECTIONS** *In Whitstable, follow the signs for the harbour. Turn left opposite the car park into the second entrance for the harbour. Follow signs to Seasalter on the end of East Quay.*

Whitstable was once famous for its Native oysters, *Ostrea edulis*. 'Native', according to Alan Davidson in his *North Atlantic Seafood*, means 'reared from indigenous stock'. Apparently most Whitstable oysters were actually '… relaid seed oysters from Brittany and none the worse for that. However Royal Whitstables, an appellation controlled by the Company of Free Fishers and Dredgers of Whitstable are genuine English Natives'. Natives, indigenous or otherwise, are all too rare nowadays due to a combination of causes – an earlier problem with disease, greediness resulting in over-fishing, and water pollution.

What you can actually buy in Whitstable are mostly Pacific oysters, *Crassostrea gigas*. Rather alarmingly, there is a move afoot to call these

---

The Royal Native Oyster Stores, The Horsebridge, WHITSTABLE CT5 1BU ☎ 01227 276856 *is a fish restaurant run from The Whitstable Oyster Fishery Company's original warehouse and still has the oyster holding tanks in the basement to prove it. Of course, you can eat oysters by the dozen here and on a sunny day there is nothing more enjoyable than to have a good fish meal while gazing out to sea. Although they have closed down the shop, you can still buy from the restaurant both Pacific and Native oysters to take away, as well as brown shrimps and cockles when supplies permit.*

MAP 3　　　　　　　　　　　　　　　　　　　KENT　　　　**151**

Pacifics 'Whitstable' on the spurious grounds that they are born and bred in Whitstable. I dread to think how Alan Davidson will react to this news.

However, there is good news to be had as far as the proper Whitstable is concerned. Seasalter Shellfish, a direct descendant of the old Seasalter & Ham Fishery Company, with premises at Whitstable harbour since 1893, have laid down stocks that show every sign of developing very nicely, thank you. The problem with the Native is that it is far less hardy than the Pacific, its spawning process is very delicate and it takes 5 years to grow to any decent size. None the less, Seasalter Shellfish have been experimenting at their hatchery at Reculver in nearby Herne Bay and the prognosis looks good. Soon – possibly in a couple of years – Whitstables should be back in full force. You can buy them now, but only occasionally (and remember only when there is an 'r' in the month). These come from fishermen who have dredged for them and are sold as size-1 ('massive'), -2, -3 or -4, graduating downwards. You can easily recognize a Native by its round shape (the Pacific is longer and comes to a point) and its advantage over a Pacific is said to be its smoother texture and its more refined delicate meat. Seasalter Shellfish farm their Pacifics off the Pollard, where once they dredged for Natives. They take about 3 years to mature and are sold either as medium – 80-100 g (3-3½ oz) – or large – 100-120 g (3½-4 oz) – anything smaller gets put back in the sea.

'Coming in like troopers' is their first crop of cherrystone clams. These were laid down a while ago and have proved a great success, adapting to our waters well and there is promise of 'thousands all year round'. Harvesting them can be a problem as it depends on the tides. In bad weather it is difficult to suck them up from the bottom of the beds where they grow. Once collected, like Seasalter Shellfish's oysters, they are passed through purification tanks and can be sent anywhere in Britain by overnight courier.

Nepicar Farm
Nepicar Farm, Wrotham Heath, Sevenoaks, Kent TN15 7SR

☎ 01732 883040 **CONTACT** *Mr Harold Woolley* **HOURS** *mid-Mar to end Dec: 10.00-17.00* **DIRECTIONS** *From Borough Green, take A25 towards West Malling. Farm is on left after about 1½ miles.*

WROTHAM HEATH
Ewes'-milk Cheeses

Harold Woolley has been making ewes'-milk cheese since 1985. Recently he turned his farm into 'The Sheep Dairy Centre of the South East', but luckily this tourist activity has not put Harold off what I think he is best at – making cheese.

He originally started with Carolina, an unpasteurized hard-pressed cheese that he claims to have been created from a recipe used by the Cistercian monks in the 12th century. Sold in small 450-675-g (1-1½-lb) or larger 2-2.7-kg (4½-6-lb) truckles, it is brined briefly and matured for about 60 days, and has a good rounded flavour with only a hint of sheep. Cecilia is made in virtually the same way, except it is rubbed in salt and buried in a barrel of hops for a couple of weeks to mature, resulting in a less intense cheese with a slight earthy sharpness. Both are interesting examples of ewes'-milk cheese suited to the average British palate (by that, I mean the sheep flavour is not over-pronounced). Harold also makes Nepicar – a pasteurized version of Cecilia. Although it is matured for 90 days, it lacks the guts and length of flavour of its unpasteurized cousins. However, anyone who objects to eating a raw milk cheese will find this a good alternative.

Perry Court Farm Shop, Perry Court, BILTING, Ashford TN25 4ES ☎ 01233 812408 *is a huge barn of a shop (literally), with a good selection of fruit and vegetables – some bought-in and the rest own-grown. Throughout the year they sell the usual vegetables and pick-your-own and ready-picked soft fruit. It is in pears, plums and apples that they really specialize. They have a good range of pears: Williams Bon Chrétien, Beth (like a Williams with the advantage that it does not go woolly), the buttery Beurré Hardy, Conference, Doyenné du Comice, Packham's Triumph (similar to a Comice but with a tougher skin), Concorde and Gloumorceau (which is ideal for poaching). They also offer plenty of different plums: Czars, Opals, Early Rivers, a gloriously meaty Giant Prune, Belles, Victorias, Marjorie Seedlings and English Gages. At the moment, they have 27 apple varieties running through the season – Discovery, Katy, James Grieve, Russet, Golden Smoothie (a Golden Delicious type), Ida Red, and Crown Gold are just a few.*

In a county that blossoms with pick-your-owns – this is after all the Garden of England – **Sepham Farm Shop, Sepham Farm, Filston Lane, SHOREHAM TN14 5JT tel 01959 522774 fax 01959 525040** *remains one of my favourites. None is quite as relaxed, informal and so tucked away as this one here in the Darenth Valley. Expect to pick rhubarb in March, asparagus in May, and from June onwards lush Hapil Honeyoye, Pegasus and Rhapsody strawberries, Admiral, Glen Prosen, Malling Leo and Autumn Bliss raspberries, which start around the 1 of August and last until the first frosts. There are sunberries, tayberries, redcurrants, blackcurrants, gooseberries, Van and Stella cherries that are usually ripe in the first two weeks of July, and such plums as Reeves, Edwards, Victoria, Cambridge Gage and Greengage, as well as various apples. They also sell honey from the farm and their own apple juice.*

While you're in the area...

Wards of Adisham, Little Bossington Farmhouse, ADISHAM, Canterbury CT3 3LN ☎ 01227 720596 make an unctuous smooth fudge with a creamy, buttery flavour from sugar, butter and evaporated milk. Flavours are: vanilla, made with essence; walnut, using chopped nuts; ginger from sugared ginger; and chocolate, from a Belgian chocolate. The fudge comes packed in 115, 450 and 675-g (½, 1 and 1½-lb) bags or boxes.

Basing Herd, Lower Basing Farm, COWDEN TN8 7JU ☎ 01342 850251 fax 01342 850022 make a crumbly Caerphilly-style cheese from the milk of their own goats' herd, matured for 3-4 weeks. From the farm door, they also sell milk, ice-cream, and a full-cream goats'-milk yoghurt.

Griggs of Hythe, Fisherman's Landing Beach, HYTHE CT21 6HG ☎ 01303 266410 is right down by the beach. With several boats from Dungeness to Dover under contract, they can be relied on for good fresh supplies 'depending, of course, on the weather'. There is a good range, including sole in several sizes – classed as Dover (large, slip) medium, and tongues (small); skate comes as wings, knobs cut from the jaw and similar to cod's cheek, and fillet cut from the back. In their smoke-holes they also smoke salmon, eels, haddock and – rather unusually – shallots and garlic.

Ladywell Dairy Sheep Products, Cobblers Yard Farm, Leggs Lane, LANGTON GREEN, Tunbridge Wells TN3 **0RQ ☎ 01892 863448** use the milk from their flock of sheep to make yoghurt, ice-cream and a soft cheese which is either plain or flavoured with black pepper, celery seed & garlic, or garlic & chive. More reports please.

I have heard good things about the champagne, kirsch and rum truffles, pralines and moulded chocolate Easter and Christmas figures made by **Mr Bienz**, a Swiss chocolatier, and sold from **The Chocolate Centre, 11 Ely Court, TUNBRIDGE WELLS TN1 2QP ☎ 01892 516167**. More reports please.

Lancashire

Map Nos. 4 and 6

A. & C. Wild

40 Warner Street, Accrington, Lancashire BB5 1HN

☎ 01254 395487 **CONTACT** Mr Wild **HOURS** Tues, Thurs and Fri 9.00-17.30 Sat 9.00-14.30 **DIRECTIONS** In town centre.

Last year I heard Jonathan Meades, anti-vegetarian extraordinary, speak at the Carnivores Club. Carnivores occasionally gather to eat and discuss meat and that night one of the subjects pursued was very near to Jonathan Meades' heart and stomach, the eating of offal. He makes no secret of his predilection. After chastizing the audience for generally being 'preposterously squeamish', he put forward an original theory along the lines that the French – predominantly a Catholic country – like offal, while the English – mostly C. of E. or chapel – do not. The exception is in and around Lancashire, which happens to be our most intensely Catholic area. This he saw as 'probably more than a coincidence' and connected with the differing attitudes to food and animals. Catholics 'eat the whole animal with great enthusiasm, the English Protestants sweep such matters under the carpet'.

How this idea actually stands up to closer scrutiny, I do not intend to pursue. Suffice to say that Lancashire is strewn with makers of black puddings and sorting the men out from the boys is no easy task. Mr Wild comes highly recommended, but trying to extract his 'secrets' is like getting blood out of a pudding. His award-winning puddings – and yes he has won Best in Britain and silver and bronze medals in France – are made twice a week in natural skins as a Bury black pudding link, which means smaller puddings about 3 to the

> **Morris's Gold Medal Black Pudding, 120 Market Street, FARNWORTH BL4 9AE ☎ 01204 71763** *is also well known for his black puddings. From the back of the shop he produces two versions: one heavily studded with diced pork fat; and a 'lean special' without. He can also be relied on to sell tripe, cowheel, pork tasties (cooked belly of pork – a meatier version of 'scratchings') sold still warm first thing in the morning, and pig's nose (which is apparently eaten with vinegar and salt).*

pound. As far as he is concerned, however, that is where any similarity to the Bury pudding begins and ends.

He makes up his own mix, 'a nice mix, neither too dry nor too mealy' with oatmeal and minimal amounts of pearl barley. What he is aiming for is a firm texture 'that doesn't stick to the knife' and a gently spiced flavour. Studded with pork fat, his puddings are quite dense and lushly textured, with a certain – but not overstated – pungency cut with a gentle pepperiness. That, says Mr Wild 'is how we like it here'. As for cooking his black puddings, he suggests simmering them in water for 10 minutes or frying them sliced, then adding vinegar or mustard to taste. He also makes various sausages and dry-cures his own bacon.

Pugh's Piglets
Bowgreave House Farm, Bowgreave, Garstang,
Lancashire PR3 1YE

BOWGREAVE
Suckling Pig

☎ 01995 602571 **FAX** 01995 600126 **CONTACT** *Barry Pugh – telephone ahead*

A young piglet still milking (suckling) the mother is how most butchers define a suckling pig. *Larousse Gastronomique* suggests that it can be as old as 2 months and weigh as much as 15 kg (33 lb). On the other hand, Barry Pugh has his sent to slaughter from 3 weeks when they weigh 3.5-4.5 kg (8-10 lb) up to 4½ weeks when they can be as heavy as 7.75 kg (17 lb). What matters, as far as he is concerned, is that they fit into a domestic cooker.

Barry does not farm himself. Instead he selects mainly from one local pig farmer who rears pigs indoors in straw yards 'it's too wet to keep them out here'. He insists that the pigs have an 'additive-free diet and obviously they get no drugs as, apart from anything else, the withdrawal period is not long enough for a suckling pig'. At 10 days the piglets 'start drinking and sniffing around for bits and pieces, are fed milk pellets, but of course we never wean them'. Suckling pig is handled differently from pork; once slaughtered, the pigs are immediately scalded and scraped to remove their hairs and the fine top layer of their skin. 'They are sent off quickly. You can't hang a suckling pig, its flesh is so milky that if you do, it turns slippy or greasy. So the turnaround has to be fast.' Its meat is softer-textured and more delicately flavoured than pork, with a gentle milkiness. They are delivered oven-ready as cleaned and paunched (gutted), complete with head and tail. Barry suggests roasting them in the oven as the most practical way of cooking and every piglet is sent out with a recipe leaflet.

This year he has also launched porchetta, which is possibly familiar to anyone who has ever wandered through a street market in Northern Italy. Whole boned pigs are stuffed with herbs – rosemary and bay leaves in Rome, fennel in Tuscany and Marche – spit-roasted and sold carved into thick juicy slabs on slices of rough country bread. They are prepared by Giovanni Matichecchia in the traditional style, with either head off or on, according to the customer's preference. The stuffing is made with fresh herbs, the actual mixture varies and you can choose whatever you prefer. He suggests dividing the porchetta into 3 pieces so it will fit into an oven. When I sampled a slice (actually several it was so good), I was with Italian food writer Valentina Harris, who knows a thing or two about how porchetta ought to taste. She pronounced it 'fabulous', rich and juicy with a crisp chewy crackling.

GOOSNARGH
Goosnargh
Cakes

Goosnargh Post Office

882 Whittingham Lane, Goosnargh, Preston, Lancashire PR3 2AX

☎ 01772 865231 **CONTACT** *Mr Reeder* **HOURS** *Mon 6.15-13.00 Tues-Fri 6.15-21.00 Sat & Sun 6.15-17.00* **DIRECTIONS** *In village centre.*

My thanks must go to food historian Laura Mason for tracking down Goosnargh cakes. Laura has been working on Euroterroir, a fascinating EU-funded project with the objective of locating traditional foods that are still produced in the area from which they originated. These cakes fit the bill perfectly.

According to Laura, 'Many Lancashire towns have their particular cakes, Eccles and Chorley are good examples. Goosnargh, known locally as Goosnargh without further qualification, are another. They are rich in butter and the Preston area has always had a dairying tradition. Their documented history can't be traced back earlier than the mid-19th century, when local historian Richard Cookson wrote 'Goosnargh has almost world-wide fame for making of penny cakes of a peculiar pastry, and great as the depression of trade at present is, about 4,000 dozen (48,000) are disposed of annually at Whitsuntide'.

The 'peculiar pastry' is a mixture of flour, butter, sugar and caraway seeds (a common enough ingredient in baking in those days). The cakes, really what we would call a biscuit and not unlike a shortbread, are a very pale off-white, round in shape, with a rich buttery flavour sharpened by the caraway, and a crumbly soft texture. Apparently there are several bakers in the area who still make the cakes but, observes Laura, 'not all of them use butter'. Mr Sidgreaves of The Corner Bakery in Longridge sticks to the proper ingredients, bakes them traditionally at the proper low temperature and finishes them bathed in caster sugar. He is, however, rather uncommunicative or, to

*Under new management, **Sellet Hall Gardens, Sellet Hall, KIRKBY LONSDALE, via Carnforth, LA6 2QF** ☎ **015242 71865** fax **015242 72208** is set in the foothills of the Dales in the Lune valley. The herb garden, sheltered by towering yew hedges, is laid out in a formal style and there is nursery with a wide range of plants for sale. Here you can find plants of bistort, which is also known as 'passion dock' or 'Easter-ledge'. It grows wild in the hedgerows in the north and in spring its leaves and young shoots were traditionally boiled and eaten as a vegetable or mixed with onion and pot barley to make Easter-ledge pudding. The nursery stocks three varieties: wild, superbum, 'an improved flowering form' and the bitter Darjeeling red.*

put it a little more politely, 'protective of his recipe'. This is why I suggest you apply to Mr Reeder who runs the Post Office, as he is more than happy to tell you about them, sell you some should you arrive in person or post them off in packets. If stored in an airtight tin, Goosnargh should keep for several weeks.

James Baxter & Son
Thornton Road, Morecambe, Lancashire LA4 5PB

MORECAMBE
**Potted
Shrimps**

☎ 01524 410910 **CONTACT** *Bob Baxter* **HOURS** *Mon-Sat 9.00-17.00* **CARDS** *Access, Mastercard, Visa* **DIRECTIONS** *In town centre.*

The potting of fish, meat or cheese is one of the great traditions in British cookery. Whatever is to be potted, the process is more or less constant. The minced, pounded or whole (in the case of shrimps) ingredient is spiced, pressed into a pot and sealed in clarified butter. Mace was invariably used as a flavouring, but quite how or why it came to be 'the hundred per cent traditional, and indispensable spice of all English potted meats and fish compounds' not even Elizabeth David writing in *Spices, Salt and Aromatics in the English Kitchen* is certain.

Bob Baxter's family has been potting shrimps for 200 years; his is the sixth generation. Whereas once the family ran their own boats, had a wet fish shop and employed a large staff, Bob is now content to buy in his shrimps, sell them from his freezer centre and has Kathleen and Doreen potting out back about 500 pots a day in a small neat kitchen. The tiny brown shrimps are still processed in the same time-honoured way. Caught in the sandy estuaries of Morecambe Bay from the traditional 25-foot boats, they are cleaned and boiled at sea in sea water, peeled by the fishermen's wives and delivered to the door within 36 hours of being caught.

Potting shrimps probably evolved as a handy way of dealing with any excess catch. For the best of all potted shrimps, the peeled shrimps should be kept whole (some recipes suggest they are pounded) and lightly cooked in spiced butter to infuse the flavours. Typically, Bob will not reveal exactly which spices he uses but, hazarding a guess, I would say he has stuck to the traditional use of mace and nutmeg. The shrimps are chilled off, packed into 50 or 200-g (2 or 7-oz) tubs, levelled off and sealed with a thin layer of butter. The ratio of butter to shrimps is one of Bob's great concerns. Some potters, he claims, put in too much butter with the shrimps or cover them with too thick a layer. His, I assure you, have copious quantities of moist succulent gently spiced shrimps which are marked for their sweet fresh nuttiness. Once sealed, he will send his shrimps anywhere in the world.

Morecambe Fishermen's Supplies, 164 Lancaster Road, MORECAMBE LA4 5QW ☎ *01524 417534 is actually a fishing tackle and net shop, but they sell tubs of frozen potted shrimps spiced with nutmegs, cloves and black pepper.*

By the sea front is Nortons Fishmonger, 23 Regent Road, MORECAMBE LA3 1QG ☎ *01524 410218 who have rough (unpeeled) and picked (peeled) shrimps piled on the fish counter, as well as tubs of potted shrimps.*

NEW ENTRY

Stockists

London: Blagdons
Partridges of
Sloane Street

Glos: Hawkins of
Shipton-on-Stour

Wilts: Mackintosh
of Marlborough

Yorks: Ramus
Seafoods

PILLING
Vegetable
Box Scheme

Growing with Nature
Bradshaw Lane Nursery, Pilling, Preston,
Lancashire PR3 6AX

☎ 01253 790046   **FAX** 01253 790046   **CONTACT** Alan Schofield – *telephone ahead*

Until 4 years ago Alan Schofield used to sell his organic (to Soil Association standards) vegetables to the multiples and wholesalers, but he was not happy. 'I wanted to get closer to the customer, market directly to them.' Now he runs box and personal choice schemes supplying crops from his 3½ acres, with 3,000 sq ft under glass, supplemented by bought-in vegetables from other local growers.

As several growers – Alan included – will tell you, growing for the multiples can be very tough. 'I objected on principle to the centralized packing and distribution – my vegetables would travel to Scotland to be packed only to come back to a store a few miles down the road. It seems ridiculous. Then the multiples expected me, a small grower, to act as their bank; they took 3 month's credit. As for their specifications, it wasn't that it was difficult to meet them but it meant that we had to grade out heavily this end. If a carrot was not long enough or a lettuce not heavy enough, it wouldn't do. They just wouldn't accept two lettuces in a bag to meet the weight. The freedom of retailing is so much more satisfying but, I assure you, it doesn't mean the quality isn't as good. It's not an excuse for selling second-class vegetables.'

Alan sells his vegetables in three ways. The first is a box scheme co-ordinated in three areas – Lancaster, Preston and the Fylde coast; the boxes are made up by price rather than weight, with seasonal produce all grown in this country. There is no choice, but his many satisfied cus-

---

The Ramsbottom Victuallers, 16-18 Market Place, RAMSBOTTOM BL0 9HT
☎ **01706 825070** *is a husband-and-wife team. Upstairs is the bistro run by the rigorous Ros Hunter and downstairs is the food shop and cellar of well-chosen wines, the domain of Chris Johnson. The recently enlarged shop is crammed with an exceptionally thoughtful selection of craft foods: bread comes winging its way from Innes see page 246, flour from Shipton Mill see page 115, chocolates from Melchior see page 81, fruit vinegars and jellies from Womersley Hall see page 312, jams from Garden of Suffolk see page 357, preserves and chutneys from Wendy Brandon see page 378, fudge from The Toffee Shop see page 58, and a rich Christmas pudding that doubles up as plum duff from Pimbletts. For the Italianophiles there is a large choice of estate-bottled olive oils and a range of Carluccio's foods see page 180.*

On the fresh food front there are cheeses nicely ripened in the cheese room outside. These include a choice of Mrs Kirkham's and Shorrock's Lancashire, Bonchester see page 324, Thornby Moor Dairy see page 61, Heydale a tangy ewes'-milk cheese see page 161, as well as several of the territorials. There are Morecambe Bay potted shrimps from Baxter's see page 157, Slack's ham and bacon see page 59, Burbush of Penrith pies see page 64, organic vegetables from Growing with Nature see above, and slices of bresaola-style beef which Chris butchers and cures himself then sends off to The Old Smokehouse see page 54 for a light smoke and finally matures himself. Altogether this a good shop for every food lover.

Possibly no one knows more about Lancashire cheeses and all its variations than Peter Gott of **Peter Gott's Cheese & Bacon Stall, 115-6 Barrow Market, BARROW-IN-FURNESS, LA14 1HX ☎ 01229 830956 fax 01229 820268**. *He sells several*   *from different makers because 'each maker makes a different cheese with a different characteristic. If we were in France they would probably all be given different names. There always have been two styles of Lancashire. From up North – that's to say north of the river Ribble – they tended to be fattier and more crumbly but as you go further South, nearer the salt plains of Cheshire, they became more acid and sharper'.*

Lancashire, unlike any other cheese, is traditionally made with curds from 2 (and occasionally even 3) days. It is, as Peter Gott says, full of subtle variations. Each maker will make a different cheese, but (s)he will also sell that cheese at different ages for a different strength. In Lancashire these are known as: Mild, with the cheese at 1-4 weeks; Creamy at 4-8 weeks; Tasty at 8-16 weeks; and Strong at 16 weeks and upwards. For my (and Peter's) money, the best of all Lancashires is made by Ruth Kirkham. She makes it with the unpasteurized milk of her 40-strong Friesian herd, 7 days a week, 52 weeks a year. Her cheese has great rich butteriness or, as Peter puts it, 'a style consistent with a farm cheese, plenty of character and a farm taste flavour'. He matures Ruth's cheese up to 7-8 months so 'it creeps up on you. It pleases the palate initially – but never bursts out too strong – and then a fruitiness opens up and lingers on'.

Other makers that Peter favours and (unlike Ruth) will also sell direct are **Carron Lodge, Carron Lane, INGLEWHITE, nr Preston PR3 2LN ☎ 01995 640352 fax 01995 641040**. *They make a Mild, Tasty and, recently, an unpasteurized Lancashire* *which he matures on for up to 9 months, as well as whey butter.* **Dewlay Products, Green Lane, GARSTANG, nr Preston PR3 1NJ ☎ 01995 602335** *(mail order only) are one of the largest and most consistent makers and Peter likes their Creamy for its soft richness.*

If you are visiting Lancashire, you should take the opportunity to try the different cheeses – you will be surprised at how good they can be. As Lancashire is a fragile crumbly cheese, 'best cut then broken off', it also means it is not suitable for pre-packing. However, the multiples like pre-packed cheese, and therefore a one-day curd Acid cheese was developed to suit their needs. It is but a pale imitation of the real thing, 'aromaless, tasteless and has the consistency of small lumps of stodgy dough stuck together with flour paste' to quote Patrick Rance, but unfortunately what most of us who live out of the county think of as Lancashire. Once you have tried Peter's recommendations, you will realize just how good this semi-soft, loose-textured, crumbly, buttery cheese can be.

tomers will testify for the range and freshness of his selection. Personal choice operates out of the same areas, as well as Blackburn, Chorley and Wigan and each week you get an itemized invoice for what you have bought with a list of next week's crops so you can ring in with an order. Finally you can ring up ahead and buy direct from the door.

His range of vegetables is wide. Several different lettuces, Japanese leaves, salad crops, cabbages and other brassicas, peas, courgettes, freshly cut herbs, at least 3 varieties of French beans, squashes (including little patty pans), potatoes, onions and tomatoes are bought in from growers down the road and he extends his season to all-year-round by joining up with a grower in Yorkshire. With Alan, growing is as much a way of life as a business. He runs a newsletter and holds open days to forge closer links with his customers. 'It's important for them to see crops in the field, so much of the criticism comes from a basic ignorance of how food is actually produced, or why we grow organically.' Nowadays Alan is altogether a happier grower.

PRESTWICH
Bagels and Challah

The Swiss Cottage Patisserie

118 Rectory Lane, Prestwich, Manchester, Lancashire M25 1GB

☎ 0161 798 0897 **FAX** 0161 798 8212 **CONTACT** Jack Maurer **HOURS** Tues-Thurs 8.30-17.00 Fri 7.30-14.30 Sun 7.30-14.00 **DIRECTIONS** From Manchester, take the A56 2 miles to Prestwich. Turn right at the traffic lights into Scholes Lane. Take the first turning on the left into Heywood Road and the shop is 400 yards down on the right.

No one is certain where bagels originate from. One theory is that they are the descendants of the 'beugal', or stirrup-shaped roll baked in honour of the victorious King of Poland when the Turks were defeated before Vienna in 1683. Another put forward by Evelyn Rose, the Jewish cookery writer, is that they are a lineal descendent of the 15th-century *pain échaudé* or boiled bread.

Jack Maurer makes something in the order of 9,000 bagels a week. 'The trick for a good bagel', so he says, 'is not to over-boil them before you bake them. Boiling alters the whole structure of the dough and gives the bagel its chewy texture. If you over-boil, they end up like rubber.' Using a synthesis of several recipes, he first makes the dough from flour, water, yeast, salt and sugar – but never, as some bakers do, with egg. It must be quite firm so it holds together. It is formed by machine into the familiar ring shape with a hole in the middle, then submerged for a few seconds in boiling water until it swells, drained, put on trays and baked off in the oven. A good bagel should have a glossy crisp but chewy crust and a creamy soft interior. Sold plain or with the tops scattered with poppy or sesame seeds or kibbled onion, he also sells them filled. The most popular choice is inevitably cream cheese and smoked salmon.

Jack runs a strictly Kosher (supervised by Beth Din) bakery that serves the large local Jewish population. As orthodox Jews cannot eat milk and meat together, he only uses vegetable margarine and vegetable oils to ensure that his products are '*parev*' (meaning neutral), so they can be eaten with both. For Friday night he makes challah, a white fluffy bread with a hint of sweetness which is traditionally always plaited. Now readers may remember that Jack holds the unofficial challah-plaiting world record and it still stands at 1,688 buns in an hour and 1,000 six-stranded loaves in 1 hour 27 minutes. He also bakes rye with caraway seeds, dark Russian rye using a recipe from his Russian grandparents, and a black rye bread. New this year are a moist Kiev pumpernickel and six-grain bread.

Stockists

Cheshire: The Deli

  Food Lover Rachel Rycroft of Goosnargh has been a mine of information about local suppliers and shops and she highly recommends **Todderstaffe's, 13a Park Street, LYTHAM FY8 5LU ☎ 01253 735325** particularly for their cheeses. They collect Mrs Kirkham's Lancashire from the farm and generally sell it at about 12 weeks' old, although they mature a few up to 6 months when it develops 'plenty of bite'. They also sell Carron Lodge Tasty at 6 months and Dewlay's creamy Lancashire at 6-8 weeks. Their remaining stock includes Keen's Cheddar see page 242, the entire range of Bonchester cheeses see page 324, Appleby's Cheshire see page 229, and Innes cheeses see page 246, as well as whey butter from Carron Lodge. Bread comes from Innes and, for the weekend, they stock rye, Italian and Greek breads from Accrington Bakeries. They sell a local chicken liver pâté, own-made salads and hot sandwiches – on Saturdays slices of salt beef tucked into barm cake are extremely popular.

While you're in the area...

Cowman's Famous Sausage Shop, 13 Castle Street, CLITHEROE BB7 2BT ☎ 01200 23842 fax 01200 25573 has a dazzling display of sausages and promises around 50 different varieties every day. Their average meat content is about 75 per cent and some come without preservatives or colourings, in a choice of medium- or coarse-textured, or even – as is the case with pork and walnut – gluten-free.

Eaves Green Game Farm, Eaves Green House Farm, Eaves Green Lane, GOOSNARGH, PR3 2FE ☎ 01772 865300 is another of Food Lover Rachel Rycroft's recommendations. During the summer, Ian Banks rears pheasants for the local shoots and, in season, sells them hung to order and dressed. He also deals in partridge, woodcock, snipe, wild mallard, rabbit and hare.

Johnson & Swarbrick, Swainson House Farm, Goosnargh Lane, GOOSNARGH PR3 2JU ☎ 01772 865251 fax 01772 86525 produce maize-fed chickens reared indoors for 9-11 weeks. Hung for 2-3 days, they have a deep yellow flesh and skin, a creamy taste and a good length of flavour. Their ducks, reared to 8 weeks and hung for 3-4 days, also have a deep intensity of flavour. Apparently Paul Heathcote of Heathcote's restaurant cooks with them.

Ashworth Confectioners, 30 Higher Deardon Gate, HASLING-DEN BB4 5QJ ☎ 01706 215099 is an old-fashioned bakery that sells, among other things, 'Sissy Green's' meat pies (made with a crisp lard pastry and a peppery meat filling) and cracknells – sometimes called sad cakes because 'they have no currants' – are made with plain pastry rolled out flat, pricked and baked.

Chamber House Urban Farm, Rochdale Road East, HEYWOOD OL10 1SD ☎ 01706 48710 use the milk from their Friesland flock to make Heydale, a soft ewes'-milk cheese with a mellow tang; Heydale Mellow and Mature (both semi-hard cheeses); a creamy full-fat and low-fat yoghurt, which comes as plain or flavoured with own-grown fresh fruit; and ice-cream.

Mansergh Hall Lamb, Mansergh Hall, KIRKBY LONS-DALE via Carnforth LA6 2EN ☎ 01524 271397 comes highly recommended by Food Lover Liz Franklin of Kent. She writes, 'I have been continuously delighted with the service, efficiency and value for money. The lamb is beautiful, and produced without the use of any herbicides, pesticides, antibiotics or food additives'. Reared on herbi-cide- and pesticide-free pastures, the lamb is hung for 'no less than a week' and sold in various joints and cuts. More reports please.

Lanigans, 74 Clifton Street, LYTHAM FY8 5EW ☎ 01253 736203 are a reliable source for teal and widgeon. As Andrew Lanigan says, 'On and around the Ribble estuary is their migrating area and there are generally plenty shot'. He also sells most game in season, as well as wet fish and fresh picked (peeled) Lytham shrimps.

Leicestershire

Map No. 4

Seldom Seen Farm
Billesdon, Leicester, Leicestershire LE7 9FA

☎ 01162 596742 **CONTACT** Claire Symington **HOURS** June to mid-Sept: 10.30-20.00; 1-24 Dec: 9.30-17.00 **DIRECTIONS** From Leicester, take A47 towards Uppingham. After about 8 miles, turn left on to the B6047, signposted Melton Mowbray. After about ¼ mile, take the first turning on the left at the farm sign, into a lane. After another ¼ mile, turn left again into the farm drive.

The Symingtons grow 30 acres of fruit and vegetables. Most of it goes off to the wholesale market, but some is kept behind for pick-your-own or sold ready-picked from the farm-shop. Here you will find 10 acres of strawberries, with 4 varieties to chose from: Elsanta, Cambridge Favourite (which, when picked fully ripe, can be piercingly sweet), Pegasus and Rhapsody. There are 5 acres planted with 6 varieties of raspberries to take you right through the season ending with Autumn Bliss. There are also tayberries, a hybrid berry bred from a cross between a blackberry and a raspberry; blackcurrants, redcurrants and, the prettiest of all, white currants; Leveller gooseberries; and Worcesterberries, a cross between gooseberry and blackcurrants, with a soft juicy centre which is splendid for jam-making or in a summer pudding. They also grow their own early- and main-crop potatoes and broad beans.

From their summer shop, they sell their own honey collected from hives on the farm. From a mixture of rape and raspberry blossom, it has a strong local following. Jams are made by a local friend, using their own fruit wherever possible. There are marmalades and a refreshing

---

Beeby Fruit Farm, South Croxton Road, BEEBY, Leicester LE7 3BL ☎ **01162 595612** *has recently been taken over by the Symingtons and has a good selection of pick-your-own soft fruit, including gooseberries, tayberries and Worcesterberries. They also grow new potatoes, broad beans and peas.*

lemon curd and sweet-sharp and intensely fruity blackberry and raspberry vinegars. Claire Symington makes masses of different cakes using geese' and ducks' eggs from the farm, including cherry & coconut, chocolate cake and banana loaf.

At Christmas, the Symingtons open up the winter shop down in the farmyard to sell their Embden-cross geese, and this year they have increased their flock size to 1,000. Their geese range free on grass and are fed on own-grown potatoes and corn. As a result the flesh is a distinctive yellow, with a deep meaty flavour. Hung for 10 days and on sale from Michaelmas through to Christmas, they weigh anything from 3.5 to 7 kg (8 to 15 lb) and are all oven-ready, complete with giblets and a chunk of their butter-yellow fat. An oven-ready 4.5 kg (10 lb) goose, Claire reckons, will feed 8 generously 'even if they have never carved one before'. Her geese all come with cooking and carving instructions. For the greatest economy, she suggests carving the breast off in one piece, then cutting it into slices across the grain.

They also sell pheasants, own-grown bronze turkeys, frozen rarebreed (Shetland and Manx) lamb from a local farmer, Brussels sprouts on the stalk so they remain fresh and firm throughout the holiday, various stuffings that Claire herself prepares (including pork & orange), mince pies, tarts, and shortbread – as well as Christmas trees from the farm.

The Manor Oven Bakery, **40-42 Sherrard Street**, **MELTON MOWBRAY LE13 1XJ** ☎ **01664 65920** *is run by Richard Greasley. He is, as he freely admits, 'a law unto himself', but there is no denying he is a good baker. A one-time winner of the bakery innovation award, you can expect to find some unusual bread combinations, including Stilton & celery. He also bakes a deep sour-dough with rye, rye and buckwheat, various seed breads and focaccia made with plenty of olive oil. His Country Gentlemen's cake, a variation of a Melton Mowbray Hunt cake (only he is not allowed to call it that), is a rich dark well-fruited version made with Barbados sugar, vine fruits soaked in brandy, cherries and 'a bit of peel'. Once baked, the cakes are brushed with brandy and stored in foil for several weeks to mature. He also makes his own Danish pastries and a Melton cheesecake with curd cheese, butter, sugar, eggs, currants and nutmeg.*

Claybrooke Mill

Frolesworth Lane, Claybrooke Magna, Lutterworth, Leicestershire LE17 5DB

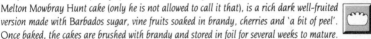

LUTTERWORTH
Flour

☎ 01455 202443 **FAX** 01455 202553 **CONTACT** David Mountford – telephone ahead

David Mountford mills his flours with bread-making in mind, so they have a reasonably high protein content. There are two ranges, conventional and organic (to Soil Association standards). Conventional has a protein content averaging 13 per cent, whereas organic flour usually hits the 11 per cent mark, 'English organic wheat is weaker, so I have to

Stockists

Leics: Currant Affairs
- - - - - - - - -
Natural Choice

Warwicks: The Health Food Shop
- - - - - - - - -
Natural Choice

blend it with Canadian'. He produces a 100 per cent wholemeal flour, an 88 per cent extraction flour, an unbleached white and two flour mixes that make interestingly textured loaves: Fieldfare is a mixture of conventional wholemeal with malted wheat flour, linseed, sunflower and sesame seeds; Nuthatch is made up from brown flour with rye flour, oat flakes, sunflower and pumpkin seeds, and chopped mixed nuts in its conventional version (the organic version has desiccated coconut instead of most of the chopped nuts as organic nuts are difficult to source). David also mills rye flour, and sells bran and semolina.

Ye Olde Pork Pie Shoppe
10 Nottingham Street, Melton Mowbray,
Leicestershire LE13 1NW

☎ 01664 62341 **FAX** 01664 62341 **CONTACT** Stephen Hallam **HOURS** Mon-Sat 8.00-17.00 **DIRECTIONS** In town centre.

For the best of all Melton Mowbray pork pies, hasten to Dickinson and Morris's Ye Olde Pork Pie Shoppe. Not only is it the oldest pork pie bakery in town but it is also the only one to make the real thing. When the shop was restored in 1992 after a disastrous fire, Steve Hallam decided to abandon so-called modern improvements and revert to making pies according to the original techniques with the original ingredients. A proper Melton Mowbray pork pie is made with a boiled paste of flour, lard, salt and water. The paste is hand-raised around a dolly (cylindrical wooden block) and, as Steve explains, 'You need a sure touch to raise the paste. If you pull too hard, you'll cause it to stretch or split. Equally the paste mustn't be too thick or uneven. But doing it by hand – once you get it right – results in a far better pie than a piece of machinery can ever achieve'.

Melton Mowbray pies also have a particularly distinctive shape. Unlike other pork pies with their straight-up-and-down sides and neatly tucked top, its top has wavy edges and bulges like a pot belly. This is because it is hand-crimped and – baked without a hoop or tin – it is completely self-supporting. Appearance is important, as Steve says, 'Not only must it look right, so you know it's authentic, but it also affects the way the filling cooks. We aim for a pie that is not just a rich pastry holding up a meat filling or a meaty filling enclosed in pastry, but a perfect marriage of the two'.

The actual ingredients for the filling are also of prime importance. When pies were first baked in Melton Mowbray, they would probably have used meat from the Tamworth pig, the local breed fattened on the whey that is a by-product from Stilton, the local cheese. Now Stephen uses good-quality lean local pork. It is hand-chopped for a good texture and, unlike most other pork pies, it is always used fresh rather than cured. This means that, when you cut it open, the filling may look dull and grey rather than a vibrant pink of cured meat; but try it, it has a far

---

With several **Walker & Son** pie shops in the county, the main one is at **4 Cheapside,** **LEICESTER LE1 5EA** ☎ **01162 625687**. Their pies are made in a state-of the-art factory on an industrial estate at the edge of town. Despite modern machinery to chop the meat, mix and press out the pastry, and fill the moulds, the pies are more than passable. The pastry may be a trifle tough and the filling lacking in texture, but they are still a whole lot better than most. For anyone who wants to make their own hot-water crust, they also sell own-rendered lard.

---

meatier fuller flavour and it packs a peppery punch, which Steve assures me is the tradition. The pies are made up with equal weights of meat to pastry. Once cooked, each pie is pricked to let the steam out and hand-filled with a proper jelly stock made from split pigs' trotters – no commercially produced substitute bought in packets. Baked freshly every day in 450 and 900-g (1 and 2-lb) pies, they are a satisfying combination of rich crisp pastry and succulent filling.

If you think making hand-raised pork pies looks easy enough, you should join Steve on one of his demonstration nights. You too can have a go; leave the pie to chill overnight and collect it cooked and jellied the following afternoon. I have tried and, although Steve makes it look like a doddle, believe me it is not easy.

Stockists

Leics: David North

London: Harvey Nichols

- - - - - - - - - -

Selfridges

Surrey: La Charcuterie

David North, 289 Station Road, ROTHLEY LE7 7LD ☎ 01162 302263 is a friendly shop with a good selection of groceries and fresh foods. What makes it exceptional is the small counter that stocks son Dominic's pâtisserie. After two years at catering college and a further two years in the kitchen of Michael Nadell's pâtisserie see page 184, he returned home, was given kitchen space in the basement and was left to start baking.

Everything is made with fresh ingredients on a daily basis from scratch. Dominic's grazed knuckles bear testament to a recent session of lemon-zesting. Most everything is made to order, although there are usually some cakes for sale in the shop. When I visited I tried a piercingly fresh lemon tart on a thin buttery layer of pastry, an unusual pyramid-shaped individual summer pudding with alternating layers of lightly sweetened berries and bread, and a deep dry chocolate mousse on a rum-soaked sponge base. The quality is good and everything was finished with true precision and finesse, the mark of a real pastry chef.

While you're in the area...

With plans to open a farm shop, Michael and Mary Bell at **Home Farm, Woodhouse Lane, NANPANTAN LE11 3YG** ☎ **01509 239228** make a range of sausages from their organically reared (to Soil Association standards) pigs. These include pork & fresh herbs, pork & garlic, pork with garlic & coriander, and 100 per cent pork. They dry-cure bacon and sell lamb from their Poll Dorset and Dorset Down flocks, and beef from their Horned Hereford herd. More reports please.

G. T. Doughty & Son, Chapel Lane, TUGBY Leicester LE7 9WA ☎ **01162 598211** are a small butchers tucked down a side lane. They still operate their own slaughterhouse and sell well-hung beef and lamb, cure tongue, make pies and sausages and prepare potted beef, faggots and brawn.

Lincolnshire

ALFORD
**Lincolnshire
Poacher
Cheese**

Lincolnshire Poacher

Ulceby Grange, Alford, Lincolnshire LN13 0HE

☎ 01507 462407 **FAX** 01507 463605 **CONTACT** Simon Jones – mail order only

Lincolnshire is not known as a dairy county. 'It's too dry' Simon Jones explained, 'we have 16 inches of rain a year as opposed to the west coast, where they have 3 times as much; and often, by summer, the grass has dried up'. In spite of what might appear serious disadvantages, Simon runs a 150-strong Holstein herd and for the past three years has been making Lincolnshire Poacher cheese with the unpasteurized milk.

A Cheddar-style cheese, he makes it 'along Cheddar lines, although we have tinkered about with the recipe'. He admits he is still 'on a learning curve' and plans to expand production but restrict making to between September and the end of May. 'Then we can dry off our cows in summer and we won't have to worry about the grass. Anyway I think it's best as a winter cheese'.

Made in 9 and 2.3-kg (20 and 5-lb) rounds with plans to make a larger – either 18 or 25-kg (40 or 56-lb) truckle, it is more open-textured than Cheddar but with the same earthy tang. When he first started making, Simon would sell his cheeses at 5 months; but now he is maturing them on either as Poacher at 9-12 months for a deeper tang, or as Vintage at 12-15 months when it has an even greater fullness but with the original underlying delicacy.

Stockists

Lincs: Comestibles

London: Neal's Yard Dairy

Lothian: Iain Mellis

Norfolk: The Mousetrap

Describing himself as a hobby farmer, **Mr Cheriton of Glebe Farm,** FORD-INGWORTH, **Market Raisen LN8 3SD** ☎ **01673 885201** *produces small amounts of free-range pork as whole or half carcasses or butchered in joints, oven-ready ducks, the odd cockerel and, at Christmas-time, a few geese. He also grows various vegetables and soft fruit.*

Belvoir Fruit Farms
Belvoir, Grantham, Lincolnshire NG32 1PB

BELVOIR
Fruit
Cordials

☎ 01476 870286 **FAX** 01476 870114 **CONTACT** Lord John Manners **HOURS** *end June to end Aug 10.00-20.00* **DIRECTIONS** *From Grantham, take A52 towards Nottingham. After about 6½ miles, turn left off the Bottesford Bypass, signposted Harby/Belvoir Castle. Drive 2 miles and turn left at the cross-roads, signposted Belvoir Castle. After ½ mile, turn left into the fruit farm at the signpost.*

The 40-acre Belvoir Fruit Farms are in the fertile vale of Belvoir, over-looked by the spectacular Belvoir Castle. During the summer about 5 to 6 acres are open to the public for pick-your-own and ready-picked fruit. Here you will find the usual soft fruit, such as strawberries, rasp-berries, blackcurrants and redcurrants, tayberries and gooseberries.

Castle apart, it is for the elegant fruit cordials that Belvoir is best known. Made from fresh fruit, the range now includes blackcurrant, strawberry, raspberry, strawberry and raspberry mixed, lemon and bitter lemon – but it originally started with elderflower. Lord John Manners used to make it on a small scale every summer in his kitchen, for home consumption. When he saw that his entire store of bottles had been drunk by October, he realized that he was on to a good thing.

Elderflower, with its muzzy-fuzzy taste, still remains my favourite. It is made with elderflowers grown on the estate's elderflower plantation, and the flowers are picked by hand so as not to bruise them. To ensure they have as much fragrance as possible, they are steeped in a cold cane sugar syrup within 3 hours of picking and left to infuse for a long time. Once the syrup is permeated with the flavour of the flowers, it is carefully filtered and bottled. A process that sounds simple enough, but it is extracting the intensity of flavour that is so important. Each of the fruit juices contains the juice of nearly 900 g (2 lb) of fruit. When-ever possible, Lord John uses own-grown fruit, and they do have good clarity of fruit. To heighten their flavours lemon is made with the rind, for that old-fashioned flavour; blackcurrant is mixed with a dash of glucose; and raspberry with lemon juice. When diluted with water, you will probably get about 20 glasses from the 74 cl (1¼ pt) bottle. These indeed are cordials to remind you of warm glowing summers.

Stockists

Avon: Pasta Galore

Derbys: Chatsworth Farmshop

Devon: N. H. Creber Ltd

London: Partridges of Sloane Street

Lothian: Valvona & Crolla

Thistledoons
Square Bays, Chapel St Leonard, Lincolnshire PE24 5TZ

CHAPEL ST
LEONARD
Cardoons

☎ 01754 872396 **FAX** 01754 872396 **CONTACT** Stephan Colback – *tele-phone ahead in season (October to January)*

Since the last edition I am sure that several readers have become thor-oughly familiar with cardoons. It would perhaps be an exaggeration to say you see them everywhere, but they are eaten – stalk by stalk – in

Jack Buck Growers, Oak House Cold Stores, HOLBEACH BANK PE12 8BL ☎ 01406 422615 *fax* 01406 426173 *is one of this country's largest growers of chicory (Belgian endive). They will supply you with a grow-your-own set of six roots, 2 plant pots, 2 pot bases and growing instructions. All you do is half-fill one pot with potting compost, plant the chicory roots, fill it up with compost, stand it in water, cover it with the other pot, put it in a dark cool place and – provided you keep it moist and dark – within 4-5 weeks you should be able to harvest your first crop.*

the more outré restaurants and households.

Just in case cardoons (*Cynara cardunculus*) have passed you by, I should explain they are a close relation of the globe artichoke C. *scolymus*, but it is their leaf stalk that we eat rather than their flowerheads.

With a texture similar to celery and a tart bitter-sweet taste rather like chicory, cardoons are grown with great enthusiasm in Southern Europe. The good news is that their revival in Britain is underway. Cookbook-seller *par excellence* Clarissa Dickson-Wright, of Edinburgh's Global Gourmet, is President of the Cardoon Appreciation Society (I am proud to be the founder – and possibly only other – member) and she, more than anyone, has brought cardoons back into our kitchens. It was Clarissa who persuaded Stephan Colback to grow them on his small-holding by the sea – ideal conditions, with its light sandy soil and frost-free climate. He has extended his cultivation, growing several varieties, and will now supply seedlings by order in April for June postage so you can grow them yourself; as well as whole plants 'stripped and ready for stalk eating', and the globes 'for the meticulous epicure or use in soups' in season from October to January. 1993 proved a disastrous year, 'over 70 per cent of the crop was lost to bolting. They produced lots of globes and flowers in consolation'; but matters have improved as Stephan's experience grows.

To prepare a cardoon, you separate the heart and stalks, strip the stalks to get rid of any stringy fibres and prickles, and cut them into suitable lengths. Then simmer them in acidulated salted water for about 15 minutes to blanch and then refresh in cold water. Finally, you cook them – by whatever method the recipe stipulates – until tender; a

Comestibles, 82 Bailgate, LINCOLN LN1 3AR ☎/*fax* 01522 520010 *is run by Kate O'Meara, a keen baker who devises her own recipes and gives them to a local baker to make for her. Her walnut & rye bread is very popular and she also sells rosemary & olive oil, herb & cheese, Marmite (which, on cutting, looks like a Swiss roll), and soda breads. New this year is a round white bread marbled through with sun-dried tomatoes and pesto.*

She has also extended her own-made range with a rich well-flavoured chicken liver pâté; a salmon & dill terrine; savoury roulades filled with watercress, crème fraîche and sun-dried tomatoes, or smoked salmon or prawns; whole honey roast, sugar-glazed hams; and, at Christmas, jars of mincemeat. She buys in glazed open fruit tarts, crème brûlée and tiramisu made especially for her and sells various cheeses, including several local ones – Lincolnshire Poacher see page 166 and Easter Dawn, made with goats' milk and similar to a mild Havarti; and soft goats' cheese in oil made by the same maker. At Christmas and Easter only, she stocks Gerard Ronay's chocolates see page 175. Comestibles is altogether an interesting shop.

total cooking time of about 30-40 minutes is all you need.

Stephan has branched out into growing 'select varieties' of potatoes, including Belle de Fontenay, Platte de Florenville, Pink Fir Apple and Viola – a new variety that Stephan is most excited about. He also grows lettuces, chicories and leaves, and makes up a mesclun salad mix containing 10 different varieties of the above including frisée Wallonne, *cresson alenoirs* and *laitue sucrine*. When we last spoke he was 'continuously experimenting with varieties of beetroot, squashes, skirret and tomatoes, all grown in the open with heaps of manure at great risk from the weather, but most wonderfully flavoursome when successful'.

Stockists
London: Tom's
Villandry

G. B. **Geese**
Lings View Farm, Middle Street, Croxton Kerrial, Grantham, Lincolnshire NG32 1QP

CROXTON KERRIAL
Geese

☎ 01476 870394   **FAX** 01476 870394   **CONTACT** Ann Botterill – *telephone for details* (end Nov to 23 Dec)

In summer, Ann's snowy white geese can be seen around the village. She keeps them all over the place, divided up into small flocks as she does not like to run more than 300 in a group. They produce somewhere in the region of 1,200 birds for Michaelmas and Christmas and rearing the birds must run in the family blood as Ann Botterill and Judy Goodman *see page* 295 are sisters.

Bought in as day-old Embden Legarth-cross goslings from May onwards, once they are old enough, they are let out to graze on the grassland. All they are fed is own-grown wheat and oats, 'the rest is grass'. At first, Ann limits the size of the field – 'if the geese walk too far, it pushes out their legs'. She is also adamant they should not have ponds to swim on, 'We keep them off water as swimming makes their meat tough. But they do have constant access to water'.

Killed on-farm at any age between 18-26 weeks, the geese are hung for 10 days and are sold from Michaelmas onwards – as long-legged

Stockists
Derbys: Chatsworth Farmshop
Humber: John Pettit & Sons Ltd
Leics: J. Morris
Notts: Chambers

---

*Grantham Gingerbread arose as a result of a 'mistake', an event that seemingly occurs all too often in the invention of our sweets and puddings. This time the local baker was making Grantham Whetstones, a flat hard biscuit. He mistook one ingredient for another and the result became Grantham Gingerbread. A hard, pale dome-topped biscuit, it was once made by Caitlin's, who had been handed on the original recipe. They are no longer in business, but the gingerbread survives at **Gadsby's of Southwell, St George's Shopping Precinct, GRANTHAM NG31 6HL ☎ 01476 743353**. The original recipe calls for sugar, flour, egg white, ground ginger and ammonium carbonate (this was in the days before baking powder was invented). I suspect that Gadsby's have altered it, particularly as egg white is notoriously difficult to work, but is essential to 'set up' the mixture and keep it light and fragile. The current version is tough, hard, slightly gungy in the middle, rather over-gingered and perhaps not as good as it could be. It is no doubt quicker and cheaper to make and probably travels and keeps better, but is it the real thing?*

(plucked but undrawn) weighing from 5.5-9 kg (12-22 lb); or oven-ready, weighing 4.5-6.5 kg (10-14 lb). The oven-ready birds, complete with giblets and a wodge of goose fat, come neatly trussed and dressed. Once game is in season, Ann Botterill also sells a splendid boned goose stuffed with a boned chicken stuffed with a boned pheasant. Be warned, however, if you want one for Christmas you will have to order it during October or November and freeze it.

HONINGTON
Seakale and Asparagus

Michael Paske Farms
The Estate Office, Honington, Grantham, Lincolnshire NG32 2PG

☎ 01400 250449   **FAX** 01400 250204   **CONTACT** *Michael Paske – telephone ahead*

Seakale (*Crambe maritima*) is a native perennial vegetable found on coastal sands, shingle, rock and cliffs around the British Isles. For centuries, young shoots – naturally blanched by growing through the banks of sand and shingle – were gathered from the wild. It was cultivated in the 19th century, then it dropped out of favour until a few years ago, when the Paske family started to grow it commercially. The wonderfully delicate flavour of the shoots was a great favourite of Mr Paske Sr., but it was impossible to find. So he gathered seedheads from Dungeness and started selectively to breed seakale. The result is the 'Sauvage' variety that, as its name implies, comes from wild stock.

His son Michael now cultivates 20 acres of seakale. Each year the crowns are transplanted into an inert compost in darkened forcing sheds for blanching. So, as the shoots sprout, they see no light and grow a creamy white. When the shoots are about 24 cm (9½ in) long, they are harvested. This year Michael hopes to extend their season, which starts in early February, and goes right through to September.

Tender and juicy, the pale-cream seakale shoots look like inner sticks of celery taken from the heart; their taste is mild and dainty, similar to an asparagus but without the grassy sharpness. Michael sends seakale out in 500-g (1 lb 2-oz) trays or 5-kg (11-lb) boxes.

If you want to try growing and forcing it yourself, he can also supply you with crowns (plants). He also sends out asparagus, guaranteed har-

---

Les Fines Herbes, 8 St Mary's Hill, STAMFORD PE9 2DP ☎ 01780 57381 *is actually a gun-shop that doubles as a game dealer, so you can buy a good selection of game in season from here too. Outback, Elinor Hawksley Beesley also brews a range of herb jellies, vinegars, oils, mustards and seasonings. Fruit, flower and herb vinegars are made by soaking the different flavourings for several months in a base of distilled white malt vinegar. Lavender is particularly pleasant, with a scented floweriness. She also produces a range of slack jellies, using apple juice, sugar and vinegar. The rose petal is perhaps the most interesting, with its musty fragrance. Mustards come as Original Tewkesbury, Spiced White Cambridge and Hot Black Lincolnshire, and all are marked with a strong punch.*

vested and posted the same day. These come in either 1 or 5-kg (450-g or 11-lb) bundles in three grades of size: the big fat jumbo (about 20 to a kilo); selected (about 30 to a kilo); and the thinner selected (about 40 to a kilo).

Jackson's Quality Butchers
118 Eastgate, Louth, Lincolnshire LN11 9AA

LOUTH
Pork
Products

☎ 01507 602797   **CONTACT** Nigel Wrisdale   **HOURS** Mon to Sat 8.00-17.00 (-13.00 Thurs and Sat)   **DIRECTIONS** In centre of Louth.

In the days when every smallholder kept a pig, writes Dorothy Hartley in Lost Country Life, 'The butcher, who rode around to small cottages to do the killing, was called the "pigsticker", and he brought his knives and tools and grisly spiked "snout holder" with him. ... The disembowelling and cutting up was done, and the soft meat, the liver and kidneys and sweetbreads were used at once. The intestines were prepared to make sausage skins, the bladders to contain the lard, the trotters, after the horn covering was scaled off, were valued being strongly gelatinous'.

From the 'pigstickers' came the pork butchers who set up in towns and had the pigs driven to them. Nowadays they are few and far between, a dying breed. Nigel Wrisdale, with his small shop in the centre of Louth, is a fine surviving example. He gave up slaughtering about 10 years ago and is content to buy in pigs that meet his specifications. 'No boars for fear of taint and, for curing, fatter pigs'. Interestingly he did flirt with free-range pork, but was 'pretty disgusted with it really. It was too lean, that caused fat separation, and wet so it wouldn't "set up" properly' and the joints were floppy'.

At the back of the shop are the preparation areas and from here he produces his Lincolnshire sausages in two sizes: chipolatas and fat. One is flavoured with sage, salt & pepper, the other with ginger, nutmeg & mace. Coarsely chopped and made with fresh breadcrumbs every day, they are good old-fashioned village sausages with a good meaty taste, nicely balanced with the spices. His Lincolnshire chine is his pride and joy. Made in the traditional way (see F. C. Phipps, *page 172*), he wraps it in muslin and hangs it up on the old hooks in the passageway to mature. The environmental health officer may not approve, 'But that's ridiculous, these hooks have been here for years. Anyway, everybody knows that meat, if properly cured, does not attract flies'. Then, with precision, he cuts the slits and stuffs it with fresh parsley from his father-in-law's garden. Sharp, salty and cut with herbs, it proved a glorious example.

Nigel also makes pork pies with a crisp clean hot-water crust pastry, a highly seasoned filling, and plenty of rich jelly. Most of the year they are machine-stamped but, at Christmas, he will hand-raise them to order in any size up to 6.8 kg (15 lb). He also dry-cures whole joints from the flick, or belly, for frying or boiling; cures loin for bacon in salt and Demerara sugar and oak-smokes it; and makes haslett and savoury ducks with onion and pigs' liver. He can let you have pigs' ears, trotters, hocks and tails and, if he buys a clean fat pig, will render down his own lard. His wife bakes a Lincolnshire plum bread rich in lard, and he cooks legs, chaps, and belly of pork with a fine crackling for the shop – in fact, all manner of things pig.

 An interesting grocery and delicatessen on the edge of Louth is **McLeod's, 11 Bridge Street, LOUTH LN11 0DR ☎ 01507 601094 fax 001507 608412.** *They sell a good choice of cheese, including Lincolnshire Poacher see page 166, Keen's Cheddar see page 242 and Tornegus see page 262; Lincolnshire sausages from Jones & Hopewood in North Thoresby, a range of locally made Indian dishes and snacks, own-made salads, and a small selection of vegetables, including own-grown fresh herbs and Good King Henry – known in these parts as Lincolnshire spinach.*

MAREHAM-LE-FEN
Lincolnshire Stuffed Chine

F. C. *Phipps*
Osborne House, Mareham-Le-Fen, Boston,
Lincolnshire PE22 7RW

☎ 01507 568235 **CONTACT** Eric Phipps **HOURS** Mon-Fri 8.00-17.00 (-13.00 Wed) Sat 8.00-16.00 **DIRECTIONS** *From Boston, take B1183 towards Horncastle. At Revesby, turn left on to A155, signposted Mareham-Le-Fen. Drive through the village and shop is on the left.*

Butcher Eric Phipps prepares a mean Lincolnshire chine (an old English word for the backbone). A local speciality, the part of the pig used is the complete forequarters (fore-rib), butchered from the spine in the centre with 7.5-10 cm (3-4 in) of shoulder muscle still attached on either side. First Mr Phipps cures for a fortnight in a brine based on an old recipe from Revesby Abbey, made up from salt, saltpetre, sugar, black treacle, juniper berries and beer; then it is dry-cured in salt for another week. Once cured, it is cut at intervals at a right angle to the spine and the resulting pockets are ready for the stuffing.

According to Mr Phipps, 'all sorts of greenery were used for the stuffing – nettles, chives, sage, raspberry or blackcurrant leaves – I have come across recipes for them all. But it's best made with fresh chopped parsley. And, although some people do add a bit of sage, I like it best with only parsley. I use masses of it, some of my customers even bring some in for me and we barter. I give them some chine in return'. After being stuffed, the chine is then slowly cooked for hours, cooled and ready for cutting in thin slices across the bone. It looks splendid – long slices of a rich pink meat studded with seams of deep green. It tastes pretty good too; pungent meat with a slightly gelatinous texture, punched with mildly bitter herbs. Eaten cold, with a strong mustard and a few drops of vinegar (one customer rather eccentrically eats his with vinegar sprinkled with brown sugar), Mr Phipps

MAP 5   LINCOLNSHIRE   **173**

thinks it is the nearest English equivalent to the French *jambon persillé*.

Food lovers may remember that Lincolnshire chine was under threat because of an EU directive. Christopher Booker, columnist in *The Sunday Telegraph* took up the case and the Government backed down. He subsequently published the whole absurd story in *The Mad Officials* and I thought you might be interested to read it. 'The regulations lay down that all pigs must now be sold split down the middle for inspection before they can be sold. This has caused consternation not only in Lincolnshire but all over the country. Pig slaughterhouses have been paying out thousands of pounds for new mechanical saws, and one company in the Midlands has even spent £50,000 on a new "dressing line". ... But it then comes to light that the whole thing is a colossal mistake ... the officials in Brussels had mistranslated one word in the original French version of the directive. The French wording had allowed for *carcasses de porc* to be inspected without being split. But in the English version the word "carcasses" has been given as "heads". Since this made no sense, when ministry officials in London came to draw up the UK regulations, instead of checking what was meant, they had simply included a requirement for carcasses to be split'.

Mr Phipps has certainly kept his slaughterhouse up to EU standards; he buys meat on the hoof from local farms, then slaughters, hangs and butchers it into all the usual cuts and joints. He also prepares first-rate hams, sausages and pies.

Welbourne's Bakery
38 High Street, Navenby, Lincolnshire LN5 0DZ

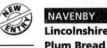

NAVENBY
Lincolnshire Plum Bread

☎ 01522 810239 **CONTACT** Pete Welbourne **HOURS** Mon, Tues, Thurs & Fri 9.00-13.00 & 14.15-17.30 Wed 9.00-12.30 Sat 8.30-14.00. **DIRECTIONS** In village centre.

Several areas in Britain boast their regional bread and Lincolnshire – with its plum bread – is no exception. Several bakers make it in the county, all claiming a 'family' or 'traditional' recipe for the yeast dough enriched with spices and 'plums' (in fact, dried vine fruit). Traditionally lard would have been added, as it was a common enough ingredient – remember the county's strong association with the pig – and it also gave a moistness and richness to the bread. Most, if not all, of the bakers I came across have now dropped lard from their recipe. Although I can understand their reasoning – we have become so fat-conscious in our diet and lard is certainly not the healthiest of fats – I think the bread suffers in the loss. Without lard, Lincolnshire plum bread is a drier version of what I imagine it must once have been.

Welbourne's Bakery date their recipe back to 1898 and it makes for fruity sweet bread that is darker than normal – due, no doubt, to the addition of black treacle. They have substituted vegetable white shortening for lard, but their plum bread remains moist. Generously fruited

Rumour has it that the Lincolnshire plum bread from **Derek Myers & Sons, 20 Bull Ring**, HORNCASTLE LN9 5HU ☎ 01507 522234 is the best in the county. Made with plain flour, three different fats (margarine and 2 shortenings), sultanas, currants, mixed peel, mixed spices, white and brown sugar, eggs, yeast, salt and water, it is exceptionally moist, rich and fruity; delicately hinting of spice, it has a flaky texture and a clean aftertaste. With a shelf-life of two to three weeks, plum bread should be kept well-wrapped in a cool place. Once it begins to dry out, it can easily be revived by toasting. They will post it throughout the country and prefer to send it out in batches of a minimum of 3 loaves.

(the trick is apparently to add the fruit quite late to the dough, otherwise it is exceptionally slow to rise), it also has mixed peel. Locally it is highly recommended to eat with cheese.

A small family bakery, the Welbournes bake a good selection of country-style breads, including a good cob with a soft interior crumb, wholemeal and Granary. Baking starts every morning at 4.00 and, although the shop does not open until 9.00, no one seems to mind if you come early and buy rolls or croissants from the side door. On Saturdays they also have their 'fancy' lines, including tomato bread with tomato paste & sun-dried tomatoes, rye, a soft pumpernickel sweetened with molasses, and a honey-roasted grain with walnuts. They make various cakes, sausage rolls, steak and chicken pies with own-made pastry and, in winter only, game pies – and they always have Lincolnshire chine on the go. They buy it in cured, soak it for 24 hours, cut and stuff it with parsley and bake it off in the bread oven.

Stockists

Notts: Cheese Cuisine

While you're in the area...

Maud Foster Mill, Willoughby Road, BOSTON TE21 9EG ☎ 01205 352188 was built in 1819 and lays claim to being the tallest working windmill in Great Britain. From the wholefood shop you can buy 100 per cent wholemeal, 85 per cent brown and untreated white flours, and maize meal for polenta. Made from a mixture of wheat, buckwheat and rye flours, they also sell a pancake flour that not only works for pancakes, crêpes or blinis but also makes an unusual Yorkshire pudding.

Special Edition Continental Chocolate, 59 Honeyholes Lane, DUNHOLME LN2 3SU ☎ 01673 860616 makes a range of various shaped and moulded chocolates, filled pralines and ganaches flavoured with fruits, liqueurs or tea. Mindful of their location, they also make Diamond Nine after-dinner mints and chocolate bars – the Red Arrow base is 3 miles up the road – and Lincoln Imps, based on the medieval carving in the Cathedral.

Syston Park P-Y-O Fruit Farm, GRANTHAM MG32 2B2 ☎ 01400 250075 is a very pleasant pick-your-own in which to while away the hours. Apart from the usual selection of soft fruits in season, they also grow very healthy-looking rhubarb.

London

Map No. 9

At last, chocolatier **Gerard Ronay, 3 Warple Mews, Warple Way W3 0RF ☎ 0181 743 0818** is sending out his chocolates by mail order, so anyone who does not have easy access to Harrods or any of his other stockists can sample his glories. However, he has asked me specifically to say that he will not welcome visitors to his door unless they have phoned in an order.

Gerard's chocolates are very lush and in~~~ cream and several different types of d~~~ their lightness of texture, b~~~ ~~~ness of flavour. His c~~~ ~~~ubarb with its sharp fr~~~ ~~~vour of the fruit; a rich ~~~ ~~~erates on and on in the palate; ~~~ ~~~nium; and a succulent red wine truffle. New ~~~ ~~~ed chocolate hearts for St Valentine's Day, which ~~~y are combed through with colour, as well as Easter eggs and ~~~ed chocolate boxes made by the same technique. These come in a variety of colours (he uses white chocolate dyed red, blue, green or yellow) and filled with chocolates; he will also inscribe them to order. These are chocolates for spoiling yourself.

NO LONGER TRADING

Bon Vivant Delicatessen, 59 Nightingale Lane SW12 8ST ☎ 0181 675 6314 is a deli stocked with plenty of good British foods. Cheeses include Caerphilly from Chris Duckett *see page* 237, and Golden Cross *see page* 274, breads come from & Clarke's *see page* 185, The Village Bakery *see page* 57, and Loaves & Fishes, and there are Martin Pitt's eggs *see page* 286, Richard Woodall's air-dried ham *see page* 62 and honey from Wandsworth.

The Real Cheese Shop, 62 Barnes High Street SW13 9LF ☎ 0181 878 6676, with branches in Wimbledon *see page* 193 and Morpeth *see page* 210 has a nicely chosen and well-kept range of British cheeses. As owner Robert Handyside hails from the North, it is very strong on Northern cheeses.

■ **Sonny's Food Shop, 94 Church Road SW13 0DQ ☎ 0181 741 8451** is a tiny food shop attached to the same-name restaurant next door. The shop has had a bit of a chequered history – opening, shutting and opening up again – and the obvious idea of selling dishes prepared in the restaurant's kitchen was not quite working when I visited, with the food cooked off the premises although the recipes are Sonny's. It is stocked with freshly made pasta sauces; a couple of terrines, including a chunky-textured salmon bound together with a rich buttery hollandaise sauce; a few dishes-to-go, including fish chowder with a pungent white wine sauce. There are also a few cheeses, plenty of good bread, chocolates from Melchior *see page* 81, freshly made cakes and – in the autumn – a tart apple chutney made by the owner's mum.

BATTERSEA

Cheeses

Hamish Johnston, 48 Northcote Road SW11 1PA ☎ 0171 738 0741 opened up shop just over a year ago and concentrates on cheese. By all accounts, he is doing very nicely thank you. British cheeses include Llanboidy *see page* 383, Tornegus *see page* 262, Devon Blue *see page* 85, Diana Smart's Single and Double Gloucester *see page* 110, and Hereford Hops *see page* 298. They also sell a small selection of British foods, such as fudge from The Toffee Shop *see page* 58, Montgomery Moore chocolates *see page* 260, The Harrow's pies *see page* 23, and Belvoir cordials *see page* 167.

Shellfish

■ Stroll past **The Grape Shop, 135 Northcote Road SW11 6PX ☎ 0171 924 3638 fax 0171 924 3670** on a Saturday and you will find mainly Scottish shellfish on sale. There are Irish or Native oysters, lobsters, crabs and spider crabs, mussels and scallops; and, if there is a wine tasting going on inside, no one minds if you down a couple of oysters with a glass of their wine.

Honey

■ **The Hive, 53 Webbs Road SW11 6RX ☎/fax 0171 924 6233** is run by James Hamill, a third-generation beekeeper. He has 120 hives in and around Tooting and Surrey and to prove his dedication to bees he keeps a hive in the shop, with a tube connected to the outside where they can buzz around. Refining is done in full view of the customers in the back and he sells honey and all manner of honey-related products. James is a great enthusiast; he loves and understands his bees, explaining how they show 'compassion' for the pollen, working one type of flower or blossom, which means that at different times of the year he gets honey with marked characteristics. Particularly splendid is the cherry honey, sweet and fruity with a soft malleable texture. He also prepares flavoured honeys mixed with nuts or fruit purées and a gentle honey & herb vinegar.

Ready-meals

■ **Mise-en-Place, 21 Battersea Rise SW11 1HG ☎ 0171 228 4392 fax 0171 924 1911** has only recently opened. Modern and spacious, it is biased towards the Continental. Sharing the kitchens with La Bouffe restaurant three doors up the road, it offers ready-meals that change according to the restaurant's menu. I tried a rabbit & mushroom casserole, which had a good gravy and plenty of succulent rabbit, as well as creamy ducks' liver terrine, punched with onions. If I lived nearer, I would certainly go back.

Breads

■ **Rae-Ra-El Bakery, 64 Northcote Road SW11 6QL ☎ 0171 228 4537** is run by a West-Indian and German husband-and-wife team. As a result you get a clash of rye and Continental and Combi cornbreads. More reports please.

Mushrooms and Wild Foods

■ As the name suggests, **Taste of the Wild, 65 Overstrand Mansions, Prince of Wales Drive SW11 4EX ☎ 0171 720 0688 fax 0171 498 7344** supplies us home cooks with an amazing array of wild foods. Its sister company, **Wild Harvest** deals with restaurants and chefs. So what are wild foods? Well, using both Roger Phillips' books *Wild Foods* and *Mushrooms* as 'bibles', they have a team of pickers who will gather fleshy sweet pennywort, salty sea beet, bright yellow gorse flowers, punchy wild garlic (ramsons), bitter Alexander shoots, tiny sharp and lemony leaves of wild sorrel or clover-shaped wood sorrel, crunchy samphire, muzzy elderflowers, and so on throughout the year.

Fresh wild mushrooms feature prominently, picked either in Britain 'even within the M25, anywhere from Wimbledon, Richmond, or Sussex, Scotland or Wales – you just have to know where to look', to as far afield as Italy, Eastern Europe, Canada – even Africa or the Himalayas – depending on the season. Expect to find a superb range that includes ceps, chanterelles, winter chanterelles, trompettes de mort (horns of plenty), pieds de mouton (hedgehog fungus), pieds bleu (blewits), puff balls, beef steak, chicken o' the woods, honey fungus, morels, mousserons, St Georges and scarlet elf-caps. Of course, you will not necessarily find everything in season all the time, but whatever they do have is always in top condition.

They will also send gift baskets of mushrooms in 3 sizes: for a snack; for a meal; and for a feast. For enthusiasts, they organize mushroom feasts. I went along to their first at Cibo, an Italian restaurant in London, and revelled in sautéed baby artichokes with wild mushrooms, and ravioli filled with cardoons smothered in a black truffle sauce. They also have plans to start drying their own mushrooms and organizing a mushroom club.

BELGRAVIA
Ready-meals

The House of Albert Roux, 229 Ebury Street SW1W 8UT ☎ 0171 730 3037, fax 0171 823 5043 is a Mecca for lazy food lovers. There are any number of dishes-to-go, pâtés and terrines, including a velvety *mousse de foie aux morilles*; French-style butchered meats, such as saddle of lamb stuffed with wild mushrooms; and, of course, a range of excellent breads, Viennoiserie, tarts, and gâteaux. All of superb quality, but no less than you would expect from M. Roux. His latest innovation is Al's Spit Shop – yes, that is its name – where a state-of-the-art rôtisserie will spit-roast boneless saddles and legs of lamb, ribs and sirloins of beef, corn-fed chickens and game birds. To go with, you can also buy such sauces as foie gras & truffle, bordelaise or shallot, unctuous gratin Dauphinois, mashed or gaufrette potatoes and prepared vegetables.

Cheeses

■ **Jeroboams, 51 Elizabeth Street SW1W 9PP ☎ 0171 823 5623 fax 0171 823 5722** is the address to which to apply for the cheese club, where members receive 4 cheeses a month. For further details of their retail selection, see Jeroboams, Holland Park *page 183*.

BOROUGH
Fish and
Shellfish

Aberdeen Sea Products, Unit 4, Toulmin Street SE1 1PP ☎ 0171 407 0247 fax 0171 407 0248 is 'a super find', according to *The Gourmet's Guide to London* by Elaine Hallgarten and Linda Collister and 'could win the prize for the best (and most modest) fish place in town'. They make their own gravadlax with fresh dill, sea salt and 'time and care', sell smoked salmon from Aberdeen, smoked eel, a good selection of wet fish and shellfish and will boil lobsters, langoustines and crabs for you.

BRIXTON
Vegetables

With members from as far east as Dulwich and as far west as Clapham, **The Cabbage Club Veg Co-op, 33 Kingswood Road SW2 4JE ☎/fax 0181 671 5358** runs a subscription vegetable box scheme. One of the few I have come across in London, once you have paid a membership fee you can expect to collect a weekly box of organic vegetables grown near the south coast. Like all box schemes, such as Little Marcle Organic Partnership *see page* 129 or Growing With Nature *see page* 158, the vegetables vary according to the season, but apparently you are always guaranteed onions, potatoes and carrots. In summer, the choice includes courgettes, spinach, 'lots of herbs'; in winter, it is more likely to be leeks, parsnips, turnips and kale.

BROMPTON CROSS

Speciality Foods and Seafood

The Conran Shop, 81 Fulham Road SW3 6RD ☎ 0171 589 7401 fax 0171 823 7015 is the epicentre of style. In the basement, housed along with stylish lighting and glass, is a small and stylishly correct food department. Gleaming bottles of recondite single-estate olive oils nestle with appealing jars of olives and Wendy Brandon's preparations *see page* 378. Her range of jams, vinegars and preserves also includes some 'specials', such as satsuma and orange & elderflower marmalades. Round the corner in the courtyard of Michelin House is **Bibendum Crustacea ☎ 0171 589 0864**. From a camionette, they sell Native and Pacific oysters, lobsters, crabs, king scallops, prawns, brown shrimps, clams, mussels, and Irish sea urchins. The quality has to be good as they are the same as served in Bibendum's Oyster Bar inside.

Fish and Seafood

■ **La Marée, 76 Sloane Avenue SW3 3DZ ☎ 0171 589 8067 fax 0171 581 3360** is the fish shop of restaurant Poissonnerie de l'Avenue next door. They have a good selection of shellfish and wet fish and, if you order, will cook whole salmon or sea bass for you.

BUTLERS WHARF

Fish and Seafood

Le Pont de la Tour Smoked Fish & Crustacea Shop, The Butlers Wharf Building, 36d Shad Thames SE1 2YE ☎ 0171 403 7573 is part of Terence Conran's 'Gastrodome'. As its names suggests, it is big on smoked fish from Loch Fyne *see page* 318 and Minola *see page* 112, as well as crustacea, including crabs, lobsters, Irish and Native oysters, clams, scallops, and winkles and whelks to order. There are wet fish as well and, at lunch-time, fish-filled bagels and slices of fish tart. Down the alley at **36d ☎ 0171 403 4030** is the **Food Store & Bakery**; here you will find at least 20 different flavoured or Continental-style breads, and various on-farm cheeses.

Bread and Cheese

CAMDEN TOWN

Bread

Lou's Bakery, 8 Ferdinand Street NW1 8ER ☎ 0171 284 4644 comes highly recommended for their various breads and cakes, and their own-made organic marmalade. More reports please.

■ **Barstow & Barr, Unit 90, Camden Lock, Chalk Farm Road NW1 8AF ☎ 0171 428 0488** are only open on Saturdays and Sundays, as is the rest of Camden Lock. For further details see Barstow & Barr, Islington *page* 183.

Cheese

CHELSEA

Ready-meals

Food from Finns, 4 Elystan Street SW3 3NS ☎ 0171 225 0733/4 is in the style of Tante Marie, that is to say good, wholesome and, perhaps, a touch old-fashioned. Dishes are cooked daily to order in the kitchen behind the shop and customers are welcome to bring in their own serving dishes. Although they will cook anything to order, the sorts of things that feature on the list are roulades, chicken in three-mustard sauce, whole poached salmon with watercress and lime mayonnaise and seemingly hundreds of puddings. The shop has some cooked dishes-to-go, cooked ham on the bone, own-made salads, mayonnaise, mustards and jams 'made on the family estate in Yorkshire' and a refreshing lemon cordial made with fresh lemons and sugar.

Cakes

■ Forget about neat round cakes with icing and candles ... if you want computers, enchanted castles or Cadillacs, **Jane Asher Party Cakes, 22-24 Cale Street SW3 3QU ☎ 0171 584 6177 fax 0171 584 6179** is the place to go. The base, Jane Asher insists, 'is a proper cake – a choice of vanilla or chocolate sponge or a richer fruit, aged and full of brandy' and these can be built to any shape or size, 'the only limitation is whether it will fit through the door'. Anything and (almost) everything is possible, although Jane draws the line this side of pornography; although she is more than happy to reconstruct a building or sculpt a person or a pet. Some people know what they want when they come to order, others have not got a clue; but helping them decide on an appropriate cake is 'all part of the service'. The cakes are covered in soft roll-on icing with pastillage (hard icing) used for their intricate models, such as the Albert Memorial on display at the time of writing. It can be mixed up in any colour and, as you can imagine, can take weeks to work. So leave as much time as you possibly can for a special order; failing that they do carry stock fruit cakes, ready-iced, which can be personalized while you wait.

Cheeses, Breads and Ready-meals

■ **Partridges of Sloane Street, 132-4 Sloane Street SW1X 9AT ☎ 0171 730 0651 fax 0171 730 7104**, grocers to HM the Queen, is a food hall on a manageable scale. You can probably find more or less everything – good British cheeses, different breads, cakes and pastries, smoked fish, cooked meats and hams, jams, pickles, thoughtfully made up hampers and so on. Food-to-go, both in the form of ready-cooked meals and buffet food, is a speciality; succulent salmon fish-cakes have a justified reputation; as do the seemingly hundreds of salads freshly prepared every day.

Chocolates

■ **Rococo Chocolates, 321 Kings Road SW3 5EP ☎ 0171 352 5857 fax 0171 352 7360** is London's wittiest chocolate shop. Chantal Coady has a great eye and packs the shop with chocolate treasures from vulgar foil-wrapped jewellery to wild animals. For Valentine's Day you will be overwhelmed by an excess of hearts. After several years as a chocolatier, Chantal confessed she now prefers 'simple' chocolates and her 'artisan' bar from Belgium fits the bill. Made with a 60 per cent cocoa content and infused with such flavours as Earl Grey tea, thyme, cinnamon or pink pepper, they are startlingly original, with their delicate flavours and textures from the flavouring ingredient. She also sells 85-g (3¼-oz) Grand Cru bars from named cocoa beans, and Rococo House bars, including a 100 per cent cocoa solids.

The chocolates she sells are made by Ackermans *see page* 192 and Gerard Ronay *see page* 175. There is also a Traditional English Hand-dipped range in 'the Charbonnel & Walker mould'. These are mainly fruit- or flower-scented creams, such as lavender, rose, violet, banana, geranium and raspberry.

Recently she has launched her own house truffles using Manjari chocolate which is made with the Criollo cocoa bean. The Criollo has an extraordinarily vibrant fruity flavour and, as a result, her truffles are imbued with it. The ganache, a simple confection of double cream, Normandy butter and chocolate, is hand-dipped in chocolate to give it the thinnest of crunchy shells and then rolled in cocoa. Bitter-sweet, with a heady fruitiness that reminds you of raspberries, these a markedly good truffles.

Fish

Covent Garden Fishmongers, 37 Turnham Green Terrace W4 1RG ☎ 0181 995 9273 fax 0181 742 3899 is run by the 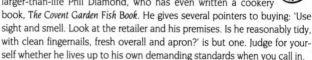 larger-than-life Phil Diamond, who has even written a cookery book, *The Covent Garden Fish Book*. He gives several pointers to buying: 'Use sight and smell. Look at the retailer and his premises. Is he reasonably tidy, with clean fingernails, fresh overall and apron?' is but one. Judge for yourself whether he lives up to his own demanding standards when you call in.

Smoked Haddock

■ Fishmonger **John Nicholson, 46 Devonshire Road W4 2HD ☎ 0181 994 0809** sells a good range of fish, but I single them out for their pearly-grey undyed smoked haddock. Mild and nutty, with the faintest touch of salt, it is a variation on the traditional Finnan haddock as the backbone is removed before curing. Once the fish has been lightly cured, it is briefly cold-smoked. I love it raw, cut into wafer-thin slices and tossed in olive oil, lemon juice and chopped flat-leaf parsley; it is also good lightly poached in milk enriched with a knob of butter, a bay leaf and a couple of peppercorns.

Wild Mushrooms

■ **Mortimer & Bennett, 33 Turnham Green Terrace W4 1RG ☎ 0181 995 4145 fax 0181 742 3068** is a tiny shop crammed full of interesting food from both here and abroad. There are usually plenty of wild mushrooms picked in Britain when the season is right, otherwise they are imported; made-up bags of Appledore Salad's leaves and shoots for a salad *see page* 143; fresh pasta from Micarelli *see page* 134; Duskin's apple juice *see page* 148; Fudges biscuits, including their light buttery Cheddar cheese wafers *see page* 92; fresh bread every day from & Clarke' s *see page* 185, La Fornaia and Innes *see page* 246; Martin Pitt's eggs *see page* 286; and various cheeses bought in from Neal's Yard Dairy *see below*. They have recently opened a second branch at **14 Cucumber Alley, Thomas Neal's, Shorts Gardens, London WC2H 9AW ☎ 0171 240 6277**.

Mushrooms, Pasta and Ready-meals

■ **Carluccio's, 28A Neal Street WC2H 9PS ☎ 0171 240 1487 fax 0171 497 1361** is fungiphile and TV chef Antonio Carluccio's shop. As you walk in, you are greeted by an impressive display of wild fungi, picked here when in season or imported when they are not. He has recently launched a collection of Italian bottled and packeted produce and gift boxes, and they are all displayed here. What I like best of all is the fresh food counter packed with pasta – try it studded with mushrooms – fresh sauces, grilled vegetables under oil, sleek thick sausages, different breads including pencil-thin freshly-made grissini, and all sorts of dishes-to-go. It is all very stylish, but then you would not expect anything less from the husband and wife team of Antonio and Priscilla (née Conran).

Bread

■ **Neal's Yard Bakery, 6 Neal's Yard WC2H 9DP ☎ 0171 836 5199** bake worthy bread; some breadies complain it is a little too heavy, others would not have it any other way. All the breads are made with 100 per cent organic flour from Shipton Mill *see page* 115 and sea salt. Apart from the plain wholemeal, they also produce 3-seed with linseed, poppy and sesame seeds; sunflower seed, cheese & herb; olive & garlic; and a breakfast loaf with fruit and malt.

Cheeses

Neal's Yard Dairy, 17 Shorts Gardens WC2H 9AT ☎ 0171 379 7646 fax 0171 240 2442 is the cheese shop for enthusiasts of on-farm cheeses from – and only from – small-scale makers for whom cheese-making is still a craft in the British Isles. Run by Randolph Hodgson and Jane Scotter, they buy direct from the farms because it enables them to build a relationship with the makers and so better understand the cheese. Most of the 100-odd cheeses sold at Neal's Yard are unpasteurized; but it is not as if it were a

MAP 9   LONDON   181

deliberate policy, rather, as Randolph explained 'It just so happens that the majority of the best cheeses are made with unpasteurized milk.

Expect to buy here the finest of our cheeses in peak condition; this is one of the very few cheese-shops that is not only air-conditioned but also ripens or matures cheeses in their state-of the-art humidity- and temperature-controlled cellars. The more I travel around, the more I come to realize just how important storing and ripening a cheese is. Too often they are ruined by being kept at the wrong temperature or in too dry an atmosphere; this, I assure you, never happens at Neal's Yard. Bringing a cheese on to peak condition is almost as important a craft as making it in the first place.

When Neal's Yard first opened, they used to make cheese. The link with cheese-making has not been severed, although the dairying side has moved to Kent and is run by Charlie Westhead. From there he makes various soft unpasteurized cheeses; a light, markedly fresh fromage frais achieved by hanging the curds to drain then lightly whipping them; Wealden Round, a Coulommiers-style cheese layered with parsley & garlic, chive, tarragon, spring onions, and black pepper & garlic; goats'-milk Perroche; and Finn, a wickedly rich full-fat mould-ripened cheese with a velvety texture and a deep flowery flavour. There are also thick crusty Greek-style and lighter low-fat yoghurts; as well as a proper crème fraîche made with rich double cream soured with a buttermilk starter. If British cheeses are now firmly on the culinary map, it is due in no small measure to the sterling work of the entire team at Neal's Yard.

Ridley Bagel Bakery, 13-15 Ridley Road, Dalston E8 2NP ☎ 0171 923 0666 fax 0171 923 0777 has shops all over London – in Clapton, Southgate, East Finchley, Hendon, Hendon Central, Bow and Finsbury Park – for their chewy creamy bagels. The Dalston shop, though, is the only one that stays open 24 hours a day, 7 days a week.

DALSTON
Bagels

The Cheeseboard, 26 Royal Hill SE10 8RT ☎/fax 0181 305 0401 is a small shop specializing in cheeses and all the things 'to go with – breads, farmhouse butter, pickles made by a friend, and wine'. There are about 50 British cheeses to choose from, with Swaledale ewes' milk *see page* 310 as the owner's current favourite.

GREENWICH
Cheeses etc.

■ The first to start up a specialist sausage shop, Bill O'Hagan of **O'Hagan's Sausage Shop, 192 Trafalgar Road SE10 9TZ ☎ 0181 858 3433 fax 0181 293 0072** is still going strong. Made with real skins, natural seasonings, fresh ingredients, proper cuts of fresh meat, his hand-linked sausages have a meat content that varies between 75 and 100 per cent, depending on the sausage, and he only resorts to bread and rusk 'when necessary to bind the ingredients together – but never to bulk up'. Apart from the more traditional ones, such as Cumberland in one long link, a herby Oxford, Lincolnshire with sage, they include Manchester 'that go back to around 1860 when a small amount of cloves gave them a distinct flavour'; or sweet Italian with pork & fennel; steak au poivre, made with prime minced beef, green peppercorns and cognac; and pork & cabbage, a mix of pork, red cabbage, apples and cider. Particular about how his sausages should be cooked, Bill says 'treat them with respect – cook them slowly and gently. As we only use natural skins, don't prick them and don't let them go too brown. Bake them in the oven on a slightly greased dish for 35-40 minutes at gas4/350°F/180°C'.

Sausages

HACKNEY
Smoked Salmon

One of the last remaining traditional salmon smokers in London's East End is **H. Forman & Son, 6 Queens Yard, White Post Lane E9 5EN ☎ 0181 985 0378 fax 0181 985 0180**. Salmon with a London-cure is traditionally milder-flavoured and silkier-textured than that from Scotland. Somewhat guarded about their techniques and times, all Lance Forman – whose family has been 90 years in the business – would tell me is that dry-curing is done with 'pure' salt. They smoke both farmed and wild salmon, with stocks of wild bought in season and frozen to be cured and smoked as and when it is needed throughout the year. They sell it in 450-g (1-lb) sliced packs, 675-g (1½-lb) pre-sliced or whole side and 900-g (2-lb) whole sides only.

HAMPSTEAD
Hams etc.

Belsize Village Deli, 39 Belsize Lane NW3 5AS ☎ 0171 794 4258 is a real village deli, with masses of own-made food to please the lazy locals. The style is hearty rather than fancy, but there is an honest approach. Own-cooked hams are generously carved off the bone; there are both sweet and savoury tarts; whole roast chickens; various cheeses; and bought-in breads, including a satisfying black rye.

Bread and Pâtisserie

■ A favourite haunt after a long walk on Hampstead Heath, **Louis Patisserie, 32 Heath Street NW3 6TE tel 0171 435 9908** bakes breads, croissants and all sorts of pastries, as well as Hungarian cakes like *dobos*, a confection of 'white' sponge chocolate buttercream topped with caramel; *rigo jancsi*, made from chocolate sponge with fresh chocolate cream running through the middle and chocolate on top; and *geszdenye*, a rich mixture of chocolate sponge and fresh cream with chestnut and brandy.

HIGHBURY
Aberdeen Angus Beef

Frank Godfrey, 7 Highbury Park N5 1QJ ☎ 0171 226 2425 fax 0171 254 1122 is one of London's few butchers licensed to sell pure-bred Aberdeen Angus beef. What this means is they sell Aberdeen Angus and only Aberdeen Angus, so even your mince will be from that noble beast. For a butcher shop as smart as Frank Godfrey it is a welcome pleasure to see several 'bits and pieces', cheaper cuts such as shoulder steaks, from the 'leg o'mutton highly trimmed and cut fine' and skirt, which is a cheap cut much neglected in Britain. At the other end of the price range there was fore-rib on the bone for roasting. They can also be relied on for caul fat, useful for wrapping around home-made sausages.

Cheeses, etc.

■ **La Fromagerie, 30 Highbury Park N5 2AA ☎/fax 0171 359 7440** is run by the indefatigable Patricia Michelson. It is a veritable treasure-trove of good food, the sort of shop in which you should spend hours just finding out what is in stock. At the back are the air-conditioned cheese rooms which double up as maturing rooms and I was overwhelmed by the choice, admittedly not much of it British. They do stock a few British cheeses, notably Mrs Appleby's Cheshire *see page* 229, Bonchester *see page* 324, all the Blues from Ticklemore *see page* 85, Tala *see page* 42 and Spenwood and Wigmore *see page* 22; but I could not help thinking Patricia's heart lies with France and Italy. What they also sell are goodies to go with cheese: apples from Brogdale *see page* 146, a farmhouse whey butter, breads from Innes *see page* 246 and & Clarke's *see page* 185, as well as some specials that are baked expressly for the shop. These include a dark rye with pecan or lexia raisins which marry well with Beenleigh Blue; and Neapolitan biscuits with nuts or figs.

Using produce from the shop, Patricia also has own-made pizzas laden with Mozzarella, crespolini, tortillas, baked ricotta, tortellini stuffed with ricotta & spinach or wild mushrooms & truffle cheese, two cheesecakes, one baked in the Bavarian-style the other creamy with uncooked Mascarpone. In season she sells wild mushrooms and the odd fresh vegetable.

C. Lidgate, 110 Holland Park Avenue W11 4UA ☎ 0171 727 8243 fax 0171 229 7160 is my local butcher and very lucky I am too. Run by David Lidgate, the fourth generation in the family, the quality of the meat is first-rate. David's brother has just started farming in Iver and we await the beef from the Angus Moray grays with interest. Pork is 'naturally' and outdoor-reared, poultry is free-range and – reared slowly at Christmas – there are Kelly's turkeys *see page* 103. Meat is properly hung – lamb for about 7 days and beef for anything up to 3 weeks – and nothing is too much trouble. If you want a piece of meat specially butchered, boned or rolled, 'it's all part of the service'; even Violet's marrow bone is chopped to a manageable size.

HOLLAND PARK
Meat, Poultry and Pies

Also particularly worth a mention are the pies. Made on a daily basis with fresh vegetables, own-made butter-based pastry and good cuts of meat, these are proper old-fashioned pies with plenty of flavour and thick flour-based sauces in 1-, 2-, 4-, 6-, 8-, 10-, 12-, 14-, and 16-size portions, made to order even at a few hours' notice. Steak & Burgundy has leeks onions and mushrooms, a touch of redcurrant jelly to sweeten the wine-based sauce and chunks of tender beef. Another favourite is the cottage pie with a blanket of cheesy mash under which nestles a gutsy mince spiked with onion and carrots. Lidgate's also sell game, ducks and gulls' eggs, a fair selection of on-farm British cheeses, Martin Pitt eggs *see page* 286, and various preserves and bottled sauces.

■ **Jereboams, 6 Clarendon Road W11 3AA ☎ 0171 727 9359 fax 0171 792 3672** is perhaps stronger on French than British cheeses, but they still have a good selection. Look out for a nicely matured 16-month Keen's Cheddar and their butter *see page* 242. Other cheeses include Gospel Green *see page* 270, Tymsboro' *see page* 16, Anne Wigmore's range *see page* 22, as well as Innes' cheeses *see page* 246 with, very occasionally, their crème fraîche.

Cheese and Butter

Barstow & Barr, 24 Liverpool Road N1 0PU ☎/fax 0171 359 4222 is a small but inviting cheese shop, with a choice of predominantly on-farm British cheeses. Some cheeses they ripen themselves (there is a humidifier in the shop to keep the air suitably moist), and they sell cheeses such as Isle of Mull *see page* 321, Wensleydale Richard III *see page* 309, and Bonnet *see page* 367 which are all too rarely seen down south. They also stock whey butter from Duckett's *see page* 237 and bread from & Clarke's *see page* 185.

ISLINGTON
Cheeses

■ **Cecil & Co, 393 Liverpool Road N1 1NP ☎ 0171 700 6707 fax 0171 700 5738** was once only a wholesaler supplying the restaurant trade. Now they have opened a shop as well, so the general public – the likes of you and me – can go and buy there. It is worth it for their fat juicy lobsters.

Lobsters

■ **Dugans Chocolates, 149a Upper Street N1 1RA ☎ 0171 354 4666 fax 0171 837 4300** is a tiny shop crammed full of chocolates. Most everything is bought in, but they do make a rich – almost meltingly – moist chocolate fudge, and a vanilla fudge that pales in comparison. They will bake chocolate sponge cakes – and indeed any kind of cake – to order.

Chocolates

■ **Steve Hatt, 88-90 Essex Road N1 8LU ☎/fax 0171 226 3963** is always bursting at the gills with people queuing to buy the fish. At that rate

Fish and Game

of turnover, the fish remains fresh and it does appear to be in sparkling condition on close inspection. I do, however, sometimes wonder why everyone makes *such* a fuss of Steve, dubbing him London's legendary fish-monger. Admittedly, his range is good and the display enormous; I was drawn by brill from Devon, Dover soles, squid also from Devon, turbot and chicken turbot, cod 'filleted less than 15 hours out of the seas' and cod flaps (cheeks) – I wish more fishmongers would sell these as they are great in soups and stews. He also has game in fur or feather, or oven-ready; and when I visited last winter, there were some particularly choice hares hanging up.

Scottish Beef and Cheeses

■ Butcher **James Elliott, 96 Essex Road N1 8LU ☎ 0171 226 3658** comes highly recommended for his beef from Scotland, hung for 3 weeks until 'you can cut it with a feather, it's so tender'.
He also has an imaginative cheese counter which features several of James Aldridge's cheeses *see page* 262.

Cheeses and Ready-meals

■ **Limoncello, 402 St John Street EC1V 4NJ ☎ 0171 713 1678 fax 0171 437 4541** is a very cheery shop, painted a bright lemon-yellow. Recently opened, when I visited early in spring I could not help thinking they had not quite 'got up to speed' yet, but they have 'plans' and I hope they materialize, as Limoncello is just the sort of food shop I approve of. There is a small but well thought-out collection of craft foods: British on-farm cheese, good breads, bacon from Richard Woodall *see page* 62, Duskin apple juices *see page* 148, and Fudges Bakery biscuits *see page* 92; plus a few useful and unusual veg (with plans to grow leaves in the garden out back) and plenty of fresh food-to-go! Cooked in the basement by Gwen Sampe and Roger David, both ex-Arts Cafe chefs, the menu varies. You may find lentil or creamy chicken with almond soups, chicken breasts stuffed with ricotta and Parmesan and wrapped in Parma ham, chicken liver pâté, spicy Italian sausage sauce for pasta, char-grilled vegetables, and puddings like chocolate and rosemary crema cotta or pears poached in white wine.

Pâtisserie

▦ **Nadell Patisserie, Units 4-5, Angel House, 9 White Lion Street N1 9HJ ☎ 0171 833 2461 fax 0171 713 5036** supplies several of London's best shops, restaurants and hotels with a glorious array of pastries, tartes, mousses, gâteaux – all impeccably finished and made with 'proper' ingredients. They will, however, supply you directly if you order in advance and do not mind picking up your order.

Bread and Baked Goods

■ A laid-back sort of place with a few tables and chairs for coffee and pastries, **Patisserie Bliss, 428 St Johns Street EC1V 4NJ ☎ 0171 837 3720** sells a small range of own-baked goods baked in the basement. Breads include wholemeal, poppy and sunflower seed, Parmesan and 'whatever else Tim the baker fancies'; flaky light plain croissants and pleasant almond ones stuffed with an almond-flavoured crème pâtissière; sticky pain aux raisins; baked cheesecakes; and a range of savoury tarts, including Stilton & spinach, anchovy, tomato & olive, and braised onion & walnut.

Polish Specialities

■ Although anyone can shop here, the **Polish Catholic Club Store, 2-4 Devonia Road N1 8JJ ☎ 0171 359 7237** is really a club for members of the Polish church, with proceeds going to charity. You can find it in the basement down the stairs by the church of Our Lady of Czestochowa and you enter under the sign *sklep* (Polish for shop). They sell a moist yeast cake, plain or stuffed with plums and twirled around a mass of poppy seeds; various breads, including Kolos Bakery *see*

MAP 9   LONDON   185

page 301; and a baked cheesecake made with curd cheese and eggs that is sweet but sharpened with lemon juice and smoothly textured. They also stock various sausages; juicy smoked pork ribs for cooking with cabbage; bags of poppy seeds; and proper *gryczana* (buckwheat), just the thing for blinis. Be warned, however, opening hours are erratic, but there is usually somebody there on Saturday mornings or Sundays after church.

KENSINGTON
Bread

& Clarke's, 122 Kensington Church Street W8 4BH ☎ 0171 229 2190 is owned by Sally Clarke of Clarke's Restaurant fame (next door). A small shop with just a couple of tables should you want to sit down for a quick cup of coffee and one of their delightful cakes or pizzas, it sells what some people consider to be the best bread in London.

What makes it so special is the combination of flavours and textures. Different flours, different shapes, textures and ingredients all combine to make a highly individual range of bread. There is a cheery yellow cornbread, Cheddar from a milk, butter & cheese dough, apricot, hazelnut & raisins, sultana & sesame, green olive & herb, black olive, sun-dried tomato, walnut, buttermilk enriched with Normandy butter, pane Toscana with low salt, little yeast and 'no real flavour of its own so it's perfect for eating with strongly flavoured Italian food', sour-dough, and a 100 per cent wholemeal that 'looks like a Hovis'. In the French line there are baguettes, ficelles, plain and raisin & walnut brioche and croissants.

Throughout the day, cakes, tarts, focaccia and pizzas appear piping hot from the kitchen; and if you think of pizza as dull or leaden, you obviously have not tried a slice of theirs. A brisk, oil-enriched dough laden with char-grilled vegetables will surely convince you otherwise. They also make nutty, round and paper-thin oatmeal biscuits, ideal with cheese; an ever-varying choice of jams and pickles 'depending on the stress and strain of the kitchen and what's in season'. There is a deep vivid-orange red pepper purée, bottled onions, marmalade, pesto olive paste or, in winter but made in summer, a rumpertoft (berries in alcohol). & Clarke's even make their own mustards – Tewkesbury, stout, lemon & honey, and Roman with pine-nuts and almonds. Their truffles are excellent: soft, silky and with a full blast of sharp chocolate, they are made with cream and chocolate, hand-rolled, hand-dipped in cocoa and made in just one flavour, 'plain – and the best'.

They stock cheeses from Neal's Yard Dairy *see page* 180 and their yoghurts, Innes cheese *see page* 246, Duskin Farm's apple juice *see page* 148, vinegars from Womersley Crafts & Herbs *see page* 312 and the occasional vegetable in season, including seakale *see page* 170. This is an imaginative shop where you can always find at least one treasure lurking.

Breads and
Ready-meals

■ Under new management, **Hamlins of Kensington, 3 Abingdon Road W8 6AH ☎ 0171 376 2191** shows signs of becoming a good food shop. Run by a brother-and-sister team, they prepare plenty of food-to-go and sell various cheeses, salads, pâtés and terrines, as well as own-baked breads, melt-in-the mouth buttery cheese sablés, pert rosemary-flavoured biscuits and rich chocolate truffles.

Bread

■ **Pierre Pechon, 27 Kensington Church Street W8 4LL ☎ 0171 937 9574** – with branches at **127 Queensway W2 4JS ☎ 0171 229 0746** and **4 Chepstow Road, W2 5BH ☎ 0171 229 5289** sell French sticks, croissants and a wide range of breads. New this year are their spelt flour bread and sugar-free banana scones *see Doves Farm Foods, page* 21 baked every Wednesday.

Organic Meat and Poultry

■ Butchers **W. J. Miller, 14 Stratford Road W8 6QD ☎ 0171 937 1777** make a point of selling organic (to Organic Farmers & Growers standards) beef, lamb and chicken. As well as the run of the mill cuts and joints, they make various sausages, roast chickens, cook salt beef for hot sandwiches, and prepare 7-spiced lamb kebabs with fresh red peppers, coriander and parsley; as well as Lebanese *sis tawouk* (chicken marinated in garlic, lemon juice and olive oil).

KENTISH TOWN
Fish and Pure Meat

B. & M. Seafoods, 258 Kentish Town Road NW5 2AA ☎ 0171 485 0346 is the London outlet for Pure Meat Direct *see page* 18. Food-writer Richard Ehrlich buys 'everything that has walked on earth or swum in the sea' from there and particularly likes the unusual 'sole-type' fish, such as dabs, witches or megrim, and the occasional octopus or red mullet that come direct from Devon.

Mushroom Accessories

■ **Mycologue, 47 Spencer Rise NW5 1AR ☎ 0171 485 7063 fax 0171 284 4058**, run by Martin Lewy, supplies equipment and accessories for mushroom collectors. There are field knives, complete with a natural bristle brush and a curved 'pruner' blade for clean accurate cutting (a deluxe version even has a compass in case you get lost); mushroom collecting baskets, drying racks, socks for 'sartorial correctness for well-dressed mushroom hunters'; books; posters and packets of common, oyster, shiitake and shaggy cap mushroom spawn. Although these do need to be grown in controlled conditions, some enthusiasts scatter them on their lawns and sit back hoping for results.

KNIGHTS-BRIDGE
Muffins

Beverley Hills Bakery, 3 Egerton Terrace SW3 2BX ☎ 0171 584 4401 fax 0171 584 1106 bakes a proper rich New York cheesecake, with cream cheese and sour cream, and proper American muffins. Real muffins, according to owner Mark Peterson, should have 'a good full-blown top. It's OK if its cracked, all it means is the mixture has overflowed on top. In the States we like them that way. The texture should be fairly light and, when you squeeze one, fairly soft. Cut one open and if there are tunnels or holes, it means the batter is over-mixed'. Flour is all-important for an authentic muffin, 'English flour doesn't work as well, so we use French cake flour. As for making them, first you mix the dry ingredients together, then the wet ones and finally you mix the two together, folding in gently until the flour disappears. You should never over-mix'.

Muffins are baked every morning and come in two sizes: mini, a 2-bite size; and large, which is quite hefty. Blueberry, the best seller, is made using a buttermilk batter with yoghurt for extra sharpness and it is soft and gooey with plenty of fruit. Other flavours include double chocolate with sugar-free cocoa and Belgian chocolate; ginger with a crisp spiced flavour; sharp and crumbly lemon made with lemon juice and zest; carrot; honey bran; and pecan orange. Depending on the time of year, Mark introduces other flavours, such as mincemeat 'it tasted brilliant but didn't sell', apple & cinnamon and, around Thanksgiving, pumpkin, made with pumpkin purée and raisins. Muffin gift baskets, with as many as 18 to 118 muffins, and their crisp buttery cookies can be delivered anywhere in London. Muffins tins can be sent all over the country. Otherwise, pop in for a muffin; there is a small café open all week, including Sunday mornings to catch the crowds from the Brompton Oratory just opposite.

■ The Food Halls at **Harrods, Knightsbridge SW1X 7XL ☎ 0171 730 1234 fax 0171 581 3946** leave me dazed – not only because there is so much to take in but also because there are so many people. Shopping, and by that I mean proper shopping for a meal rather than buying the odd-treat, there is not an experience I relish. The Food Halls (and the whole shop) seems jam-packed with tourists who have come merely to gawp, buy tea and other little luxuries with a Harrods label and they always seem to stop dead bang in the middle of an aisle just in front of me. If you persevere, however, you will be rewarded as there are good things to buy – charcuterie, cheeses, breads, and cakes in the done-up-to-dazzle new cake 'parlour' are just a few. The cheese counter is one of the best in London, look out for all the Food Lovers' favourites. Opposite the charcuterie counter you can also find some of London's snazziest party-food-to-go.

Cheeses, Charcuterie Cakes and Party Food

■ **The Fifth Floor Foodmarket, Harvey Nichols, Knightsbridge SW1X 7RJ ☎ 0171 235 5000 fax 0171 235 5020** is a happy marriage of style and content. Modern in look, with award-winning own-label packaging, The Foodmarket was conceived as a one-stop shop where you can buy the best food. The meat counter has a good selection of both Continental- and British-butchered meat with poultry from Munson's *see page* 102, Eldon Blue pork from Sutherlands *see page* 122, well-hung beef from Scotland, Goodman's geese *see page* 295 and bronze turkeys at Christmas. The fish counter always seems well stocked, with fish coming up from Cornwall – last time I bought startling fresh red mullet and slip soles. On-farm cheeses are well represented with Old Scotland *see page* 265, Mrs Kirkham's Lancashire *see page* 159, and Appleby's Cheshire *see page* 229. Bread, cakes and pastries come from various bakeries, including The Village Bakery *see page* 57 and Fudges *see page* 92; chocolates are from Holdsworth *see page* 66. There are plenty of own-label jams, mustards, olive oils, pasta, etc; as well as a good selection of vegetables and fruit. In fact, most everything for a good meal. If I have one criticism, it is that their deli counter – and food-to-go, in particular – does not quite meet the general high standard. While you are there, the café – with its huge atrium-like roof – serves a good cappuccino and very jolly light lunches. Also worth knowing about are the tastings and evening workshops held on The Fifth Floor. They vary from a session all about game to one on luxury foods, taking in foie gras, caviar, smoked salmon, Stilton and Dom Pérignon. For further details, telephone 0171 581 7562.

Meat, Poultry, Fish and Cheeses

Jefferson's Seafoods, 17 Clifton Road W9 1SY ☎ 0171 266 0811 fax 0171 266 0166 always has a good display of fresh fish laid out on ice. Even when the sun is at its hottest it remains pert and sweet-smelling. They cure their own mild gravlax with plenty of fresh dill and have recently embarked on sashimi and sushi in true Japanese style.

LITTLE VENICE
Fish

■ **The Realfood Store, 14 Clifton Road W9 1SS ☎ 0171 266 1162 fax/delivery 0171 266 1550** has just expanded into food-to-go from a new kitchen, complete with char-grill. They make 3 sandwiches that change daily so you might find a dairy version with Keen's Cheddar with own-made apricot chutney in & Clarke's walnut bread; a vegan grilled peppers with own-made lentil paste in & Clarke's olive bread; and another with tuna, own-made lime dip and salad greens in & Clarke's herb bread – these are 'realsandwiches'. They also make soups of the season each day: watercress & wild garlic; curried parsnip; fresh pasta sauces, savoury tarts and puddings, such as pear tarte tatin; dried fruit salad compote; and semolina with blood orange syrup.

Ready-meals

They stock a good range of real foods or, as I once described them, 'chosen because owner Kevin Gould believes they have been produced with integrity'. So you will find organic meat from Swaddles Green Farm *see page* 233, ice-cream from Rocombe Farm *see page* 84, wild fungi from Mrs Tee *see page* 123, cheese from Neal's Yard Dairy *see page* 180, honey from Denrosa *see page* 373, Rachel's' Dairy butter and cream *see page* 380, and organic eggs. In fact, several of the best foods are all packed into this first-rate shop.

MARYLEBONE

Fish Poultry and Game

Cheeses and Ready-meals

Blagden Fishmongers, 65-66 Paddington Street W1M 3RR ☎ 0171 935 8321 have a good range of fish, poultry and game in season. Particularly worthwhile is their plump, lightly salted and very succulent smoked cod's roe.

■ **Villandry, 89 Marylebone High Street W1M 3DE** ☎ **0171 487 3816 fax 0171 486 1370** is run by the diminutive Jean Charles Carrarini. It is a very chic shop, well laid out with shelves neatly packed with enticingly labelled tins and packets. Unlike some, however, this is one shop where food tastes as good as it looks. Cheeses and crème fraîche come from Neal's Yard Dairy *see page* 180, jams and pickles from Wendy Brandon *see page* 378, bread from & Clarke's *see page* 185, sausages from Randall & Aubin, chocolates from The Chocolate Society *see page* 310 and salads from Appledore Salads *see page* 143. The kitchens serve both the day-time Dining Room (expect such pleasures as Warm Salad of Guinea Fowl with Beetroot) as well as preparing pâtés, terrines, savoury and sweet tarts, soups, pizzas, biscuits and cakes for the shop.

MAYFAIR

Teas

For one of the most original teas in Britain, try the **Four Seasons Hotel, Hamilton Place W1A 1AZ** ☎ **0171 499 0888 fax 0171** **493 6629**. Their anniversary teas – one for each season of the year – are based around a special tea by Twinings; and the menu for the tea has been fancifully created by executive chef Eric Deblonde. Autumn is the time for Yunnan tea and brings sandwiches of herring, mushroom & exotic cress, scrambled egg & smoked salmon, and braised quail in Yunnan tea, all in complementary flavoured breads; light scones with own-made pineapple and passion fruit jam; pastries such as almond & pear tart, kumquat tart with meringue, gelée of Sharon fruit; and the delicate sorbet is pomegranate and orange lemon tea in a miniature chocolate tea cup. Served with style, you can enjoy it in the comfort of their lounge.

Pâtisserie and Vienoiserrie

■ I hear tell that good *Vienoiserrie* and pâtisserie can be bought from a pastry counter in restaurant **La Madeleine, 5.Vigo Street W1A 1AH** ☎ **0171 734 8353**. More reports please.

NOTTING HILL

Breads and Pastries

Fat Rascals, 52 Ledbury Road W11 2AJ ☎/fax **0171 792 8843** have buttery croissants with just the right hint of yeast, pain au chocolat, various savoury and open fruit tarts, and a small choice of breads, such as baguettes, ciabatta, focaccia, crostini, and a rough country bread baked for them. They also serve coffees and chocolate from the country-style shop.

Food Boxes

■ Computer buffs note, **The Fresh Food Co** is now on-line on **100600.3527 @ COMPUSERVE.COM 326 Portobello Road W10 5RU** ☎ **0181 969 0351 fax 0181 964 8050**. From here, Thoby Young runs subscription and bespoke national home-delivery services. At agreed regular intervals or on a one-off basis he will deliver a Cornish fish box, an organic vegetable or meat box (both to Soil Association standards), a game box; or a newly launched dairy box that is so new I have yet to see its contents. There are also plans for a bread box. The bespoke service is obviously more flexible and they will make up orders from their suppliers according to your needs. At Christmas they make up hampers and in the autumn can send boxes of traditional apples from Brogdale Horticultural Trust *see page* 146.

■ At the top end of Portobello Road is **Lisboa Patisserie, 57 Golborne Road W10 5NR ☎ 0181 968 5242**, with cakes rated by Portuguese food writer Edite Vieira as 'almost better than we can get back home'. Everyone's favourite is *pasties de natas* a flaky pastry case filled with a rich custard made with cream and eggs and baked until it catches on top. Edite tells me they really do have a full range of Portuguese cakes; it also includes *bolos de arroz*, similar to a muffin but made with rice flour or *bolos de coco* with coconut. They also serve very good coffee.

Portuguese Cakes and Pastries

■ **Mr Christian's Delicatessen, 11 Elgin Crescent W11 2JA ☎ 0171 229 0501 fax 0171 727 6980** has much improved over the past couple of years. There are some good pastries and interesting own-cooked food-to-go. They stock Innes and Montgomery cheeses *see pages* 246 *and* 239, Denhay hams *see page* 89 and Rocombe ice-creams *see page* 84. Saturday, come rain or shine, sees a huge table outside piled high with all sorts of breads from La Fornaia's ciabatta to pain de campagne as well as croissants, brioches and bagels.

Breads, Cheeses and Pastries

■ Every Thursday afternoon between 14.00 and 18.00 at the top end of the **Portobello Road** under the Westway flyover, there is a small **open-air food market**. Apart from two flourishing organic vegetable stalls, various own-made chutneys, jams and life-enhancing elixirs, you can buy meat and poultry from Longwood Farm *see page* 254, and some very interesting breads from The Celtic Baker. These include a fruity bara brith, Welsh barley bread, chunky well-flavoured pain de campagne and a crusty San Francisco sourdough.

Vegetables, Breads, Meat and poultry

■ Charles Campion, of Save-Our-Shops fame, loves **Joe's Bakery, 5 All Saints Road W11 1HA ☎ 0171 221 1083**. He rates it best for Afro-Caribbean bread and found a visit there a revelation. 'Joe has homesick customers who travel from as far away as Croydon to shop here. The Caribbean breads tend to be made from "milled dough" – a process where the dough is knocked back mechanically to give it a very close texture. They also contain some very un-English ingredients like coconut and molasses. On sale are hard dough, the strangely named Mastiff, as well as sweet Bajan breads'.

Caribbean Breads

■ **Sisi Edmiston, flat 1, 17 Stanley Gardens W11 2NG ☎ 0171 229 6722 fax 0171 792 8092** makes fruit cakes which are so meticulously decorated you could almost mistake them for a dried nut arrangement. Made to a family recipe which uses butter, rice flour, molasses and masses of dried Australian sultanas, Californian raisins and Greek currants, first she soaks the fruit in vintage cognac, sherry, apricot brandy and fresh lime juice for at least 7 days to plump it up, then adds nuts and even more dried fruit, such as apricots, dates, peaches, grated pineapple and grated carrots 'to give it colour'. Then she adds a minimal amount of rice flour to bind the mixture together 'the cakes are about 98 per cent fruit', a little glycerine to keep them moist and vanilla and almond essences for extra flavour. Baked in 12.5, 15, 17.5 and 20-cm (5, 6, 7 and 8-in) rounds or 17.5-cm (7-in) squares, they are matured for 'as long as I can possibly manage' and come heavily encrusted with glazed nuts and undyed cherries. In texture more like a boiled than a traditional fruit cake, they are very moist, succulent and – indeed – very fruity.

Fruit Cakes

Cheeses, Pastries and Ready-meals

■ **Tom's, 226 Westbourne Grove W11 2RH ☎ 0171 221 8818 fax 0171 221 7717** is an originally designed shop, but that is only to be expected from Tom – son of Terence – Conran. There are some good British cheeses, mostly supplied by Neal's Yard Dairy *see page* 180 as well as from Innes *see page* 246, Lincolnshire Poacher *see page* 166, and Gospel Green with their cyder *see page* 270. Sausages and bacon come from Merrivale *see page* 49; biscuits from Fudges bakery *see page* 92; potatoes and cardoons to order from Thistledoons *see page* 167; and bread and croissants from – amongst others – Bagatelle *see page* 192. The pastry counter is usually well stocked with very French-looking tarts, parfaits, florentines, amandines, individual bread & butter or summer puddings. The food-to-go counter is awash with such trendy foods as cooked Puy lentils with ginger, spinach & chilli, char-grilled vegetables, char-grilled chicken, braised fennel with tomato salsa, pissaladière, and baby quiches.

OXFORD STREET

Bread

Selfridges Food Hall, 400 Oxford Street W1A 1AB ☎ 0171 629 1234 fax 0171 495 8321 has improved tremendously in the past couple of years and makes an effort to seek out craft products to sell in the snazzy white-tiled shop. The bakery is particularly good and look out for The Loaves and Fishes Irish brown bread, properly made with Irish flour, buttermilk and bicarbonate of soda.

PRIMROSE HILL

Ready-meals

The food-to-go is adored by some but considered over-priced and a bit precious by others at **Traiteur Pagnol, 170 Regents Park Road NW1 8XN ☎ 0171 483 0401 fax 0171 916 1983**. There is no denying Melanie Pini is a good cook, but she takes her food and herself so terribly seriously. I mean anyone who says – and here I quote from the *Sunday Telegraph* – 'my food is stylish, beautiful and elegant and that's the way I strive to present myself' is bound to put a few backs up.

ROEHAMPTON

Sausages

St Marcus Fine Foods, 1 Rockingham Close, off Priory Lane SW15 5RW ☎ 0181 878 1898 fax 0181 876 0761 specialize in sausages from here and abroad. You will find *biltong*, *droëwors* (an air-dried pepperoni-style beef sausage), *boerewors* (a coiled fresh beef sausage spiced with coriander), and lamb, beef & pork *sosaties* from South Africa. There is also a coarse pork sausage flavoured with bay, basil & Chianti from Italy; a Hungarian version with sweet paprika; Lyonnais truffle (made with truffles, pistachio nuts and French brandy); breakfast pork; Cumberland with sage & thyme; and chicken & cheese. All the sausages contain at least 87 per cent meat. They also sell fresh meat, smoked sausages, smoked beef fillet and wild boar.

ST JAMES'S

Cheese and Ham

Paxton & Whitfield, 93 Jermyn Street SW1Y 6JE ☎ 0171 930 0259 fax 0171 321 0621 have been cheesemongers since 1797. Surrounded by Gentlemen's clubs and Gentlemen's outfitters, they have a reputation for being conservative in their outlook but, in fact, they have as good as selection as most for the newer on-farm British cheeses. Of course you will find well-matured Cheddars from Mrs Montgomery *see page* 239, and Quickes *see page* 86 and Stilton from Cropwell Bishop *see page* 212, but you can also buy Bonchester *see page* 324, Yarg *see page* 50, Golden Cross *see page* 274 and Cerney *see page* 118. They also stock York and Bradenham hams from Harris's and, at Christmas-time, you are bound to see gentlemen queuing up to collect their orders. Recently they have started a Cheese Society and members receive a newsletter, special offers and invitations to cheese tastings.

Brown's, 37-39 Charlbert Street NW8 6JN ☎ 0171 722 8237 do not exactly put themselves out when it comes to displaying their fish, but when it comes to quality and service they come well recommended. They stock a wide range of shellfish and wet fish – with Dover sole, turbot, hake and skate – and also have a smoked fish counter.

Fish and Shellfish

■ Food Lover Caroline Aitcheson particularly recommends the rye bread from **Le Connaisseur, 49 Charlbert Street NW8 6JN ☎ 0171 722 7070**. It has a sweet-sour – almost liquorice-like – flavour and, unlike some, is quite soft-textured. Baker Josef Keppeln also makes various other breads, proper Danish rings, baked cheesecakes and crisp buttery palmiers large enough to be called elephants' ears.

Bread and Baked Goods

■ **Panzers Delicatessen, 13-19 Circus Road NW8 6PB ☎ 0171 722 8596** is still reckoned to be *the* place to buy smoked salmon in North-west London. There is a good choice of grades and cures and it is all hand-carved with great finesse by Alec into paper-thin slices. I could stand watching him for hours. The shop has a wide range of deli foods, including breads, interesting vegetables, fruits and salads, displayed outside.

Smoked Salmon

■ My sister Sandra, who knows about such things, thinks **Platters, 83-85 Allitsen Road NW8 7AS ☎ 0171 722 5352** has some of the best fried gefilte fish, egg & onion, and chopped liver around. They also sell own-made salads and, at lunch-time, do a roaring trade in sandwiches. Their other branch is at **10 Hallswelle Parade, Temple Fortune NW11 0DL ☎ 0181 455 7345**.

Jewish Specialities

John & Sons, 103 Uxbridge Road W12 8NL ☎/fax 0181 743 9224 specialize in Yugoslavian food. Apart from huge jars of whole red peppers or red pepper sauce, smoked ribs and belly of pork, they also import pickled cabbages, *kisseli kupus*. These arrive as whole cabbages packed in barrels of their pickling mixture of salt, water, vinegar and bay leaves and are left to pickle for a couple of months in the basement. Yugoslavs buy them whole, unwrap the leaves and stuff them with a spicy meat for *sarna*. They also sell & Clarke's bread *see page* 185, rye bread from Kolos Bakery *see page* 301, piping-hot *bîrek* (cheese and spinach pie), and – rather intriguingly – Napareuli, Stalin's favourite wine.

Yugoslavian Specialities

Jenny Linford ☎ 0181 348 7767 fax 0171 278 9655 author of *Food Lovers' London* will take any food lover shopping in Soho on a Gastro-Soho Tour. With true cosmopolitan taste, she starts her tour in Chinatown, breaks for a coffee at Maison Bertaux, then takes in the 'European' – with Milroy's Whisky Shop in Greek Street, Angeluccis Coffee shop in Frith Street, I Camisa in Old Compton Street 'excellent olives, hams and salamis', Lina Stores in Brewer Street 'best for pasta', Randall & Aubin 'wonderful bacon and good butchery' and ends up at Simply Sausages in Berwick Street. With a maximum of 10 people, tours are on Saturday mornings, last about 2 hours and must be booked in advance. Jenny guides you through the morass of foreign produce, points out the goodies, answers any questions and generally tells you how to use or cook anything and everything you have possibly never seen before.

Gastronomic Tours

■ Fishmongers **Richards, 21 Brewer Street W1R 3FL ☎ 0171 437 1358** have a wide selection of fresh – and I mean fresh – fish. Service is particularly helpful and there is always advice on hand on what fish to choose for what, how to cook it and which vegetables to buy round the corner in Rupert Street market.

Fish

**SOUTH
KENSINGTON**
**French
Breads**

**Bagatelle, 44 Harrington Road SW7 3NB ☎ 0171 581 1551
fax 0171 591 0517** bake possibly the best *baguettes et ficelles* in
town. For true authenticity, master baker Jacky Lesellier insists on
using French flour, French yeast and baking in a French oven. Unlike ours,
French flours are graded according to their physical qualities, determined
by two factors – elasticity and refinement. In all, he imports 9 different
flours for his different breads, which include earthy sour doughs, *pain de
campagne* and *pain biologique*. He also makes light and glorious buttery croissants, pains au chocolat, open fruit tarts, gâteaux and mousses, as well as
finger or full party food which must be ordered at least 72 hours in advance.

Cheeses

■ Cheesemongers **Jereboams, 24 Bute Street SW7 3EX ☎ 0171 225
2232**. For full details see Jereboams, Holland Park *page 183*.

**SPITALFIELDS
Organic
Foods**

Every Sunday, **The Organic Food Market, Spitalfields Market, Brush-
field Street E1 6AA ☎ 0171 247 6590** is held in the old wholesale
market. There are about 20 stalls, selling organic flour, meat, fruit, vegetables and cheese (all to Soil Association standards).

**STREATHAM
Polish
Specialities**

**Korona Delicatessen, 30 Streatham High Road SW16 1BZ ☎ 0181
769 6647** is the haunt of many a knowing Pole. In late summer/early
autumn it has its own team of mushroom gatherers. Their finds are made
up into wild mushroom *pierogi* (the Polish answer to tortelloni), stuffed
cabbage leaves which are similar – in looks but not in taste – to dolmades,
necklaces of dried ceps threaded on string, or jars of mixed pickled wild
mushrooms in vinegar. Throughout the year they also sell countless
smoked sausages, sauerkraut made with white wine and vinegar and *pierogi*
stuffed with cheese & potato or meat which are best eaten with *smetana*, a
cultured sour cream which they sell in cartons.

**SWISS
COTTAGE
Chocolates**

Ackermans, 9 Goldhurst Terrace NW6 3HX ☎ 0171 624 2742 makes
Spartan sensible chocolates which contrast starkly with the fulsome richness of some imported chocolates. I love their dark dense hand-made mint
wafer thins that are paper-thin, quite roughly finished and jump with a dry
mintiness. Their violet and rose creams are exactly how they should be, soft
smooth centres imbued with perfume and surrounded by a plain chocolate.
Cherries soaked in brandy for 2 years then dipped in fondant and finally
dipped in chocolate, are another favourite and I also like their truffles,
doused with Irish whiskey, marc de Champagne, Cointreau, cognac or rum.

Ready-meals

■ **Gourmet Away, 3 Goldhurst Terrace NW6 3HX ☎ 0171 625 8525**
specializes in freshly cooked oven-ready meals conveniently packed in
microwave-proof packs. They also sell various on-farm British cheeses,
breads and pâtisseries.

**WANDS-
WORTH
Fish and
Shellfish**

**Condon Fishmongers, 363 Wandsworth Road SW8 2JJ ☎ 0171 622
2934** is an unpretentious fishmongers, but none the worse for that. They
have a good array of wet fish – hake, soles, brill, trout, sea trout, wild or
farmed salmon, and witches. They also have plenty of shellfish, including
cockles, winkles, shrimps from the Wash, and sometimes live clams from
the south coast. Smoking is a speciality of Ken Condon and it is all done
out in the back over oak sawdust, in his Edwardian smoke-hole (he even
has a brick built into the wall commemorating Edward VII's Coronation in
June 1902, to prove its date). Undyed smoked haddock is lightly salted with
a sweet hue backed with a gentle woodiness; salmon is firm-textured with a

good bite and with a pronounced fresh fish flavour; and smoked cods' roe is smooth and salty. Incidentally, he also sells raw and boiled cod's roe. Ken also smokes kippers, bloaters and buckling and 'nothing, absolutely nothing' he insists, 'has any dyes or colouring'. Cooks should be interested to know that he has a huge stock of fish kettles that he will lend out.

American Cakes and Pies

■ **Ewing's Classic American Bakers, Unit 12, Sleaford Street SW8 5AB ☎ 0171 498 0550** bake American-style loaf cakes. Made with unbleached white flour, vegetable fat, fresh fruits, vegetables, nuts and a good deep chocolate, Scott Ewing bakes 10 different flavours, including date & walnut, cinnamon & maple, chocolate banana marble and – best seller to date – carrot. Cakes weigh just over 900 g (2 lb). American baking tin sizes are slightly different from ours, and will cut up into 12 generous slices. New to me is the Texas pecan pie (with a name like Ewing where else could it come from?) Packed with nuts and a buttery, almost gelatinous, filling (which is how the Americans like it), it struck me as a pretty fine example.

Truffles and Fudge

■ **Sara Jayne, 517 Old York Road SW18 1TF ☎ 0181 874 8500 fax 0181 874 8575** makes seriously good truffles. The secrets of a truffle are the components of the ganache (filling), the quality of the ingredients and the techniques used. Every chocolatier has his (or her) way of making a ganache – some use butter and cream, some just butter, others eggs and cream, others eggs and butter, and some even a mixture of all three.

Sara uses just double cream with chocolate. She can see no point in using any other fats as their flavour detracts from the purity and strength of the chocolate. For every pint of double cream, she uses 2 pounds of best dark bitter couverture, with a high cocoa butterfat content. The cream is boiled, the chocolate broken up into pieces before being added and generally fussed and stirred over until it is melted. Then it is left to cool and briefly whisked for lightness; some chocolatiers, particularly the Belgians, will whisk their ganache for a long time as they like their truffles very light and airy. Next come the flavourings, and I have seen Sara pour into the ganache literally cupfuls of Tia Maria or Champagne or calvados or brandy (apparently a rough brandy works better than a smooth old cognac); they are the 'real thing' and there is no stinting with them here. Then they are either rolled out by hand or piped for Venus Nipples. Some are rolled in cocoa powder or chopped nuts, others hand-dipped into yet more chocolate to give them a glossy hard coat and a delightful contrast of textures – the hard chocolate cracks as you bite into the truffle, giving way to a rich soft yielding centre. Like Sara's nature but not – I should add – her figure, the truffles are generous in every way. Lavish in size, these are at least three-bite chocolates, lavish in flavour and deeply rich and creamy.

Sara also makes a rich crunchy – but definitely not grainy – fudge, with butter, cream and sugar. Made in the old-fashioned way of boiling it up in an open pan, whisking it and then cooling it off, hers is creamy with a taste of honey and a hint of vanilla.

Food Lover Jenny Arokiasamy writes to say that **Enzo Tartarelli, 1 Sidmouth Parade, Sidmouth Road NW2 5HG ☎ 0181 459 1952** makes amazing sausages. 'They are Italian style, not everyone's cup of tea, but I love them (especially the ones with pepper)'.

WILLESDEN
Italian-style Sausages

The Real Cheese Shop, 96A High Street SW19 5EG ☎ 0181 947 0564, for details see The Real Cheese Shop, Barnes *page* 175.

WIMBLEDON
Cheeses

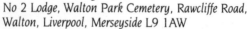

| WALTON | ### *Rice Lane City Farm* | |

Vegetables   No 2 Lodge, Walton Park Cemetery, Rawcliffe Road, Walton, Liverpool, Merseyside L9 1AW

☎ 0151 5301066 **CONTACT** Denise Turner **HOURS** 9.00-16.30 **DIRECTIONS** From Liverpool, take A59. After about 5 miles, turn left on to Rawcliffe Road and farm is at end of road.

Rice Lane City Farm is surrounded by the deconsecrated Walton Park Cemetery. Not at first sight an inspiring choice, but this a tough area. It is also part of YTS and various Community Action schemes to provide employment for the young in an area with sickeningly high unemployment. By its own admission 'it still has a long way to go', but what has been achieved so far is impressive. The farmyard houses 3 cows, 2 donkeys, 5 sheep, 3 sows, 1 boar, 2 Vietnamese pot-belly pigs, 9 milking nannies and a multitude of chickens, ducks and geese. One year – Denise Turner, the administrator, told me – they did send the animals off to the abattoir and they came back as chops, but there was such an outcry that now when they get too big the animals are sold off for store (feeding up). Instead they sell eggs and milk from the goats, and make yoghurt, ice-cream and soft cheese in the dairy. The vegetable patch flourishes, and you can buy, among other things, rhubarb, tomatoes, lettuces, cauliflowers, cabbages, onions, aubergines, courgettes, and beetroot. Any surplus is pickled and sold in jars. There are about 63 City Farms in total; some thrive others are run-down, but one way of supporting them is to buy the produce. For further information of a City Farm in your area, do contact the National Federation of City Farms, AMF House, 93 Whitby Road, Brislington, Bristol BS4 3QF ☎ 01272 719109.

  Acorn Venture Urban Farm, Depot Road, KIRKBY L33 3AR ☎ **0151 5481524** *also sells its produce to the public. You can buy chicken, pullet, goose and duck eggs, and – unlike Rice Lane – it sells chickens, free-range pork and bacon cured on the estate, beef, lamb and goat butchered into various cuts, goats'-milk, yoghurt, soft cheese and ice-cream.*

MAP 4   MERSEYSIDE/NORFOLK   **195**

While you're in the area...

Croxteth Hall and Country Park, LIVERPOOL L12 0HB ☎ 0151 228 5311 fax 0151 228 2817 has a 2-acre Victorian walled garden planted with old varieties of fruit and vegetables. It is a charming place to wander around, admiring the way the fruit trees are trained, poking about in the old mushroom house, melon pit or glasshouses. In season they sell the produce from a shed at the garden's entrance.

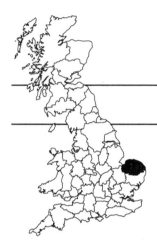

Norfolk

Map No. 5

Cley Smokehouse

High Street, Cley-next-the-Sea, Holt, Norfolk NR25 7RF

☎ 01263 740282 **CONTACT** Mike Rhodes **HOURS** Apr to end Oct: 9.00-18.00; Nov to end Mar: 9.00-17.00 **DIRECTIONS** In village centre.

The pity is that Cley Smokehouse no longer offer a mail-order service. If you want to try their produce you will have to go to Cley-next-the-Sea in person. Not that it should prove a hardship, Cley is a charming one-lane village with old clapperboard houses and a windmill facing out to sea with its sails intact. The shop itself is small and dark, with the actual smoking all done in the back in a large brick smoke-chimney. Everything is cold-smoked over oak sawdust and no dyes whatsoever are used. If there is a damp off-shore wind, the kippers can stay in the chimney for as long as 48 hours, with 18 hours the usual time. Although, if the pressure is high and there is no moisture in the air, they will be 'smoked before you know it'.

Even though this is herring country, Mike Rhodes finds the local longshore fish too small for curing, so he tends to use frozen Norwegian ones. His bloaters – whole herring unsplit and ungutted – are briefly brined, then smoked overnight. Kippers, on the other hand, are split, cured and hung on tenterhooks, and come with a marked robustness.

Further down the lane, just past the windmill, is **The Crabpot, High Street**, CLEY-NEXT-THE-SEA **Holt** NR25 7RN ☎ 01263 740218. They catch crabs and lobsters from their boat, and boil and dress the former or turn them into crab-cakes with a generous proportion of crab-meat. Likewise for their own-made fish-cakes and fish pie. In season, they also sell cockles, whitebait and freshly picked samphire.

He also smokes wild salmon, mostly from the River Tay, and cod's roe from Iceland; round, plump and a shiny pale-orange, it is a succulent example with a good balance of salt to smoke. New to me was their taramasalata made 'just like a mayonnaise' by pounding the roe and adding vegetable oil drop by drop with lots of lemon juice and garlic. Rich in flavour, slightly grained in texture and very punchy, it puts most commercial versions (diluted with bread or potato) into the shade. Also on sale are a buttery and lightly spiced crab pâté; potted shrimps made from brown shrimps caught in the Wash; a sweet pickled herring made with meaty fillets, which tasted a little on the sharp side; a fresh herring roe pâté which was surprisingly smooth but could have been a little creamier; and bags of frozen whitebait, caught in nets by a local fisherman off Blakeney Point.

CROMER
Crabs

Richard & Julie Davies
7 Garden Street, Cromer, Norfolk NR27 9HN

☎ 01263 512727 **CONTACT** Julie Davies **HOURS** mid Mar to mid Oct: 8.30-17.30; mid Oct to mid Mar: Tues-Sat 8.30-17.30 (-13.00 Wed) **DIRECTIONS** In town centre.

Cromer crabs have a certain reputation for being the best in Britain. If you ask the locals they will tell you that, although smaller than Yorkshire or Cornwall crabs, theirs are definitely much meatier and sweeter.

Mr and Mrs Davies specialize in Cromer crabs. With their son, they run two small boats that work around the chalk shelf between March and September when the sea warms up. They also run a larger boat which can supply them all year round, catching off Wells-by-the-Sea. As Mrs Davies admits, however, 'Crabs from there are probably larger and not quite as sweet'.

Their crabs are cooked daily. If they are wide awake when cooked they 'shoot off their claws' – and that would never do. Mrs Davies has several girls at the back of the shop dressing the crab-meat and there are various ways of presenting it, although she favours separating the white and dark meat 'so you can see exactly what you're getting'. They are very good – sparklingly flavoured, succulently fleshed and very rich indeed.

The Davies family sell both whole and dressed crabs and are happy to give you a bag of ice to keep them chilled on the way home. They also sell lobsters, Kings Lynn shrimps, local herrings, smoked fish from Cley and a selection of fresh fish, usually bought from Lowestoft.

You could also pop down the road to 10 Brook Street and buy a dressed crab from Buster, an ex-fisherman who sells them from a chilled display hanging out of his front window. His is a much easier life now he no longer puts to sea but, as he says, 'I spend more time picking over the crabs than I ever did catching them'.

Stockists

Norfolk: Ted's Seafoods

Fiona Dickson
Didlington Manor, Didlington, Thetford, Norfolk IP26 5AT

DIDLINGTON

Honey

☎ 01842 878673 **FAX** 01842 878673 **CONTACT** Fiona Dickson – mail order only

Fiona Dickson is an efficient and innovative beekeeper. Her honey is also judged very good, as for the last 3 years she has walked away with several firsts at The National Honey Show. Apart from heather honey, the British palate – she believes – favours light mild flowery honey 'although tastes are changing'. As well as on her own nature reserve in Thetford Forest, she places her hives in two of the Royal Parks – Windsor, in the Queen Mum's garden, Richmond in the grounds of The Royal Ballet School and, for the first time this year, is marketing honey from the Sandringham Estate. 'Each of the honeys has a different character. Sandringham grows masses of fruit, so there's a blossom honey; later in the year the bees go to the lavender or the willow-herb. Richmond is very limy, with a touch of heather at times. But, then again, honey changes with the season and with every year. And that's what I like about honey, its glorious variations'.

Stockists

London: Fortnum & Mason

International Cheese Shop

Shaws

Tom's

Surrey: Vivian's

Fiona is unusual in that she separates her honey both in terms of the location and the crop; so rather than mixing them all up together in a 'real mish-mash as some do,' hers tends to have marked characteristics of the location and season. 'Last year Windsor yielded up a wonderful deep rich amber chestnut, but it's rare. It was just that the weather was so good. And I specify my honey according to where it's collected – its geographic origin rather than the plants'. She strains her honey to get out the 'bees' knees' and wax, but never filters it. 'If you filter it, you loose pollen and pollen does give a certain flavour as it holds in the essential oils'. Far better, as far as Fiona is concerned, to have a cloudy honey full of flavour than one that is shiningly clear but with no taste at all.

*The Norfolk coast from Cromer to beyond Holkam is one of my favourite spots in England; still relatively unspoilt, I can walk for miles over the marches, with birds swooping overhead or along by the sea on stretches of golden sand and Violet chasing the waves. There are always good fish and shellfish to be had. **Andrew Athill, Scaldbeck Barn, MORSTON, Holt NR25 7BJ ☎ 01263 740306** runs a sailing school and farms mussels right by his house. Visit him down the winding lane that leads to the coast and buy them straight out of the water. **The Fish Shed, BRANCASTER STAITHE, Kings Lynn PE31 8YB ☎ 01485 210532** is run by Margaret and Stephen Bocking. They sell fresh local fish and shellfish, smoke herrings and ham, pot crabs and shrimps, and make rather good fish-cakes. **Gurneys, The Green, The Market Place, BURNHAM MARKET PE31 8HE ☎ 01328 738967** also have a roadside shed in Brancaster and sell a similar range. During the season, from May to September, you will always find at both shops bunches of freshly picked samphire (sea asparagus), crabs, lobsters, local brown shrimps, mussels and fresh fish, including grey mullet, Dover soles and local herrings. Both have their following and both are friendly fish shops.*

**Organic
Apple Juice**

Crone's Cider

Fairview, Fersfield Road, Kenninghall, Norfolk NR16 2DP

☎ 01379 687687　**CONTACT** *Robert Crone – telephone ahead*

Robert Crone makes both apple juice and Norfolk cider from his farm in the traditional way, pressing the apples to make a cheese and extracting the juice. What is unusual about both his drinks is that they are made with apples grown to Soil Association standards. In plain English this means the apples will not have been sprayed with any chemical pesticides or fungicides and therefore there should be no chemical residues in the fruit.

Norfolk cider is different from West country cider in that it is made with predominantly dessert fruit and cooking apples – as opposed to cider apples – and tends to have a lower alcoholic content. The apples Robert uses for his cider are a mixture of own-grown and bought-in, from which he produces 3 types: Original Strong Norfolk, a forceful drink with a mere 10 per cent of cider apples; User-Friendly, a milder version; and Special Reserve, which is made with predominantly cider apples and has an 8 per cent alcohol content. Sold as medium-dry, he does add a little sugar; 'not to boost the alcohol but to sweeten them at point of sale', he assures me.

The apples for his juices Robert buys in from almost all over the country 'and only from accredited symbol growers' and they won Best Beverage in the 1994 Organic Food Awards. Last year proved a bad year for Russets so he had none in stock, but normally he juices Cox, Russets, Spartan, Discovery and Golden Delicious as single-variety juices and makes up blends of Worcester & Laxton Fortune, Cox & Bramley and Cox & Russet. Pasteurized in the bottle, his juices are briskly flavoured with a good appley intensity. This year he is also trying his hand with a pear juice blended with a little apple juice 'just to get the right acidity'.

Flour

Letheringsett Watermill

Riverside Road, Letheringsett, Holt, Norfolk NR25 7YD

☎ 01263 713153　**CONTACT** *Michael Thurlow* **HOURS** *Tues-Fri 9.00-13.00 & 14.00-17.00* **DIRECTIONS** *From Holt, take A148 towards Fakenham. After about 1 mile, follow the Watermill tourist signs to the left.*

Linda Collister in the admirable *The Bread Book* singles out miller Michael Thurlow for the excellence of his flour. Letheringsett Watermill, a red-brick 4-storey building with a huge iron waterwheel powered by the river Glaven, used to supply the local communities with freshly milled flour as long ago as 1802. It was abandoned in 1944 and left to deteriorate until 1982, when its restoration started and, in 1987, Michael took over the tenancy. In the afternoons every Tuesday,

MAP 5　　　　　　　　　NORFOLK　　　199

Wednesday, Thursday and Sunday between 14.00 and 16.30, he gives formal demonstrations of how the mill works. The rest of the time he is almost always on hand to chat to anyone who is interested.

Michael mills various wheats into a range of flours. He has just started producing a flour with wheat from nearby Thornage Hall grown to Demeter (bio-dynamic) standards. The flour Linda Collister favours uses Alexandria wheat; a pre-war variety, it has – as Linda says – 'the best taste in the country. It's sweet, nutty, more intensely flavoured and, unlike many other wholemeal flours, it's never bitter'. Michael grinds his quite coarse, but he's also happy to grind to your specifications. He also mills a softer French variety, Flanders, imported from France; this bakes up into a lighter-textured product well-suited for pastry and French bread. Recently Michael changed his baker to Graves in Briston, who bakes on a daily basis a dense loaf using 100 per cent stoneground flour from Letheringsett; but you had better get there early as they are usually sold out by the afternoon.

Stockists

London: Traiteur Pagnol

Norfolk: The Bakehouse

H. V. Graves (Bakery)

C. Harrisons

Surrey: Vivian's

Clive Houlder

98 West Street, North Creake, Fakenham, Norfolk NR21 9LH

NORTH CREAKE
Wild Mushrooms

☎ 01328 738610　**CONTACT** Clive Houlder – telephone ahead

Who could have predicted how wild mushrooms – domestic wild mushrooms – would have caught on? When compiling the first *Food Lovers' Guide*, I had trouble finding anyone who dealt in them and now they are – if you will forgive the pun – coming out of the woodwork. Norfolk has never struck me as being rich in wild mushrooms, but Clive Houlder has put me right, 'Almost any county in Britain has wild mushrooms. Cambridge is an exception, but then it has hardly any trees. Norfolk is particularly good as you have plenty of woods, both deciduous and coniferous, and all types of soil from acid to alkaline'.

The season starts mid-April, with the St George's which apparently favour short grass and chalky soil. Then come (and not necessarily in this order): morels; fairy ring champignons (which the French call *mousserons*); saffron milk caps; amethyst deceivers; penny buns; bay bolete; orange birch bolete; chicken o' the woods; puff balls which, Clive generously hinted, 'grow in hedgerows and like clumps of stinging nettles, so wade in with a stick and keep an eye out for a white patch'; jews' ears; girolles; cauliflower fungus; and so

Peter Jordan of **The Tasty Mushroom Partnership, Poppy Cottage, Station Road, BURNHAM MARKET PE31 8HA ☎/fax 01328 738841** *is a self-styled 'fungus fanatic'. He works in close co-operation with Clive Houlder, but whereas Clive deals in fresh fungi Peter dries them into 30-gram packets of: English Woodland mixture, made up of various Boletus, chanterelles and fairy ring champignons; Select, with Boletus edulis and Boletus Badius; Fairy Ring Champignons only; with others on request. He has also just starting organizing foray days and weekends, with plans for one in Wales based around Betws-y-coed where 'chanterelles grow in carpets', two in Scotland and several scattered around England in Norfolk and Leicestershire.*

on – about 40 different mushrooms in all.

Clive delivers to several restaurants in the area – it was David Adlard of Adlard's fame who I have to thank for the introduction – but he will sell direct to the likes of me and you. He tends to favour mixtures, 'I like the different flavours and textures and make them up with whatever is in season' and you can be certain that most will have been foraged from the area and are in prime condition.

Stockists

Norfolk: Picnic Fare

 Groom's Bakery Market Place, BURNHAM MARKET PE31 8HD ☎ **01328 738289** *bake a wide selection of breads. Shaped like a cob, Norfolk blobs – made from white flour, with a long fermentation – are slashed on top to open them out. This, so baker Peter Groom told me, 'makes it even softer' and it does have a creamy soft interior with a crisp crust. Norfolk Harvest, a mix of wholemeal flour with honey and raisins, also has an overnight fermentation. Others, including wholemeal, rye & caraway, olive bread studded with whole olives and walnut, are made on a shorter process. New is the round-shaped mushroom bread, made with white flour, extra-virgin olive oil and dried mushrooms from Clive Houlder see above. I have heard several reports about its success, varying from 'light, fluffy and impregnated with a salty flavour of mushrooms' (Food Lover Bobby Gill of London) to 'a disappointment' (Melanie de Blank – Justin's wife). As I have yet to try it, I will leave you to draw your own conclusions, but please let me know.*

 Humble Pie, The Market Place, Burnham Market, KINGS LYNN PE31 8HE ☎ **01328 738581** *is right on the green of one of my favourite villages in the county. The shop, run by Sue Elston, maintains its standards year in year out, rotating the stock because, as Sue admits, 'I'd get bored with everything always being the same. And if I would, so would my customers'. Cheeses feature prominently, changing with the seasons. So you might find Devon Garland see page 79, Mrs Montgomery's Cheddar see page 239, or various ones from Thornby Moor Dairy see page 61. As this is serious picnic land, there is plenty of picnic food in the form of own-made salads and pâtés, raised pies from The Gingham Kitchen in Fakenham, locally baked bread, cakes, and biscuits made by 'local ladies'.*

The freezer is well stocked with own-cooked casseroles or ready-meals, such as lamb with apricots & pine nuts, Moroccan pork with apple, prunes, coriander & allspice and a couple of choices for vegetarians. There are packets of dried mushrooms from Clive Houlder see above, own-made chutneys, jams, marmalades, and pickled mushrooms. At Christmas there are Sue's puddings and fruit cakes.

STARSTON

Dairy Products

Susan Moore Dairy Products

Cranes Watering Farm Shop, Rushall Road, Starston, Harleston, Norfolk IP20 9NE

☎ 01379 852387 **FAX** 01379 852387 **CONTACT** Susan Moore **HOURS** Tues-Fri 9.00-17.30 Sat 9.00-17.00 Sun 9.30-12.30 (*closed every Thurs in Jan*) **DIRECTIONS** *From Pulham Market, take B1134 towards Harleston. Follow the road through Starston and turn right immediately after crossing the bridge. Follow the road about ½ mile to crossroads. Turn right and dairy is immediately on the left.*

 Norfolk terrain is not one that lends itself to dairy farming, so it is all the more surprising to come across Susan Moore and her 100-strong herd of Guernsey and Jersey cows. Customers can wander around the farm and buy her dairy products from the farm-shop.

Norfolk's well-drained sandy soil and (relatively) drier and warmer climate are well-suited to asparagus growing. If you drive through the county anytime from the end of April to mid-June, you can see fields striped with raised asparagus beds, the spears poking through. The asparagus is hand-picked and graded on-farm: grade 1 stands for tightly budded spears with no hint of seed and straight as ramrods. Within the grade, the asparagus is separated by width or thickness into jumbo, medium and sprue, although different growers have different specifications. Grade 2 more or less hoovers up the second quality and is useful for soups, sauces, adding to omelettes or soufflés.

Several growers do sell direct to the public from the farm, although some change their mind each year, depending on whether they are contracted to a supermarket or not. Two that can be relied on year-in year-out are listed below; if you know of any others, I would be delighted to hear about them.

W. D. Oram, Old Hall Farm, ATTLEBRIDGE NR9 5TQ ☎ **01603 867317** *only sell direct to the public and, such is their reputation, on busy days during the season there is a queue stretching from the Oram's garage right down the driveway.*

Jonathan Cave, Hall Farm, WEST RUDHAM PE31 8TE ☎/fax **01485 528238** *cut every day between 8.00 and 14.00, and no one seems to mind if you go into the fields and get your asparagus bundled up on the spot, picked to the size you want. The rest of the time they sell from the farm, in the usual grades with a 'kitchen' grade for soups and sauces.*

Most of the milk is sent off to Milk Marque, but some is kept back to be sold direct as pasteurized or green-top (unpasteurized) milk in the usual grades of full-cream, semi-skimmed and skimmed. Mrs Moore also produces a rich buttery unpasteurized double cream, a pasteurized whipping cream and, occasionally, a clotted cream. If there is any cream left at the end of the week she churns it into a well-ripened, full-flavoured butter which comes salted or unsalted.

In her neat little dairy in the barn behind the shop she also transforms the milk into various products. Her sharp loose-textured lemon curd – made with her own butter – has proved so popular that Mrs Moore now makes two more flavours, lemon & lime and lemon & orange. She is also frequently changing the flavours of her ice-cream, this year's favourite was Summer Pudding, made with fresh berries. She makes ice-cream in 100-litre (176-pint) batches, with a base of cream, milk, sugar, eggs and stabilizers (a mixture of the four gums – xanthus, carrageen, locust bean and guar). It has a variable fat content of between 12-15 per cent and a 60 per cent overrun. Flavours – apart from 'natural vanilla' (actually an essence) – are the 'real thing': Rum & Raisin is made with 'a bottle of rum and a few packets of raisins' and you can taste the rum; Autumn Glory is a mixture of poached blackberries and apples. For my money I find her ice-cream a touch thin, not quite as rich and creamy or as vibrantly flavoured as one might have hoped for, particularly if you are using Channel Island milk. New this year is an elderflower water-ice made with elderflower cordial, which I have yet to sample; Mrs Moore assures me it is 'very refreshing'.

She also makes plain and quite basic fresh soft cheeses. There is a rich full-cream cheese – plain or with garlic & fresh herbs – and an unpasteurized full-milk cheese. Simply made, it is moulded and drained for a couple of days so the texture is not unlike a Coulommiers and comes either as plain or rolled in herbs or decorated with cracked peppercorns.

Stockists

Norfolk: Natural Food Store

Natures Way

Trencherman's Deli

Suffolk: Beards Deli & Tea Room

Country Kitchen

Bryan Pickering, 30 The Street, OLD COSTESSEY NR8 5DB ☎ 01603 742002 *is a butcher with a modern approach. Convinced that the day is not far off when most of us will no longer be able to afford primary cuts, most of what he sells is prepared ready-to-cook meat. He also produces pâtés and cooked cold cuts, including natural, Virginia roast, German-style and Swiss peppered hams, as well as roast beef and haslett. Sausages come in around 52 varieties and are made in 18-kg (40-lb) batches, with a meat content of around 95 per cent and a soft finely minced texture. New this year is smoked pork with brandy, and Aunt Mirabelle's gluten-free chicken sausage. Other favourites are Oxfordshire, with fresh lemon, marjoram, sage and thyme; Somerset, a hearty blend of pork & cider; and Yorkshire, punched with cloves.*

WYMOND-HAM

Norfolk Knobs

Merv's Hot Bread Kitchen
38 Market Place, Wymondham, Norfolk NR17 0JU

☎ 01953 607118 **CONTACT** Merv Ayers **HOURS** Mon-Sat 8.00-17.30 **DIRECTIONS** In town centre.

As far as I know, Mr Ashworth – late of the Ashworth chain of bakers – is the only person to make Norfolk Knobs or, as they are locally known, 'hollow biscuits' in Norfolk. He comes in twice a week to bake in Merv's Hot Bread Kitchen.

Similar to a rusk in texture, knobs look like small pale-gold irregular doorknobs and are puffed up, with 'spent' sides which give a slightly crushed look. Made from a simple flour, fat, salt, yeast and sugar dough, they are thought to have originated from – or at least been influenced by – the Low Countries. Apparently Norfolk knobs were a great favourite of King George VI and, when he was staying at nearby Sandringham, he would always order up a supply.

Smaller than a Dorset Knob *see page* 93, they are similar in terms of ingredients but, as far I can work out, the way the dough is handled is different. The dough for Dorset knobs is mixed conventionally and the knobs are rolled out in the palm of the hand. Whereas the secret for Norfolk Knobs – according to Mr Ashworth – is to make a dough with cold water to stop it rising too quickly, then after kneading to turn and fold it to get the 'hollowness', and cut it by hand into knobs. These are then baked off in a hot oven, left to cool and finally dried out in a cool oven.

To eat a Norfolk knob, either bite into it whole or twist it gently and you will find it breaks in half, revealing the hollow centre. With a slightly sweet taste, the crunchy crust gives way to a crisp centre which dissolves in a burst of bubbles in your mouth. Traditionally spread with butter and served with jam or cheese, they are sold in packets of 12 and will keep for about 3 months.

Stockists

Norfolk: Larner's of Holt

- - - - - - - - -

The Norfolk Cake Company

Ranworth Farms, The Old House, RANWORTH NR13 6HS ☎ 01603 270722 fax 01603 270611 *juices its own apples for 3 unusual blends: Summer is a mixture of James Grieve and Katy, with the apples picked early in the season; Autumn is made with Golden Delicious and Greensleeves; and the late apples Crispin and Jonagold make the Winter's juice.*

While you're in the area...

Patrick Kemp, Evergreen Farm, Church Lane, GRESSENHALL NR19 2QH ☎ 01362 860190 is a small-scale organic grower (to Soil Association standards) with barely 1¾ acres. None the less, he comes highly recommended by chef David Adlard of Adlard's in Norwich for his globe artichokes which, depending on the winter, start in late May and go through to late October. Among other fruit and vegetables, he also grows La Ratte, Désirée, Cara and Pentland Javelin potatoes, baby broad beans and the sweet pink redcurrant called Champagne. He will sell from the door, but you should ring him first to find out what is ready for picking.

Since my visit, **Byfords, 1-5 Shirehall Plain, HOLT NR25 6BG ☎ 01263 713520** has undergone a change of management, a change of chef and a change of direction to 'more wholefoods'. They still bake their own bread, including a 100 per cent wholemeal, with flour from Garboldisham Mill, and plain focaccia or with garlic, or black olives, or fresh rosemary. More reports please.

Norfolk Larder, 35 Market Place, HOLT NR25 6BE ☎ 01263 712985 comes highly recommended by Alistair Cameron, Manager of Tom's in London *see page* 190. David Chambers runs his own in-shore boat, the Laura Jane, moored at Moorston. In summer, he catches crab and lobsters and, in winter, cod, mackerel and herring, with net and line. From the shop, he also sells local oysters and mussels from Mr Webster in Cley, who also supplies fresh whitebait in the summer months. Mr Chambers also deals in game from local estates in season, including venison, rabbit, hare, pigeon, partridge and pheasant. Teal and widgeon, shot on the marshes, are sold processed within 24 hours of being shot, otherwise they 'go off'.

Melanie Knibbs, St Nicholas, Bevis Way, KING'S LYNN PE30 3AG ☎ 01553 674703 can be found on Thursday mornings at Fakenham market and on Saturdays at Swaffham market, with her own-made preserves. Made in small 5.5-kg (12-lb) batches, with 3 pans on the go, there are 5 marmalades, including a tart Seville and a rich Old English with dark sugar; various chutneys and jams; and redcurrant, gooseberry, and quince jellies. She also bakes Victoria sponges, fruit cakes and various biscuits.

North Elmham Bakery, Eastgate Street, NORTH ELMHAM, Dereham NR25 ME ☎ 01362 668577 – with branches in Norwich Street, Dereham, Market Place, Swaffham and High Street Watton – bake 3 different breads: white; a smooth textured wholemeal; and malt crunch, similar to a Granary.

The Royal Fruit Farms, The Estate Office, SANDRINGHAM PE35 6EN ☎ 01553 772675 fax 01485 541471 have 60 acres of orchards about 2 miles from the House. Here you can PYO the same apples that are served to the Queen – Worcester Pearmain, Laxton Fortune, Cox and Bramley. They also have PYO strawberries and raspberries; some of the raspberries also end up in the new Duchy of Cornwall No. 1 Herb and Fruit drink.

Food Lover Barbara Fuller wrote to recommend butchers **Steven Smith Quality Meats, 37 High Street, WATTON, Thetford IP25 6AB ☎ 01953 885467.** 'I filled my cool-box with a range of sausages, such as Norfolk herb, and pork & apple. They are certainly worth transporting 300 miles to my freezer (in Scotland). He also looks to be a good all-round butcher'. More reports please.

Chris Bowers & Sons, Whispering Trees Nurseries, WIM-BOTSHAM PE34 8QB ☎ 01366 388752 fax 01366 386858 has all sorts of unusual fruit trees and bushes, including several older varieties of pear trees, such as Beurré Bedford, Old Warden and Vicar of Winkfield. There is also a good collection of plums, gages and damsons – including Denniston's Superb, with its large pale-green fruit streaked with a darker green and a lush honeyed flavour.

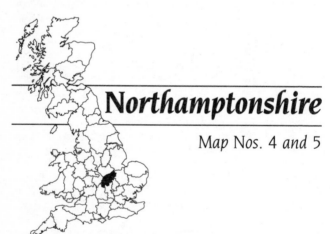

Northamptonshire

Map Nos. 4 and 5

BRIGSTOCK
Herbs

Hill Farm Herbs
Park Walk, Brigstock, Northamptonshire NN14 3HH

☎ 01536 373694 **FAX** 01536 373246 **CONTACT** *Eileen Simpson* **HOURS** *Mar to end Sept*: Mon-Sun 10.30-17.30; *rest of year: telephone ahead (Tea room: Easter to end Sept)* **CARDS** *Mastercard, Switch, Visa*

Hill Farm Herbs has a great deal of charm. Wander under the arch of the tall brick barn, past the sympathetically converted outbuildings which house the shops and tea-room and you will find yourself in the compact but attractively planted gardens. On your immediate left are the herbs for sale, laid out in their pots. There is a wide and varied selection: with several thymes, including lemon-curd with its definite lemon flavour and the variegated white-and-green leaf silver posy; white-flowered skirret, with its root used as a vegetable in much the same way as salsify; buckler-leaf sorrel which Eileen Simpson describes as having 'small shield-shaped leaves and a sour apple flavour' and the Silver-shield strain, with its green leaves marked with silver; and cardoon plants. There is an interesting collection of pelargoniums (scented geraniums); their leaves can be used to flavour jams, jellies and sugar. Here you can find the apple-scented Odoratissum, Lemon Fancy with a powerful lemon tang, and Grey Lady Plymouth with a strong flavour of mint.

> *Freebs*, *72 Watling Street East*, *TOWCESTER NN12 6AF* ☎/fax 01327 351565 *is a friendly shop filled with own-made savouries and sweets with a hearty home-made feel, including crisp chicken pies and gooey meringues.*

From the shop they sell dried herb garlands, herb seeds, chutneys and own-made herb vinegars. These are made with wine and cider vinegar, the herbs steeped for at least 6 weeks to infuse the vinegar, then they are strained and bottled with fresh herbs. Eileen makes such flavours as purple basil, rosemary, mixed herbs, tarragon and mint with a few added peppercorns. While you are there, pop in for a cup of tea. Cakes and biscuits are own-made and may include delicate rosemary biscuits, lemon balm or orange thyme cake.

> *Pass the provocatively named headquarters of the Barbara Cartland Romance Club, on down the lane and you will eventually find* **Castle Ashby Fine Foods**, **Old Farm Yard**, **CASTLE ASHBY NN7 1LF** ☎ 01604 696742 *fax* 01234 881649 *in a converted building in what was once the estate's dairy yard. Here you will find such local produce as Brixworth pâté (a chicken liver and pork pâté with sherry); various breads, including wholemeal and sunflower seed, from a baker at Olney; ice-cream from Moulton Farm, a nearby agricultural college; own-made game pie, using game from the estate; and asparagus and soft fruit from Warrington House Farm see page 28. With a band of local ladies to cook for the shop, they also sell jams, lemon curd, marmalades, different-flavoured sponge cakes, fluffy meringues (more akin to pavlovas), sweet roulades spread with fruit and cream in summer or mincemeat in winter, and Duke of Cambridge tart – an open tart filled with curd cheese, dried fruits soaked in whey and spiced with cinnamon and nutmeg. Savouries are not forgotten: there are cooked meats, stuffed brioches, and various pies, including a mammoth steak & mushroom marinated in Guinness.*

While youre in the area...

The Nuns of Daventry, **The Convent of Our Lady of the Passion Monastery**, **Badby Road West**, **DAVENTRY NN11 4NH** ☎ 01327 702569, make chocolate truffles 'while trying to maintain a prayerful silence'. Using copious quantities of alcohol – Champagne, rum, malt whisky, Drambuie, Irish Mist, Tia Maria and Grand Marnier – they are rich and smooth if a little sweet, and come in 125, 250 and 450-g (¼, ½ and 1-lb) boxes.

Essentially English, **10b West Street**, **OUNDLE PE8 4EF** ☎ 018322 74396 has some good produce packed onto its shelves and counters. There are some interesting grainy mustards, flavoured with horseradish, dill, hot or mild ginger, and garlic, made by Mustard Fields a local company; Rocombe Farm ice-cream *see page* 84; a range of frozen meals prepared by a local lady; Emmett's bacon, with hams to order *see page* 253; sausages made by Norfolk Porkers in Bressingham; and various quiches, pâtés and pizzas. At Christmas, they sell own-made Christmas puddings and cooked hams.

Ark Farm Sheep Dairy Centre, Ark Farm, High Street South, TIFFIELD NN12 8AB ☎ 01327 350202 may look a bit scruffy, but they do produce a creamy sheep's-milk yoghurt which is clear and fresh-tasting.

Northumberland

Map No. 6

Robertson's Prime

Unit 1B, Willowtree Industrial Estate, Alnwick, Northumberland NE66 2HA

☎/FAX 01665 604386 **CONTACT** Ian Robertson **HOURS** Mon–Sat 9.00–17.00 **DIRECTIONS** *From A1 travelling north, turn off at the first sign for Alnwick. Follow the road to the Shell garage, take the first turning on the right, signposted Willowtree Industrial estate. Shop is 100 yards along on the right.*

Surrounded as he is with some of the best shoots and grouse moors in the country, you would expect Ian Robertson to have first-class game in his shop, you will not be disappointed.

Grouse – mainly from Alnwick Moor, the Duke of Northumberland's shoot and other local estates – arrives straight from the shoots and is hung for about 7 days. The condition varies, 'depending on who shoots, as it can be peppered with shot,' Ian explains. After about 2 months into the season, he 'freezes them up' because, extraordinarily enough 'they're not too popular round here, people think they're too heathery'.

Also from the local estates, come hare, mallard, teal, snipe, widgeon, rabbits, pheasant and wild pigeons. Everything is hung, racked, plucked, chilled and sold oven-ready. There is a good range of wild venison, as well as a little farmed to order. A local butcher makes up venison sausages with herbs and (as the meat is so lean) pork fat; and Ian also sells a useful game-pie mix of 60 per cent venison, 10 per cent hare, 10 per cent pheasant, 10 per cent pigeon and 10 per cent rabbit, depending on season and supply. New this year is wild boar, butchered into joints; locally reared quail and quails' eggs; and for the catering trade – or any interested home cook – butchered and trimmed pigeon and duck breasts.

Fresh fish he buys straight off the boats, mainly from Amble. Sometimes he gets codling from the cobles (flat-bottomed in-shore boats) and he can generally be relied on for cod, haddock, lemon and Dover sole, monkfish, live crabs and lobsters (Ian now has a vivier), wild or farmed salmon, and turbot. From Scotland, he gets Loch Fyne kippers, fresh scallops and a range of smoked fish including salmon, eel, halibut and trout.

Charlotte Loyd

Mantle Hill, Bellingham, Hexham,
Northumberland NE48 2LB

☎ 01434 220428 **FAX** 01434 220113 **CONTACT** *Charlotte Loyd – telephone ahead*

Lucky are the guests who bed and breakfast at Charlotte Loyd's, they are served her Tarset Valley marmalade every morning. She has been making it for the last 10 years and, although she has now moved to the North Tyne valley and lives in a farmhouse on the Hesleyside estate, she has kept its original name.

Production is small, this year she reckons on making about 1,300 jars, but it is a marmalade to savour. Quite why or how it is so special, she rather modestly claims not to know, 'Perhaps it's because I use spring water. If you use water straight from the tap, it'll be chlorinated. By the time you've boiled it down – as you do for marmalade – you're bound to get a taste of the chlorine, which must interfere with the flavour'. It could also be because she uses a small amount of black treacle to give it body and a dark rich colour. Whatever the reasons, her marmalade is sharp and deeply fruity.

Stockists

Northumb:
Corbridge Larder

Isabel Wentzel of **Crowberry Hall Preserves, Crowberry Hall,** ALLENDALE, **Hexham** NE47 9SR ☎ 01434 683392 *also runs a bed and breakfast and makes a range of preserves in her kitchen. Jams are made with fruit in season, including strawberry, plum, and damson; and there are 6 different marmalades to choose from, such as three-fruit or Oxford with black treacle.*

CRASTER
Craster
Kippers

L. *Robson & Sons*
Haven Hill, Craster, Alnwick, Northumberland NE66 3TR

☎ 01665 576223 **FAX** 01665 576044 **CONTACT** Alan Robson **HOURS** Mon-Fri 9.00-12.00 & 13.00-17.00 Sat 9.00-12.00 **DIRECTIONS** In *village centre by the harbour.*

Craster kippers have been famous for generations. Still smoked in the same way, in the same towering smokehouses built in 1856, the taste has changed very little from how it was all those years ago, the only possible difference is a lighter touch of salt.

Nowadays few herrings are caught off the Northumberland coast. Instead, Mr Robson buys in wherever decent herring are landed, from Ayr or Tarbert on the west coast of Scotland or Fraserburgh or Peterhead on the east. He buys in fresh herrings when they are at their best; previously he only cured herrings when fresh, but he has just started freezing and curing throughout the year to ensure a year-round supply.

The sight of a smokehouse – its chambers packed with fish – is never to be forgotten. The walls, shiny black and sticky with tar, provide the perfect backdrop for the regimented lines of glistening mahogany-brown fish stretching up the chimney as far as the eye can soar. A warm woody aroma fills the air, as the slow gentle process of smoking carries on. At their busiest, in the height of the season, Robson can smoke anything up to 6,000 a day and, depending on the weather, they may stay in the smokehouse for as long as 14 hours.

Mr Robson reckons on his kippers weighing about 2 to the pound. As for cooking them, he follows the local squire, Sir John Craster's method of jugging them in boiling water for 5 minutes. Failing that you could pop into Robson's restaurant and treat yourself to a kipper tea – kippers, brown bread and butter and a pot of strongly brewed tea. Just what's needed after a good blow, walking along the coast. He also smokes salmon in the 'traditional' way, giving it a long cool 48 hours' smoke, using both Scottish farmed and wild fish.

Stockists
Hants: New Forest Fish Co

Northumb: Lindsay of Newcastle
- - - - - - - -
Ridleys Fish & Game
- - - - - - - -
Taylors of Jesmond

Sussex: The Weald Smokery

Swallow Fish Limited, 2 South Street, SEAHOUSES NE8 7RP ☎ **01665 721052** *is the only traditional smokehouse left in Seahouses, once a thriving fishing port. Anyone interested in the history of fishing should visit the shop; there is a display of coopering tools used to make herring barrels, as well as old photographs of fishing and kippering. From the shop, you can buy local shellfish, plump and meaty kippers, smoked salmon and haddock – all smoked over oak in their smokehouse. They also sell freshly boiled crabs and lobsters, wild salmon and sea trout. If you do visit, just ask and someone will show you around.*

ELSDON
Cheese

Redesdale Sheep Dairy
Soppitt Farm, Elsdon, Otterburn, Northumberland NE19 1AF

☎ 01830 520506 **FAX** 01830 520796 **CONTACT** Mark Robertson **HOURS** April 1 to end Oct: 10.00-18.00; Nov to Mar 31: Mon-Fri 10.00-14.00 (Sat &

Sun -18.00) **DIRECTIONS** *From Newcastle-upon-Tyne, take the A696 towards Otterburn. After 30 miles, at a brown-and-white sign 'Cheese Farm', turn right. Farm is 1½ miles down road.*

Visit Soppit Farm, home to Mark Robertson, on a sunny summer's day and the view over the moorlands of Northumberland's Southern Uplands is breathtaking; on a blowy grey winter's day I imagine it must be a little bleak, if exhilarating.

'In the dim and distant past', he told me, 'cheese was made in Northumberland. I wanted to resurrect it. But, in spite of researching, I couldn't find an actual recipe. So I fell into the way of making my Northumberland according to a wash-curd recipe. I believe there are only about half a dozen ways of making cheese in the world – the rest are variations on a theme'. His Northumberland, made with cows' milk, is matured for about 8-10 weeks and is compact, smooth and quite rich. It comes as plain or flavoured with chives or garlic or nettles or smoked. Coquetdale, also from cows' milk, is a Tomme-shaped cheese that is also matured for 8-10 weeks; at its best when the mould is ripened, the cheese softens for a salty fresh tang. Wensleydale is made with cows' milk and about 20 per cent sheep's milk; by Mark's admis-

Stockists

London: Harvey Nichols

Real Cheese Shop

Northumb: Corbridge Larder

Fenwicks

Oxon: Wells Stores

In the county there are three 'proper' farm-shops and by that I mean that almost everything they sell is own-grown or own-made. When Caroline Dickinson started the farm-shop at **Brocksbushes Fruit Farm, STOCKSFIELD NE43 7UB ☎ 01434 633100 fax 01434 632965** *her intention was 'to create a shop as near to a fresh produce stall at a village fête as possible'. Apart from PYO and ready-picked fruit and vegetables, you will find* *plenty of ready-cooked dishes, such as chicken with tomato & pine nuts; beef stew and dumplings; and lamb tagine made with their own lamb. She also cooks hams, roulades, pies, cutting pies, scones, tarts and cakes, including a 4-month matured fruit cake in 13 and 23-cm (5 and 9-in) rounds with alcohol added for Christmas. Fresh soups marketed under the label of The Real Soup Co label – which is, in fact, Caroline's company – are also on sale in 450-ml (¾-pint) cartons. Made with fresh vegetables, flavours vary according to the time of the year, but may include tomato & split lentils, or a curious-sounding courgette, basil & brie. One summer treat to look out for are own-picked strawberries dipped in white or dark chocolate.*

Roseden Farm Shop, ROSEDEN, Wooperton, Alnwick NE66 4XU ☎ 01668 217271 fax 01668 217348 *has meat from the farm, including Aberdeen Angus-cross* *beef with a good covering of fat hung for 10-14 days; grass-fed Suffolk-cross lamb; and from the son, a hill farmer, comes heather-fed Blackie lamb which graze on the moors. Free-range pork, chicken, ducks and – at Christmas – Traditional Farmfresh turkeys and free-range geese, are all bought in locally. Anne Walton cooks a wide and varying range of ready-cooked dishes, 'anything from lasagne to chicken pie', prepares pâtés, pork sausages lightly seasoned with herbs and dry-cured bacon. A keen baker, she ensures there are always plenty of scones, fruit pies, fruit cakes, meringues, tea loafs, and border tarts in the shop and a fair range of own-made jams, pickles and lemon curd. At Christmas she also makes puddings, cakes, mince pies, mincemeat and brandy butter.*

North Acomb Farm Shop, NORTH ACOMB, Stocksfield on Tyne NE43 7UF ☎ 01661 843181 *sell green-top (unpasteurized) milk, own-made butter and cream from* *their Friesian herd. They also make a wide range of own-made fresh or frozen ready-cooked meals, including Lancashire hot-pot, salmon poached in a court-bouillon with parsley sauce, and pasties. They cure bacon and ham and make sausages from their pigs, sell own lamb and Aberdeen Angus beef imported from Scotland. For Christmas, they rear turkeys and geese.*

sion it still is 'a little variable', but he persists in producing it on what can be a rather irregular supply, due to the unavailability of sheep's milk. When he can get sheep's milk, he also makes Redesdale, a hard-pressed, dry and quite crumbly cheese with a mild kick. Finally, there is Elsdon, made with goat's milk; matured for 6 weeks, it softens slightly for a mild but pronounced taste of goat. All the cheeses are on sale at the shop, with a café attached for light snacks and lunches.

 The Real Cheese Shop, 6 Oldgate, MORPETH NE61 1LX ☎ 01670 505555 *has sister shops in Barnes and Wimbledon see pages 175 and 193, and yet another just-opened branch at* **13 Acorn Road, Jesmond, NEWCASTLE-UPON-TYNE NE2 2DJ ☎ 01912 120533**. *Owner Robert Handyside is based up North, so you can expect a good selection of cheeses from that part of the world.*

While you're in the area...

 Mill Herbs, 16 May Avenue, Winlaton Mill, BLAYDON NE21 6SF ☎ 01914 141387 grow a wide selection of culinary herbs – sold as freshly cut in 100-g (3½-oz) packs – such as dill, sage, chervil, coriander, flat-leaf parsley and summer savory. In summer they also sell 450-g (1-lb) punnets of such edible flowers as pot marigolds, nasturtiums, chives, borage and violas.

 Heatherslaw Corn Mill, CORNHILL-ON-TWEED TD12 4TJ ☎ 01890 820338 is a 19th-century water-powered corn mill. Recently restored, it grinds very slowly indeed to produce wholemeal and an 80 per cent extraction flour. The flours are sold in the gift shop, along with locally-baked Tweed bannocks which are similar to a Selkirk bannock but made with their own wholemeal flour *see page* 326. There is also a range of biscuits, cakes and slices baked by the Heatherslaw Bakery, whose premises are next door in the converted cart-shed and grainstore. Everything they make contains at least a proportion of Heatherslaw Mill flour. Particularly recommended is tea brack, made with the flour, brown sugar and vine fruits soaked in tea.

 Corbridge Larder, Hill Street, CORBRIDGE NE45 5AA ☎ 01434 632948 fax 01434 633250 *is a stylish modern shop in what is a well-preserved town. Owner Richard Burt is marked by his enthusiasm for good food and you will find plenty of examples in his shop, particularly since he has just opened up the first floor, doubling his sales space to 2,000 sq ft. He runs a team of local cooks who bake for him, so do seek out one of the best Border tarts I have ever tasted. Made by a Mrs Archer, the crisp and buttery pastry is lined with a light vanilla sauce and piled high with raisins, sultanas and currants oozing in yet more butter. Mrs Stafford rustles up lemon & orange drizzle cakes; a Pakistani family based in Newcastle make crisp and noticeably well-drained samosas; and there are brownies, Cheviot fruit cakes, terrines and pies.*

Local produce comes in the form of Tarset Valley marmalade see page 207, flour from Little Salkeld Mill see page 57, bacon and sausages from Richard Woodall see page 62, various cheeses, bread from the Village Bakery see page 57, and a (sadly erratic) supply of an aromatic melissa bee honey.

Chain Bridge Honey Farm, HORNCLIFFE, Berwick-upon-Tweed TD15 2XT ☎ 01289 386362 fax 01289 386763 sells honey gathered from the 1,000-odd hives kept in the Scottish borders. The Ling heather honey is rich and particularly clear-tasting.

The Good Life Shop, 50 High Street, WOOLER NE71 6BG ☎ 01668 281700 stocks various local cheeses, including two new ones made by Neill Maxwell. Made on a small scale with the unpasteurized milk of his Friesian/Normandy mixed herd, they are: Doddington, similar to Leicester; and Berwick Edge, a Gouda-style cheese. More reports please.

Nottinghamshire

Map No. 4

Colston Bassett & District Dairy
Harby Lane, Colston Bassett, Nottinghamshire NG12 3FN

Stilton Cheese

☎ 01949 81322 **FAX** 01949 81132 **CONTACT** *Ernie Wagstaff* **HOURS** *Mon-Fri 9.00-12.30 & 13.30-16.00 Sat 9.00-11.30* **DIRECTIONS** *From Leicester, take A46 towards Newark. Turn right at sign for Colston Bassett, about 3 miles after the roundabout junction with the A606. Follow the road for about 2¾ miles through the village. Dairy is on the right as you leave the village.*

Unlike any other British cheese, Stilton is the only one to be legally protected along similar lines to the French *Appellation d'Origine Contrôlée* or *Label Rouge* schemes. Its legal definition, given the backing of a High Court judgement in 1969, is as follows: 'Stilton is a blue or white cheese made from full-cream milk, with no applied pressure, forming its own crust or coat and made in cylindrical form, the milk coming from English dairy herds in the district of Melton Mowbray and surrounding areas falling within the counties of Leicestershire (now including Rutland), Derbyshire and Nottinghamshire'.

Several other Stilton cheese-makers sell their cheese direct to the public. In the county is **Cropwell Bishop Creamery, Nottingham Road, CROPWELL BISHOP NG12 3BQ ☎ 0115 9892350**. Out of the county but still within the controlled Stilton-making area, are **Websters Dairy, Main Street, SAXELBYE, Melton Mowbray, Leicestershire LE14 3PH ☎ 01664 812223** and J. M. Nutall, of Dove Dairy who run **The Olde Cheese Shop, Market Place, HARTINGTON, nr Buxton, Derbyshire SK17 0AH ☎ 01298 84496**.

Unfortunately the judgement made no mention of whether the cheese should or should not be pasteurized. At that time only Colston Bassett Dairy was producing unpasteurized Stilton, so to have prohibited it would not have been in the interest of the other Stilton makers. Since then Colston Bassett Dairy, under pressure caused by the listeria scare about 6 years ago, was also forced to pasteurize and now no unpasteurized Stilton is made. What is interesting is how their pasteurized cheese, generally thought to be the most interesting, goes from strength to strength. Initially there may have been the odd dip in flavour, but now it seems to have regained its mellow fruitiness, its rich butteriness, its complexity, depth and length of flavour. Of course you are unable to compare it with an unpasteurized version, but most experts would agree that it is as good as it ever was.

A small farmers' co-operative, Colston Bassett Dairy get their milk from 5 local farms, the furthest away is a mere 2½ miles from the dairy. They make between 60 and 100 cheeses a day (about 4 per cent of the total Stilton output). The cheeses are still turned by hand – every day for the first 20 days, then 3 times a week until they are pierced to encourage the veining. When buying Stilton, always look for evenly distributed veins, a good blueing and a good contrast between the paste and veins. Although you may be tempted to buy a small 450-g (1-lb) truckle, it is not necessarily a good idea. The flavour is not nearly so highly developed because such a small cheese dries out far more quickly so they mature when far younger. Colston Bassett do not even make small truckles for this reason and advise buying a piece off a large cheese. Always keep Stilton in a cool place, preferably a larder; if you do not have one, a fridge will do. Some people wrap it in a lightly moistened cloth to stop it from drying out, others use foil or cling wrap; but do not forget to unwrap and leave it at room temperature a good couple of hours before you intend to eat it.

Stockists

Avon: The Fine Cheese Co

Devon: N. H. Creber Ltd

Ticklemore Cheese Shop

London: Neal's Yard Dairy

Norfolk: The Mousetrap

CROPWELL BUTLER

Pork Pies

Mrs Elizabeth King

Hardigate Road, Cropwell Butler, Nottinghamshire NG12 3AG

☎ 0115 9332252 **CONTACT** Ian Hartland **HOURS** Mon-Fri 9.00-17.00 Sat 9.00-12.30 **DIRECTIONS** From Newark, take A46 towards Leicester. Turn left at sign for Cropwell Butler about 1 mile after roundabout junction with A52. Shop is in centre of village.

What is unusual about Mrs Elizabeth King's hand-raised pies is that they are sold frozen for you to bake yourself. The thinking behind this is to ensure maximum freshness. It works. Each pie comes complete with baking instructions and a little sack of jelly and I dutifully followed the instructions. First you thaw it out, then bake it for 1 hour at 200°C/400°F/gas 6, leave it to cool for 30 minutes, heat the jelly and pour it into the centre. You must be careful at this point; if you pour it in too enthusiastically it bubbles over, something not mentioned in the instructions. Then you have to sit back and wait for the pie to cool. You can, of course, eat it hot with the jelly as a gravy, but by the time I realized this it was too late as the jelly had already gone in. I might as well confess that I could not wait long enough for the jelly to set and when I cut the pie open, it flooded out. None the less it was extremely good. The hot-water pastry – made with flour, water, lard and salt – was crisp and clean; the pork filling – made with chopped pork shoulder – was perhaps a little solid, as if it had been a trifle over-processed, but the flavour was unquestionably good, porky and peppery. The pies, sold in 450-g, 675-g, 1.35-kg and 2.3-kg (1, 1½, 3 and 5-lb) sizes have a good balance of meat to pastry and of texture and taste.

She also sells frozen sausages with a meat content 'towards 90 per cent' in collagen skins, including leek & tomato, garlic & sage, sausage bombs (sausagemeat wrapped in pastry), sausage rolls, sausagemeat, pork burgers, Eccles cakes and – should you be determined to make your own with a bit of help – 600-g (22-oz) packs of pastry. Everything is frozen, so do remember to take a freezer bag with you when you call in.

Stockists

Cambs: Chivers Farm Shop

Derbys: Chatsworth Farmshop

Notts: Hortors Farm Shop

Plumtree Farm Shop

Thaymar Farm Shop

Fresh Farm Choice, White Post Modern Farm Centre, FARNSFIELD NG22 8HL ☎ 01623 882977 *is a farm-shop on a working farm open to the public. From the shop you can buy own-grown vegetables, including bunched carrots, beetroots with their tops, and Brussels sprouts still on their stalks, fresh or frozen own-reared free-range chickens and pork, as well as dry-cured bacon, hams and pork pies made by butcher Mike Maloney in nearby Ollerton. There are various pies, cakes, treacle and Bakewell tarts, ready-cooked frozen meals, quails' and hens' eggs, and a selection of British cheeses including a creamy fresh goats' cheese made on a very small scale by Mrs Clarke in Derbyshire.*

Mrs Potter's Perfect Pork

The Manor House, Langford, Newark on Trent,
Nottinghamshire NG23 7RW

LANGFORD

Pork Products

☎ 01636 611156 **CONTACT** *Trudy Potter – telephone ahead* **HOURS** *Wed & Fri 9.00-16.00 at Newark Market; Sat 8.30-15.00 at Southwell Market; Tues mornings at Melton Mowbray Cattle Market* **DIRECTIONS** *Markets in town centres.*

If you have ever seen Trudy Potter serving at her stall, you cannot fail to remember her. There she is, come rain or shine, complete with straw hat trimmed with a mass of flowers; a rural idyll personified. If you visit her farm, you will see that it too is a rural idyll. Her pigs are free-range in the true sense of the word, as they are both reared and fattened outdoors. She has banished all inhumane husbandry practices – namely farrowing pens, teeth-clipping, tail-cutting, castration and early weaning. The pigs live in family groups and are fed on a mixture made to her specifications, containing milled barley-meal and beans. Everyone is invited to come and see for themselves, 'it's the best way, then you see we're not conning anyone'.

Currently her pigs are either pure-bred Gloucester Old Spot or purebred Oxford and Sandy Black or crossed with the Large White boar. She likes rare or old breeds, particularly Oxford Sandy and Black. 'They are', she told me a touch controversially, 'to the rare-breed pig world what the Jack Russell is to the kennel world. They never breed true. One might be all ginger with a few black spots, another the other way round'. Apparently they do qualify as a rare breed, although not recognized by The Rare Breed Survival Trust as such'.

Pork is processed on farm and either sold as fresh, as bacon sliced from dry-cured middle (either green or smoked), or transformed into an ever-changing range of sausages. Coarsely ground with 80 per cent meat content, they are made from shoulder and belly, with either wholemeal rusk or oatmeal and packed in natural casings. Apart from plain pork, original sage, and pork & bacon, flavours are as varied as sour cherry, chives & honey, mushroom & onion with garlic, chilli & ginger, and tomato, basil & chilli. New this year are the 100 per cent meat sausages – either plain or flavoured with sage or rosemary – and Thai gluten-free, made with pork, coconut, rice and various spices.

On Trudy's market stall you will also usually find pig's fry – a mixture of pig's offal that should include trimmed liver, heart, kidney, sweetbread, brain, tongue and skirt (mesentery or frill) – which in this area is traditionally eaten with boiled onions and greens. Occasionally she has grass-fed beef from her own herd of Aberdeen Angus crossed with British White, which has been hung for a minimum of 3 weeks.

NEWARK
Hams

The Country Victualler
Winkburn Hall, Newark, Nottinghamshire NG22 8PQ

☎ 01636 636465   **FAX** 01636 636717   **CONTACT** *Richard Craven-Smith-Milnes – mail order only*   **CARDS** *Access, Diners, Mastercard, Visa*

When it comes to ham, there are two schools of thought; one is that you must buy the best-quality welfare-friendly-reared breed-specific pig, the other is that more or less any pig will do and it is how you cure and cook it that really matters. Richard Craven-Smith-Milnes belongs to the latter school. This is not to say that he does not choose his hams carefully, but he never specifies breed or worries about how they are reared. To cure his hams, first Richard injects them with a sugar and brine mixture, then they are brined for 2 days. Now you may have heard dubious reports about brine-injecting to pump up the ham. Richard assures me that he injects only to speed up the process and anyway cooks out all the excess water. Once brined, the hams are hung for 10 days to give the salts time to spread out, then they are steam-cooked for 3 hours, coated with their flavours and then dry-roasted for 4 hours. It is in the dry-roasting that the secret of his hams' flavour lies. Many producers just flash-roast so the coating adheres to the skin 'purely for cosmetic purposes. If you dry roast the flavour permeates right through'.

He produces 5 hams in total and is most proud of the Alderton, a whole ham on the bone weighing between 5 and 6 kg (11 and 13 lb) and covered with a lush tangy coating of marmalade. The boned Vict-uallers ham weighs around 5 kg (11 lb) and has a glossy honey, mar-malade and Guinness finish. Both have moist firm-textured meat and plenty of tang.

They also produce terrine de campagne, a coarse pork pâté with a hint of nutmeg, and a gutsy wild boar with juniper berries pâté en croûte. At Christmas they also sell puddings.

Stockists

London: Fortnum & Mason

Harrods

Partridges of Sloane Street

Selfridges

Notts: Christy's Farm Shop

Spring Farm Shop, The Moor, TROWELL NG9 3PQ ☎ 0115 9282076 *is perched on the side of a hill, with a bird's-eye view over Nottingham. Barbara Haynes makes all her own jams, pickles and chutneys, including a meaty apricot jam complete with kernels; wild plum and damson jams; a tart rhubarb chutney; beetroot relish; and pickled eggs. Ready-picked fruit and vegetables include peas, runner beans, broad beans, bunched beetroots still with their tops, Désirée and Wilja potatoes, cherry tomatoes, gooseberries, damsons and Victoria plums. Chickens are barn-reared and hung for around 4 days and, at Christmas, they sell own-grown turkeys and Barbara's puddings.*

P. J. Onions (Farms)
Shelton Lodge, Shelton, Newark, Nottinghamshire NG23 5JJ

SHELTON
Chickens

☎ 01949 850268   **FAX** 01949 850714   **CONTACT** *Peter Onions – telephone ahead*

I want to get one thing absolutely straight – I think Peter Onions' chick-ens are very good indeed. Well-matured birds having well-textured moist meat with plenty of deep – almost gamy – flavour. What I was worried about, however, when I visited him in the summer of 1995, was how they were reared, given that they were sold under the banner 'organic'. True they were fed organic grain, kept in airy well-ventilated houses with a low stocking density, but they were not free-range and had no access to the outdoors. One of the stipulations for organic poultry is that they must be free-range and not permanently housed.

Before I get deeper into the issues at stake I should declare my interest not only as a consumer but also as a council member of the Soil Association, one of the governing bodies for organic food. The standards to which organic food is produced are strictly regulated by the United Kingdom Registrar for Organic Farming (UKROF), in conjunction with the Soil Association and Organic Farmers & Growers. They stipulate, among other things, consideration for the animal's welfare. Their intentions are clear – to raise animals and poultry as humanely as possible; that is what we, the public, believe and, equally important, want to believe in – happy hens that can run about outside.

In Peter's defence, the UKROF's standards were initially a little ambiguous, particularly as far as housing was concerned. Realizing this, however, they were amended in September 1994 and now state categorically 'All poultry production systems must be planned to allow birds to have continuous and easy daytime access to open-air runs, except in adverse weather conditions. The land to which the birds have access must be adequately covered with properly managed and suitable vegetation'.

You may think that it does not matter a jot whether the birds range freely outdoors or, even if they did, whether they would be better. That is not the point; no one has ever said the eating quality of organic produce is necessary superior rather that it has been produced to clearly set-out rules and standards.

I have always believed that if you know what you are buying (and can have confidence in it) you will become a more discerning shopper and make more informed choices. That is one of the reasons I set out to compile this guide. Since my visit Peter has conformed to the improved standards and his birds are free-ranging. All is right with the organic world and my faith in the policing of their standards has been restored. So you can buy Peter's poultry in full confidence of both standards to which they have been reared and the flavour and texture they attain.

Stockists

London: G. G. Sparks

While you're in the area...

The Cheese Shop, 14 Market Street, BINGHAM NG13 8AB ☎ 01949 837409 has another branch in the county at **Cheese Cuisine, 10 Saracen's Head Yard, NEWARK NG24 1XA ☎ 01636 703313**. Both sell a selection of on-farm British cheeses, including Colston Bassett Stilton *see page* 211 and Lincolnshire Poacher *see page* 166. They also sell tubs of locally made Thaymar ice-cream.

The Beacon Smokehouse, Beacon Dene, Beacon Hill Road, NEWARK NG24 2JJ ☎ 01636 71631 is recommended by Trudy Potter for their farmed smoked salmon, with a medium to heavy smoke. It is sold in 115, 225 and 450-g (¼, ½, and 1-lb) packs as well as whole sliced and interleaved sides. More reports please.

Oxfordshire

R. S. Malcolm
41 High Street, Banbury, Oxfordshire OX16 8LA

☎ 01295 257724 **CONTACT** Raymond Malcolm **HOURS** Mon-Fri 9.00-17.30 Sat 8.30-17.00 **DIRECTIONS** In town centre.

Banbury cakes are really small pies or covered tarts. There are various theories as to how they came into being, but what seems clear is that they are variations on a theme, each taking its name from the town or region in which they were first made. Good ones, as far as I'm concerned, should have a light crisp pastry case positively crammed with a moist filling; it's so disappointing when bakers skimp on the filling – and so many of them do – as it makes for a very dull dry cake indeed.

Raymond Malcolm, you will pleased to hear, does not fail us with his Banbury cakes. They are generously stuffed with an oozing mincemeat of butter, brown sugar, currants, sultanas and mixed peel, subtly flavoured with rose-water, rum and lemon essence, and nutmeg. For once, the fruits are not over-chopped, so it has a chunky texture studded with whole vine fruits. The pastry, rich and flaky, comes sprinkled with icing sugar; so when, as Raymond suggests, you gently heat the cake in the oven before eating, it crispens to a crunchy sweet coating that explodes as you bite into it.

Raymond sends Banbury cakes all over the world, but you can also buy them freshly made at his shop – along with a range of breads, cakes, pies and slices – or direct from his bakery around the corner at 53, Middleton Road, which has a tiny shop attached.

BANBURY
Banbury Cakes

Stockists
Oxon: Mr Soden
- - - - - - - -
Ride-a-Cock-Horse Café
- - - - - - - -
Banesberie Coffee Shop
- - - - - - - -
The Granary Restaurant
- - - - - - - -
The Old Bakehouse

Grove Farm Shop, MILTON HILL, Abingdon OX14 4DP ☎ 01235 831247 *sell ready-picked apples, pears, strawberries, raspberries and plums. If you enjoy unusual plums, try to time a visit for some time in September, when the golden-yellow Warwickshire Drooper is ripe. Large, extra-sweet and juicy, it is an old-fashioned variety which lasts a mere day or two. They also have about 18 different ready-picked varieties of cherry, starting in June with the densely black sweet Early Rivers through to the meaty Stella in mid to late July.*

CHALGROVE
Leaves and
Herbs

Halcyon Herbs

10 Hampden Close, Chalgrove, Oxfordshire OX44 7SB

☎ 01865 890180 (mobile 0374 723103) **CONTACT** Richard Bartlett – telephone ahead.

Richard Bartlett has been a gardener most of his working life, but he did not start growing vegetables until he joined Raymond Blanc at Le Manoir 6 months before it opened, to set up the vegetable garden. Now he tends his own 5-acre field on the Waterperry Road near Wheatley and supplies some of London's trendiest restaurants, such as Bruno's Bistro, Les Saveurs and Nicole's.

With 8 poly-tunnels and the artful use of huge sheets of downy fleece to protect his plants from both the winds in winter and the full force of the sun in summer, he grows an exciting selection of more than 25 different leaves with an Eastern bent. Mizuna, with its deeply serrated dark-green leaf and mild mustard flavour, is reasonably well known. Far more unusual is leaf radish jaba, which grows a mooli-type radish and the young leaves of which are succulent with a pepper-free radish flavour; red mustard, a member of the Chinese mustard green family, is the same colour as an oak-leaf lettuce but has a catch to the throat and a fiery back bite; tatsoi is quite punchy; mibuna watery and succulent; Celtuce offers a mild bitterness; and serrated leaf santo, a lime-coloured leaf, is nutty and sweet.

Richard also grows rhubarb chard; mitsuba (a Japanese parsley); various herbs, such as wild rocket; and much, much more. Still not content with the varieties, he is 'trying wild weeds' and has just written off to 50 seed merchants all over the world to see what else they can offer.

Mail Order

55-g (2-oz) bags of mixed leaves with a minimum order of 6 bags.

The best way to try his young leaves, he thinks, is 'to dress them lightly in the best possible olive oil you can afford'. When they are more mature they can be stir-fried, steamed or used in a soup. He makes up mixtures in 55-g (2-oz) bags, depending on what is in season. During the day you can usually reach him in the fields on his mobile number to discuss an order.

Locals praise the bread from **The Old Farmhouse Bakery**, STEVENTON, **Abingdon OX13 6RP** ☎ **01235 831230**. Their aim is to produce bread as baked at home, and it is done in a 1930s brick oven in an old barn converted from a cart-shed to look very spick-and-span. Using flour from various local millers, the 30-odd breads are made up from the 14 different flours on hand; some white flour is unbleached, as 'customers like it that way', and most breads are left to prove twice. Thursday is 'organic' day, when organic breads are made; otherwise choose one of their flavoured breads: such as walnut plait, made with a mixture of 3 flours with wholemeal predominating, fresh walnuts and a pinch of curry powder to spice it up; tomato & basil with fresh tomatoes; pecan, bay & olive; or a strong cheese & onion, using English Cheddar. They also make remarkably sticky gingerbread, open fruit flans, buttery croissants and brioche, and various cakes. They also sell cheese, local Jersey cream and yoghurt, and own-made frozen pastry.

Wells Stores, 29 Stert Street, ABINGDON OX14 3JF ☎ 01235 535978 *is a rambling shop, with small rooms running one into the other and a cheese-ripening room at the back. It is run by Gill Draycott who has a passion for British on-farm cheeses. With over 70 to choose from, she has a selection of most of the best, including Old Scotland see page 265, Finn from Neal's Yard Creamery see page 181, Bonchester see page 324, and Llanboidy see page 383. It is also a good source of local produce, including Shaken Oak's mustards and dressings; Martin Pitt's eggs see page 286; fresh asparagus in season from Bothy Vineyard, as well as their wines; own-grown fruit and vegetables; Mrs Jameson's truffles see page 224; and bread from The Old Farmhouse Bakery, delivered on Fridays and Saturdays, supplemented by Innes sourdough and cheeses see page 246, fresh in on Thursdays. Gill also runs a tiny café where you can have a plate of cheese with salad, a few olives and a chunk of bread or a slice of one of her cakes.*

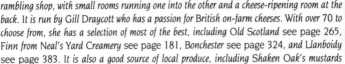

The Oxford Pick Your Own Farm
Elsfield, Oxford, Oxfordshire OX3 9SW

ELSFIELD
Baby Vegetables and Asparagus

☎ 01865 358873   FAX 01865 351463   CONTACT Peter Clarke   HOURS June to end Oct: 9.30-19.00; Nov to end May: 9.30-17.00   DIRECTIONS From Oxford, take A40 towards Wheatley. Turn left at sign for Elsfield. Drive through the village and turn left on to B4027. Follow road ½ mile and farm is signposted on the left.

Peter Clarke is one of a tiny band of pick-your-own farmers who not only grow unusual varieties but also positively encourage you to pick baby produce. He is resigned to the fact that this might be a losing battle, 'Most people pick for size; it's easier and quicker. And though they may buy baby vegetables in the supermarkets, they don't like paying the prices if it's at a PYO'. Actually he does sell ready-picked, but prefers customers to pick (or dig) their own.

Apart from the more usual vegetables, he also grows globe artichokes in season in June and July; baby round carrots; bright yellow courgettes, tasting of honey when picked at finger-size; ivory-coloured patty-pans, which remind me of a fluted brioche and are best steamed or gently stewed in butter; baby sweetcorn; Florence fennel; mangetout peas which you nip off with your fingernails while the pods are so young they are almost transparent; plain and ruby spinach (and, yes, you can pick the pousses or baby leaves); green or purple kohlrabi (best for eating raw, grated in salads when the size of a golf ball); and pak-choi, a mildly flavoured succulent Chinese leafy brassica. In the dig-your-own line – and forks are provided – there are various potatoes, including the much-favoured Pink Fir Apple; leeks for pulling when ribbon-thin; Jerusalem artichokes; and celeriac. New this season are rocket, and a startling red Brussels sprout which can be eaten raw grated into a salad or cooked, although it does lose its colour.

There is a good selection of strawberries and raspberries, with varieties chosen for taste and to last through the season; redcurrants, white currants and blackcurrants; various apples, starting with Discovery; plums from Early Rivers, running through to the newer varieties,

While you are in pick-your-own mode, visit nearby **Rectory Farm, STANTON ST JOHN OX33 1HF ☎ 01865 351214** for pick-your-own asparagus. To pick, they recommend you hold the asparagus spear (shoot) about 15 cm (6 in) from the tip and snap it off. If you prefer the sharper French-style white asparagus (the same variety just grown in trenches or banked soil to exclude light), all you do when you see a tip just breaking through the soil is to burrow down with a long knife and cut it off a few inches underground. In season from around the end of April to mid-June, they will sell ready-picked and there is an answerphone (01865 351677) for daily updated crop information. Later on they also have strawberries and raspberries.

Excalibur and Avalon; and Conference and William's pears. He now has a barn of a shop filled with own-produce in season or bought-in to fill the gaps – but he does meticulously label everything with its source so you will not be confused. He also sells hens', geese' and ducks' eggs, free-range turkeys, geese and ducks at Christmas, Lady Wills' Guernsey cream in the soft fruit season, locally baked cakes and biscuits, and bakes bread for his local customers.

RADLEY
Free-range
Turkeys

Homewood Partners
Peach Croft Farm, Radley, Abingdon, Oxfordshire OX14 2HP

☎ 01235 520094 **FAX** 01235 522688 **CONTACT** John Homewood **HOURS** Farm-shop: 9.00-17.00; **PYO**: extended hours **CARDS** Access, Eurocard, Mastercard, Visa **DIRECTIONS** From Abingdon, take the 12 Acre Drive (the peripheral road) towards Radley. Farm adjoins 12 Acre Drive and is signposted.

John Homewood is a member of both the Traditional Farmfresh Turkey Association and British Goose Producers Association. Every year he produces, to their standards, about 1,200 geese *see Goodman's Geese page* 295 and 3,500 turkeys for Christmas. The TFTA standards are, John admits, rigorous and have been set to take into account the birds' welfare and eating qualities.

To explain them as simply as possible: turkeys must be grown for a minimum of 18 weeks (John keeps his for 20 weeks), fed a mainly cereal diet free of all antibiotics (unless prescribed by a vet) and growth-promoters. Barn-reared birds must be kept at a stocking density at or below that laid down by the Animal Welfare code, in naturally lit and ventilated building on a bedding of freshly topped-up straw or softwood shavings (John uses straw); free-range birds after 8 weeks must have daylight access to open-air runs, with an area mainly covered by vegetation of at least 6 square metres per bird.

Most of John's birds are free-range and, of these, the majority are bronze birds *see Kelly Turkey Farms, page* 103, the rest ordinary whites. All free-range birds are kept in groups of 250-300 and he literally 'drives them out of the barn at first so they can experience grass, after that they go out of their own accord'. John believes that it is the exercise and 'the extra succulence from the grass that goes right through to their wing tips' that puts them points ahead on texture and flavour.

Mail Order

Christmas orders for turkeys and geese to be placed by end of November

Stockists

Avon: Bartlett & Son (Butchers)

Hants: C. E.Evans & Sons

London: Harrods

Surrey: Horton Park Farm

Once slaughtered, he complies with TFTA standards by dry-plucking and hanging them uneviscerated for a minimum of 7 days to allow their flavour to develop. Sold in weights ranging from 4.5-11.5 kg (10-25 lb) oven-ready, a couple of years ago I tried his free-range white; it was creamy and moist with a hint of game and that marked length of flavour I have come to expect from all TFTA birds. Believe me, after that, a mass-produced bird just pales into insignificance. The rest of the year he sells own-grown soft fruit, potatoes and various vegetables.

Eastbrook Farm Organic Meats

50 High Street, Shrivenham, Oxfordshire SN6 8AA

SHRIVENHAM
Poultry

☎ 01793 782211 **CONTACT** Helen Browning **HOURS** Tues-Thurs 8.00-17.00 Fri 8.00-18.00 Sat 8.00-14.00 **DIRECTIONS** From Swindon, take A420 towards Oxford. After about 4 miles, turn right after the railway bridge at sign for Shrivenham. Follow the road 1 mile to village and shop is signposted on the left.

Helen Browning is one of the leading lights in the organic movement in Britain. From Eastbrook Farm in Bishopstone, Wiltshire, covering 1,350 acres of prime downland she runs 150 beef cattle, 2 dairy herds, 650 breeding ewes, chickens for eggs, and 80 Saddleback pigs producing up to 1,600 piglets a year, all reared to Soil Association organic standards. Pigs are her passion, and to visit them free-ranging on the hills – with their arks as shelter – is to see very happy fully outdoor-reared animals. Saddlebacks, easily recognized by their bold pink stripe against black, 'make great mums', so Helen told me, 'and one of the reasons why some outdoor pig units fail is they don't use the right pig. You can't expect a modern hybrid pig to know instinctively how to rear their young. They roll over and squash them. That's just one of the reasons we chose an old-fashioned breed'.

Another reason is the quality and flavour of their meat; the pork is markedly well-textured with a fresh earthy flavour. They also cure hams and bacon and make their own sausages using only the 'real' fresh ingredients. There is a chunky gutsy Cumberland with a good whiff of spices; cider & apple; plain pork; beer & garlic; Welsh leek; beef & Guinness. The beef from the mixed herd of Angus, Hereford and various Continental breeds is also first-rate; hung for a minimum of 14 days, it has a well-developed taste and a good length of flavour. Lamb is reared on the downland clover pastures, which gives it a pleasant hazy taste. They also sell organic chickens, eggs from the farm and, at

> Butcher **M. Newitt & Sons, 10 High Street, THAME OX9 2BZ** ☎ **01844 212103 fax 01844 217715** has a reputation for quality and choice. He stocks Aberdeen Angus certified beef, Scotch beef and – when supplies are available – beef from Duchy Home Farms as well as from his own farm. There is a range of 50 different sausages, although you will probably find no more than 12 in the shop at any one time. With an average meat content of 85 per cent, favourites include: Oxford, using bread instead of rusk as a binder and a secret blend of herbs and spices; and venison with pork & red wine. Newitt's stock game, boar from Barrow Boar see page 241 and organic chickens, and prepares various marinated cuts and joints as well as ready meals and pies. Look out for own-reared free-range Maran eggs, they come from Mr Newitt's own flock.

Christmas, organic turkeys. 'Specials' – in the form of prepared meats, such as lamb fillet marinated in red wine, olive oil, garlic & rosemary or boned stuffed chicken – are another of Helen's lines. However, it has to be said that they are not a patch on her fresh meat.

Mail Order

☎ 01793 790460

THAME
Breads

De Gustibus

9 Greyhound Walk, Thame, Oxfordshire OX9 3DY

☎ 01844 214040 **FAX** 01235 555777 **CONTACT** *Dan Schickentanz* **HOURS** *Mon-Sat 9.00-17.30* **DIRECTIONS** *In town centre.*

Food lovers living in and around Oxford may already be familiar with Dan Schickentanz's lively breads, as they have been on sale in several shops in the area for the past few years. Now in his own recently opened shop in Thame, you have the chance to buy direct, although I doubt if you will ever find all of the 59 breads he lists on sale at one and the same time. What makes his breads so interesting is his use of sour-dough starters. He keeps three on the go: a rye German-style starter; a San Francisco-style; and a medium starter with a 'lesser flavour'. These he adds to all his breads in varying quantities depending on the recipe, the type of bread, the flour – even the time of year, 'in summer the action will be more vivid than winter, it'll ferment faster, so I adjust proportions accordingly'.

Whereas British bakers traditionally made bread with a long overnight fermentation, at times even adding some of the previous day's dough and giving it 2 (sometimes even 3) risings, Dan – a German – resorts to the more Continental approach of using a proportion of starters with yeast. For him, 'no bread is complete without the tang, no matter how mild. If it hasn't got it, I always feel something is missing, like listening to a full orchestra without any violins'. I know what he means, sometimes when you bite into a slice of bread, you immediately notice its lack of depth, there is nothing in the background, it has no resonance ... no back up to it.

He makes his bread in a large unit, using untreated flour and purified water. Water, he feels, is one ingredient most bakers ignore and ridding it of its major impurities – chlorine and pesticides – he is convinced improves his bread.

Dan's range is large: large and chewy bagels are a speciality and rightly so; his Italian-style Tuscany is rich in tomatoes, peppers and olives; his bready ciabattas are generously studded with spinach or sun-dried tomatoes; rosemary & sea salt focaccia is terse and rich in oil; and herb & onion is a good combination of sharp dough tempered with sweet onions. My favourites of the samples I tried (and, no, I have not tried all 59, yet...) is the Six Day Sour and the Old Milwaukee Rye. The former is made by the long drawn-out process of fermenting and feeding the flour and water over 6 days, then adding salt almost at the end so the natural yeasts are not retarded. His is surprisingly light in texture, with a good rough-looking crust and a sharp sour zing to it that mellows out the longer you keep the bread. Incidentally, if you wrap it in plastic it should last for about 10 days, provided you have not eaten it first. The Old Milwaukee Rye, a deep-dark-brown loaf made with a mixture of 35 per cent rye and 65 per cent wheat flours, caraway and treacle, was sheer delight; punched with the sourness of the dough and the gentle sweetness of the sugars, it was moist and lingeringly subtle. There are several others that I cannot wait to try: honey & lavender sounds as if it could either be a disaster or triumph; stout; mead; and saffron with sultana & sherry all sound unequivocally intriguing. I think another trip to Thame is called for.

Mail Order

sour-dough only
☎ 01993 881263

The Old Dairy Farm Shop
Path Hill Farm, Whitchurch-on-Thames, Reading, Oxfordshire
RG8 7RE

WHITCHURCH-ON-THAMES
Poultry, Meat and Dairy Produce

☎ 01734 842392 **CONTACT** Elizabeth Rose **HOURS** Wed-Sat 10.00-17.00
DIRECTIONS *From Reading, take A329 about 3 miles into Pangbourne. Turn right at The George Hotel on to B471, cross the toll bridge and follow the High Street to Whitchurch-on-Thames. Take the first turning on the right into Hardwick road, just opposite a shop on the left called Heron Pictures. Follow the road out of the village and up Path Hill. At the top, turn right into the farm lane, just opposite the sharp left bend in the road. Follow lane and shop is in front of you.*

The Old Dairy Farm Shop, converted from the old dairy, is on the 1,000-acre Hardwick Estate owned by Sir Julian Rose and, as a committed member of the Soil Association, he farms it organically. Of the produce sold in the farm-shop run by his wife Elizabeth, about 80 per cent is certified organic. If, however, you think this means a dreary but worthy selection you could not be more wrong. There is a riot of temptingly good 'proper' food to indulge in; the fact that it is farmed organically seems almost incidental.

    Almost half their turnover is meat and, even though the shop has been open for 3 years, surprisingly there is not enough volume to justify stocking every meat fresh, every week. There are always frozen supplies, but if you prefer it fresh, Elizabeth has devised a system that works efficiently; a big blackboard in the shop offers up a timetable of what will be in fresh and when, giving everyone plenty of notice and the opportunity to order. Beef comes mainly from their mixed herd of Aberdeen Angus, North Devon, and Guernsey crossed with a particularly docile North Devon bull. The calves are reared on their mother's milk for the first 6 months to give them a good start, they then graze on organic pastures supplemented with cereal and silage, and are slaughtered at anything between 2 and 3 years. Hung for about 3 weeks, this is beef at its best; well-grained and juicy, with a deep meaty taste and a superb length of flavour, it demands to be noticed. Lamb is hung for 2 weeks and again has that glorious full flavour.

Chickens and, at Christmas, turkeys are also first-class. I must point out here, however, that they cannot be sold as certified organic because of a mere (although, to the Soil Association, important) technicality. The Roses buy in chicks and poults (day-old turkeys) which are not fed organic chick-feed as it is difficult to buy and its cost is prohibitive. So, although they are reared in optimum organic conditions and are truly free-ranging (you can see the turkeys out in the fields scratching around for nettles), they do not qualify for the symbol. I only wish other producers would be as scrupulous. Also from the estate are wild rabbits either whole or jointed, wild venison, and wood pigeon breasts throughout the year, with pheasant and partridges in season. Pork is bought in, mainly from Eastbrook Farm Organic Meats *see page* 221; hams are cured for them at Minola *see page* 112 and they make their own sausages. These come as chipolatas with a 75 per cent meat content (Elizabeth has reduced it down marginally as people complained the sausages were 'too heavy'). The flavours are Mild, with nutmeg & sage, also made in a plump Succulent; Spicy, with coriander and ginger; lamb with garlic & rosemary; and English country with sage & thyme.

Julian was one of the champions of the Save our Green Top (unpasteurized) Milk, so you will be certain to find full-cream and low-fat skimmed milk, as well as a rich buttery yellow unpasteurized cream from the Guernsey dairy herd. Recently the dairy has been revived to process their unpasteurized Guernsey milk. The fruits of their labour are a thick, seriously creamy, strained yoghurt and a fresh creamy curd cheese, which comes either plain or with fresh parsley & chives or black pepper. Dairy-maid Jane King is being ably abetted by James Aldridge *see page* 262 to perfect her rind-ripened soft cheese with its buttery interior. Still at early-days stage it promises very well indeed.

From the shop you can also buy a full range of organic vegetables, salads and soft fruit, grown in a 10-acre field on the estate or in the 2-acre walled garden behind the big house; bread from The Old Farmhouse Bakery *see page* 218, including a few specials baked exclusively for them; eggs; organic flour, grown by Julian and milled at Bartley Mill *see page* 269; and various other superior organic products, such as Rocombe Farm ice-cream *see page* 84 and Rachel's Dairy produce *see page* 380. This is a glorious spot and Elizabeth encourages visitors to walk around the 600 acres of woodlands 'provided you keep to the paths'.

While you're in the area...

Mrs Jameson of Bayworth, 11 Brumcombe Lane, BAYWORTH OX13 6QU ☎ 01865 730158 makes about 100 different chocolates on a small scale, supplying several of the High Tables at the Oxford colleges. Truffles have a ganache using fresh cream from a local farm and are flavoured with marc de champagne, amaretto, and banana & rum. Centres for moulded chocolates include chestnut & marzipan and sherry & walnut. At Easter she makes truffle-filled eggs; at Christmas, various solid figures.

Butcher **Richard Walton, 1 Mill Street, EYNSHAM OX8 1HE ☎ 01865 881219** comes praised to the skies by Penny Marcus, wife of food writer Paul Levy. 'He's literally the best traditional British butcher I've ever come across. There's nothing he doesn't do or can't get for you, from pigs' cheeks to caul fat. His sausages, made with fresh herbs, are wonderful; his dry-cured bacon excellent, and his meat well-hung – steak for 3 weeks. Now I've found him, I won't go anywhere else'.

Shaken Oak Products, Shaken Oak Farm, HAILEY, Witney OX8 5UX ☎ 01993 868398 produce a range of coarse-grain mustards, including: original; hot, with chillies; with herbs; and with garlic; Arthur's peppercorn; and a self-explanatory hot & smooth. They also make a mustard & garlic dressing with olive and sunflower oil, cider vinegar and their mustard, as well as a picante sauce.

What's for Dinner?, 23 Market Place, HENLEY-ON-THAMES RG9 2AA ☎ 01491 412128 fax 01491 412098 is a new shop modelled on a French-style *traiteur*, with plenty of food-to-go cooked by the chef on the premises and a menu that changes daily. The day I dropped in starters included pigeon salad, 'caveached' salmon and chicken terrine; puddings included treacle tartlets, tarte au citron and lemon & walnut meringue cake.

Maison Blanc, 3 Woodstock Road, OXFORD OX2 6HA ☎ 01865 510974 fax 01865 311027 bake a good range of rough French country breads, baguettes, ficelles and full-butter crois-sants and brioches, as well as pâtisserie finished in the French style, such as religieuse and a satisfyingly sharp tarte au citron.

The Covered Market in the centre of Oxford just off the High is, according to Food Lover Bob Gee, 'arguably the finest of its type in the country … (it) is a must for any self-respecting Food Lover who wants really high-class service by very knowledgeable vendors'. He recommends **M. Feller Son & Daughter, 54 and 55 The Covered Market ☎ 01865 251164** for their 'stunning array of home-cooked meats and pork scratchings'; and **Hayman's 21, Avenue 1, The Covered Market ☎ 01865 242827** for the 'variety, freshness and quality' of their fish. Recently opened at 96 is **Stroff's Speciality Sausages, Oxford OX1 3DY ☎ 01865 200922** and it is recom-mended by Laura Mason for their Oxford sausage, made with shoulder of pork, veal, lemon, herbs, and high-baked breadcrumbs instead of the more usual rusk. **The Oxford Cheese Shop, 17 The Covered Market ☎ 01865 721420** has a good selection of on-farm cheeses.

Mapledurham Watermill, Mapledurham Estate, READING RG4 7TR ☎ 01734 723350 gets my vote as the prettiest mill in the country. It is also the last working corn and grist mill on the Thames and there has been a mill on the site since Saxon times. Mildred Cookson, one of the few female millers I have met, runs the mill single-handedly and sells 100 per cent and 81 per cent stoneground flours.

Shropshire

Map No. 4

Womerton Farm

All Stretton, Church Stretton, Shropshire SY6 6LJ

☎ 01694 751260 **CONTACT** *Ruth Lawrence – telephone ahead*

It is always thrilling to discover a new cheese, particularly when it is made by as conscientious a cheese-maker as Ruth Lawrence. She has packed in several years of cheese-making, starting at agricultural college, then a few months under John Curtis's watchful eye making Bonchester *see page* 324 and on to France, somewhere near Dijon, where it was all goats' cheese and – as a bonus – 'glorious wines'.

Starting from scratch is never easy, but Ruth and her husband have built up a goat herd of about 60 – mainly Anglo-Nubian – goats and built their own dairy. She makes 2 cheeses, with ambitions for others, but realizes that she still has work to do 'perfecting' her current cheese. Working with goats' milk can have its problems, 'you want to achieve a cheese with a fine balance of a distinctive flavour but not one that's too goaty. On the other hand, if it's not goaty enough, you might just as well be working with cows' milk.' Goats' milk must also be handled gently otherwise it taints, 'if you shake it around you disturb the fat globules, which are not as stable as in cows' milk. That is one

---

Wrekin Honey, Southview, WROCKWARDINE TF6 5DJ ☎/fax 01952 254894
*has unfortunately closed down its shop, but the distinctive honeys are still sold by mail order.
With 300 hives, which Ralph Palmer moves around the county depending on the blossoms
and seasons, he produces a pale rape-seed (not one of my favourites); a charmingly light general
hedgerow; a deep aromatic wild flower; clover with a dense lingering aftertaste; a vividly fruity raspberry; a thick unctuous broad bean; sunflower; and a Ling heather honey from the Long Mynd in
South Shropshire in 115, 350 and 450-g (½, ¾ and 1-lb) jars. Unlike large-scale honey producers,
Ralph never flash-heats his to dissolve the crystals and keep it liquid. The very process, he says destroys
the enzymes and sugar and reduces the immediacy of the honey's flavour. This does mean that some
will crystallize, but honey can always be easily liquefied by gently heating it in a bain-marie.*

MAP 4   SHROPSHIRE   227

way of getting off-flavours'.

Currently Ruth is making Womerton, a 1.35-kg (3-lb) hard-pressed cheese that is milled twice, pressed for 24 hours, then brined and matured for 3 months. Light and very fresh, with only the gentlest of goat characteristics, Ruth modestly describes it as 'getting there'. Her other cheese, a soft St Frances, made with a penicillin mould, has still 'got to get there', as when I tried it was still rather soapy. I have every confidence in Ruth, however, she will 'get there' very soon.

Stockists
Salop: Ludlow Larder

Dukeshill Ham Co Ltd
Deuxhill, Bridgnorth, Shropshire WV16 6AF

BRIDGNORTH
York Ham

☎ 01746 789519 **FAX** 01746 789533 **CONTACT** *George Morley – mail order only* **CARDS** Access, Amex, Visa

George Morley's mother was a Marsh of Marsh & Baxter, one of the great producers of York ham. So it seems only logical then, when he left the family company, that he should start his own business specializing in what he likes to think of as 'the smoked salmon of the meat trade – York Ham'. He buys in legs of pork with a good fat cover, as 'for curing it's important they're not hyper-lean', and dry-cures them for 3 weeks in salt and saltpetre, brushing off and changing the cure three times. The hams are hung to mature for about 12 weeks, until ready, and have a markedly deep punchiness and a firm chew to the meat. They can be matured longer but, according to George, this will affect not so much their taste as their texture; which becomes even denser, due no doubt to the moisture loss.

New this year is the Shropshire Black ham. As far as I know it is an invention of George's, rather than a traditional cure of the county; actually it is strikingly similar to a Suffolk-cure but, I assure you, none the worse for that. To start with, the hams are cured exactly as for a York, then after a couple of weeks they are immersed in a brine flavoured with molasses and various spices, including juniper. Left for 3 weeks to pickle, they are then hung for 12 weeks, by which time they have acquired their meatiness with a back-up of sweet-saltiness.

George also sells a milder Wiltshire-cure, with the hams brined for about 2 weeks. All his hams are sold either cooked or uncooked on the bone, with a choice of a whole ham weighing 6.3 kg (14 lb), a small whole ham at about 4.5 kg (10 lb) or half a ham at 3 kg (6½ lb). Sold uncooked or cooked, on-the-bone (he will bone them, but is reluctant to do so because they do not cook so well) and as hams rather than by actual weight, with a guaranteed minimum weight of 3 kg (6½ lb) for half a ham, 5 kg (11 lb) for a small and 6.3 kg (14 lb) for a whole one. Definitely not ham for the faint-hearted, they have a stronger punch than the milder Wiltshire-cure hams George also sells.

Blackhurst Of Shropshire
Drawwell, Clive, Shrewsbury, Shropshire SY4 3JN

☎ 01939 220329 **CONTACT** Jim Blackhurst **HOURS** Mon-Fri 9.00-18.00 Weekends by arrangement **DIRECTIONS** From Shrewsbury, take A49 towards Whitchurch. Follow the road about 10 miles into Preston Brockhurst and turn left signposted Clive. Follow the road 1½ miles into Clive and take the first turning left in the village, at sign for Drawwell. Smokery is 100 yards along on the right, opposite the church.

Jim Blackhurst spent a fair amount of time in Finland and Scandinavia where he learnt to smoke. Possibly as a result, their products have an obvious flavour of the smoke – not overpoweringly so, but very definitely present. Smoking takes place in 2 small smoking cabinets across the courtyard from their house. They use oak chips with the addition, at times, of different aromatic woods.

Imported corn-fed chicken, cold-smoked for 36 hours then roasted to cook it through, is succulent with a well-married taste of salt and smoke; pheasant from a local shoot, cured in salt and brown sugar and smoked over oak mixed with applewood, is fairly gamy, cut by a pleasant sweet haziness; and their hot-smoked trout, farmed over the borders near Chirk, has a definite bite of salt.

They also smoke imported corn-fed guinea fowl; Barbary duck breasts smoked for 8-10 hours to ensure a dense smokiness; poussin; quail; and haunch of farmed venison, sold thinly sliced; farmed salmon from Scotland is cold-smoked and they have just started smoking whole heads of garlic. Theirs are all gutsy products, favoured by anyone who likes a sense of smoke.

The Blackhursts cure salmon with fresh dill for gravadlax and here the Scandinavian influence is discernible; theirs is far more full-bodied than most. They also have some 'prepared-to-order' products: smoked salmon terrine, a creamy mousse wrapped in slices of salmon; smoked salmon; smoked trout; and ducks' liver pâté.

Mail Order

smoked products only

Dalesman's Ice Cream
Cruckmoor Farm, Prees Green, Whitchurch, Shropshire SY13 2BS

☎ 01948 840217 **CONTACT** Andrew Fawcett **HOURS** Easter to mid-Sept: Thurs-Sun 10.30-17.30 **DIRECTIONS** From Whitchurch, take A49 towards Shrewsbury. After about 5½ miles, go over the bypass and turn left at the 'Farm ice cream sign'. Farm is 600 yards along on the left.

Dalesman's ice-cream strikes me as one of the better on-farm ice-creams. Cruckmoor is still very much a family farm, run by Andrew Fawcett, his brother and father. The milk for the ice-cream comes from their 120-strong Friesian herd. There are 2 unusual things about Dalesman's ice-cream – its ingredients and its texture. Made from own-milk, sugar, cream and fresh eggs, it does contain stabilizer and emulsifier in the forms of sodium alginate, guar gum and mono- and diglycerides of fatty acids respectively; but, unlike virtually every other ice-cream, it does not contain any skimmed milk powder. This is because, having worked out a mix to suit their old-fashioned Italian ice-cream maker, they found they did not need it.

The over-run (added air) is also exceptionally low, between 15-20 per cent; as a result, this is one ice-cream with a very heavy, dense texture. The overall impression is one of a deep richness, an ice-cream that you can 'bite' into, with plenty of substance. You either love it or hate it. Rather misleadingly, its actual fat content ranges between 4 and 7 per cent, but this is because it is gauged on the ice-cream's liquid state and Dalesman's is far thicker than most. So, if it were to have a usual over-run, its fat content would rise to the more normal range of 10-14 per cent.

They make a range of 8 flavours: some, namely hazelnut, mint and toffee, are bought in from an Italian flavour house; others are own-made and much the better for it. Try as they may, these flavour houses can never exactly reproduce the true flavours and I only wish more ice-cream producers would leave well alone. Vanilla is made with ground-up pods and you can see the little black speckles which, so Andrew says, actually put some people off. I loved it, buttery and not over-sweet it was laced with a true musk rather than a synthetic syrupiness. Banana is again made with the 'real' thing – mashed fruit – and again it had the true taste; chocolate, from a dark Belgian couverture, was rich and strong-bodied. Andrew also makes raspberry and strawberry fruit ices, with egg white, sugar and fruit purée. More of a sorbet than an ice-cream, they were refreshing and fruity, if a touch on the sweet side for my – but not Violet's – taste. Sold from the farm in cones or 1 and 4-litre (1¾ and 7-pint) packs, remember to take your cool-bag along.

Appleby's of Hawkstone

Hawkstone Abbey Farm, Weston-under-Redcastle, Shrewsbury, Shropshire SY4 5LN

☎ 01948 840221 **FAX** 01948 841199 **CONTACT** Edward Appleby – telephone ahead

WESTON-UNDER-REDCASTLE
Cheshire Cheese

Although not actually in the county of Cheshire, the Applebys make a very fine Cheshire cheese. The special flavour of the Cheshire cheese is, according to John Arlott, due to the soil of Cheshire, which contains rich deposits of salts. The Appleby's land, not far from the county border is, they assured me, rich in the correct minerals.

Mrs Lucy Appleby is still in charge of the cheese-making. John Arlott states that in 1939 there were about 400 farmhouses turning out some 6,000 tons a year, almost all of it a pale orange (coloured with

T. O. Williams of Wem, 17 High Street, WEM SY4 5AA ☎ 01939 232552 fax 01939 235151 – with shops in Shawbury, Shrewsbury and Whitchurch – make a point of selling local as well as many other cheeses. Here you will find Cheshires from Appleby's, Hares and Windsor's, all past and current champions of the Cheshire and Nantwich Cheese Shows.

anatto); now there are a mere handful, with the Appleby's the only one to make a clothbound unpasteurized version. They make it 6 days a week, with their own milk from their Friesian/Holstein-cross herd and they also make it a lot slower than most. Cheshire has a reputation for being quite a sharp acidic cheese, due partly to the amount of starter used. The Applebys use far less (about 0.5 per cent as opposed to as much as 5 per cent by others); this means the acidity level in the milk takes far longer to rise, but the result – a richer, buttery, more mellow cheese – makes it worth it.

Cheshire is well-known for its loose crumbly texture, which is achieved by cutting the curds, then breaking them by hand and finally – when all the whey is drained off – milling them. The downside is that it is notoriously difficult to store as it is prone to cracking (which is how it blues naturally) or drying out. The Applebys wrap theirs in calico, then smear it with a bought-in edible paste (originally flour and water) and mature it for at least 6 – but possibly up to 10 – weeks. (Randolph Hodgson at Neal's Yard Dairy, *see page* 180 will mature it on for as long as 12 months). Sold in truckles ranging from 900 g to 22.5 kg (2 to 50 lb), it is a delight; moist and sharp, cut with a subtle saltiness that lingers on the palate. One of the oldest cheeses this country boasts, I believe it was even mentioned by name in the Domesday Book.

Mrs Appleby also makes a soft mild salted whey-butter which is still churned by hand every day in the wooden butter churn, and a mellow Double Gloucester.

WESTON-
UNDER-
REDCASTLE

Bacon

Maynards Farm Bacon
The Hough, Weston-under-Redcastle, Shrewsbury, Shropshire SY4 5LR

☎ 01948 840252   **CONTACT** Maynard Davies   **HOURS** Wed-Sun 9.00-17.30
DIRECTIONS *From Shrewsbury, take A49 towards Whitchurch. Farm-shop is on the left after about 12 miles.*

When it comes to bacon, Maynard Davies has an interesting theory along the lines that the further north you travel in Britain, the stronger the cure of bacon. Certainly his dry-cured Shropshire is harsh and rasping, a no-nonsense bacon that demands to be noticed; otherwise I am not totally convinced.

In all, Maynard produces at least 10 different cures, each with a different flavour; and each one of the 10 comes as a choice of cut from the middle or back (streaky) and as green (unsmoked) or smoked over applewood. Pigs are carefully chosen for a good covering of fat or, that is to say, a 'proper bacon pig. You can't dry-cure properly if the pig's too lean. The meat goes hard. You need the fat to absorb the salt,' and the butchering and curing is done in his converted barns behind the shop. Traditional, dry-salted with an iodine-free salt 'so it won't weep in the pan', has a good biting texture and a well-developed earthy flavour; Shropshire is dry-cured for longer; Welsh, cured in a mixture of salt and saltpetre, is softer-textured; County, the mildest of them all, is brined with sugar; Honey, brined in an English honey, has a shy sweet flavour; English Gold, cured in a treacle brine, has a thicker richer flavour; and Staffordshire Black, easily recognizable by its dark rind, is cured in black treacle for an even thicker, soupier taste. New this year are Suffolk, in which the bacon is brined in beer and treacle for 5 weeks, and Low-salt, where less salt than usual is used. By Maynard's admission '(this) doesn't keep as well. Frankly it's a bit like drinking weak coffee'.

Maynard also produces 5 different sausages with natural skins which he fills with lean shoulder meat. These include: Shropshire with a 100 per cent meat content, mildly seasoned with salt and pepper; a more heavily seasoned Cambridge; and Lincoln, flavoured with dried sage. Then there are his dry-cured hams. He works them relatively fast as the actual process from curing to maturation takes him about 4 months and the range includes York dry-cured in salt and saltpetre, and a brightly coloured – almost cherry-blossom-pink – Honey Ham. If you like good old-fashioned bacon, this is one place to find it.

Meadow View Quail

Meadow View Farm, Church Lane, Whixall, nr Whitchurch,
Shropshire SY13 2NA

WHIXALL
Smoked Salt

☎ 01948 880300   **CONTACT** Mr Eddie Reeves – telephone ahead

If you like the flavour of smoked food but do not want to eat food that has been smoked, there is a solution – smoked salt. You use it exactly as you would ordinary salt – perhaps a little more sparingly – with whatever you are cooking, whether it is fish, meat, game or poultry. About 1 heaped teaspoonful mixed with a little butter and rubbed into a 1.25-kg (2½-lb) chicken is one of Eddie Reeves's suggestions. The smokiness permeates right through and you will end up with a moist bird that does have a delicate smoky haze. Trust me, it really does work.

Buying asparagus from **Golding Hall**, **PITCHFORD**, **Shrewsbury SY5 7HG** ☎ **01694 731204** is an experience. On your way to the 4 acres of asparagus fields, you saunter past the Tudor gabled Hall with a later red-bricked facade that belies its true age. From about the beginning of May through to mid-June, you can pick-your-own asparagus. Baskets, knives and a demonstration are provided, but bring your own gloves. If you prefer, you can telephone ahead to order asparagus ready-picked.

Eddie Reeves makes no claim to dreaming up the idea, it was a suggestion from one of his customers, who had stumbled across it in Spain. After several months experimentation, however, he does think he has perfected the technique. Using a quality sea salt which he imports from Spain, the problem was, as he explained, 'getting the right degree of intensity of flavour'. He cold-smokes it over oak chips in trays, stirring and turning it until it is done, 'that can be anywhere from 7 to 14 days, depending on weather. You need that long to get the depth'. By that time the finely grained salt has turned a dark honey-brown and is well imbued with smoke. Packed in 30-g (1-oz) sachets, do make sure you store it in an airtight jar, otherwise it could overpower the entire kitchen.

Eddie also makes up 2 flavoured dipping salts, which he sees as alternatives to the ubiquitous celery salt. These are Herb, made with bay, thyme, fennel & black pepper; or spiced, made with a potent mix of chilli, turmeric & coriander. He also produces quails' eggs (hence the dipping sauce), packed in 300-g (10½-oz) jars – with a minimum of 13 eggs to the jar – in quite a vinegarish pickle. They are sold either pickled or smoked and pickled, although he will do plain smoked to order.

Stockists
Salop: T.O. Williams

While you're in the area...

Ellesmere Road Organic Nursery, COCKSHUTT, Ellesmere SY12 9AB ☎ 01939 270270 grows a wide range of produce to Soil Association standards. These include strawberries, raspberries, broad beans, tomatoes, cucumber and piercingly sweet hothouse melons, ripe during July and August.

Butchers **C. G. Sadd, DORRINGTON, Shrewsbury SY5 7JD ☎ 01743 718215** dry-cure hams in salt, saltpetre and brown sugar, mature them up to 12 months for a strong meaty flavour and sell them smoked or unsmoked, raw or cooked, on or off the bone. They also cure for bacon.

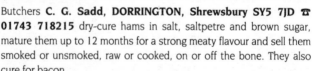

Carter's High Class Family Butchers, 6 King Street, LUDLOW SY8 1AQ ☎ 01584 874665 still farm 'in a small way'; the rest of the meat is bought in on the hoof at auction and hung for 2-3 weeks. Ham and bacon are own-cured in salt and brown sugar. More reports please.

Arthur Hollins, Fordhall Farm, TERN HILL, Market Drayton TF9 3PR ☎ 01630 638255 sells either from the farm or from his stall at Altrincham Organic market, fresh beef, pork, lamb and good strong and immensely well-flavoured chickens, weighing from 1.8-4 kg (4-9 lb).

Somerset

Map No. 2

Swaddles Green Farm

Swaddles Green Farm, Hare Lane, Buckland St Mary, Chard, Somerset TA20 3JR

☎ 01460 234387 **FAX** 01460 234591 **CONTACT** Charlotte Reynolds **HOURS** Thurs-Fri 10.00-18.00 Sat 10.00-13.00 **CARDS** Access, Visa **DIRECTIONS** From Ilminster, take A358 towards Taunton. After about 100 yards, turn left at sign for Broadway. Drive through Broadway and, after about 1½ miles, signpost for farm-shop is on the right.

Swaddles Green Farm, a 35-acre holding in the Blackdown Hills, has been farmed by Charlotte and Bill Reynolds since 1987. Here they farm chickens, ducks, geese and – at Christmas – bronze turkeys to UKROFS (United Kingdom Register of Organic Food Standards). Meat is bought in from various local organic farms and processed on their farm in an old flint barn converted into a cold store, chilled cutting rooms and a poultry processing unit.

    The shop is on the other side of the yard and from here they sell their poultry, lamb hung for 1 week, beef hung for 3 weeks, and pork all butchered into various cuts. The quality of their mince remains impres-

Nori and Sandra Pope have, according to Garden Illustrated 'created one of the most beautiful border gardens in England' at **Hadspen Garden & Nursery**, **CASTLE CARY BA7 7NG** ☎/**fax 01749 813707**. Better still, after a lazy saunter through 'a 5-acre canvas of melding hues' you can have tea in the blue patio – a paved courtyard with a riot of blue flowers. Lunches and teas are served every day from Easter to the end of September. The food is cooked in the kitchens of the nearby Bonds Hotel and brought up to an old gardener's cottage which has what can, at best, be described as 'a cramped charm'. If the weather is fine, you must sit outside, inhale the scented air and tuck in. Teas are honest affairs: own baked scones liberally spread with Elliscombe cream see page 243; generous sandwiches; and splendid cakes, such as meringue roulades, apple cake, or open fruit tarts. On a sunny day you may want to stay all afternoon.

sive. There are 3 grades: Everyday, from flank, bits of brisket and trimmings; Lean, from chuck, clod and sticking (the top end of the rump); and Ground Steak, from the top rump and steak trimmings. Chunky sausages, made with shoulder of pork, have a 95 per cent meat content and come as plain, herb, garlic (made with fresh garlic), tomato & chilli, tomato, basil & garlic, and red wine. They also cure for bacon and ham and make a range of charcuterie. Improved since last year, I must admit I still find their *saucisson sec*, a little leathery and unsubtly spiced.

New this year are their pies and prepared meals. There are mini pork pies with a rich pastry and a meaty (if a little densely textured) filling. Both chicken and steak & kidney pies are generously filled and, while there is no denying the quality of the meat, the flavour was a touch ordinary.

Charlton Orchards
Charlton Road, Creech St Michael, Taunton, Somerset TA3 5PF

☎ 01823 412959 **FAX** 01823 412959 **CONTACT** Matthew Freudenberg **HOURS** *mid-Aug to end Mar: Mon-Sat* 10.00-18.00 *Sun* 14.00-17.00 **DIRECTIONS** *At exit 24 of M5, take A38 towards Taunton. Follow the road for about 3 miles, turn left on to A361, direction Glastonbury. Take first turning right into Creech St Michael. After about ¾ mile, turn left at the sign for Charlton Road – No Through Road. Orchard is 1 mile down the road on the left.*

Unlike many other commercial apple orchards where 'yield per tree, regularity of cropping and uniformity of fruit size' are the major preoccupations, Charlton Orchards choose their varieties for flavour and texture, 'We only grow them if they are really good to eat'. Grown under an 'integrated pest-management system' (meaning they do not blanket-spray trees but rather monitor them closely and only spray when necessary), they have over 20 varieties and are always adding to them.

The apple season starts in mid-August, with the lightly strawberry-flavoured Discovery, and moves on to Katy and Worcester in September. Next come late-season apples (varieties ripening for eating in October to December), including the nutty Cox, the orange and red-cheeked Lord Lambourne and (one of my great favourites) the creamy white-fleshed slightly russeted sweet and intensely aromatic Orléans Reinette – the ideal Christmas apple. They grow a few extra-late season apples (for eating in December to March), namely Ashmead's Kernel, an old variety famous for its 'pear-drop' taste, Gloucester 69 and the firm juicy Suntan with plenty of acidity.

This year sees the first tasting of varieties planted 3 years ago. When first planted, a tree should always have its blossom stripped for at least the first 2 years 'to get a reasonable tree going and it takes about 5 years to get a good crop'. However, the Freudenbergs are leaving some blossom on, so with any luck you might be able to sample Claygate Pearmain with its rich nuttiness and refreshing zest; the nutty Egremont Russet; Ribston Pippin, with its firm deep cream flesh; and Adam's Pearmain, a favourite of the Victorians.

All Charlton Orchards' apples are kept in cold storage until ready, and are sold from their grading shed by the pound or in 4.5- and 9-kg (10- and 20-lb) trays. There are 'always apples for tasting so visitors can try the varieties and see what is in season'. The Freudenbergs also mail out a 2.7-kg (6-lb) Traditional English Apple box, made up of either Cox, Suntan or Orléans Reinette (or a mixture of the 3), with each apple hand-wrapped in tissue. These make an imaginative – and welcome – Christmas present.

French's Escargots
Beechfield Farm, Curry Rivel, Langport, Somerset TA10 ONP

☎ 01458 252246 **FAX** 01458 253072 **CONTACT** Nicola French – *telephone ahead*

The British have never embraced snails with quite the same enthusiasm as the French. In the West Country, where they are known as 'wallfish' (because they float along walls?), they are supposed to be a local delicacy. I have yet to meet a local who indulges.

There must be a demand, however, because Nicola French farms them there. Admittedly most of her customers are local restaurants, but she is more than happy to sell them directly to the public. Her snails are superior garden snails – '*petit gris*', the variety favoured by the French. Grown outdoors in poly-tunnels between April and September and fed on mixed greens, they are then brought indoors into a barn to hibernate. Available throughout the year, Nicola needs at least 24 hours' notice to collect an order. The advantage of buying snails from her is that they are so fresh they are still alive; the disadvantage is the lengthy preparation this incurs.

Actually, it is not that difficult. Once you have collected the snails (and do remember to take a box with a tightly fitting lid – otherwise

---

Barnard & Gooding Dairies, Keward Farm, River Road, PAWLETT, Bridge-water TA6 4SE ☎ 01278 685173 fax 01278 684664 *make an ice-cream using milk and double cream, sugar, egg yolk, dried skimmed milk and carob bean gum as a stabilizer. With a fat content 'heading for 16 per cent' and an over-run (added air) of 30 per cent, it is creamy and dense. Joining the existing range – Banana made with fresh bananas for a fruity punch; Coffee; a sweet Cointreau & Orange, a mixture of the liqueur and orange zest; Ginger; Vanilla; Chocolate Chip; Chocolate; and Strawberry, replete with pips – are Blackberry made with bought-in purée; Fudge a mixture of caramelized sugar, chopped fudge and larger pieces to give it texture; and Toffee, which also has toffee pieces. At Christmas they also make a Christmas Pudding ice-cream, and throughout the year can be relied on for 500-ml (16-fl oz) cartons of frozen goats' milk from their own herd.*

they will escape all over the car), the first thing is to kill them. This is achieved simply enough by plunging them in boiling water. Once cooled down they have to be hoicked out of their shells. Again a simple enough operation, provided you have a skewer and a strong wrist-flicking action. Then they have to be thoroughly washed under cold running water until it runs clear; finally they must be gently simmered (too high a heat and they turn rubbery) for about an hour – preferably in a court-bouillon made with water, cider or wine, bay leaves, onion, carrot, mixed herbs, salt and pepper. At last they are ready to be stuffed back in their shells and baked in garlic butter or whatever you fancy.

Brown & Forrest

HAMBRIDGE
Smoked Eel

The Smokery, Bowdens Farm, Hambridge, nr Curry Rivel, Somerset TA10 0DR

☎ 01458 251520 **FAX** 01458 253475 **CONTACT** Michael Brown **HOURS** *Mon, Tues & Thurs 10.00-13.00 Sat 9.30-12.00* **CARDS** *Access, Eurocard, Mastercard, Visa* **DIRECTIONS** *From Taunton, take A358 towards Chard and Yeovil. After 2 miles, turn left on to A378 towards Langport. After 6 miles, turn right in centre of Curry Rivel on to B3168 towards Ilminster and Hambridge. After 1½ miles, Hambridge is signposted on verge. 50 yards after sign, turn left at farm-track, signposted Bowdens Farm, directly opposite a red-brick house in trees. Follow track to farm courtyard. Smokery is in stone barn on left.*

The natural habitats of the common or freshwater eel are rivers, ponds and lakes, although it can survive out of water. Because of our current problem of pollution, it is vital that eels come from clean, unpolluted water and Michael Brown collects his from the upper reaches of the rivers Avon, Itchen, Stour and Test. 'They're all chalk streams, good clean rivers upstream with good feed'.

For smoking, the best of all eels are silver (mature) eels. Plump and juicy with a rich succulent flesh, the eel turns silver in autumn as it is ready to start its extraordinary exhausting journey downstream and on to its breeding grounds in the faraway Sargasso Sea. 'You know intuitively when they're going to run. Usually it's with a deluge of rain after a dry spell. Then they run downstream with a vengeance. They're caught on racks straddled across the rivers because, if the river's in full spate, you can't get the nets out. The brown or younger eels have already hibernated, so what you catch is 99 per cent silver eel'.

Michael blast-freezes the eels, as 'it's the most efficient and painless method of killing them'. It also means that he has a supply of eels in prime condition throughout the year and draws on his stock as and when he needs them. First he brine-cures them for 2-3 hours 'Although you can dry-cure, I always brine them because I learnt the trade in Germany and that's how they do it over there. I also believe you get a more even uptake of salt'. Then he hot-smokes them over beechwood to cook them right through. Sold as whole eels, usually weighing about

900 g (2 lb), and in 225 g (8 oz) and 450 g (1 lb) packs of skinned and neatly cut fillets, they have a full meaty flavour and a soft succulent – almost gelatinous – texture. Michael recommends eating them simply seasoned with freshly ground black pepper and a squeeze of lemon juice to cut their richness.

He also smokes wild Scottish salmon, and hot- or cold-smokes trout. The cold-smoked trout is cured in a mixture of salt and brown sugar, which results in a mild sweet flavour. New this year is his smoked cheese.

---

*Phil Bowditch of 7 Bath Place, **TAUNTON TA1 4ER** ☎ **01823 253500** fax* **01823 421875** *has the reputation as the fishmonger in Taunton. His shop is very cool, with white tiles, designer plants in baskets and simple uncluttered displays of fish bedded in crushed ice surrounded by seaweed. Most importantly, the fish is first-rate, with freshness a priority. Mostly he gets his fish from Brixham Market and from his own two boats. With a good display in the shop, if you are after a particular species do ask as Phil keeps a larger selection out back. In summer you could be tempted by gleaming wild salmon caught in the West Country from the rivers Exe, Dart and Teign (Phil now favours Dart salmon); stiff silvery sea-bass; or a cheaper and 'adequate' alternative, black bream.*

R. A. *Duckett*
Walnut Tree Farm, Heath House, Wedmore, Somerset BS28 4UJ

HEATH HOUSE
Caerphilly Cheese

☎ 01934 712218   **CONTACT** *Chris Duckett – telephone ahead*

Although thought of as a Welsh cheese, Caerphilly has a tradition of being made in Somerset. This is the third generation of Ducketts to produce it. Chris's mother still remembers when cheeses were taken to market at Highbridge and sent by rail to Wales. During the last century, demand for Caerphilly increased. As not enough milk was produced in Wales to fulfil the demand, the farmers on the other side of the Bristol Channel saw the opportunity and swiftly went for it. Already producing Cheddar, the idea of adding Caerphilly to the list suited them as it is a quick cheese to make, with a fast turnover. Cheddar takes at least 6 months to mature, but Caerphilly is ready within 5 days.

Chris, his brother Phil and their mother make Caerphilly every day with unpasteurized milk from their herd of 120 Friesians. Using the night and morning milk, it is started and renneted (with a vegetarian rennet). From then they have to work very fast as the whole process takes a mere 2 hours. The junket is cut in 3 directions, stirred for 45 minutes and quickly drained until the whey has settled. The curds are then piled in a 'semi-cone' and stacked at one end of the vat, cut with hand-held knives into 2.5-cm (1-in) cubes, salted and – if making the chive-flavoured Wedmore – the dried herbs are added. Finally they fill the moulds: traditional Caerphilly moulds (made from metal) have a cap or rim at the top, making the cheese instantly recognizable by its distinctive curved shape. The Ducketts still use them (several farmers have gone over to more convenient straight-sided plastic) and they also still use their magnificent ornately-decorated, cast-iron upright cheese presses, dated 1866. The cheeses are lightly pressed for about 18 hours, depending on their size – they produce 3.5-4-kg (8-9-lb), 1.8-2.3-kg (4-5-lb) and 900-g-1.35-kg (2-3-lb) rounds – then brined for 24 hours and kept until about 4-5 days old.

Eaten when young, Caerphilly is moist and crumbly, with a sharp fresh lemony flavour punched with salt. Unlike most other Caerphilly, however, these can also be successfully aged. Randolph Hodgson of Neal's Yard Dairy *see page* 180 matures them for 2-3 months, until they acquire a richness and a nutty mellowness. James Aldridge *see page* 262 washes the rind and bathes them in Penshurst wine from Kent – the result is Tornegus, similar in texture to a Pont-l'Evêque, but with a cleaner, sharper flavour (also sold at Neal's Yard Dairy). Chris usually keeps back a young plain and a Wedmore to sell from the farm to his local customers. As by-products from the whey, he also makes a rich sharp clotted cream and, at the end of the week, churns that into a ravishing butter.

Stockists

Avon: The Fine Cheese Co

Devon: Ticklemore Cheese Shop

London: Neal's Yard Dairy

The Real Cheese Shop

Somerset: The Good Earth

The Somerset Cider Brandy Company
Burrow Hill, Kingsbury Episcopi, Martock, Somerset TA12 5BU

☎ 01460 240782 **FAX** 01460 240782 **CONTACT** Mr Julian Temperley **HOURS** *Mon-Sat 9.00-17.00* **CARDS** *Mastercard, Visa* **DIRECTIONS** *From Martock, take B3165 towards Long Sutton. After about ¾ mile, turn left sign-posted Coat. Follow signs to Kingsbury Episcopi. At village, follow the Hambridge Road past The Rusty Axe pub. Cider farm is ½ mile along on left.*

Julian Temperley, a roistering colourful individual, is just the sort of person required to give cider a much-needed short sharp shock. He eschews foreign apples and chemical concoctions, opting for Somerset apple varieties, such as Dabinetts, Porter Perfection, Yarlington Mill, Chisel Jersey, Somerset Red Streak and, of course, the famous Kingston Black. He ferments his cider in oak vats, in his wooden-slatted cider house. Sold from wooden barrels, you should be warned that visitors are positively encouraged to sample before buying.

Somerset Royal Cider Brandy, however, is the fulfilment of a dream. Cider Brandy (similar to Calvados) had not been distilled in England for several hundred years until the mid 1980s, when Hereford Cider Museum was granted a licence. In 1989, Julian Temperley was also awarded one, although due to the vagaries of HM Customs and Excise, the distillery has to be sited 2 miles away and is not visitable. But Somerset Royal Cider Brandy can be tasted and bought at Burrow Hill. Aged for 3 years in oak barrels, with a fine spicy bouquet and a fresh appley palate, it slips down the throat like a dream, but with plenty of kick. Made from a variety of apples, including Royal Somerset with a bottled alcohol strength of 42 per cent, each year produces a different vintage.

Stockists

Avon: Averys

Devon: County Stores

London: Fortnum & Mason

Harvey Nichols

Waitrose

MAP 2　　　　　　　SOMERSET　　　239

Also new is Burrow Hill Bottle-Fermented Sparkling Cider, made by the *méthode champenoise see also Bollhayes Cider, page* 75. Wine writer Kathyrn McWhirter, writing in *The Independent* describes it as 'very dry, with a complex rich flavour, the traditional cider apple tang and a lovely fine fizz'. It is a drink to savour, 'a classy alcoholic summer drink' and an interesting alternative to wine.

Mrs Montgomery
Manor Farm, North Cadbury, Yeovil, Somerset BA22 7DW

☎ 01963 440243　**FAX** 01963 440243　**CONTACT** James Montgomery – telephone ahead

Mrs Montgomery's family has been making Cheddar on the farm since the 1930s. The tradition of a clothbound Cheddar using unpasteurized milk is deeply embedded and Mrs Montgomery would not have it any other way. Now only she and S. H. & G. H. Keen *see page* 242 make a traditional Cheddar. The now-defunct Milk Marketing Board defined a 'traditional Cheddar' as made on-farm by a registered milk producer with a proportion of milk from that farm and the balance coming from identifiable farms, and by traditional 'in-vat' methods. It omitted to mention anything about how the cheese should be matured and this, I believe, was a very grave error. The problem arose as several makers of Farmhouse Cheddar produce a 'block' cheese that is made in exactly the same way up to the point of pressing; it is pressed in cloth-lined rectangular moulds, turned out, wrapped in plastic coating and packed in wooden slats to ripen for only 6 months. Unlike the traditional clothbound truckle, it does not breathe or lose moisture or develop a rind and it matures a lot faster. It makes for a denser and less interesting cheese. Currently, however, traditional cylindrical and block forms are marketed as the same cheese and this is misleading. They are not the same cheese as they are not matured to the same traditional recipe and I honestly think the reputation and future of Traditional Farmhouse Cheddar will be undermined unless the cheeses are differentiated. Worse is to come as I have just heard that some makers are now making Cheddar truckles to mature in a plastic coating; soon you will buy a wedge and no longer be able to tell from its shape how it has been matured.

You can rest assured that both Mrs Montgomery's and Keen's Cheddars are clothbound and properly matured. Mrs Montgomery's is eating particularly well at the moment; I tried a 13-month cheese and it was a triumph. Creamy, tangy, it hit the teeth at first bite and then generously opened out to reveal a lingering rich flavour. Made in 11-kg (56-lb) cylinders or 2.3-2.7 and 3.5-4-kg (5-6 and 8-9-lb) truckles, Mrs Montgomery will sell from the estate office, but for smaller quantities she suggests you go to the village shop next door where there always is a supply. They also sell her lightly cheesy whey butter.

Stockists

Heref: The
Mousetrap

London: Harrods
- - - - - - - - -
Neal's Yard Dairy
- - - - - - - - -
Paxton & Whitfield

Oxon: Oxford
Cheese Company

PILTON
Preserves

The Bay Tree Food Company
Perridge House, Pilton, Somerset BA4 4EN

☎ 01225 310754 **FAX** 01225 310754 **CONTACT** Lucy Green – telephone ahead **CARDS** Access, Mastercard, Visa

New companies come and go but, as far as I am concerned, The Bay Tree Food Company looks set for a dazzling future. Run by Lucy Green (no relation) and Emma and Jennifer Sheldon, from a Georgian manor house (where you can also stay the night), they produce an imaginative and finely-judged range of relishes and pickles attractively packaged in small and medium-size Kilner jars, with refill packs available.

Tasting them with food writer Claire Clifton, we both felt that here were products with a freshness and texture that all too often seems missing. Everything is made in small batches to preserve the textures and to ensure an even cooking; and, when necessary, pickles are aged so the flavours meld and mellow out.

Everyone's favourite was a charming cucumber relish. Made with fresh cucumbers left to salt in bowls then mixed in a marinade of distilled malt vinegar, sugar, pickling spice and cinnamon, it has a crisp texture and a nicely rounded sweet-sour flavour. With a rich jammy fragrance, Green Tomato chutney is thick and juicy, with an edge of spice; Marinated Figs, made with dried baby figs soaked in white wine, rum, sugar, mixed spice, cinnamon, vanilla and lemon, are incredibly moreish, in a lushly scented syrup; Caramelized Apple Compote with Thyme has great appeal, with its slices of apple in a buttery purée spiked with thyme, and what a clever combination of flavours that turns out to be. Aga-dried tomatoes also deserves a mention; they actually do use English tomatoes, drying them for 24 hours in the Aga, then packing in extra-virgin olive oil with baby capers, salt and pepper. Milder than their Italian cousins, they have a gentle sweetness that would suit their addition to a salad. They also make a fresh salsa with peppers, tomatoes, onions and jalapeño peppers; an apple & apricot relish; and marmalades.

Stockists

Avon: The Butler's Choice

Glam: Howells

London: Harvey Nichols

Mortimer & Bennett

Northumb: Corbridge Larder

Burrow Products, Higher Burrow Farm, TIMBERSCOMBE, Minehead TA24 7UD ☎ **01643 841427** *buy in day-old Gressingham ducklings and fatten them on farm. These were first bred a few years ago by Lancashire breeder Peter Dodd, who set out to 'improve' the mallard by hybridizing with other breeds to ensure a better meat-to-carcass ratio while retaining its leanness. Slaughtered on-farm at 7 weeks 2 days, Anthony Rusher told me emphatically '2 days later they develop their pin feathers … then they're like hedgehogs and you can't pluck them', they are hung for 2-3 days to give them their gamy flavour. Dry-plucked and wax-finished, they are sold oven-ready in a range of sizes from 900 g to 2 kg (2 to 4½ lb). With finely grained meat and a well-pronounced and clean flavour, they are very moist and surprisingly lean, with a skin that crisps up very satisfyingly. Anthony also sells 255-g (9-oz) supremes cut from the breast with the first pinion bone and, in season, the 'odd' oven-ready partridge from local shoots, hung for a couple of days.*

MAP 2　　　　　　　　　　　　　　　　　SOMERSET　　　　　　　　**241**

Coombe Farm, WEST MONKTON, *Taunton TA2 8RB* ☎ 01823 413228 *fax* 01823 412366 *grows several varieties of plums in a 3-acre orchard. Starting in mid-July with the reddish purple Opal, then moving through the season with Avalon, Excalibur, the larger blue-black Edwards, Victorias and Greengages, they end with the delicately bloomed Marjorie's Seedling in September. There are also a few unnamed trees which were planted several years ago as part of a fruit trial to find new varieties with commercial possibilities. Owner Stephen Piper admits that most were not that successful, although WJ16 has a certain following. Plums are sold ready-picked or as pick-your-own.*

Barrow Boar

Foster's Farm, South Barrow, Yeovil, Somerset BA22 7LN

SOUTH
BARROW
Wild Boar

☎ 01963 440315 **FAX** 01963 440901 **CONTACT** *Christina Baskerville* **HOURS** *Mon-Fri 8.30-17.00 Sat 8.30-13.00* **CARDS** *Access, Eurocard, Mastercard, Visa* **DIRECTIONS** *From Wincanton, take the A303 into Sparkford. Turn left towards South Barrow, opposite Haynes Publishers. After 1 mile, turn right after the church on an 'S' bend. Farm is 200 yards along on right.*

Whereas wild boar still roam the fields, forests and scrublands of France, Northern Italy, Poland, Germany and Austria, in Britain they became extinct in the 17th century. What we do have, however, is farmed 'wild boar'. If you think it sounds like a contradiction in terms, I had better explain that Wild Boar is an actual species, *Sus scropha*.

Nigel Dauncey's pure-bred herd – or 'troop', or 'sounder' as he would have it – roam in fields, in conditions that approximate to the wild, with a stocking density that varies from 1 to 5 sows per acre. Each field is securely fenced and furnished with bales of straw for nesting, water holes for wallowing and trees for shelter.

Although wild Wild Boar is thought by the French to be best eaten as *marcassin* (up to six months), Nigel does not slaughter his until at least 18 months. 'The wild Wild Boar have a much more varied diet, so they will be tastier when younger', he explained. 'Ours do not develop a full-flavoured meat until later. At 6 months, frankly you wouldn't notice a marked difference between their meat and pork'.

Nigel's boar are always bled after slaughter; so, although their flesh is a darker red than pork, it is not as deeply coloured as you might expect. All the boar is hung for a minimum of 14 days, the older the beast the longer he will leave it. As for the taste, it does have a deeper and more resonant flavour than pork – gamier, more rounded and gutsier – but it was pleasingly subtle and not at all intrusive or musty. It is also in the texture that you notice a difference, boar meat has a much closer longer grain – actually rather like beef – and is surprisingly lean.

Recently Nigel has converted a barn into an on-farm butchery. You can order whole butchered carcasses or joints, including eye of loin steak, shoulder or saddle – either on-the-bone or boned and rolled. In conjunction with Christina, he also makes wild boar sausages with 85 per cent meat content and flavoured with herbs or juniper berries.

Stockists

Avon: Bartlett & Son (Butchers)

Glos: Jessie Smiths

London: Harrods

Harvey Nichols

Game Larder

WINCANTON
Cheddar
Cheese

S. H. & G. H. Keen
Moorhayes Farm, Verrington Lane, Wincanton,
Somerset BA9 8JR

☎/FAX 01963 32286 **CONTACT** *Stephen Keen – telephone ahead*

As far as I know, only 2 farms exclusively make unpasteurized traditional Farmhouse Cheddar; here at Moorhayes and Mrs Montgomery *see page* 239. Now most people believe, and rightly so, that an unpasteurized cheese is more interesting and complex than a pasteurized one; and, as Randolph Hodgson of Neal's Yard Dairy aptly said, 'the difference is the same as listening to music in stereo or mono'.

It is a constant source of surprise that people are worried about the risks of unpasteurized cheese. If the milk is carefully handled, regularly tested and scrupulous hygiene is practised, there should be no danger. The Keen family use milk from their 160 Friesian cows to make their Cheddar. In 1990 they built a new state-of-the-art dairy with a 1,000-gallon vat, and they make most days in the time-honoured way.

To explain the lengthy process as simply as possible, once the starter and rennet have been added to the milk, it coagulates and forms a junket which is cut by knives to separate it into curds and whey. These are then 'scalded' at a temperature of 40-41°C (104-106°F) until the desired acidity level is reached. The whey is drained off and the curds cool, then these are cut into large rectangular pieces ready for 'cheddaring'. This is done by hand and is incredibly hard work, as the curds are stacked and re-stacked and turned to assist the draining of the whey. It continues until the whey runs clean and the level of acidity is right. Next the curds are milled, salted and finally shovelled into cloth-lined moulds, ready for pressing.

Initially pressed for 24 hours, they are then grease-bandaged (in muslin dipped in lard) to help the rind form. A rind allows a cheese to breathe as it matures, but prevents mould penetration. The cheeses are stored and turned until ready to eat, which for a mild cheese could be as little as 9 months and for an extra-mature as long as 20 months.

The Keen's Cheddar is quite marvellous. I tried a wedge cut from a 16-month truckle: golden yellow, quite firm and dry, it cut 'clean' and had a nutty honeyness with the merest hint of salt. Its flavour builds in the mouth and, like all the best Cheddars, has a 'kick' as it glides down the throat. They do make small 1.35-1.8-kg (3-4-lb) truckles, but these never seem to develop the same length and complexity of flavours. If visiting, try their creamy whey butter and unctuous double cream.

Stockists

Devon: Ticklemore Cheese Shop

Dorset: Sabins

London: Jeroboams
- - - - - - - - - -
Neal's Yard Dairy

Lothian: Iain Mellis

While you're in the area...
The Post Office, Bathway, CHEWTON MENDIP BA3 4ND ☎ **01761 241325** is a good source of bread, biscuits and cakes, baked on a daily basis by Richard St John, son of the postmistress. Breads include a nutty 100 per cent stoneground wholemeal (with or without sunflower seeds), crusty white and brown.

MAP 2   SOMERSET   243

With several orchards in the county, there are 2 more worth a mention – **West Bradley Orchards, near GLASTONBURY BA6 8LT ☎ 01458 50227 fax 01458 51008** and **Stawell Fruit Farm, Stawell, BRIDGWATER TA7 9AE ☎ 01278 722732**. Both offer a wide range of ancient and modern apples, as both PYO and ready-picked.

Elliscombe Farm, HOLTON, Wincanton BA9 9EA ☎ 01963 32393 is recommended by Food Lover Philippa Grant for its rich untreated (unpasteurized) milk and double cream from the Wisteria herd of Jersey cows, the very same that can be seen prancing about on the Anchor butter commercial. They also sell whey butter from Mrs Montgomery *see page* 239 and very occasionally 'when there's a lot of cream' they make their own.

R. T. Herbs, Orange Farm, KILMERSDON, Bath BA3 5TD ☎ 01761 435470 is a magical herb garden. A quiet gentle place, the only noise you are likely to hear is the constant fluttering of pigeons as they fly back and forth into their loft in the middle of the gardens. Apart from the usual culinary herbs, you will find some interesting varieties, such as garlic chives, wild celery, silver-grey buddleia mint, and buckler's sorrel. They also sell pots of edible flowers and the odd old-fashioned vegetable, including alexanders, cardoon, and good king henry.

With the exception of the soft Baby Brendon, made from goats' milk, all the other cheeses are blue from **Exmoor Blue Cheese, Willett Farm, LYDEARD ST LAWRENCE, Taunton TA4 3QB ☎ 01984 667328 fax 01984 667460**. There are 6 cheeses in all, using local unpasteurized goats', sheep's, or Jersey cows' milk. Each is made up into an unpressed hard cheese, then matured for 2-4 months, or into a younger softer cheese 'similar to Bleu d'Auvergne' matured for 1 month.

Now under new management, **West Country Stile, Greenway Farm, Moon Lane, NORTH NEWTON, Bridgwater TA7 ODS ☎ 01278 663801** produces a range of pork sausages with an 80 per cent meat content. Flavours include coriander & garlic, herbs, and spicy. More reports please.

The Cheese and Wine Shop, 11 South Street, WELLINGTON TA21 8NR ☎ 01823 662899 'tries to be as local as possible' in its produce. As a result, there are plenty of cheeses from the South-West; chunky duck & apricot and game cutting pies, baked by 2 local ladies; pies; cakes; quiches; chocolates by Melchior *see page* 81; bacon and sausages from West Country Stile; and much more.

Laurelbank Dairy Co, 14 Queen Street, WELLS BA5 2DP ☎ 01749 679803 is owned by Ford Farm cheeses. Naturally they stock their full range of Cheddar, as well as an unpasteurized version, cream, butter and milk. They also sell other cheeses, Hobbs House Bakery bread *see page* 12 and wild boar sausages from Barrow Boar *see page* 241.

Staffordshire

Map No. 4

Staffordshire Organic Cheese
New House Farm, Acton, Newcastle, Staffordshire ST5 4EE

☎ 01782 680366 **CONTACT** Betty Deaville **HOURS** Mon 9.00-16.00 Fri 9.00-17.30 Sat 9.00-13.00 *(and by arrangement)* **DIRECTIONS** *From Newcastle-under-Lyme, take A53 towards Whitmore. After 4 miles, at Mainwaring Arms in Whitmore, turn left towards Acton and Farm is ¾ mile on.*

Stockists

Heref: Organic Options

IOW
Godshill Organics

Lothian: Iain Mellis

Strath: Roots and Fruits

Sussex: Wealden Wholefoods

Michael and Betty Deaville, with their son David, have been farming organically to Soil Association standards since 1975, but it was not until 1984 that they decided to make cheese using unpasteurized milk from their mostly Friesian herd.

As Staffordshire has no history of cheese-making, there was no local traditional recipe, so Betty opted for a Cheddar-style recipe instead. Unlike a Cheddar, hers is a fast-maturing cheese ready for eating at 2 months. When eaten young at about 3 months, it is moist and buttery with a mild grassy tang; as it matures, it hardens slightly and develops a deeper resonance and more punchy kick. Betty also makes 3 flavoured versions: mixed herbs, made with dried herbs which were far too overpowering; chives, fresh from the garden, which gave it

Essington Fruit Farm, Bognop Road, Essington, WOLVERHAMPTON WV11 2BA ☎ **01902 735724** *was voted regional winner by the Farm Shop and Pick-Your-Own Association. They grow a wide range of pick-your-own and ready-picked fruit and vegetables. Strawberries start the season in June and carry through to the end of July; and there are raspberries, tayberries, gooseberries, redcurrants and blackcurrants, blueberries in an acidified bed, and marionberries – a cross between an American black raspberry and a blackberry. In the vegetable line, they grow a good range of brassicas, including various cabbages, Brussels sprouts on the stem, cauliflowers, broccoli and borecole (curly kale). Then there is spinach, beetroot, carrots, onions, shallots, peas, sugar-snap peas, broad beans, French beans, runner beans, leeks and sweetcorn. Potatoes are not forgotten as they grow over 10 varieties, starting with the early Maris Bard through to Wilja, Cara and the red Stemster.*

a mild light touch; and wild garlic, gathered from the local woods, which lend a 'certain pungency'. If you like garlic-flavoured cheese, you will enjoy this one.

These are sold as 1.35, 9, or 18-kg (3, 20, or 40-lb) clothbound truckles or in vacuum-packed portions from the farmshop, which Betty has now reopened and which stocks various other local products.

Baked in Staffordshire's only surviving front-room oatcake shop, journalist Steve Dixon rates the oatcakes from **Sue & Glenn's 62 Waterloo Street, Hanley, STOKE-ON-TRENT ST1 3PW ☎ 01782 261883** *as 'exceptional'.*

Food Lover Mrs Pickering of Barnsley recommends **Asplins Oatcakes, 2 Haywood Street, LEEK ST13 5JX ☎ 01538 387556** *as 'a little corner shop selling only oatcakes – local mill factory workers go at lunch-time etc. Seems pretty authentic to me'.*

High Lane Oatcakes
599 High Lane, Burslem, Stoke-on-Trent, Staffordshire ST6 7EP

BURSLEM
Staffordshire Oatcakes

☎ 01782 810180 **CONTACT** Roy Gavin **HOURS** Tues 10.30-17.30 Thurs-Sat 7.00-18.00 Sun 7.00-12.00 **CARDS** Access, Visa **DIRECTIONS** From Hanley, take Town Road towards Chell. After about 2 miles, go straight across the Smallthorne roundabout. Follow road about ¾ mile and shop is signposted on left.

Staffordshire oatcakes are completely different from Scottish oatcakes; both are made with oats, but that is where the similarity begins and ends. Scottish oatcakes are crisp and baked like a biscuit, whereas Staffordshire oatcakes are soft and floppy and made from a batter. There are, according to writer Steve Dixon, at least 23 oatcake bakers among the pottery towns of Stoke-on-Trent alone and their recipes and methods are virtually unchanged from the turn of the century. 'The switch from coal- to gas-fired hotplates, known as bakestones, has been the major technological advance since the earliest days of the Industrial Revolution'.

Roy Gavin makes about 5,000 oatcakes a day, with a batter of fine oatmeal, white flour, water, sugar and yeast. His bakestones (griddles) are kept permanently warm and larded to stop the batter from sticking. A hopper moves back and forth dispensing the batter, although I have seen some bakers still ladling it by hand. The oatcakes bubble up so they look like the pitted surface of the moon, then flatten out and – with a flick of the wrist – they are turned over. Once they are a golden brown, they are racked to dry and are ready to eat.

Quite chewy, these oatcakes have a soft pliable texture and a slightly sharp flavour, from the oatmeal. The size of a plate and only a few millimetres thick, I think the oatcakes are best eaten on the day, although Roy disputes this as he sends them all over the country to grateful customers. He recommends reheating them in an oven, in the microwave or under a grill and eating them spread with butter or honey, served stacked on a warm plate for breakfast, or with cheese, sausages, or any savoury filling you care to name. On the griddle, Roy also cooks either plain or fruit pikelets, similar to a crumpet.

STATFOLD
Breads and
Cheeses

Innes
Highfields, Clifton Lane, Statfold, Tamworth,
Staffordshire B79 0AQ

☎ 01827 830097 **FAX** 01827 830628 **CONTACT** Andy Bakewell – telephone ahead

Hugh Lillingston has a clear aim in life, 'to produce here in Britain our own good products instead of being forced to import them from abroad'. To this end he set up, on the family estate, two separate but complementary businesses: a bakery and a dairy.

Since the last edition, there have been several changes in the bakery, both in the expansion of the range and the methods of production. Dealing with Innes sour-dough bread first. It is no longer made from scratch, starting off with flour, salt, water – and nothing else – and leaving it to rise for a natural fermentation; nowadays it is 'helped' on its way with a sour-dough starter, or 'mother' as it is affectionately called. The sour-dough is still made on either a 4- or 5-day process; this means that on each day the dough is split in half and then doubled up with new flour and water and continues doubling up each day, giving it plenty of time for a long deep fermentation. The sour-dough is now the only bread to be baked in the igloo-shaped wood-burning stone oven that Hugh brought back from St Tropez and lovingly rebuilt stone by stone on the farm. A pity that, as it does bake glorious bread; but, as Hugh told me shrugging away any regrets, 'you have to be commercial'. It is a dense, very solid bread (some say too dense), with a tooth-jarring crust; it is heavy, with a reverberating sour aftertaste, which still reminds me of a properly brewed bitter. It comes as a huge 1.6-kg (3¾-lb) loaf; 800-g (1¾-lb) loaves either plain or pain aux noix (mixed with hazelnuts, walnuts and raisins); and 400-g (14-oz) loaves, also plain or flavoured with olives, sun-dried tomatoes & mustard seed, and sultanas & walnuts.

New this year are Hugh's Italian breads, which bear an uncanny resemblance to the Manoucher breads which seem to have taken this country by storm. Made with a little 'mother', flour, yeast and olive oil, fermentation times that vary according to the breads, and baked off in new electric steam ovens, they are quite doughy and spongy, but that Hugh told me firmly 'is how people like them'. Sunshine loaf is packed with bitter-sweet sun-dried tomatoes and pesto and has a good tear to it; focaccia, either plain or with sun-dried tomatoes and olives, had a gutsy flavoured dough but was a little too puffy and lacked that open texture that I associate with this style of bread. He also bakes a Greek-style bread, with pesto, ouzo & honey, and is planning a range of properly fermented British breads. Quite right too.

There has, however, been no change with the cheese. They are still made by cheese-maker Stella Bennet using unpasteurized milk from the Saanen and Toggenburg herd. She makes two types: a fresh light and fluffy curd that is drained in muslin bags and sold in 170-g (6-oz)

and 1.8-kg (4-lb) pots, either plain or flavoured with herbs, armagnac & black pepper. She also makes a round moulded cheese which is sold fresh at 3 days, semi-mature at 3-5 days and mature at 5-14 days. Aperitif are tiny bite-size cheeses on a cocktail stick in various flavours, sold as collections of 12s and 56s. Button, the next size up, is 5 cm (2 in); when fresh it is smooth-textured with a startlingly pure taste and the mildest hint of goat that develops as the cheeses matures; Clifton, with a 7-cm (2¾-in) diameter, is sold as plain, with herbs or a mature version wrapped in a leaf that mellows out to a fine rounded tang. Bosworth has a diameter of 11 cm (4½ in) when fresh and comes either matured in ash or wrapped in a leaf. As all the cheeses age they shrink, so the sizes – be warned – are approximate. If you come across a demi-sec Button, snap it up; it is the nearest equivalent I have found to a Crottin de Chavignol, the little hard cheese that grills superbly.

Mail Order

Long-life breads only

Stockists

London:

C. Lidgate Ltd

Fortnum & Mason

Harrods

Harvey Nichols

La Fromagerie

Rosemary Barnes runs **The Old Stables, Packington Moor Farm, LICHFIELD WS14 9QA ☎ 01543 481223** *from a converted barn. Most of what is sold is either grown on the farm or cooked in the barn; there are pick-your-own or ready-picked gooseberries, raspberries, redcurrants and blackcurrants, and a few varieties of strawberries – Pegasus and Cambridge Favourite. You can buy bunches of their own herbs (sage, parsley, thyme, chives and mint); bags of their main-crop Maris Piper or Wilja potatoes and 'Barney Bakers' (which are washed scrubbed and ready for the oven), local apples, peas, beans, onions, roots crops such as turnips and swedes, cabbages and excellent creamy cauliflowers. They also sell a limited supply of their own bacon, ham and sausages processed from their own pigs by Rosemary's father – a butcher who lives nearby. At Christmas, they rear a few turkeys, geese, ducks and cockerels, which can weigh as much as 5.5 kg (12 lb). With a bakery on the premises using, whenever possible, the Barnes' own flour, they bake farmhouse bread; scones; feathery-light Victoria sponge cakes filled with lemon, chocolate or coffee buttercream; sponge slices; biscuits; Dundee fruit cake; sausage rolls and savoury quiches; as well as a wide range of dishes, pies and casseroles baked to order. Own-made jams are gooseberry, strawberry, raspberry, damson, rhubarb & ginger, and redcurrant jelly – all made with their own fruit.*

While you're in the area...

W. J. Robinson & Sons, 103 High Street, CHASETOWN, Burntwood WS7 8XQ ☎ 01543 686461 comes highly recommended by Food Lover Nicola Smith as 'the best butcher I know. All his meat is of the highest quality. He slaughters his own animals and is very particular from whom he purchases animals. But perhaps his greatest strength is in his bacon, sausages and black pudding. His dry-cured bacon cooks in a trice, it is mouth-watering and wonderful. Unlike most nowadays, when it is cooked the pan doesn't fill with water. His thick pork sausages are superb. Full of real tasty meat. I am not a big fan of black pudding, but my husband tells me that Mr Robinson's is the best ever'. More reports please.

Amanda Gray, Riverside Farm, CHEBSEY, Stafford ST21 6JU ☎ 01785 760125 may live in Staffordshire but she farms the Devon breed of cattle on a small scale. She sells 13.5-kg (30-lb) packs of mixed joints, braising steak and mince for the freezer.

ASHBOCKING
Apple Juice

James White Apple Juice & Cider Company

The Farm Shop, Helmingham Road, Ashbocking, Suffolk IP6 9JS

☎ 01473 890111 **FAX** 01473 890001 **CONTACT** *Lawrence Mallinson*
HOURS *Mon-Sat 9.00-17.00 Sun 10.00-16.00* **DIRECTIONS** *From Ipswich, take B1077 towards Debenham. After about 7 miles, farm-shop is on the left.*

What is extraordinary about James White apple juices is their clarity and intensity of flavour, particularly when you realize that these juices, unlike most made on-farm, are filtered. Now most juicers will tell you that when you filter a juice to make it clear, the particles you remove inevitably hold flavour; so it follows that a clear juice will not have the same vibrancy and strength of flavour as a cloudy (unfiltered) juice. Apparently Lawrence Mallinson has several tricks up his sleeve, as his juices offer up what wine writers would call 'a good nose'. Made with fresh English apples and – apart from Vitamin C to stop the juice from turning brown – nothing else, they are pressed by variety and bottled in clear glass.

Each apple gives a distinctive flavour: Bramley is dry and crisp with – borrowing again from wine-speak – 'a thin nose'; Cox is far fuller, with a deep fruity bouquet that hints of nuts; and Russet is superbly rich with a flowery sweetness that, as Lawrence suggests, 'is best drunk with a dessert or cheese or as an indulgence on its own'.

They also produce English pear and English grape juices, cider vinegar and a range of ciders made with a mixture of cooking and eating apples. This is an accepted East-Anglian tradition, according to David Kitton in *The Good Cider Directory*, as cider apples as used in the West Country are regarded over here as too bitter. Suffolk Cider, naturally fermented to over 8 per cent alcohol and matured for at least 5 months, has a crisp dry flavour; October Gold, matured for 8 months and then blended with pear juice, is fuller-bodied and fruitier; and Special edition is blended with Bramley apple juice.

Stockists

Derbys:
Chatsworth
Farmshop

Northants: Daily
Bread Cooperative

Strath: Peckhams

Yorks: Lewis &
Cooper Ltd

Majestic Wine
Warehouses

Maynard House Orchards, BRADFIELD ST CLARE, Bury St Edmunds IP30 0DX ☎/fax **01284 386264** *started juicing their own apples 2 seasons ago. On the principle that 'younger, fresh apples make for a better juice' most of their apples are juiced between August and Christmas. Sold in 250-ml (8-fl oz) and 1-litre (1¾-pint) bottles, their unfiltered juices include a blend of Cox and Bramley, a refreshing Bramley, well-rounded Cox, flowery Discovery, Russet and James Grieve.*

Alder Carr Farm Shop

Alder Carr Farm, Creeting St Mary, nr Needham Market,
Ipswich, Suffolk IP6 8LX

CREETING
ST MARY
Ice-cream

☎ 01449 720820 **CONTACT** Joan Hardingham **HOURS** May to Christmas: Tues-Sun 9.30-17.30 (open Mon PYO season); Christmas to May: telephone ahead; **DIRECTIONS** In Needham Market, at junction of A14 and A140, take the Creeting sign near the church. Drive past Hawksmill over the river. Farm is on right after ¼ mile.

When I first visited Alder Carr Farm Shop, the own-made ice-cream was no more than a sideline. Fast-forward a few years and now it is a thriving cottage industry. Unlike several producers who 'adapt' their recipe or methods of making to suit increased output, I am sure you will be relieved to hear that Joan Hardingham has not changed the ice-cream one jot.

Actually her ice-cream is really more like frozen mousse 'what I'm sure they ate in the grander houses years ago'. Made by the astonishingly simple process of whipping up whipping cream in a mixer with sugar and fruit. It is sublime. Joan did try using Jersey cream ('too rich') and even investigated an ice-cream-making machine 'it tasted different'; so that is how they still make it. It has no flavourings, no stabilizers, no emulsifiers, no nothing added; and it is rich, tempting velvety and pure. Even more surprisingly – and in contradiction to what mass manufacturers say – it has a shelf-life of at least 6 months when stored in a domestic freezer 'after that the water crystallizes'; and if that does not put paid to the idea that stabilizers and emulsifiers are essential, what will?

Sold in individual 100, 500 and 1500-g (4-oz, 1 and 3-lb) cartons, there are about 12 flavours 'although other combinations are still being dreamt up'. Most of the soft fruit used is own-grown, but this not being a top fruit-growing area, they buy in apples, plums and damsons. Fruit is used fresh in season and frozen in batches for the rest of the year. Flavours currently include strawberry, a lush gentle raspberry, tayberry, blackberry, blackcurrant, meaty damson, a piercing gooseberry & elderflower, apple & honey, spicy apple with sultanas & cinnamon, blackberry & apple, summer pudding and – at Christmas only – a Christmas pudding, with apple, dried fruit, nuts, brandy & mixed spices. Should you be concerned about all that cream, you might be tempted by the sharper strawberry & raspberry made with half yoghurt.

From the farm-shop, Joan also sells own-grown asparagus (incidentally they supply Marks & Spencer); soft fruits such as strawberries, raspberries, redcurrants, gooseberries (including the dusty-red Whinham's Industry), various potatoes, a good selection of lettuces, decorative and edible squashes, Hamburg parsley (a mild root vegetable that looks like a small parsnip for adding to soups and stews), spinach, celeriac, and Brussels sprouts sold on the stalk. She also makes a good selection of jams from their own fruit – greengage, tayberry, strawberry, and rhubarb. They sell some good local produce, including a Suffolk-cure bacon from Creaseys in Peasenhall, fruit pies made with, whenever possible, their own fruit by Mary Noy who lives nearby.

Stockists

Suffolk: Denham Estate

Fish & Fayre

J. R. Creasey

HEMINGSTONE

Jams and Preserves

Stonham Hedgerow Products

Hemingstone Fruitique, Main Road, Hemingstone, Ipswich, Suffolk IP6 9RJ

☎ 01449 760482 **FAX** 01449 760280 **CONTACT** *Kathy Neuteboom* **HOURS** 10.00-17.30 **CARDS** Access, Visa **DIRECTIONS** *From Ipswich, take A45 towards Bury St Edmunds, then A140 to Norwich. Turn off immediately to Coddenham on B1078. Follow this road through Coddenham, then turn right towards Ipswich at the crossroads. Drive up the hill, with the orchards on the right. Fruitique is in the main fruit farm on the right.*

Kathy Neuteboom's jams are her passion and she has very firm ideas about how they should be made, 'I want to stick to basic principles, like using real whole fruit and chopping it by hand – too much machinery only bruises it. A good raw cane natural sugar – ours is from Mauritius. It may make the jam darker and give it a definite taste but I – and my customers – like it that way'. Jams are made on a small(ish) scale, 'mostly in 20-30 lb batches, although we do have a 100-lb boiler for easy-preparation jams like strawberry. The home-made feel is important and we want to keep it that way'.

Fruit is bought from local growers when the quality and price is right, then frozen and used accordingly throughout the year. Jams are made with fruit, cane sugar and, although Kathy goes for a slack set, she does add pectin. With a sugar content of 'anything between 60 and 66 per cent' the wide range includes greengage, mixed fruit (apple, strawberry, blackberry and loganberry), a reddish gooseberry brimming with whole fruit, a nutty-flavoured apricot made with fruit imported from Cyprus and whole kernels, a sharp apple & ginger 'made with my

Nowton Farm Shop, NOWTON, Bury St Edmunds IP29 5LT ☎ **01284 828566** *is a small but useful farm-shop, open only during the soft fruit season, for pick-your-own and ready-picked fruit. From the shop they also sell own-made jams, such as plum, damson and raspberry, untreated Jersey cream and various own-made cakes and biscuits, including a rich buttery shortbread.*

MAP 5　　　　　　　　　　　　　SUFFOLK　　　　　　　　　251

father's Bramleys – he'd never forgive me if I used anyone else's', and sunberry which 'looks like a raspberry but tastes more like a black-berry'. There are several 'reasonably clear' jellies – crab apple, quince, redcurrant, and morello cherry 'from fruit grown here that take hours to stone'. Various marmalades and chutneys include a novel Uncooked Fruit. Made by soaking raw chopped bananas, apples, onions, sultanas, raisins and currants with salt and spices in vinegar overnight, I found it a little harsh. I much preferred Suffolk Chutney, a powerful blend of cooked apple, black treacle seasoned with mustard and curry powder.

Kathy also makes reduced-sugar jams; legally known as 'conserves', as they have a sugar content of 40-45 per cent. Unfortunately, in order to achieve a set, Kathy is forced to add extra pectin and, particularly in the case of the strawberry, its taste comes through. Undaunted she is working on a 'no-sugar' range, more of a fruit spread. I wish her luck.

J. T. Cole
Newcombe Road, Lowestoft, Suffolk NR32 1XA

Stockists

Ches: Bridgemere Garden World

Kent: Polhill Garden Centre

Suffolk: Corncraft

Friday Street Farm Shop

LOWESTOFT
Kippers

☎ 01502 574446 **CONTACT** Terry Jones **HOURS** Mon-Fri 4.00-16.30 **DIRECTIONS** *On the beach.*

Terry Jones comes from a long line of smokers. His great-grandfather started the business and he himself has been smoking herrings 'all (his) life'. Walking into the smokery down an alleyway, it looks as if nothing much has changed since then; high ceilings, stone floors, baskets of fish and smoke-holes lining one wall, with their wooden slatted doors tightly shut and no trace of modern machinery or any mod-cons. Nowadays he mostly uses frozen herring as 'Herrings are my trade, the other fish – haddock, cod, whiting – are just a side-line' which he processes, curing

> *Raglan Smokehouse, The Old Smoke-house, Raglan Street, LOWESTOFT* ☎ **01502 581929** *is another old-fash-ioned smokehouse down an alleyway. Here you can buy meaty kippers with a strong salty tang straight off the speats, as well as a small selection of fresh fish.*

and cold-smoking over white shavings and oak dust for kippers, bloaters (whole ungutted fish) and red herrings. Terry is of the school that believes you never really master a craft even if you have been practising it at long as he has (I was too polite to ask exactly how long that was, but I guess at least 40 years), so he was not prepared to impart the secrets of his trade. All he would volunteer was how the weather 'be it fog, heat, off-shore winds, gales or any other conditions' affects his curing and smoking, and a little information about red her-rings. An old-fashioned curiosity, they are a bright tandoori-red and will keep for up to a year; dry-salted 'for a while', then smoked continu-ously for 6-8 weeks, until they are completely dried-out – rather like a fish biltong, they have a harsh strong taste not much suited to the modern palate. Far better to stick to Terry's juicy kippers, gently salted with a mild smoky overlay.

Stockists

Norfolk: Burden Gorlston

J. R. R.'s Place

Mastersons

Suffolk: John's Fish Shop

ORFORD
Smoked Fish

Butley Orford Oysterage
Market Hill, Orford, Woodbridge, Suffolk IP12 2LH

☎ 01394 450277 **FAX** 01394 450949 **CONTACT** William Pinney **HOURS** Mon-Sat 9.00-17.00 (-16.00 Winter) Sun 11.00-16.00 **DIRECTIONS** In *village centre.*

For good fresh or smoked fish, Butley's is the place to go. The Oysterage Restaurant has not changed since the last edition and still serves remarkably fresh and simply prepared fish, own-smoked fish and oysters. Daily specialities are chalked up on a blackboard and – with an emphasis on produce rather than cooking – food tends to be simply prepared but none the worse for that. Open daily during the tourist season for lunch and supper (check for times out of season), I strongly recommend a brisk walk to the castle at the top of the hill just outside the town to work off a satisfying lunch.

Tucked behind the restaurant is their shop, selling fish – either fresh, caught by the two boats Bill Pinney runs off the coast; or smoked from their smokehouse down in Butley Creek, which is where they also farm their plump, juicy and sea-scented Pacific oysters. All the fish is smoked over oak logs.

There is a choice of farmed Scottish or wild Irish smoked salmon, with the latter particularly impressive. Lightly cured mild lean and easy-textured, it was like biting into butter and slipped down the throat with resounding waves of pearly fish. They also smoke trout; chubby cod's roe with a strong sense of salt from which they now make a tara-masalata; kippers; bloaters; chewy densely-flavoured sprats; juicy mackerel; and fat eels caught in the local dikes and ditches. Incidentally, if you are wondering, they are related but no longer connected with Pinney's smoked salmon of Scotland.

Stockists

Suffolk: Harveys

John's Fish Shop

Loaves and Fishes

Revetts

ORFORD
Smoked Meat and Game

Richardsons Smokehouse
Bakers Lane, Orford, Suffolk IP12 2LH

☎ 01394 450103 **CONTACT** Steve Richardson **HOURS** Apr to end Oct: 10.00-17.30; Nov to Mar: 10.00-16.00 **DIRECTIONS** Off Market Hill, in *centre of Orford.*

Just around the corner and down the lane from Butley Orford Oysterage is Richardsons – 2 smokeries in the same village, how can they both survive? Steve Richardson smokes in a blackened old lean-to smokehouse divided into 2, which may look a bit ramshackle but works a treat. One side, with the boiler (fired with oak logs), is for hot-smoking; and the smoke is vented through to the other compartment for a longer cooler smoke.

Until recently, Steve concentrated on meat and game, but he has changed emphasis and now also smokes bloaters, mackerel, sardines,

MAP 5   SUFFOLK   **253**

trout, haddock and prawns. Smoked ham and dry-cured bacon are bought in, but pigeon – with a light woody haze – is very definitely done on the premises, as are the whole chickens. They are brined for 6 hours, then smoked for more than 15 hours and emerge soft-fleshed, with a musky flavour. Wild duck, guinea fowl and pheasant looked equally tempting.

Also new this year are smoked garlic and, extraordinarily enough, smoked Stilton ... will the craze never end? They also sell ham hocks marinated in black treacle and cider; own-made sausages, including pork & venison, cider, pork & leek, spicy Old English, and pork & garlic; and smoked salmon fish-cakes, made with own-smoked Alaskan salmon and mixed with potatoes, lemon juice, mixed herbs and oregano. Satisfyingly rough and chunky-textured, these bulged with fish and were cunningly spiked with lemon.

The Leaping Hare Cafe, Wyken Hall, STANTON, Bury St Edmunds IP31 2DW ☎ *01359 250287 is simply one of the most heavenly places, with food served all day on Thursdays, Fridays and Sundays in the 400-year-old barn. Eat indoors or, on a warm day, outside – with a view over the fields, where the Jacob and Shetland sheep munch, and beyond. Cooking is a dazzling but well-judged mixture of California and French cuisine, using local ingredients; favourites include chicken pan-smoked over vine prunings (Wyken produce far-better-than-most English wines). Teas are equally stylish; there are scones with own-made jams, but – the Reubens (salt beef & Swiss cheese) apart – no sandwiches. Instead enjoy a slice of almond tart with crème fraîche, a piercingly lemony lemon tart, 'proper' chocolate brownies, or any of the other American-style cookies and cakes ... then wander through the elegantly planted gardens and grounds.*

Emmett's Stores
Peasenhall, Saxmundham, Suffolk IP17 2HJ

**PEASENHALL
Suffolk Ham**

☎ 01728 660250 **CONTACT** Nigel Jerrey **HOURS** Mon-Sat 8.30-13.00 14.00-17.30 (-17.00 Sat) **DIRECTIONS** *In village centre.*

Emmett's store is actually the village supermarket, newsagent and haberdashers rolled into one. The only give-away that something special might be going on, is the huge royal warrant (granted by HRH the Queen Mum) plastered over the front door. Inside, among the jumble of woolly socks, Woman's Own, cat food, processed peas and the like, is one of the best examples of the Suffolk-cure hams and bacons you will find in this country. Quite how and why Mr Jerrey Senior (now handed down to Mr Jerrey Junior) started making their Suffolk-cure ham has never been fully explained. It is enough that they do.

The traditional Suffolk cure is made with black treacle, sugar, salt and stout (one recipe I found also added vinegar, but this was the only time I have seen it suggested) and he also produces a lighter Suffolk cider-pickled ham, using cider instead of stout. Both hams are made in the same way in the backyard behind the stores. Mr Jerrey buys in pork, 'mostly,' as he puts it, 'from happy pigs because it is important to

F. E. Neave & Son, 20 Cross Green, DEBENHAM, Stowmarket IP14 6RW ☎ 01728 860240 *cure their Suffolk hams in black treacle, molasses and local beer for 6-8 weeks, then hang them for 14 days for a sultry sweet meat. Sold as whole hams on the bone, weighing 5 kg (12 lb) upwards, they also produce a Suffolk-style bacon.*

some customers, but I can't guarantee it'. Curiously enough, 'one in every 200 hams won't take a pickle'. Although not exactly sure why this is, Mr Jerrey has a few ideas; but, at the moment, he is not letting on. First he brines the pork in salt, saltpetre and water, then pickles them in either cure for about 3 to 4 weeks. Next they are gently smoked for about 5 days in the smoke-holes over oak sawdust; and finally they are hung for at least a month to mature.

Sold vacuum-packed, either as whole hams weighing 6.5-8 kg (14-18 lb) or half hams weighing 3.5-4.5 kg (8-10 lb), they have a rich deep blackish brown skin. The taste is unique; these are strongly flavoured hams with a biting texture. The Suffolk sweet pickle is sweet, punchy and very meaty; the cider cure lighter, even sweeter, with a hint of fruit. Also worth trying is the sweet-pickled bacon; again it has a good firm texture with a sweet-smoky flavour, but not overly so. Beware of pale imitations, however, I tried a competitor's bacon and it was quite disgusting – cloyingly flavoured with a sweet-sour aftertaste and it spluttered and shrank away merrily in the pan. Mr Jerrey's is without rival in the county.

To cook his hams, Mr Jerrey recommends soaking them overnight in water, then sealing them in a large piece of foil with about 5 cm (2 in) of cider and baking them in an oven preheated to gas 4/180°C/350°F for about 25 minutes to the 450 g (1 lb).

TUDDENHAM ST MARY
Organic Meat and Poultry

Longwood Farm
Tuddenham St Mary, Bury St Edmunds,
Suffolk IP28 6TB

☎ 01638 717120 **FAX** 01638 717120 **CONTACT** *Louise Unwin* **HOURS** *Farm-shop: Mon, Wed and Fri 9.30-16.30 Sat 9.30-17.30; Spitalfields Market: Sun 8.30-16.30; Portobello Road Market: Thurs 12.00-19.00* **DIRECTIONS** *From Bury St Edmunds, take A14 towards Newmarket. After 8 miles, take slip-road on left, signposted Tuddenham. At top of slip-road, follow road to right, signposted Tuddenham, to High Street. Turn left, past church on right. At top of village green, turn sharp right up the green past the pond and up an incline. On right is grain-store, marked Longwood Farm. Go into yard and follow track to shop.*

Most farmers selling a complete range of organic meat and poultry do not actually produce everything themselves, they tend to buy in from other farmers who farm to similar standards. Longwood Farm is different; they currently produce about 85 per cent of the meat and poultry they sell, with the avowed intent of being '100 per cent self-sufficient

---

John's Fish Shop, 5 East Street, SOUTHWOLD IP18 6EH ☎/fax 01502 724253 *is a first-rate fishmongers, run by John Huggins. The white-tiled shop in a side street leading down to the promenade has a well-earned reputation for its range of wet fish and a serious selection of herrings – fresh and variously cured and smoked, each one with its different nuances. In autumn, when the local long-shore herrings are in season, he can be relied on for supplies caught about 4-5 miles offshore. Whenever possible, he buys them weighing about 285 g (10 oz), 'the best size to eat' and caught in drift nets. 'You can tell because they still have their scales on; trawled herrings are usually bruised and battered'. They are sold whole or as fillets. He also sells a choice of fresh sweet herring roe; the hard and darker roe from the female and the softer milky male roe that pop in the mouth like tiny bubbles. He also sells kippers (gutted, split down the middle and cold-smoked); bloaters (whole unsplit herring cold-smoked for a milder mellower flavour); meaty but delicate buckling (head-off, gutted, unsplit, hot-smoked and meaty) and overpowering red herring see J. T. Cole, page 251. During the summer, when local herrings are not in season, he buys them from Scotland. He also sells local samphire and Norfolk crabs.*

---

within the next 2 years'. Louise Unwin prefers it this way 'as then I can have total control and know exactly what I am selling'.

The Unwins farm to Soil Association standards. Their mixed beef herd is single-suckled for about 10 months and slaughtered at between 2 and 3 years; free-ranging pigs from Gloucester Old Spot and Saddle-backs are fattened for 6 months. The chickens, as anyone who has visited them will know, are kept out in the fields and are killed between 8 and 13 weeks, then hung for a week. The only animals they do not keep on the farm all year round are the lambs; after lambing on the farm, they are grazed extensively on the edge of the Brecklands in a nature conservation area, jointly owned by Suffolk Wild Life and English Nature, to which the Unwins have the tenancy.

From the farm-shop they sell all the meat butchered into various cuts by their on-farm butcher. The sirloin was well-textured, firm to the chew with a nice meaty resonance, and the butterfly lamb chops flowery with a good rim of clean-tasting fat. They also make sausages, cure for bacon, ham, tongue and salt beef, and have a range of produce such as on-farm cheeses, beans and grains.

D. J. Rolfe, Hatchmere House, WALSHAM-LE-WILLOWS IP31 3BD ☎ 01359 259225 *attracts customers to his small village butcher's shop from miles around, such is the quality of his meat. He buys locally and everything is well-hung, even the maize-fed chickens that are kept uneviscerated for between 4-6 days. David Rolfe also makes a point of his butchering; he will bone and stuff all manner of things, including saddle of lamb (which comes with a stuffing of sea-soned minced lamb with apricots & almonds), turkeys, chickens, ducks and geese. He also prepares to order ballotines of boned birds, with one stuffed within the other. He Suffolk-cures bacon in a brine of ale and molasses for 21 days and, at Christmas and Easter, whole hams; with both available smoked or unsmoked. He dry-cures silverside of beef for 14 days, then rubs it with mustard and spices for another 4 days for a pungent but well-judged spiced beef. Sausages are plump and meaty, with at least 4 flavours on sale at any one time; these may include pork & fresh leeks or an intensely flavoured pork & tomato made with both fresh tomatoes and a purée of tomatoes and onions. He also sells local bread and vegetables and occasionally you can also buy saladini, a mixture of various leaves grown by Joy Larkcom, the salad guru who lives nearby.*

Describing himself as a transporter/wholesaler, John Streeter of **Pure Suffolk Foods, PO Box 7, LEISTON, Aldeburgh IP16 4UB ☎ 01728 830575** runs a countrywide organic meat box delivery service. Beef and lamb are bought in from Wales, pigs from Derbyshire, and chickens from P. J. Onions see page 215. They supply these butchered to your choice.

WOODBRIDGE
Pork

The Happy Hogs
Kyson Hill, Woodbridge, Suffolk IP12 4DN

☎ 01394 383922   **CONTACT** *Sarah Pinfold – telephone ahead*

A small producer who takes great care with her livestock, throughout the year, Sarah Pinfold rears her 'happy hogs' in what she refers to as 'happy conditions'. These are Large Black sows crossed with the leaner Large White boar for a Blue and White pig, a 'true bacon pig'. Kept outdoors to rummage away and fed an antibiotic-free diet, they are sent off to slaughter at 6 months. Only frozen pork is available butchered into legs and shoulders, and loin chops. The meat is firm-textured, with a deep flavour and a covering of skin that makes a crisp crackling. Bacon is cured and smoked by Mr Jerrey at Emmett's Stores *see page* 253; and mild and meaty sausages with an 82 per cent meat content are made to a 'secret' recipe by a butcher in Norfolk. At Christmas only, Sarah also has hams for sale, cured by Mr Jerrey from her pigs.

Sarah also grows about 200 Norfolk Black turkeys for Christmas. In June she buys them in as day-old poults from Kelly Turkey Farms *see page* 103 and, as soon as they are 'paddock-trained, meaning they won't fly all over the place and up on to the roof, I turn them out on to grass'. They stay out all day, pecking away at wild berries, nettles and greens and are fed grain supplemented with fruit and vegetables (they have even been know to eat avocado); and at night are locked up to stave off the foxes. With plenty of space to move around and varied diet, Sarah's turkeys resound with flavour and well-textured moist meat. She even manages to produce Norfolk Blacks with plump generous breasts, no

---

 Suffolk Larder, 17 The Thoroughfare, WOODBRIDGE IP12 1AA ☎ 01394 386676 is run by Tony Constantine-Smith and his wife, Sue. Most of what they sell is either made by – or exclusively for – them to recipes they have developed. First off is a crumbly moist Suffolk Cyder cake made with eggs, sugar, butter, flour, sultanas, raisins and, of course, Suffolk Cyder (from James White, see page 248). Then there is Suffolk-spiced lamb; whole boned-out leg of lamb cured in a rosemary-flavoured salt and hot-smoked until the meat is a deep-pink right the way through, with a pungent grassy nuance. They make their own flavoured vinegars, using cider vinegar as a base – elderberry; a muscat-tinged elderflower; a fruity blackcurrant; strawberry; raspberry; and redcurrant. Then there are the mustards, based on a Sole Bay (Southwold) recipe: Master's Own, with green peppercorns; pungent Boatyard, with paprika and black peppercorns; mild Sweet Honey; a hot and strong Horseradish; and Christmas, made with honey and whisky (delightful with slices of cold ham). There's a fair range of cheeses with a British bias: unpasteurized Cheddar, various Dale cheeses, and a mild clean fresh-tasting hard-pressed goats' cheese made at nearby Otley College of Agriculture.

MAP 5　　　　　　　　　　　　　　SUFFOLK　　　　　257

mean achievement for – as a breed – they have a notorious reputation for scrawny, scrimpy ones. Killed on site at about 25 weeks, they are dry-plucked while still warm 'to keep their bloom and it's easier to pull out those tough feathers', and hung uneviscerated for 10-14 days; hen birds weigh 4.5-6.8 kg (10-15 lb) and stags 7-10.5 kg (16-24 lb).

During the season – from the end of June to the end of September – Sarah also picks samphire. This she sells fresh in bunches or pickled in 340-g (11½-oz) jars to an Eliza Acton recipe.

Mail Order

turkeys only

Last edition's winners of Best Jams and Preserves Rosette was **Garden of Suffolk Preserves**, *run under the watchful eye of Mary Holmes. In December 1994 she retired and sold the business to friend and neighbour Anne Bloomfield. The premises have moved to* **The Granary, Woodhill Farm, Willow Marsh Lane, YOXFORD IP17 3JR ☎/fax 01728 668329**. *While Mary assures me that everything is 'staying exactly the same', I have not had the opportunity to try this year's jams and to taste for myself whether the high standards are being maintained. If you have, do let me know. Meanwhile, I wish Mrs Bloomfield luck.*

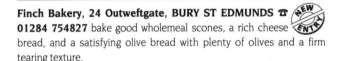

While you're in the area...

D. G. M. Woodhouse, 28-30 Blyburgate, BECCLES NR34 9TB ☎ 01502 715711 not only sells just about everything you would need for cake decorating but also makes chocolates. Worth seeking out are the ginger chocs, which explode with a burning fieriness, and the bars of dark dry bitter chocolate.

Finch Bakery, 24 Outweftgate, BURY ST EDMUNDS ☎ 01284 754827 bake good wholemeal scones, a rich cheese bread, and a satisfying olive bread with plenty of olives and a firm tearing texture.

Brown & May, 7A Broad Street, EYE IP23 7HN ☎ 01379 870181 fax 01379 870673 sell fresh fish as well as a range of smoked fish, including a mild buttery smoked salmon.

Opposite the characterful 16th-century timber-framed Guildhall are bakers **Sparling & Faiers, Market Place, LAVENHAM CO10 9QZ ☎ 01787 247297**. Bread is baked on the premises and the well-fruited currant loaf and nutty Granary 'pat' are interesting.

The Cheese Shop, 74 Beccles Road, OULTON BROAD, Lowestoft NR33 8QY ☎ 01502 564664 has a deserved reputation for selling an interesting British – and Continental – cheeses.

Stowbeck Cheese Dairy, Meadow Farm, WEST STOW, Bury St Edmunds IP28 6EZ ☎ 01284 728862 have only recently started making cheese using unpasteurized milk from their Jersey and goat herds. Stowbeck, made with the cows' milk, is a Cheddar-style cheese; and Stowa based more on Caerphilly.

EGHAM
Vegetables

Green Landscape Nurseries
Hurst Lane, Egham, Surrey TW20 8QJ

☎ 01784 435545 **CONTACT** Mario Mingoia **HOURS** mid-June to end Oct: 6.00-20.00 **CARDS** Access, Mastercard, Visa **DIRECTIONS** From Egham, *follow road across the railway line towards Virginia Water. After about 50 yards, take the last exit off the roundabout, signposted Virginia Water. Follow the road about 1 mile to the next roundabout and drive straight across, signposted Virginia Water. After about ½ mile, take the first turning on the left after the Great Fosters Hotel, into Hurst Lane. Farm is signposted on the left.*

If you live in or around London and want to buy your vegetables from the same source as Quaglino's, The River Café, Cecconi's, The Ivy, Le Caprice and many more, then visit Mario Mingoia at Green Landscape Nurseries, who imports out of season and grows-his-own in season.

Mario is actually half-Sicilian, half-Cockney; but as all his seeds come from Italy his produce definitely has an Italian bent. Grown mostly under glass, with no sprays or artificial fertilizers ('only horse manure'), you will find cardoons; rucola d'orta, a deep-green rocket with a hot peppery flavour as ready-picked only; at least 10 different lettuces; green and Valeriana radicchio; green and white baby zucchini (courgettes) and, of course, their flowers for stuffing; fat green, yellow and red peppers; glossy and plump deep-purple aubergines; both large

The Game Larder, Rushett Farm, CHESSINGTON KT9 2NQ ☎ 01372 749000 *is a good source for game. Pheasant comes from local shoots and is hung to order, depending on the time of the season it is usually around the 5- to 7-day mark. He also sells red-legged and the finer-textured grey (English) partridge, Roe and Fallow deer stalked mainly in Hampshire, woodcock, various wild duck, hare, pigeon, rabbit, wild boar from Nigel Dauncey see page 241 and live crayfish in season. Then there is bison, ostrich, crickets, crocodile, squirrel and locusts, and all those other curious – if not to say outré – meats that seem to have found a following over here.*

and baby cucumbers; artichokes cut 'for babies' in June and grown to their full glory in July; various herbs; and an unusual range of beans which includes cornetti gialli (yellow French beans); runner beans; and, for eating either fresh or dried, borlotti beans. This year promises tomatoes in various shapes and sizes, including round Turbo; Chio 111, an Italian plum tomato; and Coure de Bue, a beefsteak tomato which is big, fleshy and extraordinarily sweet when ripe.

Wentworth Exotic Mushrooms
1 Hurst Lane, Egham, Surrey TW20 8QJ

EGHAM
Mushrooms

☎ 01344 842795 **FAX** 01344 845002 **CONTACT** Peter Hawton **HOURS** 9.30-17.00 **DIRECTIONS** As Green Landscape Nurseries.

Last edition, I featured Peter Hawton's grow-bags of composted straw inoculated with the fungus strain for oyster mushrooms; either as the grey (*Ostreatus pleurotus*), yellow (*Cornucopiae pleurotus*), pink (*Samoneostramineus pleurotus*) or two different but similar-tasting brown (*Sajor caju* or *Pulmonarius pleurotus*). Unlike the common cultivated mushroom (*Agaricus bisporus*), oyster mushrooms thrive on daylight, and the ideal place to keep the bag is in a warm and humid bathroom or kitchen. You cut slits about 2.5 cm (1 in) long, no more than 6, evenly spaced over the bag; then sit back and wait. After about 10 days, the mushrooms should start to appear and from then on they should be lightly sprayed with water every day.

New this year are the shiitake mushrooms. Peter supplies grow-bags of sawdust impregnated with the mycileum and, from starting them off, they take 2-3 weeks to fruit. On average, each bag produces about 25 per cent of its weight in mushrooms; as a bag weighs 450 g (1 lb), you can expect 250 g (8½ oz) of mushrooms. If you pick the first flush when quite small, you may well get another 2 or 3 flushes appearing, with approximately 10 days between each one. Shiitake are meaty, relatively strong-flavoured (far more powerfully flavoured than the oyster) and tend to hold their shape well in slow cooking.

Also new are the oak or hazel saplings he is importing from France. Inoculated with the truffle mycelium, the theory is that you plant the tree in a suitable chalky soil and then sit back and wait; after any time between 6 and 8 years, you should start harvesting truffles of any sort from the French *Tuber melanosporum* to the white Italian T. *magnatum*, depending on which tree you ordered. Definitely a long-term view and, as far as I could find out, a bit of a punt, as there is no money-back guarantee.

Peter is also 'playing around with the weird and wonderful' and has plans to introduce grow-bags for horse mushrooms and blewits, and possibly even trees inoculated with ceps. If growing- and picking-your-own is your dream, then Peter is obviously a man to watch.

Priory Farm, Nutfield, REDHILL RH1 4EJ ☎ 01737 823304 fax 01737 823568 *has all the usual soft fruit and vegetables as well as pick-your-own cherries from late June through to early July. The season starts with Merchant and ends with large black Colney, with Merton Glory, Merpet, Mermat, dark and juicy Van, Stella, Sunburst and Lapins fitting in between. Later on in the autumn they have pumpkins, such as Becky, Tom Fox, Small Sugar, Sumo and Howden; and Onion, Delica, Rowlet and Vegetable Spaghetti squashes. At Halloween, they organize tastings and cookery demonstrations.*

GUILDFORD
Chocolates

Montgomery Moore
17 Tunsgate, Guildford, Surrey GU1 3QT

☎ 01483 451620 **FAX** 01483 451620 **CONTACT** Sheila Torrance **HOURS** Mon-Thurs 10.00-17.30 Fri and Sat 9.00-17.30 **CARDS** Access, Mastercard, Switch, Visa **DIRECTIONS** In town centre, first shop through Tunsgate Arch, just off the High Street.

Now I know that as a nation we are supposed to have a sweet tooth, but I am relieved to discover that Montgomery Moore have determinedly stuck to their guns to produce a better class of chocolate, definitely ones that 'are not too sweet'. To this end they use a couverture (chocolate) with a high cocoa solids content, relatively unsweet fillings and never add sugar to the ganache. Chocolates are made on a daily basis in the kitchen behind the shop and the whole premises are conditioned to maintain a constant cool temperature.

Truffles – made with a ganache of cream and chocolate and flavoured with raspberry, rum, coffee, Champagne or Cointreau – are fresh and creamy with a clean aftertaste. They are quite dense as, unlike the Belgian ones, the filling is not whipped. Tea chocolates, a ganache infused with Earl Grey, Lapsang Souchang, Orange Pekoe or Passion fruit, are rather unusual. I tried the Earl Grey and it had a subtle flavour with the merest hint of the smoky brew. There is an obvious interest in textures such as *feuilletines*, with layers of thin palettes of chocolate lined with a crunchy filling, and hazelnut clusters.

With an innovative approach, they are constantly developing and experimenting. New this year is a white chocolate range; apparently certain people find eating chocolate gives them a migraine. (Can you imagine what a hardship that must be?) Well, according to Sheila Torrance, this is induced by the cocoa husk; but, as white chocolate (with a cocoa solids content of 35 per cent) is free of the husk, this range has been developed particularly with these sufferers in mind. The range includes: Orange Surprise, with a white chocolate and cream ganache flavoured with fresh orange peel; Fruit & Nut, with a white chocolate praline in a white chocolate cup topped with pieces of apricot, lemon, hazelnut & pecan; and a white chocolate truffle with the ganache lightly scented with fresh vanilla. They still make their spoonable chocolate sauces using a 61 per cent cocoa solids chocolate mixed with cream and stock syrup. They come as Original (plain) or laden with

Stockists

Lancs: Merediths

London: Harvey Nichols

Heal's

Selfridges

Oxon: The Old Farmhouse Bakery

Cointreau or cognac. Another range of useful sauces is the coulis; these are made with fruit purées and stock syrups and the flavours available are mango, blackcurrant and, new this year, blueberry. At Christmas, look out for chocolate tool sets and a wide range of gift-boxed chocolates.

Surrey boasts two better-than-average pâtisseries. **Delicieux Pâtisserie, 31 Church Street, REIGATE RH2 0AD ☎ 01737 221740**, *with a couple of tables for indulging on the spot, benefits from pâtissier Stephen Haver's stint in France at Jean Millet. Pastries, tartes and gâteaux are very much in the French mould; tarte au citron comes with a peerlessly crisp buttery pastry and a filling that was perhaps a little grainy and lacking in the piercing sharpness of lemon; truffe au chocolat was delightfully rich, smooth and light, with that glorious dryness only ever achieved when chocolate is of good quality and properly worked; tarte paysanne, with apple flamed in calvados covered with crème pâtissière mixed with meringue, was a heady mixture of textured apple and floaty topping; and pain aux raisin, pronounced by Food Lover Jill Springett of Dorking as 'better than anything we've had in France'.* **The Belgian Pâtisserie**, *with branches at* **86-8 High Street, DORKING RH4 1AY ☎ 01306 880998** *and* **72 Walton Road, East M⁻lesey KT8 0DL ☎ 0181 979 8123**, *shows signs of a marginally heavier hand; pear frangipane, a cunning mixture of almond and pear in a puff pastry case had a buttery afterglow, but was short on the almonds; and the pastry of the raspberry chiffon was a touch heavy, but the intensity of the fruit a welcome compensation.*

The Granary
32 West Street, Haselmere, Surrey GU27 2AB

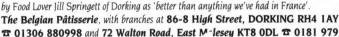

☎ 01428 653226 **CONTACT** *Steve Cooper* **HOURS** *Mon-Sat 8.30-17.00* **DIRECTIONS** *One block behind High Street. Follow signs to Town Hall.*

Some of the signs of a thriving bakery are a brisk trade and shelves half-emptied of bread by lunch-time. I arrived at The Granary at 12.00 and almost all the white bread was sold. Baked in various shapes and sizes – farmhouse, sandwich bloomer, cob and cottage – the dough is given an 18-hour ferment for a better deeper flavour and a denser, firmer texture. Another advantage of a slow-fermented dough is its keeping quality; the bloomer I bought lasted for a good 4 days which, let's face it, is not what we have come to expect from a white loaf. Steve Cooper worked as a baker in the merchant navy where 'there were high-speed machines, so there was less work and less trouble'. For the past 12 years he has run his own shop and, although I would not say it was exactly machine-free, there is an emphasis on craft methods, careful mixing in small batches and quality ingredients. Apart from the white breads already mentioned, there is an enterprising range of flavoured and foreign breads. Inevitably, some work better than others: ciabatta was not, I think, quite right, a little too 'bready' and not quite rich enough in olive oil; tomato, herb & olive oil, made with sun-dried tomatoes, tomato paste and mixed dried herbs, was an orangey red with a good tomato tang; soda bread, made unusually with a lightly malted flour, has a well-judged resonance; and the flat potato & herb was well-textured, with an earthy flavour.

Steve also bakes an interesting range of rye breads. The 100 per cent was dense and tangy; plain rye, made with 60 per cent rye flour and 40 per cent wheat-flour, was lighter and chewier with a dark rich brown crumb; sunflower rye, again made in 60/40 proportions, had a deep rye 'nose' but a surprisingly light rye flavour, mixed with the nutty flavour of the seeds; 6-grain rye, made with 98 per cent rye flour, has a busy mixture of wheat, sesame and sunflower seeds, linseed, millet and barley; and herbina had, for added interest, mixed herbs and caraway seeds and was finished by dipping it in paprika and mixed seeds.

What strikes me particularly about The Granary is that here is a baker with a sure deft touch, who knows and cares about his bread and is forever encouraging his customers to try interesting combinations.

OXTED
Cheese

Eastside Cheese
59 Station Road East, Oxted, Surrey RH8 0AX

☎ 01883 723890 **FAX** 01883 743617 **CONTACT** James Aldridge **HOURS** Tues-Sat 9.00-17.30 (-13.00 Wed) **DIRECTIONS** In town centre, near station.

Like several other cheese enthusiasts, I believe that James Aldridge is probably Britain's finest cheese-maker. You may well have tried his rind-washed – or, as James would exactingly have it, 'smear-ripened' – Tornegus. 'Technically speaking, rind-washing means that the first wash is with a bacteria culture, and that's not how we do it'. James, it is only fair to warn you, can be a trifle tricky to deal with, which is such a shame as his knowledge and expertise know no parallel in this country.

Back to Tornegus: using a fresh Caerphilly made by Chris Duckett see page 237, the cheese is 'massaged' with a white-wine brine every few days over a period of about 7 weeks. As James says, 'This is all-important in the development of the thin apricot-coloured rind, the flavour and the softening of the interior'. Along similar lines is Celtic Promise, from a cheese made by Patrice Savage see page 381, but here cider is used and the cheese develops its supple texture and full taste.

Recently James, in conjunction with Pat Robinson and her daughter Alison, opened the shop Eastside Cheeses in Oxted, not exactly what I would have thought of as a promising area. The shop, simply tiled, has an exciting selection of the best of the on-farm cheeses, some matured by James in the cellars under the shop or at his maturing rooms a few miles up the road. From here he also makes cheese and these are rare and wonderful jewels. Using only unpasteurized milk in the form of cow's milk from Old Scotland Farm see page 265, a local goats' milk (incidentally milked by hand) and a sheep's milk from 'around the corner', he is constantly trying out cheeses, perfecting his favourites and ever varying the range. Passionate about cheese, he is a perfectionist, every aspect of cheese-making fascinates and is known

MAP 3　　　　　　　　　　　　　　　　　　　　SURREY　　　　　263

to him and he says 'hard work and a lot of soul go into making cheese'.

He has his regulars, such as a creamy sparkling fresh Eastside goat, on sale in the shop every weekend; or St Francis, a creamy soft light-textured goats'-milk cheese, with a bloomy rind that when relatively young has a hint of lemon and sweetens out as the cheese matures. Others are: Lord of the Hundreds, made with sheep's milk and matured for about 5 months until it develops a mouth-warming caramel flavour; cows'-milk Willow, with a rich Marmite taste; Wachlestede, with charcoal running through the centre like a Morbier; and a 'proper' Wensleydale, where the curds are broken up by hand so you can control the acidity. James makes this seasonally with sheep's milk, which is what the monks – the originators of Wensleydale – used to use. I could go on and on. James himself produces more than 35 cheeses, but you will never find them on sale all at the same time, with the shop stocking about 90 in total. The pity is that the shop is struggling; if it were in France, on Saturdays there would a queue around the corner instead of no more than a spasmodic flow of customers. If you are at all interested in cheese, and British cheeses at that, I urge you to go. If you try James's cheeses, there is no way you could possibly be disappointed.

John Patrick Coles of **Upper Ridgeway Farm**, THURSLEY, **Godalming GU8 6QR** ☎ **01428 604508 fax 01428 604707** *has been growing for 35 years and is known locally as the Strawberry King for the superb flavour of his fruit. Varieties, chosen for flavour 'rather than ease of growing or travelling', are sold ready-picked from the barn. For the first 3 to 4 weeks of the season, you can buy the pointy Cambridge Vigour, with its biting sweet five-star flavour; with Elvira and Honeyoe as two other earlies. Then come Elsanta, Pegasus, Hapil, Symphony and Rhapsody, followed by Bogota. Also I am grateful to Janet Allan, chief National Fruit Advisor for MAFF, for pointing out that Patrick Coles' raspberries are so good that they too are worth a mention.*

The Original Maids of Honour
288 Kew Road, Kew Gardens, Richmond, Surrey TW9 3DU

RICHMOND
Maids of Honour

☎ 0181 940 2752 **CONTACT** Mr Newens **HOURS** Mon-Sat 9.30-18.00 (-13.00 Mon) **DIRECTIONS** Opposite Kew Gardens, Cumberland Gate.

As with so many of our traditional dishes, several legends have sprung up as to how or when Maids of Honour acquired their name. Newens, who own the trademark for Maids of Honour, would have you believe it comes from King Henry VIII. On inspecting the kitchens at Richmond Palace, he saw a group of women of the bed-chamber (Maids of Honour) eating the tarts; he tried one, liked it and named it after the women courtiers. Another story is that, as the tarts emerge from the oven, the effect of the cool air on the filling is to draw it down making it look like it is bobbing in a curtsy like any good Maid of Honour.

Be that as it may, the tarts are actually rather pleasant. Newens keep the recipe very close to their heart, but the rough puff pastry is filled with curd lightly flavoured with (and here I guess) ground almonds, eggs, a little lemon rind and sugar. The effect is a creamy, fresh and slightly sharp centre, set off by a flaky pastry. Newens make them every day and you can either eat them in the tea-room attached to the shop or take-away for an impromptu picnic in Kew Gardens just opposite. Also to be recommended are the glorious crisp macaroons, generously filled open strawberry tarts, choux buns piped full of fresh cream, crumpets, a rich and moist walnut cake and savoury cutting pies.

RICHMOND
Cheese

Vivian's

2 Worple Way, Richmond, Surrey TW10 6DF

☎ 0181 940 3600 **FAX** 0181 332 1276 **CONTACT** Vivian Martin **HOURS** *Mon-Fri 9.00-19.00 Sat 8.00-18.00 Sun 8.30-12.00* **CARDS** *Access, Euro-card, Mastercard, Visa* **DIRECTIONS** *From Richmond town centre, take Upper Richmond Road towards Sheen. After about ½ mile, turn right at crossroads just before Red Cow Pub. Shop is immediately behind pub.*

Vivian's is an extraordinarily good food shop. Its only drawback, as far as I am concerned, is that it is held back by lack of space; both in the shop, so it is unable to stock even more good food, and out back, where currently there is no room for a kitchen, so they are unable to prepare their own food-to-go. What makes the shop so special is that everything is chosen by Vivian Martin, with quality and flavour in mind or, as he puts it rather less diplomatically, 'I try not to sell any s...t at all! I never sold marmalade until I found a good one, now I stock Garden of Suffolk' *see page 257*.

Cheese plays a big part in the shop, there is a large refrigerated open counter down one wall; and they are ripened by Vivian to optimum condition. For example, I have always thought that Sharpham *see page* 70 would deepen in its creaminess if properly kept, but I have never come across a truly satisfying example; Vivian's was ripened until flowing and much improved by the waiting. Yarg *see page 50* is another cheese that mellows into a honeyed glory when properly matured and Vivian has the knack. Expect to find the Food Lovers' favourites and, among others, are the Blunts' cheeses *see page 274*, Berkswell *see page* 282, and Chris Duckett's Caerphilly and whey butter *see page 237*.

Chef Stephen Bull cooks exclusively for them; although supplies can be a bit spasmodic if he is too busy in his restaurants. He prepares lush well-textured and innovatively layered terrines. They can vary from week to week and can be difficult to cut into slices, but they are special. On offer the week I was there was a velvety-smooth chicken liver, with a well-defined orange resonance; crab & leek, with a buttery fresh crab interleaved with thin strips of leek; duck confit, with bite-size pieces of confit set in jelly studded with vegetables and wrapped in lightly blanched cabbage leaves; and omelette, a terrine of cunning layers of paper-thin omelettes with spinach and sweet pepper between. Stephen also makes a creamy black pudding, boudin blanc, St Emilion au Chocolat, and various puddings and pies. Also worth a try is the broad bean salad prepared by one of the Queen Mum's ex-chefs.

There are plenty of good jams, pickles, Richmond Park honey *see page* 197, Womersley vinegars *see page* 312, breads, croissants and locally baked leek tarts. Half the fun of shopping at Vivian's is that he keeps all sort of things hidden away; I did warn you that the shop was overflowing, so if you want a slice of rare-breed ham or Soay lamb from Ann Knowles *see page* 277 and cannot see it in the shop – ask. He may well have a supply hidden away in the freezer.

Old Scotland Farmhouse Cheese
Staple Lane, Shere, Guildford, Surrey GU5 9TE

SHERE

Cheese

☎ 01483 222526 **CONTACT** Pat Vigar **HOURS** 14.00-18.00 **DIRECTIONS** *From Guildford, take A246 towards Leatherhead. After about 5 miles, turn right signposted Shere. Follow the road about ½ mile up the hill. Farm is signposted on the right.*

Old Scotland is a Cheddar-style cheese made on-farm with unpasteurized Friesian milk by Pat Vigar, ably abetted by David Doble who, you may remember, once produced a similar cheese, Castle Hill. With a close texture and a well-formed natural rind, Old Scotland is made into whole cheeses weighing approximately 4 kg (9 lb), half cheeses, truckles weighing 1.8 kg (4 lb), and mini truckles at 550 g (1¼ lb), Old Scotland is remarkable in that a comparatively young cheese should have such a rich mellow flavour with a flowery nuttiness. Incidentally, the fridge outside the farmhouse is kept well stocked with 450-g (1-lb) wedges.

As luck would have it, when I arrived, Pat was just cutting into her new cheese Tillingbourne, 'the result of fiddling around for 18 months'. Similar to a Tomme de Savoie, it is made in a 50-gallon vat; the curds are packed into 900-1,350-g (2-3-lb) square moulds with rounded corners (the traditional Tomme shape). Left for about 30 hours, during which time they are turned several times to self-press, they are then turned out of the moulds and racked overnight. The following day the cheeses are brined for about 9 hours, put back on the racks to drain, then ripened on wooden boards for about 4 weeks.

With a supple springy texture, Tillingbourne was quite creamy, with an interesting – almost mushroom – flavour, if a little salty. Pat was its fiercest critic, dismissing it as having 'too up front a taste'. So, with the

Stockists

London: Harvey Nichols

Surrey: Secretts Farm Shop

Sussex: Brighton Cheese Shop

Horsham Cheese Shop

Say Cheese

Parsons Pantry, 12 Upper Church Lane, FARNHAM GU9 7PW ☎/fax 01252 735758 *specializes in on-farm British cheeses. They stock a good selection, including Old Scotland see above, Keen's Cheddar see page 242, Avanti (an English Parmesan made locally) and the range of blues from Ticklemore Cheese see page 85. To go with the cheeses are Denhay butter see page 89, breads from The Granary see page 261 and various biscuits. There is a selection of frozen puddings cooked for them, such as lemon mousse or tarte Normande, and a local Guernsey cream.*

help of James Aldridge *see page 262* who has been advising her, it is back to the dairy to improve on it. You cannot help but admire Pat – and all our other on-farm cheese-makers – for their dedication; the best ones are constantly experimenting and improving on their cheeses.

WISLEY
Top Fruit

The Royal Horticultural Society
RHS Enterprises Limited, The Royal Horticultural Society's Garden, Wisley, Woking, Surrey GU23 6QB

☎ 01483 211113 **FAX** 01483 211003 **CONTACT** *Wayne Garrigan* **HOURS** *Mon-Fri 13.15-16.00 Sat and Sun 12.00-16.00* **DIRECTIONS** *Gardens are signposted from Junction 10 of M25.*

The Royal Horticultural Society's Garden at Wisley is interesting not only for plantsmen but also for vegetable and fruit growers. There are various trial gardens for herbs, salad plants, vegetables and soft fruit, where you can see unusual varieties and experimental methods of growing. The orchards are a rare treat; the apple collection boasts about 650 cultivars (varieties); the pear collection 130 varieties; and the plum collection contains around 100 cultivars of mainly high-quality dessert and culinary plums, and gages raised in the 19th and 20th centuries. According to Jim Arbury, Technical Supervisor in the Wisley Fruit Department, 'excluding damsons, bullaces and cherry plums, some of the oldest in the collection are Old Green Gage and White Magnum Bonum, known in France since 1700 as Dame Aubert'.

What you may not know, as the RHS never seem to advertise the fact, is that you can buy fruit and vegetables grown at Wisley. You do not need to be a member nor do you have to pay an entrance fee, as the produce hut is sited outside the gardens. It opens sometimes in June, through to the end of November, 'depending on the crops'. Everything is freshly picked and you can often pick up some unusual varieties in excellent condition but supplies are a bit spasmodic.

The season kicks off with soft fruit: various strawberries, raspberries, gooseberries and currants; there may be vegetables, depending on 'what's on trial this year. Last year it was lettuces and cauliflowers, and lots of them. Next come plums, 'in short supply this year because of the late frost', but worth looking out for is Late Muscatel with its oozing sweet juiciness or the reddish Royale de Vilvoorde with its rich flavour. Then come the pears and apples: Dumelow's Seedling is thought to be very good for mincemeat and Golden Noble Mr Arbury recommends as 'the finest of cookers'. Quinces are very popular, if in limited quantities; the 4 varieties grown

In a county studded with pick-your-owns, **Garson Farm, Winterdown Road, ESHER KT10 8LS** ☎ **01372 464778** *fax 01372 470410 and* **Secretts of Hurst Farm, Chapel Lane, MILFORD GU8 5HL** ☎ **01483 426543 fax 01483 861703** *are worth recommending for their scope and variety of fruit and vegetables. Secretts run a huge farm-shop* ☎ **01483 426789**, *which also has to be admired for its breadth and choice of products.*

are Bereczki, Champion, Portugal and Apple-shaped, but there usually
is a waiting list, with eager customers putting their names down early in
the season. Wayne Garrigan is trying to organize a weekly list, so you
can ring up and find out what is for sale.

While you're in the area...

**Bonnetts Farm, Horsham Road, CAPEL, Dorking RH5
5JW ☎ 01306 711598** sell own-reared beef, lamb and pork,
in various cuts and joints. They also produce a pork pâté and various
sausages made with an 85 per cent meat content and breadcrumbs.
More reports please.

Butchers **R. G. Young, Sussex Cottage, Petworth Road,
CHIDDINGFOLD GU8 4TY ☎ 01428 683434** sell nicely
hung meat and game in season. They also produce very good sausages
in natural skins, with an average meat content of around the 80 per
cent mark: pork & leek is meaty and well-textured, with fresh chopped
leeks; wild boar has a well-rounded punchy flavour; pork & honey is
coarsely-textured with a pleasant sweetness; and pork & apple is
gently spiced and studded with fresh apples.

**At Home Catering, 40 High Street, COBHAM KT11 3EB ☎ 01932
862026 fax 01932 867617** 'offers gourmet solace to weary com-
muters' who can buy anything there from a loaf of ciabatta to a prepared take-away dinner party if they are too tired to cook.

**La Charcuterie, High Street, CRANLEIGH GU6 8AU ☎
01483 277072** is an unpretentious village deli with an interesting selection of local cheeses, including Old Scotland *see page* 265,
locally smoked trout, and various cakes made by local ladies.

Thanks to Food Lover Mrs Wedgbury of Guildford for recommending butchers **C. H. Wakeling, 41 Farncombe Street,
GODALMING GU7 3LH ☎ 01483 417557**. 'When needing good-
quality well-hung beef, I go to Mr Wakeling, whose Aberdeen Angus is
excellent... (also) local lamb, free-range pork and a selective range of
cheeses – two locally produced'.

**Jarvis & Sons, 56 Coombe Road, NORBITON KT2 7AF ☎ 0181
546 0989 fax 0181 296 0139** has a justified reputation for the freshness and quality of their fish. With several Japanese customers, they
will gut and fillet as part of the service and even prepare fish for *sushi*.

Tim Dommett of Parsons Pantry *see page* 265 recommends
butcher **Michael Humphries, The Long Road,
ROWLEDGE, Farnham GU10 4DQ ☎ 01252 792204** with a branch
at **West Street, MIDHURST GU29 9NQ ☎ 01730 813135**. All the
meat is well-hung and they make various pies, pâtés, meat en croûte,
potted venison and pheasant, brawn with added salted silverside, dry-
cured bacon and ham, and pickled tongue, brisket and belly of pork.

Sussex

Map No. 3

The Weald Smokery

Mount Farm, Hawkhurst Road, Flimwell, Sussex TN5 7QL

☎ 01580 879601 **FAX** 01580 879564 **CONTACT** Andrew Wickham **HOURS** Mon-Sat 9.00-17.30 (all year); Sun 11.00-17.30 (Easter to end Sept only) **CARDS** Mastercard, Visa **DIRECTIONS** From Flimwell, take A268 towards Hawkhurst. Smokery is first property on the left.

The smoked products from The Weald Smokery have a distinctive smoke taste. For cold-smoking, Andrew uses oak sawdust; but for hot-smoking, or 'cooking', he uses whole oak logs. Their advantage is that they burn to create heat, then smoulder away to create smoke and thus give better heat control. This enables Andrew to smoke for a longer period of time and without overcooking the food.

The result – a powerful woody flavour – is particularly obvious in the trout and locally made Toulouse-style sausages. The salmon, farmed in Argyll then dry-cured in salt for 15 hours and smoked for 2 days (which struck me as an extraordinarily long time) has a buttery texture with a salty woody overlay. Hot-smoked boneless breasts of chicken, first brined in salt and sugar, were sweet and moist. New to me are the smoked eel and venison. Using either local eels or some from the Isle

---

Halstead Home Preserves, 8 Stirling Way, HORSHAM RH13 5RP ☎ **01403 218086** make a range of jams, mustards and chutneys, but it is for the Spicy Apple Butter that I single them out. Fruit butters belong to the old tradition

of boiling fruit down to a pulp in order to preserve it, in the times when sugar was in short supply or beyond the pockets of ordinary country-folk. Using mainly Bramleys, Margaret Halstead makes hers by stewing the apples with a strong dry cider, puréeing, sieving and

finally cooking them with sugar and spices. Packed into 225 g (8 oz) jars, the light rich-brown dense butter is grainy-textured, with a well-judged sweetness of apples backed by a complexity of spice that warms and reverberates in the mouth. Serve it with cold meats or spread on toast.

MAP 3   SUSSEX   269

of Bute (sent live), they are frozen on arrival and smoked throughout the year. Andrew brines his for about 2 hours, puts them in the kiln initially to cook them, then blocks off the chimney for a hot-smoke. Sold either as whole eels or in pieces weighing 140-350 g (5-12 oz), they are meaty with a salty punch. Venison is farmed 'for consistency of quality', dry-cured in salt, brown sugar, and juniper berries for about 1 week, then cold-smoked for another week. Sold thinly sliced with or without olive oil and herbs as a dressing in 115 and 225-g (4 and 8-oz) packs, it has a mild gentle flavour. They also smoke haddock and mussels, prepare smoked trout and salmon pâtés and a smoked chicken terrine.

From the shop they also sell kippers from Craster *see page* 208, a wide range of cured and smoked products from Mooreland Foods *see page* 38, as well as a well-chosen range of on-farm British and French cheeses, wines, jams, pickles, sauces and mustards.

Stockists

Kent:
Chiddingstone
Causeway Stores
- - - - - - - - -
Perry Court
Farmshop
- - - - - - - - -
Todds Vintrey

Sussex: Corbin's

Bartley Mill
Bells Yew Green, Frant, Sussex TN3 8BH

FRANT
Flour

☎ 01892 890372 **FAX** 01892 890101 **CONTACT** Piers Garnham **HOURS** *Apr to end Sept:* 10.00-18.00; *Oct to end Mar: Sat and Sun only* 10.00-17.00 **CARDS** Access, Visa **DIRECTIONS** *From Tunbridge Wells, take B2169 towards Lamberhurst. 1 Mile east of Bells Yew Green, fork right to Wadhurst. After about ½ mile, Mill is on right.*

Piers Garnham is a fourth-generation miller. The family mill was in Kent and when it burnt down over 10 years ago his father gave up the ghost. Piers, who obviously has flour sifting through his veins, persevered and bought Bartley Mill, a 13th-century working water-mill on the river Win. Then he then set about renovating it.

Using French burr stones for milling, Piers mills organic (to UKROFS standards) and conventionally grown wholemeal and brown flours; white flour he buys in ready-milled. An important part of his business is the blending of flours: some are relatively straightforward, such as Pastry flour – a mix of soft English wheat milled for pastry – or Sussex bread flour with wheat and rye flours, rye flakes, linseed and sunflower seeds, or Ciabatta flour with white flours specially milled for a low starch damage and mixed with a European sour-dough powder and aged. A large part of his work is tailor-making flours for specific bakers. 'They come to me and tell me they want to make a "such and such

Piers Garnham of Bartley Mill *see above recommends* **Rye Bakery, 89 High Street**, **RYE TN31 7JN** ☎ **01797 222243** *for both his straightforward but 'properly' made breads and the breads he bakes with Piers's flours and sometimes supplies to the mill shop. These include Italian-style red or green pesto twists and various ciabattas, such as plain, cheese, sun-dried tomato & onion, arrabiata and a hijiki seaweed bread.*

bread", and then I create a specific flour for them'.

From the mill-shop he sells his flours, but it may be wise to check first as not everything is always there. if you ring first, providing the flour is in stock, Piers will bag it up into a 6-kg (13¼-lb) bag. However, you should remember these flours are made up for a baker's convenience and so do contain such ingredients as powdered cheese in the Cheese, sun-dried tomato & herb flour or powdered onion & potato (to give it a creamy texture) in the Seaweed flour. He also sells a range of biscuits using his flour, but baked by a baker in Scotland and Fudges *see page* 92. A selection of bread made from his flour is also on sale, baked either by Rye Bakery *see page* 269 or on-site.

Last, but by no means least as far as Violet is concerned, are the dog knobs – hard round biscuits packed in 340-g (11½-oz) bags and made with organic cereal, legume seeds, grains, oil seeds, vitamins, minerals & herbs. I have to tell you that Violet found them too much like hard work, she just could not get her teeth around the hard texture. Her Jack Russell boyfriend Jack, however, cannot get enough of them; all I can surmise from that is do not give them to lazy spoilt dogs.

Mail Order
flour & dog knobs only

Stockists
Hants: Durleighmarsh Farm

Oxon: Old Dairy Farm Shop

Surrey: Fanny's Farm Shop

Sussex: Crumbs of Comfort

Middle Farm Shop

GOSPEL GREEN

Cyder & Cheese

Gospel Green
Gospel Green Cottage, Gospel Green, Haslemere, Sussex GU27 3BH

☎ 01428 654120   **CONTACT** James Lane – *telephone ahead*

James Lane makes 2 different but complementary products to high standards – Gospel Green cheese and 'cyder', as he would have it spelt. The cheese is made with equipment dating back to Victorian times – a water-jacketed curd bin, curd knife and fork and sturdy cheese presses. The equipment has done him proud, as he has now been making for 8 years.

Using about three-quarters of the morning and one-quarter of the unpasteurized evening milk from his father's Friesian herd, he makes a buttery and fruity hard-pressed cheese which is notable for its mildly grassy flavour. Made in a 400-litre vat, usually about 3 times a week, the cheese is a bit of a hybrid. 'I don't know how to bracket it,' James told me, 'it's not as hard-pressed as a Cheddar, but it does have a high butterfat content of around 55 per cent. And the curds are cut, milled, then broken up by hand, similar to both a Cheshire and Caerphilly'. Its texture changes with the time of year; the cows calve in August and the earlier cheeses, made in September through to Christmas (and sold after 3 months) tend to be softer, crumblier and creamier. As the season progresses, the cheeses turn out to be firmer and harder with a deeper fuller flavour. Made in 900-g, 1.8 and 3.2-kg (2, 4, and 7-lb) truckles, they are interesting any time of the year.

James also makes a *méthode champenoise* cider. It was he who pio-

MAP 3   SUSSEX   **271**

neered the idea and since the last edition he has been joined by Boll-hayes *see page* 75 and Somerset Cider Brandy Company *see page* 238 and both acknowledge their debt to him. His is a blend of two-thirds eating apples and one-third cookers, including Mère de Ménage from Nor-mandy but 'definitely no bitter-sweets (cider apples), as I've a horror of them ever since I got drunk as a lad on scrumpy'. The apples are lightly pressed to maintain fruitiness. The juice is stored in stainless-steel vats; after 6 months, when it has completed its first fermentation, it is racked, fined (clarified), blended in an active champagne yeast solu-tion, with cane sugar, bottled in full-strength champagne bottles and stored for 12 months. During that time a second fermentation takes place, 'the longer the fermentation and the more constant the temper-ature the finer the mousse – meaning the size and longevity of the bubbles in the glass'. Then, in the traditional champagne method, the *rémouage* takes place. The bottles are stacked in a *pupitre* and there follows the highly skilled process of turning the bottles so the sedi-ment falls on to the cap, then freezing to remove it and finally giving it a dosage of cider to bring it to the level of *brut* as champagne-makers would say. The result is highly successful; a sophisticated, very French, evenly balanced dry cider with a lingering apple flavour. Almost, but not quite, as satisfying as drinking champagne.

Stockists

London: Harvey Nichols

Jeroboams

Surrey: Guildford Cheese Shop

Sussex: English Wine Centre

Pallant Wines

The Horsham Cheese Shop, 20 Carfax, **HORSHAM RH12 1EB** ☎ **01403 254272** *can be relied on for stocking a good choice of local cheeses from their 200-odd selection. Here you will find Gospel Green see above, Tornegus see page 262, Old Scotland see page 265 and the little waxed Chabis from Nut Knowle Farm. They also sell Carfax, a dill-and-chive-flavoured cheese espe-cially for them in Devon, own-made pasta, pesto sauce, tea-breads, shortbreads and cheese straws baked every day. Upstairs is a café serving ploughman's, using – of course – cheeses from the shop.*

Carr Taylor Vineyards
Westfield, Hastings, Sussex TN35 4SG

HASTINGS
Verjuice

☎ 01424 752501 **FAX** 01424 751716 **CONTACT** David Carr Taylor **HOURS** 10.00-17.00 (*closed Christmas and Easter*) **CARDS** Access, Visa **DIRECTIONS** *From Hastings, on A21 take A28 and follow signs to Carr Taylor vineyard.*

David Carr Taylor is one of our more innovative wine-makers. Fortu-nately I do not write about wines, as I have never perfected the art of 'spitting' at tastings – can you imagine what a problem that would be, careering from one vineyard to another?

What I do want to tell you about is Carr Taylor's verjuice. As Tom Stobbart writes in *The Cook's Encyclopedia* the word 'from the French *vert* (green) *jus* (juice) means the sour juice of unripe fruit and was more used in the past as a souring agent than it is today. In France, it was the juice of unripe grapes and in Britain, the juice of unripe apples or crab apples'. David's green juice or 'green wine' as he likes to call it, is a by-product of the wine-making. After about 4 weeks, at the very early stages of fermentation, he racks the wine off into clean vats; the yeasts and sediments that are left behind are left to settle then he draws the liquid off the top, filters and bottles it in 33-cl (12-fl oz) bottles. As David positively encourages a heavy degree of oxidization, it is actually a sherry-style wine at its very early stages, but it can be used in exactly the same way as a wine vinegar for dressings, marinades or in cooking. Quite acidic but not nearly as sharp or as obvious as vinegar, it has a slight sweetness that comes from the unfermented grape sugars and it is mild and grassy and surprisingly gentle.

Mail Order

minimum order 6 bottles

KIRDFORD
Apple Juice

Kirdford Growers Ltd
Kirdford, Billingshurst, Sussex RH14 0NQ

☎ 01403 820274 **FAX** 01403 820560 **CONTACT** Colin Head **HOURS** Mon-Sat 9.00-17.00 Sun 10.00-17.00 **CARDS** Access, Switch, Visa **DIRECTIONS** In centre of village.

Kirdford Growers is a co-operative of about 15 apple growers in Sussex, Dorset and Somerset. A couple of years ago, they invested in a modern juicing plant and now produce three single-variety clear juices with plans to develop others over the next few years.

All the apples are stored at Kirdford, in a central facility atmosphere-controlled cold-store. Juicing takes place from harvest through to the spring, in batches using what are known in the trade as 'outgrades'. To obviate any possible problem of patulin, no rots or damaged fruits are allowed and all the fruit is pre-washed. Once the apples are pressed, the juice passes through filters into stainless steel vats and then it is fed into the pasteurizer and on to the bottling plant; the only addition being ascorbic acid (vitamin C) to prevent oxidization (discoloration). They are sold in green bottles, which normally I think is a pity as it means you cannot see the colour, although in this case it does not matter as – extraordinarily enough – they are all the same honey-yellow colour. All the juices are well-balanced, with a pleasant freshness: Bramley is dry with a good balance of fruit acids and a tight fruitiness; Cox is sweeter, with a hint of pear; the even sweeter Russet has a fragile floweriness and a lingering tang; and they also produce a Sussex juice, a blend of various apples.

Stockists

Surrey: Secrects of Milford

The Horsham Cheese Shop

Pallant Wines

The Salmon Shop

The Weald & Downland Open Air Museum

Costrong Fruit Farm and Nursery, Plaistow Road, Kirdford BILLINGHURST RH14 0LA ☎ 01403 820391 *grow several apples, including such older varieties as* King of the Pippins (*the apple for* tarte Normande), Orléans Reinette, Egremont Russet *and* Blenheim Orange. *In late summer they also produce melons and grapes from their glasshouses.*

MAP 3　　　　　　　　SUSSEX　　　　　273

Old Spot Farm Shop, PILTDOWN, Uckfield TN22 3XN ☎ 01825 722894 fax
01825 723623 *buy in local outdoor-reared and finished pork from a Saddleback hybrid-
cross pig. They brine-cure for bacon for 3 weeks and ham for 4 weeks in a mixture of rock
salt, saltpetre, herbs and spices, and sell it green or smoked over oak chips. Sausages are a
speciality, with about 20 varieties in total: made from shoulder, belly and hand meat, they
are coarsely textured, and packed into natural skins with own-grown fresh herbs as flavourings. These include: Medieval, with a 100 per cent meat content with chives, parsley, sage & black
pepper; pork & leek; and Orchard Pork, with fresh apples & cinnamon. They also make hand-raised
pork pies with a hot-water crust and full of juicy meat, enriched with a 'proper' jelly made from the
pigs' trotters. From their shop they also sell various cheeses, including a locally made unpasteurized
soft and hard-pressed goats' cheese from Willowdown Dairy Goats.*

Rumbolds Farmhouse Cheese
Rumbolds Farm, Plaistow, Sussex RH14 0PZ

PLAISTOW
Cheese

☎ 01403 871404 **CONTACT** *Alison Gibbs* **HOURS** 10.00-18.00 **DIREC-
TIONS** *In village centre.*

A trip to Rumbolds Farm is like stepping into picture-postcard land.
The granary, now converted into a farm-shop which operates on a
serve-yourself policy, overhangs an old fish stew (pond) that once
served the monks. On the bank opposite, glimpsed between the
rushes, is the farmhouse.

Alison Gibb is a relative newcomer to cheese-making and she
makes no more than a 45 kg (100 lb) a week, using the unpasteurized
milk from the family's Guernsey herd which also has a few Jerseys for
good measure. Using the morning milk, 'the evening's milk is too high
in fat and is too creamy for a cheese', she makes Rumbolds to a
Cheddar recipe 'with a few adaptations', in 4.5-kg (10-lb) wheels and
450-g (1-lb) waxed babies. Matured for 4-8 months, it is a close-
textured cheese with an obvious creaminess; mild and buttery, it has a
pleasant if not terribly well-developed resonance. From the shop, she
also sells cartons of their unpasteurized cream which is so thick you
can dig a spoon into it, as well as eggs from the farm.

Stockists

Hants:
Durleighmarsh
Farm

Surrey: Gusto
Classico

Sussex: Country
Produce

C. R. Upton
The Lodge, 4 Top Road, Slindon, Arundel, Sussex BN18 0RP

SLINDON
**Pumpkins
and
Squashes**

☎ 01243 814219 **CONTACT** C. R. Upton **HOURS** *mid-July to end Oct: 9.00-
19.00* **DIRECTIONS** *From Fontwell, take A29 towards Watersfield. Follow the
road and turn left signposted Slindon. Follow the road through Slindon to the top
of the hill, past The Newburgh Arms. House is about 300 yards along on the left.*

Mr Upton grows about 30 varieties of pumpkins and 30 varieties of
squashes, revelling in such glorious names as Pink Banana, Golden
Hubbard, Funny Faces (pumpkins) or Golden Nugget, Sweet Dumpling,

Crookneck or Turk's Turban (squashes). Mr Upton's record-breaker topped the scales at 29 kg (60 lb), others are tiny; some are soft-fleshed and custardy, others incredibly stringy or pappy; some are stuffed with seeds, others have virtually none. Visit him when they are in season and there they are stacked all over the place – on wheelbarrows or piled outside his house – it is a sight not to be missed.

The Weald & Downland Open Air Museum, SINGLETON, Chichester PO18 0EU ☎ 01243 811348 fax 01243 811475 *is a fascinating place to visit. On a 50-acre site, they have re-erected over 35 historic domestic and agricultural buildings which give an insight into how our ancestors lived and farmed. These include an old smithy; Winkhurst House, a medieval house from nearby Chiddingstone; Bayleaf Farmstead, complete with a garden planted out with medieval herbs and vegetables, and a farmyard stocked with rare-breed animals; and a working water-mill from Lurgashall which dates back to the 17th century. You can regularly see the water-mill in action, and from the shop you can buy the coarsely stone-ground 100 per cent wholemeal flour from English wheat, along with biscuits made with their own flour and other local products.*

WHITESMITH

Goats' Cheeses

Kevin & Alison Blunt

Greenacres Farm, Whitesmith, Lewes, Sussex BN8 6JA

☎ 01825 872380   **CONTACT** *Kevin Blunt – telephone ahead*

Kevin and Alison Blunt have now been making unpasteurized goats'-milk cheese for over 6 years and their cheeses continue to improve, manifesting deeper and more complex flavours that could easily compete with our Continental cousins. Using a mixture of evening and morning milk from their Toggenburg and British Saanen flock, they turn it into Golden Cross, Chabis and Laughton Log (aka Greenacres) – 3 differently shaped and sized cheeses, but made to more or less the same recipe. The basic recipe they use is as for a Saint-Maure, a soft creamy goats' cheese from Touraine. First the milk is started, renneted and injected with a penicillin culture; after a 24-hour ripening period, the curds are cut and gently ladled into the different moulds – Golden Cross comes as a 225-g (8-oz) log, Greenacres weighs 900 g (2 lb) and Chabis, an 85-g (3-oz) truncated cone. These are then left to drain for 24 hours.

The following day they are carefully unmoulded, drained, put into the drying room for one day, then salted by hand. After a couple of days they are removed to a maturing room kept at a constant temperature of 10°C (50°F). From this point the techniques for the cheeses

---

Say Cheese, Gardner Street, HERSTMONCEUX BN27 4LE ☎ 01323 833871, *with a branch at* **Riverside, LEWES BN7 2AD ☎ 01273 487871**, *make a point of selling local cheeses, including Flower Marie and Laughton Log see above; Duddleswell and all the other sheep's-milk cheeses from Sussex High Weald Dairy; Burndell a hard-pressed goats'-milk cheese and Chancton, both made by Jenny Ferris at Ashington; Old Scotland see page 265 and Tornegus see page 262.*

differ: Chabis, creamy with a fresh lemon fruitiness and a deep smoothness, is eaten while still quite young; Golden Cross and Laughton Log, on the other hand, are rubbed in charcoal to encourage the penicillin to grow. After a few days the mould starts to develop and forms a furry coating on the outside. The Blunts sell their cheese at about 2 weeks, although it is at its best when matured on for a further couple of weeks, by which time they have opened out in flavour for a well-rounded creamy floweriness and a gentle hint of goat.

New this year is the mould-ripened Flower Marie, made with an unpasteurized ewes' milk the Blunts buy in from Dorset. Made to a recipe developed in conjunction with James Aldridge *see page 262*, the curds are carefully ladled into moulds, left to drain, unmoulded, brined briefly for about 30 minutes then matured. After about 1 week its furry coat starts to grow and, although the Blunts do sell it at about 2-3 weeks, it is at its best at about 6 weeks, by which time it has turned creamy and starts to run at the edges. Gloriously and delicately smooth, with a sweet creaminess and a full richness, this is a very fine cheese which deserved the gold award it won at the 1995 London International Cheese Competition.

Stockists

Kent: James's

Surrey: East Side Cheese Company

Vivian's

Sussex: Corbin's

Say Cheese II

Hunts Fruit, Sharewood Farm, New England Lane, SEDDLESCOMBE, Battle TN33 0RP ☎ 01424 870354 *grow about 150 different apples, although most of them are cider varieties. Eating apples include Worcester Permain and Charden, a French variety with a honeyed sweetness. They mail-order 4.5 kg (10 lb) boxes of Kidd's Orange Red, Egremont Russet and Cox only. They also send their apples for juicing and sell as single-variety juices Crispin, Kidd's Orange Red, a piercingly sweet Egremont Russet, Cox, and Sturmer Pippin – which if left on the trees until late November produces a sweet full-flavoured juice with a lasting tang. They also sell cider, again made off the farm using a mixture of their own dessert and culinary apples.*

Anglo Dutch Rye Co.
Unit 9, Amelia Road, Worthing, Sussex BN11 3AS

WORTHING
Pumpernickel

☎ 01903 237664 **CONTACT** Wil van der Meij – *telephone ahead*

Wil van der Meij was 'practically weaned on pumpernickel'. When she moved here from Holland about 12 years ago, she was forced to buy it imported from abroad, 'but it was awful, not how I remember it as a child'. The idea came to her that she should make her own in England – having a baker as a partner obviously helped – and so about a year ago they set up in business after several months of intense tutoring with a baker in Friesland. Pumpernickel, as Wil explained, 'is very difficult to make and it takes such a long time – about 5 days from start to finish. Perhaps that's why no one else makes it in England'.

To explain the process briefly: using cut rye (Wil buys hers from Shipton Mill *see page 115*), you soak it in water until it is the consistency of porridge, then you cook it in the oven for about 8 hours until it

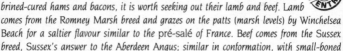

J. Wickens Family Butchers, Castle Street, WINCHELSEA TN36 4HU
☎ **01797 226287** *is a proper family butcher. Apart from their good sausages, brined-cured hams and bacons, it is worth seeking out their lamb and beef. Lamb comes from the Romney Marsh breed and grazes on the patts (marsh levels) by Winchelsea Beach for a saltier flavour similar to the pré-salé of France. Beef comes from the Sussex breed, Sussex's answer to the Aberdeen Angus; similar in conformation, with small-boned carcass, it produces soft well-marbled meat with a sweet flavour which Wickens hang for between 2 and 3 weeks.*

Stockists

London:
Portobello
Wholefoods

The Haelan Centre

Wild Oats

Sussex: Infinity
Foods

Waitrose

darkens and all the starches have converted to sugar. Then you mix it with more uncut rye to stiffen the mixture, leave it for a while, mould it into long loaves and finally bake it off for 12-14 hours. It must be cooled down, for 'even though there is no yeast and rye has a very low gluten content, it tends to rise so you must let it die down'. Finally it is carefully sliced, packed into 250-g (8½-oz) packs and pasteurized.

Now I have no great experience of pumpernickel, but I was struck by the freshness of Wil's. The thin dark-brown slices were moist and chewy, with a gentle sweetness and a mild earthiness which was exactly what Wil is aiming for. Recently they have started baking spelt flour *see Doves Farm Foods page 21* into a range of loaves and are currently experimenting with a spelt and rye sour-dough. I will keep you posted.

Mrs Stickland *makes jams in her kitchen in Wisborough Green, but actually sells them from a help-yourself-stand outside her mum's bungalow* **Ellington, in KIRDFORD RH14 0LX** ☎ **01403 700265**. *I can heartily recommend the meaty apricot, made with the dried fruit and flaked almonds; and the tangy strawberry with whole large fruit.*

While you're in the area...

Pallant Wines, 17 High Street, ARUNDEL BN18 9AD ☎ **01903 8822880 fax 01903 882801** has a reasonable collection of English wines as well as bottles of Sussex Spring water and Gospel Green cyder *see page 270*. There are plenty of local foods, including various cheeses, Kirdford apple juice *see page 272*, bread delivered on a daily basis from The Slindon Bakery and a selection of Gina Burt's cakes, including her lemon drizzle and fat-free Sussex fruit made with Gospel Green cyder.

Dalton's Natural Food Centre, Barnham Road, EASTER-GATE PO20 6RP ☎ **01243 543543** smoke quite a wide range of produce, including a firm and salty Sussex eel and salmon with a salty bite. They also sell fresh fish and crabs and lobsters from Selsey.

Friend Virginia Ironside tells me that **Springs Smoked Salmon, EDBURTON, Henfield BN5 9LN** ☎ **01273**

857338 fax 01273 857228 is 'rather an amazing shop – stuffed with every kind of frozen fish. They do their own smoking, including a well-flavoured smoked salmon'. More reports please.

Boathouse Farm, ISFIELD, Uckfield TN22 5TY ☎ 01825
750302 is a mixed organic (to Soil Association standards) farm. They mill their own wheat for a 100 per cent stoneground flour, sold in 1.35, 16 and 32-kg (3, 36 and 72-lb) bags, and a local baker bakes a straightforward dense and nutty wholemeal loaf for them. They also sell own beef, lamb and a few own-grown vegetables.

Ann Knowles of Burstye Soays, Burstye Farm, LINDFIELD, Hay-wards Heath RH16 2QY ☎ 01444 483376 keeps Soay lamb, a small – almost deer-like – sheep, with lean gamy meat. She has a small amount available as boned joints, mainly between October and December.

Lurgashall Winery, Windfallwood, LURGASHALL, Pet-worth GU28 9HA ☎ 01428 707292 fax 01428 707654 is
very 'picturesque', with the winery in a 17th-century converted cattle barn. Here they make country wines, meads and liqueurs; some, I have to say, more successful than others, but then I am no great fan. To be admired is the walnut liqueur, made from crushed and marinated walnuts, then fortified to a 17 per cent alcohol content. Thick and limpid with a light nuttiness, you can serve it chilled with cheese.

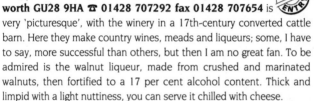

I have heard good comments about the produce from **Old**
Plawhatch Farm, SHARPTHORNE, East Grinstead RH19 4JL ☎ 01342 810857, farmed to Biodynamic and Soil Association standards. Using the unpasteurized milk from their Meuse-Rhine-Isel herd, they sell milk; thick, whipping and single cream; Cheddar; quark, as plain or with blackberries or strawberries; yoghurt as plain, low-fat or flavoured with the same fruit; and vanilla and organic chocolate ice-cream. They also sell their own beef, lamb, and pork; cure and smoke their own bacon; and grow various vegetables. More reports please.

Maynards, Windmill Hill, TICEHURST, Wadhurst TN5 7HQ ☎/fax
01580 200394 have the usual pick-your-own soft fruit during the height of summer. From late July to early August they also have morello cherries which are ideal for bottling, Kent Cob and White Spanish cob-nuts and Shropshire Prune damson in September and, at the end of the month, Vranja quinces.

Warwickshire

Map Nos.2 and 4

Take Two Cooks

Rosello, Harbury, Leamington Spa, Warwickshire CV33 9JD

☎ 01926 612417   **CONTACT** *Caroline Iacaruso – telephone ahead*

Take Two Cooks, a husband-and-wife team of Pino and Caroline Iacaruso, continues to flourish and bake to a consistent high standard. Pino's cooking pedigree is impressive; it includes stints at Nyffenaggars, the pâtisserie in Lausanne, and with various Royals – last heard of he was making a batch of rose-petal jelly from Royal roses. Everything is cooked to order and, although there is a list, Pino will make almost anything in any size and will even cater for any number up to 150.

He works from a large kitchen that – large fridges, freezers and 2 ovens apart – is pretty much like yours or mine. His forte is Continental pâtisserie: bavarois in lemon, chocolate & orange, and raspberry; roulades of chocolate and vanilla sponge filled with fresh cream, cherries & kirsch; French apple flan with a rich butter pastry covered with a thin layer of crème pâtissière and glazed bitter-sweet apples that he has contrived to keep crunchily textured; gâteau St Honoré, with either chocolate or toffee; fruity lemon or orange tartes and a serious chocolate truffle cake. Made with layers of light sponge infused with alcohol, spread with layers of light-as-air chocolate truffle, it is finished with a deep rich dark chocolate – definitely for sophisticated chocolate lovers, it is moist and finely judged, neither too sweet nor too mean.

At Christmas, there is a meltingly rich Yule log; and panforte di Sienna covered with own-made crystallized fruit. Lighter in colour and texture than the imported versions you see in just about every Italian deli, Pino's is heavily based on various nuts and has a yielding toffee texture. He also bakes flavoured shortbreads in packets of 8 or 16 portions; and chicken & ham pies with generous quantities of the meat bound together in a creamy sauce. In fact it strikes me there is very little that Pino cannot make and make very well at that.

Fosse Way Honey, Northcote, Deppers Bridge, LEAMINGTON SPA CV33 0SU ☎/**fax 01926 612322** *run 350 hives. They sell 3 honeys: a lighter flowery honey from a mixture of fruit blossoms, chestnut, lime, blackberry, willowherb, clover and the inevitable rape, as either runny or soft set (seeded); a deep rich and pungent Ling heather, gathered when the hives are taken up to the National Park in Derbyshire above the Chatsworth Estate in late summer; and an English honey, a mixture of the two.*

Meg Rivers Cakes
Middle Tysoe, Warwickshire CV35 0SE

☎ 01295 688101   **FAX** 01295 680799   **CONTACT** Meg Rivers   **HOURS** Mon-Sat 10.00-17.00   **CARDS** Access, Mastercard, Switch, Visa   **DIRECTIONS** *From Stratford-upon-Avon, take A422 towards Banbury. After about 8 miles, turn right just before the Edgehill escarpment, signposted Tysoe. Follow the road about 2 miles into Middle Tysoe and shop is signposted on the left.*

The small one-storey converted outbuilding that houses Meg Rivers' shop and bakery is set at right angles to the quiet main street of Middle Tysoe. A gleaming white-washed front, colourfully planted hanging baskets, a mounted shop sign creaking gently in the breeze and a large bow-window set the scene. Inside, the tiny shop is charmingly laid out: an old pine dresser displays the cakes and tucked under the table are pine chairs for customers to use while considering which of Meg River's 30 fruit cakes to choose. The pity of it is that few of Meg's 8,000-odd customers ever see the shop – they order their cakes by post. With the possible opening of a tea shop, however, that should change.

Meg's cakes are made with the very best natural ingredients: raw sugar, organic flour, local free-range eggs and English butter, 'If I use alcohol – rum brandy or kirsch – that's what I pour in. I don't use any essences. Unbleached white flour is organically produced and the dried fruits are the best money can buy'. Baking powder has been banished, 'you don't need it if you cream the butter properly'. Although it may sound a contradiction, Meg places an emphasis on healthy eating, 'Some, like the apricot & nut or fig & nut contain no added sugar, they don't need it, the natural sugars in the fruit make them sweet enough'. Others have minimal or no added fat; and one of the rich fruit cakes is made with rice and soya flour for anyone allergic to wheat flour.

Meg's cakes change with the seasons. During the summer there are lighter fruit cakes: cherry cake made with cherries soaked in kirsch or a old-fashioned seed cake with caraway seeds soaked in lemon juice and orange and lemon peel. There are sporting cakes: for summer, a lawn-tennis cake tinged with sherry, a sailing cake doused in rum and packed with walnuts, cashews, hazelnuts, almonds and Brazil nuts; in winter there is a rich dark rugby cake soaked in stout, and a huntsman's cake made to an old Cotswold recipe. Easter produces a proper Simnel cake, but without its marzipan balls to commemorate the apostles; winter, a choice of rich fruit cakes with or without alcohol. Her

Christmas cake is spectacular – a confection of vine fruits, nuts, mixed peel and spices laced in brandy. All of the cakes come carefully decorated on top with whole nuts or fruit, tied up in a band or ribbon and well-packed for safe transport. What I have always liked about the cakes is their 'wholesomeness', their clarity of flavours and freshness. Generously packed with fruit or nuts, they are rich but not overly so, sweet without cloying the palate and dense without being too heavy. Due to popular demand, Meg has started selling iced cakes, using a natural almond paste with a fondant icing. These are the rich fruit and Madeira, although she will ice any cake to order.

As a treat for yourself or a present for a friend, you can join Meg's Cake Club. New members receive a storage tin with their first cake and for the first week-end of every other month you receive a cake weighing approximately 1 kg (2¼ lb). In 1995 members indulged in light fruit cake in February, apricot & almond in April, pineapple in June, date & walnut in August, cherry in October and a rich fruit cake for December.

Paxton & Whitfield, 13 Wood Street, STRATFORD-UPON-AVON CV37 7DJ ☎ 01789 415544 fax 01789 297972, *sister shop to Paxton & Whitfield in London see page 190, sells a creamy mildly salted Mozzarella made from buffalo milk by Robert Palmer in – would you believe – Idlicote near Shipston on Stour. Like the best mozzarellas, when you bite into it, it reveals flaky layer upon layer of rich milkiness. They also stock various territorial cheeses, several local ones including Cerney see page 118, Smart's Double Gloucester see page 110 and Charles Martell Single Gloucester matured at 3 months, Longman's butter, bread from a local French baker and Innes cheese and bread see page 246.*

RYTON-ON-
DUNSMORE

Seeds

Ryton Organic Gardens

Ryton-on-Dunsmore, Coventry, Warwickshire CV8 3LG

☎ 01203 303517 **FAX** 01203 639229 **CONTACT** *Jackie Gear* **HOURS** *10.00-17.00 (Restaurant also open Sat eve)* **CARDS** *Access, Visa* **DIRECTIONS** *From Coventry, take A45 towards the M45. After about 5 miles, turn left on to B4029, signposted Ryton Organic Gardens. Gardens are 200 yards along on the right.*

As ever, there's an awful lot going on at Ryton Gardens. As the National Centre of Organic Gardening, it is also the headquarters for the Henry Doubleday Research Association and, as such, promotes, advises, runs courses and carries out research for organic gardening. The 10-acre gardens are a pleasure to wander around, as well as a source of great interest. Divided into areas for soft fruit, apples, pears, plums, vegetables growing in beds, a no-dig vegetable garden, weed control, composting and soil fertility, herbs, and many others, there is much to enjoy as well as to learn. For anyone at all interested in growing produce or flowers without chemicals, this is the place to visit.

Jackie Gear, Executive Director of the HDRA runs the recently expanded shop and café. Under her management the café serves wholesome salads, soups and meals from organic (to Soil Association standards) produce, while the shop sells a wide selection of organic produce – meat, cheese, vegetables, fruit, bread and possibly the widest range of organic wine in this country. Throughout the year there are special events: last year Ryton Organic Gardens held the first ever potato day, with 60 kinds of seed potatoes on sale, tastings and talks. Every year at the beginning of July is the National Organic Food & Wine Fair, where visitors are positively encouraged to try the produce.

Another vital aspect of their work is the Heritage Seed Library, run by Jeremy Cherfas. As he explains, 'For any vegetable or fruit seed to be sold in this country, it has to be registered on the national list. As that costs a lot of money, you'd have to sell a lot of seed to make it worthwhile for the seed merchants. Some varieties, although popular with gardeners, are just not commercially viable. The merchants can't afford to register them and so they are dropped. Now the danger is these varieties will just disappear forever. To prevent this, we have established a seed library – a genetic bank to keep them going. We need to preserve these seeds; they represent diversity, a range of colours, textures, sizes and shapes and, of course, tastes. Flavour from old-fashioned varieties isn't something we can afford to lose'.

Anyone can join the Heritage Seed Programme and membership entitles you to, amongst other things, a choice of seeds from 5 varieties. Last year's most requested seed was the Crimson-flowered broad bean, next came the Banana-Pink squash with the Ne Plus Ultra pea as third. As they cannot afford to offer everything every year and 'besides' as Jeremy says, 'we want to encourage people to save their own seeds' the 1995 list offers different varieties, such as Lazy House-wife climbing French bean whose young pods are 'quite tasty but it is at its best as a drying bean'; Asparagus kale, whose young flower shoots can be blanched and eaten like asparagus; Bath Cos lettuce, which dates back to before 1885 and is apparently 'deliciously meaty and crunchy'; and Carlin peas the Northern pea which dates as far back as Elizabethan days. As Jeremy is always on the look-out for any information about threatened varieties and, indeed, the seeds, do get in touch if you have any. This is the only way we have of ensuring our glorious cornucopia of vegetables will survive.

While you're in the area...

Hiller's Farm Shop, Dunnington Heath Farm, ALCESTER B49 5PD ☎ 01789 773057 is highly recommended by friend Tim Finney. 'A converted barn, the shop is light and airy and always well stocked with fresh locally grown vegetables and a good selection of British cheeses'. More reports please.

Thanks to Food Lover Hugh Sheldon of Lea for recommending ducks from **Mr D. S. Marland, Whitehouse Farm, IDLI-COTE, Shipston-on-Stour CV36 5DN ☎ 01608 663247** as 'the only ducks I know large enough for 12 people – and not a bit fatty'. Apparently they are Barbary ducks and weigh from 1.8-5.5 kg (4-12 lb). More reports please.

Patricia's Cotswold Fudge, Unit 4, Shipston Industrial **Estate, Darlingscote Road, SHIPSTON-ON-STOUR CV36 4PR ☎/fax 01608 662252** produce a fudge made with sugar, glucose syrup, evaporated milk, butter and margarine, cut into irregular squares with a hardish texture that crumbles in the mouth. The 7 flavours include plain; rum & raisin with whole raisins and a warm honey flavour; coffee; and a fiery ginger.

Snitterfield Fruit Farm, Kings Lane, SNITTERFIELD, Stratford-upon-Avon CV37 0QA ☎ 01789 731244 fax 01789 731712 sells ready-picked soft fruit, including strawberries, raspberries, gooseberries, redcurrants, white currants & blackcurrants, tayberries, marionberries (a loganberry-raspberry cross) and tummelberries (a tayberry-raspberry cross). There are also various vegetables, such as sweetcorn, asparagus, broad and runner beans, 20 apple varieties, plums and pears.

West Midlands

Map No. 4

BERKSWELL
Berkswell Cheese

Ram Hall Dairy Sheep
Ram Hall, Berkswell, West Midlands CV7 7BD

☎ 01676 532203 **CONTACT** *Stephen Fletcher – telephone ahead*

Would that all cheese-makers were as assiduous as Stephen Fletcher. He started 'dabbling' at making his cheese in 1989, with a Caerphilly-type recipe; from that 'our own technique evolved. It doesn't follow any written recipe, nor does it even resemble how we first started making it. No one who tried it then would recognize it now'. This slow

Judged best British cheese-shop by Good Cheese Magazine, **Langmans Fine Cheeses, 3 Manor Walk, Solihull B91 3SX ☎ 0121 705 2535** has a good selection of on-farm British cheeses, including Berkswell see below, as well as bread baked on the premises.

and careful evolution carried on for several years and when I approached Stephen for the first edition of the *Food Lovers' Guide* he turned me down on the grounds that he was still not confident of his cheese and how it was maturing; but now – and rightly so – he is.

Berkswell, made with the unpasteurized milk from their flock of 160 milking Friesland ewes, is a glorious cheese. It is a seasonal cheese, made only between February and October, when the ewes are in milk. Stephen tends the flock, while his mother Sheila and wife Tessa do the actual making. Working in a 454.5-litre (100-gallon) vat, no more than a couple of times a week they make about 40 2.7-kg (6-lb) wheels. Turned regularly, they drain in colander moulds for 48 hours before being hand-salted and then left to mature for a minimum of 4 months. With quite a dense texture, it has all the flavour you would hope for from a well-made ewe's-milk cheese; flowery with the characteristic sweet caramel, it lingers in the mouth, opening up to reveal a warm glow. Incidentally, I judged the sheep's-milk class at the 1994 British Cheese Awards and Berkswell was a deserved winner of gold; its depth of flavour and its purity made it stand out a mile.

They also make 2 Coulommiers-type soft cheeses, Kelsey, with its chopped curds and sold as plain or flavoured with garlic & chives or tarragon; and the two-tone Marlow, in which the curds are sliced for a creamier flavour, then half is mixed with anatto to give it an apricot colour. If you are wondering about the appropriately named Ram Hall, the Elizabethan double-gabled manor house where the Fletchers live, Stephen assures me it dates back to Saxon times and was so-called long before he started making ewes'-milk cheese.

Mail Order

Berkswell only

Stockists

Derbys: Chatsworth Farmshop

Pugsons of Buxton

London: La Fromagerie

Neal's Yard Dairy

Surrey: Vivian's

Fowler's Forest Dairy, Small Lane, Earlswood, SOLIHULL B94 5EL ☎/fax 01564 702329 make Little Derby cheese. The 'Little' signifies it is made out of the county, although as far as Pat Fowler knows, no one within the county is actually making it on-farm. Pat makes hers with the pasteurized milk of their Friesian/Holstein herd, in both block and traditional wheels. Lightly pressed with a soft golden rind, Pat washes the cheese in red wine and matures the wheels for 7 months for a close-textured cheese with a soft mellow tang. New this year, but as yet unsampled by me, is the Warwickshire Truckle; a 6-kg (13½-lb) cloth-bound and waxed truckle, it is an offshoot of the Derby recipe.

While you're in the area...

If the thought of knocking at the door of a convent to buy chocolates daunts you, you will find Nuns of Daventry truffles *see page 205* at **Southfield Farm Shop, 841 Kenilworth Road, BALSALL COMMON, nr COVENTRY CV7 7HB ☎ 01676 532212**. Now under new management, they also sell both the local cheeses, Fowler's Little Derby *see above* and Berkswell *see opposite*.

Wiltshire

Map No. 2

Sandridge Farmhouse Bacon

Sandridge Farm, Bromham, Chippenham, Wiltshire SN15 2JL

☎ 01380 850304 **CONTACT** Roger Keen **HOURS** Mon-Sat 9.00-17.30 **DIRECTIONS** From Chippenham, take A4 towards Devizes. Turn right on to A342, towards Devizes. After about 7 miles, turn right at sign for Melksham. Follow the road for 2 miles and turn left at sign for Bromham. Farm is on the right after about 150 yards.

All the pork products from Sandridge Farm come from Roger Keen's own pigs. In summer you can wander down and see them out in the fields, but in winter they are kept indoors in straw yards on the grounds that Roger Keen claims the wet land causes the sows considerable discomfort. He feeds them on pig rations, from mostly home-grown cereal without any artificial hormones, routine growth promoters or antibiotic feed additives. Roger used to supply bacon pigs to the local Harris bacon factory, so he must know how to finish a bacon pig. When it closed down several years ago he started to process the meat.

He now sells a wide range of village hams – so-called as each one is named after a local village. The strong-bodied, heavily-salted and darkly-fleshed Brunham takes about 8 months to mature, as first it is dry-cured then steeped in molasses flavoured with juniper berries – it is certainly not a ham for the faint-hearted. Trubridge is what Roger Keen describes as a York Ham *see Harris-Leeming Bar, page 308*, as it is dry-cured. Devyses is brined in the local brew (Wadworths 6X); the result is a robust, slightly hoppy ham (fine if you like beer); Chipnam is a Wiltshire-cure ham which means that it is brined rather than dry-cured, and Golden Rind is the smoked version.

He also prepares an apple-cure bacon, with a sweet overlay, and both smoked and unsmoked (green) Wiltshire-cure bacon. Food lover Bronwyn Williams Ellis writes, 'All very good, especially streaky apple-cure and smoked streaky – the added bonus to the latter, in particular,

MAP 2 WILTSHIRE **285**

is lack of shrinkage'. Bath Chaps are also splendid; they come from the fleshy part of the pig's jaw – the jowl (although I have heard the lower cheek and tongue are sometimes used). The meat is salt-cured, cooked, boned and then rolled to look like a miniature ham. Usually eaten cold and sometimes coated in breadcrumbs, it can be a little fatty, so it is best served with a sharp vinaigrette to cut the richness. Roger also makes coarse sausages from shoulder of pork; these include pork & herb and an interesting smoked pork which is smoked over oak for a woody finish.

Stockists

Berks: G. Machin

Glos: Jessie Smiths

Warw: Country Bumpkins Delicatessen

Wilts: E. Hall
- - - - - - - - -
Reeves the Baker

In the middle of the busy high street is **Mackintosh of Marlborough, 42A High Street, MARLBOROUGH SN8 1HQ ☎ 01672 514069**. *Run by Nigel Mackintosh, an ex-employee of Justin de Blank, whose London food shop is sadly missed. No doubt following his former boss's example, Nigel's policy is to stock unusual hand-made products made by small – and, whenever possible, local – producers. Here is a shop after my own heart, as it stocks most of my favourite products from the county – and more. You will find Berkeley Farm Dairy cream and butter* see page 291, *a selection of* Wild Food Tamed *see below, Rushall Mill's bread – delivered on Fridays only, a superbly fruity well-balanced apple juice made by Peter Pitman of Pewsey, Hotshop's sparklingly fresh-tasting unusual pickles and chutneys, Mere Fish Farm's* see page 288 *cold- and hot-smoked trout, worthy rich fruit cakes and chocolate, coffee and Victoria sponges baked by local ex-WI ladies, Eastbrook Farm Organic Meats* see page 221 *free-range eggs and, occasionally, their bacon and sausages, Baydon Hill cows' and sheep's cheeses, Rosary log cheese* see page 292. *From out of the county come Ackerman's truffles* see page 192, *Alderton Ham* see page 215, *a full range of* Wendy Brandon Preserves *see page 378, a good choice of mostly unpasteurized farmhouse and ter-ritorial British cheeses, Innes bread and their mature cheese* see page 246, *and James Baxter's potted shrimps* see page 157.

Nigel also sells a range of own-prepared foods, either fresh or frozen pâtés, roulades, main dishes, puddings and canapés, including strongly flavoured crumbly and sharply cheesy Parmesan short-breads. They are an idea he 'borrowed' from Justin, but are none the worse for that.

Wild Food Tamed
31-2 Lower Horsehall Hill Cottages, Chisbury, Marlborough, Wiltshire SN8 3HX

CHISBURY
Pickles and Sauces

☎ 01672 870639 **CONTACT** Louisa Maskill – *telephone ahead*

Louisa Maskell lives at the edge of Savernake Forest, down at the end of a leafy track in an enchanting idyllic cottage. A natural inventive cook with an intuitive sense of flavour, she also is passionate about using indigenous ingredients. From spring to autumn, you may come across her, loaded down with baskets filled with leaves, nuts and berries gathered from the forest.

Her fruit cheeses are in the traditional style of a thick paste; they vary with the seasons, but are always made with English fruit. Last year she made rhubarb with ginger, elderflower with gooseberry, elderberry with apple and damson with kernels. The latter was a shiny ruby-red confection, tart – Louisa by her own admission does not like sweet things – and bursting with ripe fruitiness; so good you could eat it on its own or serve it as the Spanish serve their quince paste, with cheese.

She pickles walnuts from her own trees. First the green walnuts are pricked, soaked in brine and left to dry until they turn black in our so-called sun. Then they are stored in a spiced vinegar for 2 months, until they emerge with a flowery taste spiced with a hint of cloves. Fighting back the invasion of pesto, Louisa has come up with a British answer – Savernake nut and herb pastes. Again these vary according to the season, but you might try wild forest mushrooms in oil, one made with her pickled green walnuts, or piquant green sauce made with parsley, elderberry capers and ground hazelnuts. 'As far as the nuts are concerned, it's a matter of who gets there first – the squirrels or me. Hazelnuts are fine, but they usually beat me to the ripe walnuts'.

New this year is nettle & sorrel sauce, made with nettles gathered from her garden, sorrel and wild garlic (ramsons) flowers. It is a thick dark-green purée, with a mild earthy flavour and a hint of sharpness; Louisa suggests diluting it with oil or cream and spreading on toasted bread for crostini and as a sauce with pasta or rice. She is currently experimenting with lemon balm and wild mint, so you can expect additional new flavours soon. Everything is charmingly presented, tied up in brown paper – yet another example of Louisa's style and flair.

Stockists

London:
Jeroboams
- - - - - - - - - -
Mise-en-Place
- - - - - - - - - -
The Real Food
Store

Wilts: Mackintosh
of Marlborough

CLENCH
COMMON

**Free-range
Eggs**

Martin Pitt
Levetts Farm, Clench Common, Marlborough, Wiltshire SN8 4DS

☎ 01672 512035 **FAX** 01672 514976 **CONTACT** Martin Pitt **HOURS** Mon-Fri 8.00-16.00 Sat 8.00-12.00 *(Inspections until 1 hour before closing)* **DIRECTIONS** *From Marlborough, take A345 towards Upavon. The farm is just before Clench Common on the right.*

'Free-range' can be very loosely interpreted; but when it comes to eggs it does, in fact, have an EU legal definition. The hens must have continuos access to open-air runs during the day and these must be mainly covered with vegetation; inside, in the hen-house, the birds must be kept at no more than 25 per square metre (giving each a space the size of an A4 sheet of paper), with perches allowing 15 cm per hen.

Martin Pitt, however, is an egg farmer who thinks the EU definitions are just not good enough. They do not control feed – most farmers add antibiotics and chemical colorants (or, at best, natural ones) to turn the yolks the sunshine yellow we have come to expect. Martin Pitt adds nothing. He feeds them a home-grown mix that includes wheat, barley, soy bean oil, limestone, ground oyster shells (for the egg shells), maize (for their yolks), and a seaweed meal bought in from the west coast of Ireland which gives the yolk a deeper colour and is a further rich source

---

 West End Farm, BISHOPS CANNINGS, Devizes SN10 2LL ☎ **01380 86059** *sell 'proper' free-range eggs sold at the farm gate. Reared on a diet of wheat and barley, supplemented with proteins and minerals, you can see the hens pecking about in the paddocks.*

of minerals. He also refuses to buy in chicks that have been de-beaked – farmers usually burn off the tips to stop the hens from attacking each other. Martin Pitt believes this only happens if they are given an imbalanced diet and/or housed in poorly ventilated buildings with too many birds crammed in. Anyway, as he points out, 'if they are de-beaked, they won't be able to grub for food or pick at the grass. It defeats one of the objects of "free-range"'.

Martin's are mollycoddled hens, kept at one-third of the usual stocking density in small separately housed flocks of 1,800. His henhouses are specially designed airy barns with several huge doors and his hens do go out into the fields. They lay their eggs in his own design 'potty' system which provides them with space and comfort. His eggs may come more expensive than most, but you are guaranteed that they come from sleek happy hens (visitors are welcome to inspect the hen houses). They taste remarkably good and, because of his unique collecting and date-laying stamping procedure, are also remarkably fresh. Widely distributed throughout the south of England, you can also buy them direct from the farm, secure in the knowledge you are buying the 'real thing'.

Stockists

London: C. Lidgate Ltd

Hockneys

La Provencal

Selfridges

Oxon: Gluttons

The Real Meat Company
East Hill Farm, Heytesbury, Warminster, Wiltshire BA12 0HR

Fresh Meat and Poultry

☎ 01985 840501 (01985 840436 for general information) **FAX** 01985 840243 **CONTACT** *Richard Guy – mail order only* **CARDS** *Access, Amex, Mastercard, Switch, Visa*

I have real problems with The Real Meat Company; not – I hasten to add – about the eating quality of their meat and poultry, but rather about their welfare standards. In my last edition I wrote criticizing their use of farrowing crates (a means of confining sows in a small restricted space for a period prior to and during birth – and, on some farms, until weaning – to prevent them from rolling over and squashing their piglets) and teeth clipping for pigs. In a long and somewhat hectoring letter, its founder Richard Guy took me to task, I quote: 'Farrowing crates are the safest form of indoor farrowing and our bias has to be away from temporary sow discomfort and towards the piglet's life chances. We insist on solid floors, straw bedding and they are not used until weaning, but until the piglets are strong enough to move to a group suckling area. As there is no profit and certainly no PR gain in allowing the use of crates, our motive is clearly welfare only … As for teeth-clipping … We prefer not to teeth-clip, but in large litters where competition for teats causing face-biting and udder damage are a predictable risk, it would be cruel not to'.

Now the last thing I want to indulge in is a slanging match and no doubt Richard Guy could run rings about me arguing the technical toss. But I have visited hundreds of farms, seen pigs kept in all sorts of conditions and I maintain that any company whose logo carries the words, 'Quality, Purity, Welfare' has no business keeping pigs in farrowing crates. It may be good livestock management, it may save piglets lives but no matter how hard Richard Guy tries to convince me, if he makes the claim that Real Meat animals are reared to high welfare standards, I believe this should not include farrowing crates. Other 'alternative' meat producers who make similar welfare claims have banned them on the grounds they are not welfare-friendly, they distress the pigs and, anyway, in a well-planned, stress-free system, they are as unnecessary as teeth-clipping.

One of the reasons I have raised these issues is because I think it is important that we, the consumers, do try get to grips with what exactly it is we are buying, particularly when it comes to meat. All sorts of extravagant claims are made for animal husbandry, but they cannot always be justified. Another consideration is, of course, taste. Again some 'alternative' producers make the claim that because their animals are reared extensively and fed a well-balanced additive-free diet, they have a better taste and texture. However, it is not as simple as that. The eating quality of meat depends on several factors – breed, feed, age, slaughtering, hanging and butchering; each one – and no particular one – is vital to the end result.

Stockists

Essex: Elmer & Sons

Glos: Andy Howse

Leics: Roy Hendersen Butchers

London: Brimarks
Henry Reed Butchers

MERE

Cold-smoked Trout

Mere Fish Farm
Ivymead, Mere, Warminster, Wiltshire BA12 6EN

☎ 01747 860461 **FAX** 01747 860461 **CONTACT** Janet & Chris Wood **HOURS** Mon-Fri 9.00-17.00 Sat 9.00-13.00 **DIRECTIONS** In Mere, pass the public car-park on your right and after about 50 yards turn right into Water Street. Then turn first left into Ivy Mead and, ignoring the bend in the road, drive straight on. Follow the track to the Fish Farm.

Mere Farm's cold-smoked trout continues to be one of the best in the country. It looks like – and is prepared in exactly the same way as –

Le Hérisson, 90-2 Crane Street, SALISBURY SP1 2QD ☎ 01722 333471 fax 01722 716547 is named after the French for 'the hedgehog', which is why this delicatessan/brasserie is known locally as 'Prickles'. A modern uncluttered shop in a period street just by the Cathedral, food is served all day from the café at the back. There is an ongoing menu of light meals/large starters, croissants, own-made cakes and savouries throughout the day, with 'proper' courses at meal times. The deli is out front and here you can buy own-made pâtés – the ducks' liver is particular rich and creamy – and such trendy affairs as own-made roast Mediterranean vegetables. They stock Hobbs House Bakery bread see page 12 collected every Monday and Friday, Finns' jams see page 178, Fudges biscuits see page 92, Fjordling smoked fish see page 292, and some cheeses including Blue Vinney see page 94 and Charles Martell's Stinking Bishop. A busy place – when I went it was only recently opened and by the owners' admission the kitchen was having difficulty keeping up. By now it should have settled down.

Rushall Mill, Devizes Road, Rushall, PEWSEY SN9 6EB ☎ 01980 630335

stone-grind wholemeal flour from wheat farmed to Soil Association standards on Rushall Farm. There they grow 'hard' or strong varieties, meaning wheat with a high protein content. As the more protein the flour contains the more gluten there will be in the dough, their flour is well suited to bread-making. Flour is sold in 25-kg (55 lb) sacks, and 12.5 and 1.5-kg (28 and 3½-lb) bags; and for anyone who is determined to grind their own flour, whole wheat is available in 25-kg (55-lb) sacks. Using the flour, miller David Fuller doubles up as baker; he bakes a 100 per cent wholemeal loaf with a solid texture and a pleasant earthy taste, light scones, crisp and very strong garlic croûtons, a sultana loaf stuffed with fruit, a sticky malt loaf – and Wookey Woofs, twice-baked dog biscuits given a wide berth by Violet who has still not learnt how to crack them. New this year are pizza bases, rolls and baps, sweet and Chelsea buns, bread pudding made to a Scottish recipe using local free-range eggs; and the farm manager's wife makes cakes, and savoury and fruit pies. Anyone making a special trip should phone in advance (they have a 24-hour answering machine) as they can sell out very quickly.

Mail Order

wholemeal flour only

smoked salmon. First the trout is cured, smoked for several hours over a cold smoke (Mere use beechwood), then thinly sliced and vacuum-packed in 225 and 450-g (8-oz and 1-lb) packs or whole sides. What Mere Farm do to make theirs so special, I cannot imagine; but it is delicate, finely textured and moist. As local aficionado Michael Murphy said in the last edition (and finds no reason to revise his opinion), 'It's like eating smoked salmon, but paying trout prices'. Also available are hot-smoked trout, an excellent butter trout terrine and fresh trout.

Truffles
72 Belle Vue Road, Salisbury, Wiltshire SP1 3YD

**Plum
Pudding**

☎ 01722 331978   **CONTACT** *Mrs Barbara Bayfield – mail order only*

Although one-time private cook Barbara Bayfield does supply tea-shops with various cakes and scones, it is for her 'Traditional Olde English Plum' – aka Christmas – puddings that I single her out. Using her grandmother's old-fashioned and laborious recipe, she starts making in May through to 'the start of the summer holidays', so the puddings will have been aged for about 6 months.

Working in 9.5-kg (21-lb) batches 'for no other reason than it's easier for me that way', first vine fruits (sultanas, raisins and currants) are soaked overnight in a dark stout and medium cream sherry. Wholemeal breadcrumbs are crumbed by hand 'I can't get sufficient supplies of fresh. Also they must be the right size; if they're too large they make holes in the puddings'. All these are mixed with beef suet (sunflower suet for the vegetarian version), muscovado sugar, glacé cherries, mixed peel, fresh eggs, mixed spices and plain white flour, 'even though I only use 1 lb for every 21 lb mix, wholemeal flour would make too heavy a pudding'. Then she adds copious amounts of the stout and sherry, and pressure-cooks the puddings for about ¾ hour for the smallest 225-g (½-lb) size up to 2 hours for the largest 1.8-kg (4-lb) size.

Stockists

Ches: Goose Green Delicatessen

Hants: Hockeys Farm Shop

London: Fox's Delicatessen

Oxon: Aubrey Newman & Daughters

Wilts: The Nadder Catering Food Shop

While still hot, they are treated to a liberal dose of brandy or rum or Cointreau or Drambuie ('if you add the liqueur before it is cooked, most of it boils away in the cooking'), and then they are stored until Christmas-time. Packed in plastic bowls in 6 sizes, they come complete with heating instructions either for steaming or in a microwave. Speaking personally and as a traditionalist, I do not terribly like the inclusion of mixed peel, but I was in the minority here. Barbara's are proper Christmas puddings; dense and quite firm, substantially spiced and generously fruited, they are the sort of pudding that demands to be noticed.

SHERSTON
Mustard

The Wiltshire Tracklement Company
The Dairy Farm, Pinkney Park, Sherston, Malmesbury, Wiltshire SN16 0NX

☎ 01666 840851   **FAX** 01666 840022   **CONTACT** *William Tullberg – mail order only*

'Mustard should never up and hit you on the forefront of your palate. Initially it gives a mild sensation, then creeps back increasing as it goes', is how William Tullberg, a large jocular man, defines a good mustard. Mustard has been made for centuries in England and William has been in the mustard business for a mere 25 years. Still making it more or less by hand in the traditional way, he started off with a recipe found in a John Evelyn diary and is one of the very few to grind his own seeds.

To explain the process briefly: first he mills or grinds the seeds – usually a mixture of locally grown white (B*rassica alba*) and black (B. *nigra*) mustards – to crush them. For a smooth mustard he may have to grind them up to 4 times. Then he mixes them with water, wine and cider vinegar, beer, honey, spices or herbs – again it depends on the mustard he is making – and leaves them to stand in huge drums for around 14 days. The weather plays a part: the colder it is the longer the time it takes for the seeds to absorb the liquid – but William can tell instantly as he stirs them with a huge paddle, 'It's just a question of feel and smell'.

Stockists

Devon: N. H. Creber Ltd

Norfolk: Larner's of Holt

Surrey: Garson Farm Shop

Wilts: Skidmores Butchers

Yorks: Lewis & Cooper Ltd

The strength of a mustard depends on the mix of seeds, how finely they are ground and the quality of the vinegar and the spices. William uses the best possible for his 8 coarse-ground and 8 smooth range. For Tarragon he mixes in frozen French tarragon to give it that sharp distinctive flavour; Original is robust and gently tickles your throat; English Beer, made with Wadworth's 6X, is full and creamy; and Green Peppercorn delightfully piquant.

William also makes other 'tracklements' (a Lincolnshire word for meat accompaniments) – jellies, sauces and condiments – and new this year, jars of grated horseradish mixed with cream. They are all of first-rate quality.

John Hurd's Organic Watercress
Hill Deverill, Warminster, Wiltshire BA12 7EF

☎ 01985 840260 **FAX** 01985 840260 **CONTACT** John Hurd **HOURS** Mon-Fri 8.00-17.00 Sun 8.00-12.00 **DIRECTIONS** Call at Packing Shed.

As far as I know, John Hurd is the only organic grower (to UKROF Standards) of watercress. He farms 5½ acres on the edge of the Wiltshire Downs and his 47 beds are fed every day with 3 million gallons of pure spring water pumped up from bore holes 36.5 metres (120 feet) down in the chalky land. Growing watercress organically means that he uses neither pesticides nor fertilizers other than fibrophos (slag).

If he is lucky he crops continuously throughout the year, although a severe temperature drop can halt the growth. During the winter he grows a French-American cross, like virtually all the growers; but from May to September John grows what he calls the English variety with pointier less-round leaves, as he claims it has a better flavour. Buy his watercress hand-picked in 10-g (3½-oz) bunches direct from the packing sheds; or, if you prefer, call in at Deverills Trout Farm, Longbridge Deverill, Warminster BA12 7DA ☎ 01985 840522, which borders John's farm.

Stockists

Wilts: Warminster Fish and Fruit

Berkeley Farm Dairy
Berkeley Farm, Wroughton, Swindon, Wiltshire SN4 9AQ

☎ 01793 812228 **CONTACT** Mrs Christine Gosling **HOURS** Mon-Fri 9.00-16.00 Sat-Sun 9.00-12.30 **DIRECTIONS** From Swindon Old Town, take A4361 towards Avebury. After about 3½ miles you reach Wroughton. Dairy is about ¾ mile into the village on the left.

The Goslings run a mixed arable farm with a 100-strong Guernsey herd; they sell the milk from the local milk rounds they run or from the dairy-shop as pasteurized Channel Island or Gold Top (with a minimum 4.9 per cent fat content), semi-skimmed (1.5-1.8 per cent fat) and skimmed (less than 0.3 per cent). They also sell cream with a rich vibrant buttery flavour, made from the skim; but, unlike most dairies, they do not double-pasteurize it. What often happens is the milk is first pasteurized, passed through the skimmer and then re-pasteurized; this results in a 'dead'-tasting cream with a slightly plastic smell.

Using a 3-day ripened (aged) cream, Christine Gosling also makes full-cream butter. This she makes in an 11-litre (2½-gallon) churn on wheels which her father-in-law made for her; to see it at work in the state-of-the-art modern stainless steel dairy, a tiny wooden churn that looks like a dog on wheels wagging away as it vibrates when churning, is a hilarious sight. Butter-making is, I can assure you however, very hard work. Once the butter has been churned to get rid of the butter-milk, it is washed, then worked by hand in a rough sort of kneading-squeezing action, until smooth. Christine let me have a go and it is not easy, plus you need serious muscles and elbow-power. Salted at about 1 teaspoon per lb to give it a 2 per cent salt content, it is then weighed and patted with wooden butter pats into 250-g (8½-oz) pieces and wrapped in butter paper. The butter is gorgeous; unbelievably creamy and clear, clean and fresh-tasting, with a thick heavy spread. In the spring, when the cows have just gone out to grass, it can be an extraordinary bright orange; the rest of the year it is a clear vibrant sunshine yellow.

Sadly Christine is one of a dying breed; most farmers – or their wives – no longer make butter; if they do, it is usually with whey (a by-product of cheese-making) rather than cream. They tell me that it is not worth their while or they cannot make it pay; yet we are prepared to buy French farmhouse butter at vast expense – it does not make sense.

Stockists
Wilts: B. V. Berry & Son

- - - - - - - - - -

Mackintosh of Marlborough

While you're in the area...

Future Foods have moved from Gwynedd to **20 Gastard Lane, GASTARD, Corsham SN13 9QN ☎ 01249 712749**, but they still supply (by mail order only) an astonishing collection of unusual seeds, tubers and spawns, such as Wood Blewit or Shaggy Cap imported from France. Home-bakers can buy sachets of Tunnel Hill sour-dough culture from California in powder form, which is easily reconstituted according to the directions on the pack.

Rosary Goats Cheese, The Rosary, LANDFORD, Salisbury SP5 2BB ☎ 01794 322196 make their cheeses with pasteurized milk from their British Saanen herd. Their fresh cheese – in 115-g (4-oz) rounds or 1-kg and 275-g (2¼-lb and 9-oz) logs, either plain or with garlic & herbs – has a mild goaty flavour tinged with a tangy freshness and a crumbly, relatively dry texture.

A. Pritchetts & Son, 5 Fish Row, SALISBURY SP1 1EX ☎ 01722 324346 is an old-fashioned butcher right in the centre of town. It comes highly recommended for its chitterlings by Jonathan Meades, whose love of offal is well catalogued .

Fjordling Smokehouses, Dunstable Farm, Pitton Road, WEST WINTERSLOW, Salisbury SP5 1SA ☎ 01980 862689 fax 01980 863944 smoke a whole range of meat and fish, including a moist Fjordling, a cold-smoked trout, eel, chicken and hot- or cold-smoked Welsh lamb legs.

The Nadder Catering Food Shop, 4 North Street, WILTON, Salisbury SP2 0HE ☎ 01722 744707 fax 01722 744724 has plenty of food-to-go as well as prettily packaged food for presents. At Christmas it is crammed with flavoured oils, mustards and spices, as well as own-made mince pies, stuffings and royal-iced Christmas cake.

Worcestershire

Kite's Nest Farm

Kite's Nest Farm, Broadway, Worcestershire WR12 7JT

BROADWAY
Beef

☎ 01386 853320 **FAX** 01386 853621 **CONTACT** Rosamund Young – telephone ahead

The organic philosophy is to work with nature rather than dominate it, to avoid pollution, to enhance the soil and to maintain and develop its fertility. What this actually means in farming terms is no chemical fertilizers and pesticides; rotation of nitrogen-giving plants with arable or vegetable crops; conserving the environment; and, in the case of animals, following the laid-down regulations of feed, housing, welfare and veterinary treatment. What most people possibly do not realize is that to farm organically is more than just a philosophy – it is a farming system, with legally binding standards set by the EU and implemented in this country by the United Kingdom Registrar for Organic Farming (UKROF), a Government regulatory body working in conjunction with the Soil Association and Organic Farmers and Growers. If farmers or growers do not adhere to these standards, have not registered and not been inspected by any one of these groups, they are breaking the law if they use the word 'organic' to describe their produce.

Kite's Nest is farmed organically (to Soil Association standards) by the Young family. The standards practised on the farm are extreme – some say too extreme and question whether they are practical or realistic, let alone commercially viable; but this is how they choose to farm and no one could possibly question their commitment to the organic system. Their herd of mixed cattle (primarily Lincoln Red and Welsh Black, with a sprinkling of Hereford, Aberdeen Angus and Charolais) is a closed herd, meaning that they have bought in no animals since 1974 but rely on rearing own-bred stock. That, coupled with the fact they have not bought in any cattle cake, since 1967 as they grow all the feed, also means that there is no possibility of BSE infection.

Cattle are reared on a single-suckler system, with the calves feeding from their mothers for at least a year. They are allowed to stay in family groups throughout their lives; if you wander around the farm you will see small groups of a mother, her children – and even grand-children. They are free to go out or stay in the barns as they choose, any time of night or day the gates are always open. As Rosamund Young says 'Our cattle are completely free from stress, they're never cold or miserable, can exercise whenever they feel like it on a variety of grazings, both young and old grasses. Their environment, welfare, medication and feed are of prime importance. They are incredibly healthy, rarely – almost never – falling ill as I believe they even practise their own herbal medicine. We're a fanatic family. We mightn't live well but our animals certainly do'.

In spite of what you may have heard, if an animal falls ill, the Soil Association does, in fact, allow the use of drugs. What is banned is their prophylactic (i.e. preventative rather than curative) use; and once the animal has been treated, a suitable period of withdrawal must be enforced before the animal is allowed to return to the herd and its meat or milk can be sold as organic. Slaughtered as humanely as pos-sible at around about 24 months, their 30-odd carcasses a year are hung for about 14 days, then butchered into traditional cuts, with the cheaper stewing cuts – such as brisket, sweet rib (from the forequar-ter), skirt and cheek – being both tasty and good value. They also sell offal: heart, liver, pickled tongue, suet and – dog lovers please note – pet mince. When I tried the topside, I found it to have a resisting texture but great depth of flavour, a subtle richness underlayed with a gentle grassiness. What was really extraordinary was how long it kept its flavour; all too often the flavour evaporates after the first bite and you are left chewing the culinary equivalent of cotton wool. You can also buy organic flour from their corn which Rosamund mills herself in an electric mill, and occasionally pork, bacon and eggs. In keeping with their philosophy, prices for all produce are kept as low as possible.

T. H. Checketts, Main Road, OMBERSLEY WR9 0EW ☎ 01905 620284 *is a 'proper' butcher. Too many factors – supermarkets, EU and our own MAFF's regulations, plus changing social and dietary habits – contrive to make the butcher's lot a hard one; but Tony Checketts is determined to carry on. He buys meat locally and still slaughters and hangs it himself, 'the only way to keep complete control of the quality'. Beef comes from mostly heifers, 'because of their marked tenderness', and he favours a Hereford/Friesian cross 'as it takes a lot of beating'. Hung for 'a good 14 days, a special piece will go to 21 days and in practice, most everything is', it eats succulently and richly. A rib comes highly recommended by food writer Philippa Davenport as 'the most vibrantly flavoured I've had in years'. Lamb, mostly Charolais or Suffolk cross is well-marbled and finished and is hung for a few days. Pork has a 'pearly' finish and Mr Checketts processes his own tongues, hams, dry-cured bacon (which won a gold medal at the Smithfield Show), as well as Cumber-land, pork, and pork & beef sausages. He also sells haggis, an unusual white pudding made with leeks, groats, flour and pork fat by a small producer in Worcester, farmed venison, wild duck, hare, pheasant and – at Christmas – fresh cockerels weighing up to 4.5 kg (10 lb) and hung for 10 days, Judy Good-man's geese see opposite and bronze turkeys.*

Evesham and the surrounding area is known for its asparagus. Every year on the Sunday of the last bank holiday in May, **The Fleece Inn, The Cross**, BRETFORTON WR11 5JE ☎ 01386 831173 holds an asparagus auction. The money raised goes to the village's silver band and 100 of the best buds in the county are selected, bundled up and sold off, some years fetching as much as £500.00. The less extravagant can bid for rounds (bunches) weighing 800 g (1¾ lb).

Failing that, during the season from May to mid-June, you can always stop and buy asparagus in one of the small stands along the Evesham Broadway road, such as **R. G. Collis Leelands, Broadway Road**, EVESHAM WR11 6RN ☎ 01386 446537 who grows about 3 acres.

Goodman's Geese

Walsgrove Farm, Great Witley, Worcester, Worcestershire WR6 6JJ

GREAT
WITLEY
Geese

☎ 01299 896272 **FAX** 01299 896889 **CONTACT** Judy Goodman **HOURS** Geese 26 Sept to Christmas – telephone ahead; Asparagus May to early June; Strawberries May to end July: 9.00-17.00 **CARDS** Diners **DIRECTIONS** From Worcester, take A443 about 12 miles into Great Witley. Turn left on to B4203 at sign for Bromyard. After 100 yards, take first turning on the left. Farm is ¼ mile along on the right.

Judy Goodman is possibly the largest producer of free-range geese in Britain; this year she promises around 3,000 over the Christmas period. Followers of the tangled negotiations and specifications of the Poultry Meat, Farm Game, Bird Meat and Rabbit (Hygiene and Inspection) Regulations 1995, will be interested to know that she is also the proud owner of an EU-approved low-throughput slaughterhouse; this means that she can now legally send her geese anywhere in the country without fear of officialdom.

Now, although Judy is a member of the British Goose Association, on closer enquiry it stands for nothing at all in terms of standards. Most anyone at all connected with geese – from hobbyists with perhaps no more than 50 birds to large-scale producers with 250,000 birds – can join. Even among the 'traditional' geese producers there is no code of practice as such. For optimum flavour, as Judy says, it is important to buy a bird that has been free-ranging, reared for a minimum of 24 weeks and hung, 'The colour of the skin is a good sign. If it's golden, you know the bird must have been grass- and corn-fed, and that makes for a creamier flesh'.

Her geese waddle about in the fields, kept at about 100 to an acre, and peck away contentedly at the grass, supplemented with a compound feed of minerals, vitamins, wheat and barley made up to Judy's specifications. They are slaughtered by dislocation of the neck (the approved way) at any age between 22-28 weeks, dry-plucked, hung for about 10 days, cold-eviscerated, and sold oven-ready, weighing between 4.5 and 6 kg (10 and 13 lb). For the last 4 years now, I have had geese from Judy for Christmas. They are magnificent meaty birds, with moist deeply resonant flesh. Carefully plucked for an unbruised, unbroken skin, they are beautifully presented, trussed with string to make stuffing easier, and come with a full complement of giblets, a chunk of goose fat and a bunch of fresh herbs. What is particularly striking about Judy's birds is their finish; unlike some other geese, they have a good meat-to-bone ratio – a 4.5-kg (10-lb) goose is ample for 8 greedy eaters – as they are comparatively lean and, unlike some, do not shrink during cooking. Some geese swim in fat and shrink to almost half their size when cooked, not so Judy's.

Mail Order

Geese only

Stockists

Avon: Gerald Millhouse Butchers

Oxon: M. Feller Son & Daughter

W Mids: Rackhams

Worcs: T. H. Checketts

Getting the bird right is, for Judy, no more than 'a question of good management. First there's the breed. I choose a Legarth-cross. It's a large meaty bird from Denmark and I always buy them from the same trusty source. And you have to look after them; feed them well, take care they're never frightened or frustrated. And we only kill them when they're mature, you get better, deeper-flavoured meat. We don't try to bring them on too fast, if we did, they'd only turn to fat'. Starting in May, from the pack-house Judy sells ready-picked asparagus in 3 grades: sprue, choice and jumbo; and following on, from mid-June through to the end of July, she also has pick-your-own or ready-picked strawberries, raspberries and tayberries.

SUCKLEY

Poultry and Pork

Parsons Nose Poultry
Grove Court, Greenhill, Suckley, Worcestershire WR6 5EJ

☎ 01886 880617 **FAX** 01886 880617 **CONTACT** *Andrew Dobson – telephone ahead*

Andrew Dobson of Parsons Nose Poultry currently rears all his livestock on his 50-acre farm, 'in a completely natural and traditional way – free-range and additive-free'. Aware, however, that this rather loose description can be open to interpretation and is often misunderstood by the general public, he is apparently in the throes of applying for organic (to Soil Association) registration.

As the foundation of his operation was poultry, let us deal with that first. He rears chickens and Aylesbury ducks – which are, in fact, Aylesbury/ Pekin cross and tend to weigh 1.5-2.3 kg (3½-5 lb), but have (by all accounts as I have not tried one) a well-flavoured firm flesh with not too much fat. At Christmas, he rears 'a few' geese, bronze and Norfolk black turkeys. Although the latter have a bad reputation for a poor breast meat-to-bone ratio, Andrew claims 'they're as good as the poorest bronze birds and beat them hands down for flavour'. All his poultry is kept outside during the day but locked up at night, fed a corn-based diet, dry-plucked and hung for a minimum of a week.

Breed is something that also interests Andrew, because of 'its flavour advantage'. Thus he rears a few grass-fed Herdwick lamb, and pork from 2 different pig breeds – Oxford Sandy Black (actually thought to be extinct as a breed) and Wild Blue. This is a hybrid from a Wild Boar Gloucester Old Spot-cross sow crossed with a boar of the same parentage, as Andrew says 'neither Wild Boar nor Gloucester Old Spot are known for their fast growth, we let our Wild Blue run for at least 8 months, sometimes as long as 12 months. And the longer we rear them, the more their flavour develops'. Sold in various joints, it makes for meat with a deeper flavour than conventional pork, more earthy and pungent with a good chew. They also dry-cure both breeds for bacon and hams; make coarsely chopped sausages, such as pork & red cabbage, and pork & leek with fresh vegetables; and 3.2-kg (7-lb) cutting pies, such as goose & ham, duck & pork, and Oxford Sandy Black with cider.

Cotswold Orchard Farm Shop, Childs Wickham, nr BROADWAY WR12 7JA ☎ 01386 443142 fax 01386 49641 *opens in mid August at the start of the plum season. Here you can buy a whole range of plums, including Pershore Yellow Egg and Pershore Purple Egg, yellow Magnums for a meaty jam, Black Swan which is good for cooking, Victorias, Opal and Marjorie Seedling; damsons include the Prune Damson the 'proper' damson, the small full-flavoured Pin Damson, and the round Damazine 'loved by supermarkets, but lacking in flavour'. The plum season is finished by mid-October, but the farm-shop stays open until January to sell such apples as Blenheim Orange and Kidd's Orange Red, as well as own-made ciders.*

Lisle's Lemon Cheese

The Forge, nr Tenbury Wells, Upper Rochford,
Worcestershire WR15 8SP

☎ 01584 781349 **CONTACT** Lisle O'Driscoll **HOURS** Cirencester Craft Market: 2nd & 4th Sat of month

According to Lisle O'Driscoll, who has been selling her lemon cheese for the last 15-odd years, the difference between lemon curd and lemon cheese 'is the quantity of sugar. Lemon curd has above 55 per cent sugar, our lemon cheese has around the 33 per cent mark'. Obviously the amount of sugar affects the texture: lemon curd is usually quite solid or, as Lisle describes it, 'firm enough to trot a mouse across'; lemon cheese – Lisle's in particular – is soft, and very spoonable.

Made with fresh lemon juice and rind, butter, sugar and eggs, each small batch takes a good 1½ hours of constant stirring over a bain-marie. Now, I do not know whether you have ever tried making it yourself, but it requires an awful lot of looking after; the heat has to be just so, otherwise the eggs scramble and turn into an unholy mess of rubbery eggs running with water, not a pleasant prospect. Lisle's is smooth, an ultra-bright yellow (which she assures me comes from the ingredients and 'nothing else') with a clear bright lemon tang; a pleasing combination of sharpness and richness that melts in the mouth.

Lemon cheese is the main product, but she also produces a whole range of jams, mustards, chutneys and marmalades. Made in small batches using 'proper' ingredients, Elizabeth Rose of The Old Dairy

Farm Shop particularly rates the tayberry & apple jam, with its high fruit content and deep fruity flavour; and Old Man Driscoll's Irish Marrow Chutney made in memory of Lisle's 'wild' father-in-law. It has more than a drop of the hard stuff poured in once cooked. Look out for Lisle as she pops up all over the country at various shows and if you want to find out exactly where and when, do ring her for details.

Stockists

0xon: The Old Dairy Farm Shop

WORCESTER
Cheese

Malvern Cheesewrights
Pond Farm, Church Lane, Whittington, Worcester,
Worcestershire WR5 2RD

☎ 01905 350744 **FAX** 01905 350788 **CONTACT** Nicholas Hodgetts **HOURS** Mon-Fri 9.00-17.00 **DIRECTIONS** From Worcester take A44 towards Evesham. At roundabout, turn left signposted Whittington. Turn left almost immediately at T junction. Follow road through village and sign to farm is on left after ½ mile

The Malvern Cheesewrights is run by Nick Hodgetts. As lynch-pin of the whole operation, not only does he actually make an interesting and varied range of cheeses but he also acts as sales co-ordinator for its members' see Richard Rogers page 299 and Fowlers page 283 as well as his own, cheeses.

Nick has moved to new premises – so new, in fact, that I have yet to visit him. His milk is delivered directly to him; and to ensure it has the quality and characteristics he needs for cheese-making, it all comes from single herds. For Worcester Gold, he uses a Channel Island milk (Jersey and Guernsey mixed) from Sandwell Priory, home to one of the few remaining herds run by Benedictine monks. A lightly pressed cheese matured for around 14 weeks, it has a creamy rich flavour with a buttery texture.

Hereford Hops, made with local unpasteurized Friesian milk, is a Gloucester-type cheese, but it is pressed for 48 hours, then coated in hops and left to mature for anything from 6 to 10 weeks. The result is a smooth buttery cheese with a mild lemon astringency. Based on a similar recipe is Hereford Red, with a more biting flavour and coloured red with anatto Single Worcester, a Single Gloucester-type cheese, is made with the same milk, 'but skimmed in the old farmhouse way', as Nick explained. 'Once it has settled and the cream has risen to the top, I just skim it off and use it in Hereford Hops. The remaining milk I use for the Worcester'. Moist, mild and delicately spiced.

All Nick's cheeses have a rich butteriness about them; this he puts down in part to the quality of the milk, and in part to the particular way he makes them. He tends to scald the curd at a relatively higher temperature than most – as is the case for Bedwardine, also from Friesian milk, a melting rich cheese, similar to a Port Salut but with a far gutsier, more complex punch. The curds, once scalded are washed through with water, pressed briefly for 5 hours, brined for about 12 hours and

Richard Rogers of **Little Lightwood Farm, Cotheridge, nr WORCESTER WR6 5LT ☎ 01905 333236** lives a ½ mile from Elgar's birthplace, so it seems only proper and correct that he should name one of his cheeses after the famous composer. The other, Severn Sisters, takes its name from the river running in his valley, a tributary of the river Severn. Both of Richard's cheeses are unpasteurized,

Ansteys of Worcester, Broomhall Farm, Kempsey, WORCESTER WR5 2NT ☎/fax 01905 820232 make Old Worcester White, a hard-pressed cheese matured for 4 months; anatto-coloured Double Worcester made along similar lines to a Double Gloucester; and, packing a fair punch, a Worcestershire Sauce cheese.

made with vegetarian rennet and are distributed by the Malvern Cheesewrights see opposite. Elgar, in 1.8-kg (4-lb) truckles, is a semi-hard rich and creamy cheese, whereas Severn Sisters, made in 1-kg (2¼-lb) truckles from semi-skimmed milk, is crumblier and has a more forceful tang.

then left to mature for about 5-6 weeks, until a pliable rind develops.

While you're in the area...

Robbins, 35 Port Street, BENGEWORTH, Evesham WR11 6AD ☎ 01386 446161 fax 01386 40811 make particularly good faggots, fresh every day. Made with pork liver and pork meat 'but no lights and the other bits because people think they are a health risk', breadcrumbs, rusk, various spices and seasoning, they are cooked wrapped in caul fat for a juicy succulence. They also produce a range of cooked meats, sausages and sausage rolls, meat pies, bread and cakes.

The Avoncroft Museum of Historic Buildings, STOKE HEATH, Bromsgrove B60 4JR ☎ 01527 831363 is home to a working windmill removed from Tanworth in Arden, Warwickshire. Weather permitting, you can see it at work and buy the stoneground flour from the shop. There is also an orchard planted in 1992 with a number of different varieties of traditional cider apple and perry pear trees. With some trees mature enough to pick, in season they demonstrate cider- and perry-making, using a horse-drawn perry mill and press rescued from Hunt End near Redditch.

Teme Valley Honey Farm, Sutton House, SUTTON, nr Tenbury Wells WR15 8RJ ☎ 01584 810424 runs about 90 hives, keeping the bees on hillsides and rough woodlands. The honeys are strained rather than filtered, for a more stated flavour and come in 225 and 450-g (½ and 1-lb) jars. Mixed blossom honey is best described as medium to light with a gentle floweriness; and lime honey is also available in comb.

Yorkshire

Map Nos. 4 and 6

Ampleforth Abbey Apples
Ampleforth Abbey, Ampleforth, Yorkshire YO6 4HA

☎ 01439 788485 **CONTACT** Stuart Murfitt **HOURS** All year (for walks): 8.00-17.00; Sept to Apr (for fruit): 8.00-17.00 **DIRECTIONS** From Oswalkirk, take the Ampleforth Road towards Coxwold. After about 1 mile, orchard is sign-posted on the left.

Ampleforth Abbey Orchards was started by an asthmatic priest who was advised by his doctor to get out in the fresh air and take some exercise. He planted 5 Bramley and 1 Grenadier trees; now there are over 58 cultivars with 2,500 trees. Stuart Murfitt, Keeper of the Apples, has been tending the orchards for the last seven years, helped by three or four novice priests – but only during picking-time. 'I prune and keep the trees tidy, Mother Nature does the rest', he told me rather san-guinely, 'This being quite far north and not that well sheltered, late frosts can knock us back' and if he gets past mid-May without mishap, he reckons he is home and dry. The risks may be greater, 'As a rule of thumb we're about 14 to 21 days behind Kent', but the advantage of growing apples this far north is fruit which is more intense and deeper flavoured. For apples and most temperate fruit, it is warm days and cool nights that make ideal growing conditions; too warm a day will bring on the fruit too fast, whereas a cold night – provided of course it is frost-free – can only intensify the flavour.

The apples are kept in large wooden boxes in a narrow dark barn that serves as the orchard's store. As it is not refrigerated, the varieties have been chosen with their natural keeping qualities in mind. Most of

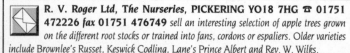

R. V. Roger Ltd, The Nurseries, PICKERING YO18 7HG ☎ 01751 472226 fax 01751 476749 sell an interesting selection of apple trees grown on the different root stocks or trained into fans, cordons or espaliers. Older varieties include Brownlee's Russet, Keswick Codling, Lane's Prince Albert and Rev. W. Wilks.

them are late- and extra-late-season varieties, meaning that although picked in September to early October, they are ready for eating only from late October through to the New Year or even later, to provide a succession of fruit throughout the late autumn and winter. 'Earlies are eaten directly off the tree, the others we store off and mature like wine'. Stuart's favourite is the early high-shouldered Red Gravenstein which he describes as 'firm, crisp and juicy, it lasts well. Early on it's got a good smack to it, then it mellows out'. Another splendid and rare early is Irish Peach, with its greenish-white flesh tinged with red and its aromatic flavour. Unusual late apples include the yellow-skinned Belle de Boskoop, the irregularly shaped and briskly juicy Kings Acre Pippin, Ribston Pippin with its original tree at Ribston Hall in nearby Knaresborough, and the acid Lane's Prince Albert. With fruit to sample and an honesty box for leaving money when Stuart is not around, Ampleforth is a relaxed, informal orchard to visit.

New this year to **M. L. & R. C. Snowden, Wharfedale Grange,** HAREWOOD LS17 9LW ☎ 0113 288 6320 *fax* 0113 288 6206 *is asparagus packed in 1.8-kg (4-lb) boxes from late April to 20 June. Apart from the asparagus, they are only open in July for the likes of you and me – the rest of the year, sadly, they are wholesale only. Even so, it is worth noting them for pick-your-own soft fruit, such as various strawberries, raspberries, tayberries, blackcurrants and redcurrants and their vegetables, salads and salad leaves. These include coloured lettuces, chicories, purslane, corn salad, rocket, baby spinach, radish pods (which are picked when the radishes are left to go to seed and have a mild peppery flavour and a crisp biteable texture), and Perilla frutescens with its leaves of deep rich purple which taste like sweet nettle. Vegetables – both baby and normal size – include carrots, golden beetroot, broad beans, peas, calabrese, turnips, courgettes and courgette flowers.*

Kolos Bakery
128-132 Parkside Road, Bradford, Yorkshire BD5 8EH

BRADFORD
Sour-dough
Rye Bread

☎/FAX 01274 729958 **CONTACT** *Jaroslaw Prytulak* **HOURS** *Mon-Fri 7.00-18.00 Sat 7.00-13.00* **DIRECTIONS** *Turn off M606 at the last exit, signposted Bradford. Follow the slip-road to the roundabout and turn right off the roundabout towards The Rooley pub. Turn left immediately after the pub into Parkway Road. Follow the road about ¼ mile to a T-junction and turn left. Bakery is signposted about 500 yards along on the left.*

When Ivan Prytulak bought an existing bakery in Bradford in 1961 it seemed logical to name it Kolos (Ukrainian for an ear of wheat) after the bakery in Stanislav where he served his apprenticeship before World War II. As Bradford had one of the largest Ukrainian communities in the United Kingdom, it also made sense to carry on making the rye breads he had been taught to make.

Kolos is now run by Ivan's three sons and what was once a corner shop has grown into a large wholesale bakery. It still services the local community, as throughout the day the door bell rings and another customer pops in to buy bread, but it also distributes it around the country. They do make white and brown wheat bread, Vienna bread, French sticks, tea-cakes, baps and – new this year – a ciabatta, but it is for the sour-dough rye breads that I sought them out. These come as Ukrainian rye, a comparatively light bread with a mix of 50 per cent rye and 50 per cent wheat (and, according to Jaroslaw, 'best for the English taste'); Bauernbrot, a German-style rye with 70 per cent rye and 30 per cent wheat, which is closer textured; Estonian, with 80 per cent, is closer still; and Bavarian, with 100 per cent, verges on the solid, as it follows the higher the rye content the denser and darker the bread.

All the breads are made with the same sour-dough starter kept in a huge bin in the bakery and which goes on and on for years provided you feed it with flour. The bread, left to rise once, is knocked back and rises again 'like nature intended' in order to develop its flavour. When tasting, none of them had a very pronounced sourness, although the higher the rye flour content, the more marked it became. Rather they were moist, slightly sweet and delightfully dense, the sign of a good solid rye; and they have good keeping qualities.

Stockists

Cambs:
Continental Store

Cumbria: E. H.
Booth & Co

London:
Selfridges

Oxon: Palms
Delicatessen

W. Mids:
Rackham's

DANBY
Breads and Jams

Botton Village Foods
The Camphill Village Trust, Danby, Whitby, Yorkshire YO21 2NJ

☎ 01287 661270 **FAX** 01287 660888 **CONTACT** Paul Abel **HOURS** Mon-Fri 9.00-12.00 & 14.00-17.30 **DIRECTIONS** *From Middlesborough, take A171 towards Guisborough. After about 12 miles, turn right signposted Castleton/Danby. Follow the road about 5 miles and turn right signposted Botton Village. Follow the road about 3 miles to the end of Danby Dale into the village. The trust is in the village.*

Botton Village – a busy thriving community set in isolated countryside, with five farms, a bakery, dairy and a food centre as well as craft workshops and a printing press – is one of many of The Camphill Communities in Britain. Established by Dr Karl Koënig, their purpose is many-stranded: primarily it is to work with the mentally handicapped; to give them a life, an occupation and a purpose in a community where everyone, according to his or her ability, contributes what he or she can towards the well-being of his or her fellows. To this end co-workers (trained staff or volunteers) run the workshops, helped by villagers, with the goal of producing good products (to Biodynamic standards) that stand up on their own.

They are possibly best known for Botton, their hard-pressed Cheddar-style cheese, but sad to say at the moment it is no longer being made because they lost their cheese-maker. Hopefully, a new cheese-maker will soon be found and normal service will be resumed.

From the bakery workshop comes a hearty choice of breads and biscuits made from either their own or bought-in (to Soil Association standards) flour. These include a splendid herb & cheese loaf (using Botton cheese when available), bread rolls (or buns as they are called in this part of the world) made with two-thirds wholemeal flour and one-third white; and a substantial tea bread. The Food Centre produces a range of fruity jams, some made with their own fruit, others from bought-in: there is a deep and very fruity blackberry; a well-spiced rhubarb & ginger; and a nutty damson; thick-cut orange marmalade made with raw cane sugar and no added pectin for a sharp slack-set preserve; there are cordials made in the fruit press, which come in apple, blackcurrant, redcurrant and strawberry flavours; a thick mayonnaise from their whole free-range eggs and olive and sunflower oil; and a cloudy apple juice.

The products are good; but more, much more than that, the dedication of the co-workers and the enthusiasm of the villagers made visiting Botton Village a memorable experience.

For a good choice of Yorkshire cheese visit **The Cheeseboard, 1 Commercial Street, HARROGATE HG1 1UB ☎ 01423 508837**. *Cheeses include Wensleydale Creamery young and mature Wensleydale see page 309, both ewes'- and cows'-milk Swaledale and Old Peculier Swaledale see page 310, Iain Hill's Ribblesdale cheeses see page 310 and a new(ish) goats'-milk Braythorne. They also have a good range from all over the country.*

Bettys and Taylors by Post & Bettys Café Tea Rooms

1 Parliament Street, Harrogate, Yorkshire HG1 2QU

HARROGATE
Breads and Cakes

☎ 01423 886055; tea-room 01423 502746 **FAX** 01423 565191 **CONTACT** Ian Jackson **HOURS** *Shop & Café*: 9.00-21.00; *Bettys by Post* 9.00-17.00 **CARDS** Access, Visa **DIRECTIONS** *In town centre*.

In Yorkshire Bettys is an institution and whether it's for a cup of coffee and a 'fat rascal' (a cross between a rock cake and a scone, which hails from the Moors) or just a loaf of wholemeal bread, who can resist popping in? Bettys first café tea-room was opened in Harrogate in 1919 by Frederick Belmont, a Swiss confectioner, and it remains a family firm with everything baked at a central bakery and whisked around the county in Bettys vans. Standards are kept high by using the best ingredients (butter, fresh cream, unbleached white flour) and by working by hand in small daily batches to ensure peak freshness.

The range is a comfortable balance of traditional – parkin (a dense spiced cake made with black treacle and fine oatmeal), rich Yorkshire curd tarts, pikelets, Yule loaf (a fruity tea bread from Ripon), Yorkshire tea-cakes (similar to Yule Log, but with the addition of spices and mixed peel), comforting egg and cress sandwiches and feather-light baps – and Continental – rich Sachertorte, vanilla slice (aka *millefeuille*), Venetian Festival cake (a heavenly confection of Genoese sponge soaked in apricot brandy syrup, layered with apricot preserve, topped with almond paste, and decorated with French glacé figs, cherries and angelica), gaudily coloured marzipan fruit; an authentic *panforte di Siena*, plain and pesto ciabatta, and wreaths of mixed olive, rosemary and sun-dried tomato bread.

If you cannot go in person, the next best thing is to order from Bettys by Post. Offering a selection of goodies from the huge range in the shops, at Easter there is Simnel cake and fancily decorated chocolate eggs; at Christmas there are dark puddings, rich fruit cakes steeped in sherry, Swiss *Lebkuchen* (gingerbread), tree hangings and an array of chocolate novelties. All through the year, there are fine teas and coffees (Bettys now own Taylors of Harrogate, the tea and coffee merchants) and fruit cakes in tins. Each weighing 750 g (1 lb 10 oz), these include Earl Grey with vine fruit soaked in the bergamot-rich tea, a darker Old Peculier with its malty flavour as this time the sultanas, raisins, currants and cherries are steeped in Yorkshire ale, and Sloe Gin with glacé apricots, plums, cherries and a good measure of sloe gin.

Stockists

Yorks: Bettys, Northallerton

Bettys, Ilkley

Bettys, York

 Arcimboldo's Delicatessen, 146 Kings Road, HARROGATE HG1 5HY ☎ **01423 508760** *has a small kitchen out back that prepares soups; frozen ready-meals; sweet and savoury tarts, including a nicely caramelized French onion;*

 a gutsy chicken & pork pâté and a richly jellied jambon persillé; dishes to go, such as coq au vin and chicken meatballs; salads and pasta sauces. They make their own sausages in natural casings with a meat content between 80 and 90 per cent and, writes Food Lover G. Adams of Leeds, 'the farmhouse are first class'. They also offer a well-chosen selection of on-farm cheeses, including Swaledale see page 310, Richard III Wensleydale see page 309 and Braythorne, a locally made mould-ripened goats'-milk cheese. They also stock Krousti breads, an interesting range of Continental and flavoured breads baked in Leeds, and various jams, pickles and chutneys from – amongst others – Rosebud Preserves see below.

 A couple of shops away is **Ramus Seafoods, Ocean House, Kings Road, HARROGATE HG1 5HY** ☎ **01423 563271 fax 01423 531040**. *They* *sell fish from all over the country, including Whitby plaice, turbot, sea bass, clams to order, samphire from Norfolk, langoustines, kippers from Seahouses see page 208, Morecambe Bay potted shrimps from Baxters see page 157 and live lobsters imported from Canada (sadly). Salmon is both wild and farmed from Scotland and they hire out fish kettles, but equally offer a cooking service which actually works out cheaper.*

HEALEY

Jams and Chutneys

Rosebud Preserves

Rosebud Farm, Healey, Ripon, Yorkshire HG4 4LH

☎ 01765 689174 **FAX** 01765 689174 **CONTACT** Elspeth Biltoft **HOURS** 9.00-18.00; *Masham market: Wed (weather permitting), Sat & Bank Holiday Mons* **DIRECTIONS** *Market in town centre.*

Elspeth Biltoft's 'secret' is to work in small batches of no more than 120 jars of jam or jelly at a time; if you work in larger batches you have to boil for longer and risk boiling away all the flavour. Using a light golden granular sugar, lemon juice and plenty of fruit and no pectin, as she finds she just does not need it, she describes her jams as 'honest products with a soft set, but I – and my customers – like it that way'. Strawberry is classified as an extra-jam (with a fruit content of over 65 per cent), but 'in fact they're all pretty high in fruit and relatively low in sugar. Rhubarb & ginger, rhubarb & orange and apricot & almond actually fit into the reduced-sugar category'. Low sugar or not, the apricot & almond is stunning; sharp, meaty and intensely fruity, it is punched with slivers of whole almonds which Elspeth buys in from California whole and unpeeled, then she gets the 'girls' to peel and blanch them, 'they're so much brighter-flavoured than buying them in ready-peeled and blanched'. Damson was full of body and made in the good old-fashioned way, with the stones thrown in for good measure.

Jellies have a sparkling translucence and an unusual – and welcome – sharpness which comes from adding Bramley apple. She makes wild crab apple; an astringent wild rowan to complement a rich meat; and cranberry orange for the Christmas turkey. Chutneys and pickles are made using a light muscovado sugar, fresh spices, cider vinegar and sea salt. Elspeth divides them into two distinct categories: traditional British, such as spiced plum, green tomato; and from India and the Far East, with a spicier headier base, such as hot lime, aubergine & chilli, and Malay vegetable. This powerful blend of roasted peanuts with crunchy pieces of carrots, cucumbers and cauliflowers punched with fresh chillies and garlic, is remarkable for its crisp texture and a mild hotness that creeps up on you unawares. They are all matured for at least a month in the jar to allow the flavours to meld together and they certainly do improve with keeping.

Stockists

London: Conran Shop

Harvey Nichols

Neal's Yard Dairy

Yorks: The Dales Kitchen Tearoom

Wensleydale Creamery

The Castlegate Bakery & Café
10-12 Castlegate, Helmsley, Yorkshire YO65 AB

☎ 01439 770304 **CONTACT** Andrew John Rivis **HOURS** Mon-Sat 9.00-16.30 **DIRECTIONS** Just off the Square.

HELMSLEY
Curd Tarts

When in Helmsley, walk out of the Square towards the castle and you will find The Castlegate Bakery in front of you, with most everything here own-baked. Owned by Andrew Rivis, it struck me it was the six ladies who run the kitchen who were really in charge, with Maude as 'queen bee'. Baking is done in small batches, without resorting to much machinery; one of Maude's daily tasks is to make the curd for the Yorkshire curd tart and, although I would not put hand on heart, I do not think many – if, indeed, any – other bakers still do that.

Maude heats preserving pans full of milk, she usually does two at a go; the milk gently simmers for a quarter of an hour until the butterfat comes to the surface. Then she adds, of all things, Epsom Salts 'to turn it – vinegar would do the trick but it'd flavour the milk'. As she stirs, the milk separates into whey and curds and once it has cooled down, it is ready for straining. Then in go sugar, eggs, plenty of currants, nutmeg and margarine (surprisingly this is one of the few times they do not use butter) and it is beaten for 20 minutes 'for texture' and set aside for the next day. Curd tarts are baked every day and are usually sold out by

The Old Police Station Café, 17 Market Place, HELMSLEY YO6 5BL ☎ **01439 770413** *has close connections with The Castlegate Bakery, Mrs Rivis is Andrew's mother. She also makes curd tarts and, although not so keen to share her recipe, did admit to adding double cream to the bought-in curd. This makes for a splendidly creamy closer textured filling, but she lost marks for the (comparatively) dry pastry.*

lunch-time. Set in a crisp 100 per cent lard pastry, there are two sizes – individual and large. By the time Maude has beaten the filling it is smooth and relatively rich, with an obvious – but not overstated – touch of nutmeg. Unlike far too many bakers who skimp with the curd, their tarts are generously filled, so the proportion of curd to pastry is most satisfying.

Parkin is also made 'properly', Cynthia showed me the old recipe to which they work, which calls for equal amounts of flour and medium oatmeal, brown sugar, ginger, mixed spice, butter, golden and dark syrup. Everything is mixed up together and baked into rounds for a gorgeous bite of oatmeal with a build of ginger in the mouth; sticky and soft, a good parkin should never be brittle. They also make a nicely fruited fruit cake, puffed-up sandy-textured rice tarts, and rich Eccles cakes full of currants, to name but a few, as well as jars of own-made marmalade and chutneys.

Adjoining the bakery is the Castlegate Café, open from Easter to October. Here you can try all the triumphs from the bakery and, if it is warm enough, sit outside in the garden.

HOVINGHAM
Bread

Hovingham Bakery
Brookside, Hovingham, York, Yorkshire YO6 4LG

☎ 01653 628898 **CONTACT** Penny Jones **HOURS** Tues-Fri 9.30-17.30 Sat 9.30-17.00 **DIRECTIONS** In the village, by the ford.

Penny Jones came to bread-making relatively late in life. She trained as a nursery school teacher and, after her third child went off to school, she started making bread. One thing led to another and soon it was all too much for her kitchen and it was a question of 'either doing it properly or not at all', which is why you will find her installed in a cheery bakery, very much in the red-and-white-gingham mode.

Her bread is 'as near to traditional home-made as is commercially possible'. At home she would leave it to rise covered with tea-towels, so she has adapted a proving cabinet to give just the right moisture and heat. Using flour from Village Craft Flours *see below* and fresh yeast, she works in 13.5-kg (30-lb) mixes, allowing two rises to develop

Village Craft Flours, Thorpe Mill, GREWELTHORPE, Ripon HG4 3BS ☎ **01765 658534** *stone-grind about 18 different flours in different grades of coarseness and mixtures of strong through to softer wheats for cake-making.* **Crakehall Water Mill, Little Crakehall, BEDALE DL8 1HU** ☎ **01677 423240** *stone-grind a mixture of strong Canadian and softer English wheat for a good 100 per cent bread flour.*

flavour and texture. This is good honest bread; nothing too fancy, but well made – neither too pappy nor too solid – with good fresh flour.

Her 100 per cent organic has a great taste of wheat and a well-judged density; white, made with unbleached flour, is creamy with a moist creamy crumb; seed, a mixture of sesame, sunflower, millet, rye, barley and pumpernickel 'when we can get it' is mixed with treacle for a powerful spiciness that struck me as being splendid with cheese; and rye is surprisingly soft, with a sour aftertaste. There are 'fancy' breads; onion swirl; a strong herb & cheese; and a generously studded walnut. Yorkshire tea-cakes are very successful; they actually have a texture that fights back as opposed to collapsing as soon as they meet your teeth, as well as a good yeasty resonance and plenty of currants. Wednesday is 'the big cake day', with filling day on Thursday in preparation for the week-end rush, so try Penny's sticky lemon made with fresh lemon juice or the Victoria, orange & raisin or coffee & walnut sponges. Her range may be restricted, but what she makes she makes very well.

Stockists

Yorks: The Armstrong Delicatessen and Wine Shop

- - - - - - - - - -

Burdettes

Weegmann's, 6 Market Place, OTLEY LS21 3AQ ☎ 01943 462327 *is a traditional pork butcher. On market day the queue snaking up the street testifies as to how good it still is. Pies – from bite-size to large enough for a hungry family – have a rich crisp pastry and a succulent filling; haslett is remarkable for its strong flavour of sage; and slices of roasted pork belly are satisfying, if the crackling is a little limp. There is own-made brawn, potted meats, a cutting block of sage & onion stuffing, cooked gammon joints, and dry-cured bacon cut on an old-fashioned slicer.*

R. & J. Lodge
Greens End Road, Meltham, Huddersfield, Yorkshire HD7 3NW

MELTHAM
Meat Pies

☎ 01484 850571 **CONTACT** Raymond Lodge **HOURS** Tues-Fri 8.30-17.00 (-13.30 Wed) Sat 8.30-12.30 **DIRECTIONS** From Holmfirth, take A635 towards Manchester. After about 1½ miles, turn right just after The Ford Inn, signposted Meltham. Follow the road about 1½ miles into the village centre and turn left just after the church into Greens End Road. Shop is immediately on the left.

I defy any food lover to spend time in Yorkshire and leave without trying at least one meat pie – assuming, of course, they are not vegetarian. The better general – or specifically pork – butchers still make their own. Raymond Lodge, a one-time butcher, now makes nothing but hand-raised pies.

He starts with a hot-water crust; lard is 'melted not too hot 'cos it would make pastry too hard', then he mixes it with flour and leaves it to rest overnight. It is hand-raised around a wooden die (mould) ready for the filling. Now, whereas several butchers may use leftovers or scraps for the fillings, Raymond will have none of that – his pork pie is made with freshly minced shoulder. He also does not just stick to pork pies, branching out to all manner of fillings: turkey, ham & cranberry has good chunks of both meats; game is a shredded mix of rabbit,

For meaty juicy pork pies with a rich crisp pastry I think butchers **J. B. Cockburn & Sons, Market Place**, BEDALE DL8 2EQ ☎ 01677 422126 *take some beating. Mind you, Food Lover Owen Wells of Ilkley upbraided me for omitting from the first edition* **Stanforths Old Pork Pie Shop**, 11 Mill Bridge, SKIPTON BD23 1NJ ☎ 01756 793477. 'It is,' *as he writes,* 'rated by many local people as producing the finest pork pies. Their speciality is hot stand pies and they make the finest picnic snack for anyone visiting Skipton'. *Mind you', he goes on to say,* 'I don't think there is much to choose between theirs and **Clayton's Butchers**, 35 Brook Street, ILKLEY LS29 8AG ☎ 01943 608015. *You must judge for yourselves.*

In spite of the stories you may have heard about how York hams were smoked over oak chippings while the Minster was being built, do not believe a word. York ham is a green (unsmoked) ham. Traditionally it is dry-cured in salt, saltpetre and brown sugar for about a month, then hung to mature.

Harris-Leeming Bar, Leases Road, LEEMING BAR, Northallerton DL7 9AW ☎ **01677 422661 fax 01677 424986** *age theirs for about 4 months for a mild moist version. They also produce the black-skinned Bradenham ham, which is dry-cured for 2 weeks.*

Butchers George Scott, 81 Low Petergate, YORK YO1 2HY ☎ **01904 622972** *hang theirs for about a year for a deep pink ham punched with salt and a firm texture, and sell it either as whole uncooked hams weighing from 7 kg (16 lb) upwards or in moist very succulent cooked slices.*

Radford's Butchers, 81 Coach Road, SLEIGHTS, Whitby YO22 5EH ☎ **01947 810229** *mature theirs for 1 to 2 years and its punchy saltiness underlayed with a clear clean taste of pig is impressive. Sold as whole hams weighing between 9 and 13.5 kg (20 and 30 lb) or sliced from the shop, it has a meaty clear clean rasping quality. They also produce the Admiral Ham which is first dry-cured, then marinated in Guinness and molasses 'for quite a long time' and finally hung for 4-6 months.*

hare, pigeon, mallard, venison and wild boar stewed in red wine; and Fidget, traditionally a harvest pie, contains pork cut from the shoulder, ham, and sage & onion stuffing, topped with slices of apples. Then there is wild boar, blackberry & mushroom; to satisfy the vegetarians a mix of potatoes, carrots, peas, tomatoes, sweetcorn, garlic, basil and cheese in a pastry made with vegetable shortening; and, new this year, chicken & ham with apple & apricot stuffing.

Raymond does produce a range of machine-moulded 115-g (4-oz) pies, but all the larger pies, weighing from 285 g to 1.8 kg (10 oz to 4 lb) are 'stand' pies, meaning they stand up by themselves and are baked without hoops or tins. The tops are hand-crimped, then they are baked in the oven and washed in an egg glaze for a golden finish. Once cooled, they are pierced and filled with Raymond's 'gravy'; this he makes in a huge saucepan from 'pig's feet, tails, bones, rind, ribs – anything to boil off for a jelly' to give them a moist succulence.

NEWTON-LE-WILLOWS
Wensleydale

Fortmayne Farm Dairy

Fortmayne Cottage, Newton-le-Willows, Bedale, Yorkshire DL8 1SL

☎ 01677 450660   **CONTACT** *Suzanne Stirke – telephone ahead*

Wensleydale cheese is thought to go back as far as the time of the Norman Conquest. As the story has it, Norman soldiers stationed up

North complained bitterly about the food and King William persuaded his uncle, the Abbot of Savigny, to send over some monks to make cheese. The first monastery was built in Fors, in Upper Wensleydale, but they soon moved to Jervaulx in Lower Wensleydale, where the weather was more clement and the natives less hostile. The cheese, made with ewes' milk, was similar to a Roquefort and would blue naturally. Quite how and why it changed from ewes' to cows' milk, no one is too sure and, as far as I know, James Aldridge *see page* 262 is the only person making a ewes'-milk Wensleydale in Britain.

After the dissolution of the monasteries, it was the farmers' wives who made the cheese. And so they carried on, although their numbers slowly diminished with the formation of the creameries, until the Second World War. What then brought farmhouse production to an abrupt halt was the edict that all milk available for cheese should be brought into factories and turned into hard cheese with a maximum moisture content of 40 per cent – unachievable with Wensleydale. Somehow, after the war, only the creameries started making it again and it was thought to be lost from the farmhouses for ever.

Suzanne has been making for the last seven years and deliberately set out to achieve the same pre-war moist cheese. She makes Richard III Wensleydale with unpasteurized milk from the next-door Friesian herd in a small 100-gallon vat. 'A simple cheese to make', the milk is started and renneted for about 1 hour, the curds are cut and stirred with a ladle, left to sit in the whey for an hour, then the whey takes about an hour to drain away. The curds are cut into blocks, turned and broken up or 'snapped' in a small hand mill. Then they are packed into cloth-lined moulds and turned. The following day they are turned again and lightly weighted for 24 hours; then turned again, washed in salt and water and bandaged.

Made in 450 and 900-g and 2.3-kg (1, 2 and 5-lb) cheeses, it is eaten young at only 2 weeks or it can be kept to about 5 weeks for a deeper-flavoured, slightly drier cheese. New this year is Suzanne's matured Wensleydale which she is keeping for 10-12 weeks for an even firmer deeper flavour, but I am afraid I have yet to sample it. What I have tried is the young cheese and I was delighted by its moist butteriness, its loose crumbly texture and a taste that hints of honey. According to the descriptions in old books, that is how it is meant to be.

Stockists

Yorks:
Arcimboldos

Durants

The Farmhouse Kitchen

Hunters of Helmsley

J. & M. Reah

Apart from Fortmayne see above there are only two other makers of Wensleydale cheese left in the dale: **Wensleydale Creamery, Gayle Lane,** HAWES DL8 3RN ☎ 01969 667664 fax 01969 667638 make a crumbly pasteurized cheese that mellows out as it ages. A visit to the dairy now includes a 'cheese experience', a cheese museum and a viewing gallery where you can watch the cheese being made. **Fountains Dairy,** KIRBY MALZEARD HG4 3QD ☎ 01765 658212 also make a pasteurized Wensleydale. At 3 weeks it was green but buttery and very crumbly. They also make a blue version which is quite soft and pasty with a sharpness softened by an underlying creaminess; it gets sent off to the 'bluers' for maturing. Sold throughout the county, you can buy them at Kirby Malzeard Village Stores along with their full-cream well-salted butter.

Two other Dale cheese-makers are particularly worth singling out. **The Swaledale Cheese Company, Mercury Road,** RICHMOND DL10 4TQ ☎ 01748 824932 *make Swaledale, which was originally made by the monks using ewes' milk. They do make a ewes'-milk version using pasteurized milk from a Friesland flock which graze in the Dales; moist and quite crumbly, it is fuller bodied than the cows'-milk Swaledale they also produce. This too is made with pasteurized milk from local herds and has a light open texture with an open freshness. It comes as plain; Old Peculier, with the curds soaked overnight in the ale for a hoppy flavour and a marbled effect; mixed with fresh apple-mint; and fresh chives & garlic. Made in 450 and 900-g and 1.5 and 2.3-kg (½, 1, 3½, and 5-lb) rounds and sold at 3 weeks, Swaledale softens with age and turns creamy; it is probably at its best when matured on to 5 weeks. They also make Beamish at the Beamish Museum in Co. Durham; it is harder pressed than Swaledale and tends to have a stronger flavour and crumblier texture.*

Chris & Iain Hill, Ashes Farm, HORTON-IN-RIBBLESDALE, Settle BD24 0JB ☎ 01729 860231 *make Ribblesdale following a Wensleydale-style recipe. Like all Dale cheeses, it is eaten when quite young; made with pasteurized goats' milk, it is light and delicately sweet; whereas the sheep's-milk version is richer and the cows'-milk offers a touch of lemon.*

NORWOOD
BOTTOM
Chocolates

Norwood House Chocolate

Norwood Bottom Farm, Norwood Bottom, Otley,
Yorkshire LS21 2RA

☎ 01423 322230 **FAX** 01423 322253 **CONTACT** Nicola Porter

Serious chocolate devotees take note, Norwood House Chocolates not only make exceptionally good chocolate truffles but also run The Chocolate Society. Among the advantages of being a member is the bi-monthly newsletter full of chocolate gossip, information, recipes, invitations to tutored tastings, lectures and events (one that caught my fancy was a summer picnic at Kew Gardens with the Head Gardener giving a guided tour of the Palm House to view the cocoa tree).

Their 100-g (3½-oz) bars are for afficionados – the chocolate world's equivalent of single-estate extra-virgin olive oils. Cocoa Pod no. 1 with 64 per cent cocoa solids is produced from pure Criolla beans imported from 'Islands in the Indian Ocean'. Intense, clear and bitter-sweet, it has an intriguing fruity flavour that reminds me of redcurrants. No. 3 with 66 per cent cocoa solids, made from the Trinarario bean, is stronger, headier with a deeper blacker finish. No. 2 with 70 per cent cocoa solids is a mixture of rare beans and is the strongest and most intense of the 3, with a dry smoky aftertaste and the same velvety smooth finish.

The fresh square chocolate truffles have a similar depth of chocolate and are made in a 3-day process with a ganache of fresh double cream from Yorkshire, unsalted French butter and Valrohna chocolate. Once the ingredients are mixed together, they are poured into a frame, left to set, cut by wires into squares, doubly enrobed in tempered chocolate and finally dusted in cocoa powder. Sold as plain or flavoured with a choice of fresh fruit purées, such as raspberry for a piercing fruitiness, pear or liqueur and raisin or champagne, they are particularly glorious both for their sense of chocolate and their contrast of texture. The centres are meltingly smooth, surrounded by a wafer-thin coating (enrobement) of chocolate. At first bite you 'crack' the casing and then it is luscious delight all the way down the throat. They also make drinking chocolate that frankly puts Cadbury's to shame, as well as some very rich chocolate pouring sauces.

Haley & Clifford Delicatessen, 43 Street Lane, LEEDS LS8 1AP ☎ 0113 237 0334 *is well served by John Vennel, the chef at Haley's hotel, who cooks both for the hotel and the shop. The shop produces a menu of prepared dishes, but 'there is a degree of flexibility' and more or less anything can be cooked given a few days' notice. When I visited I noticed chargrilled vegetables in extra-virgin olive oil; a rich chicken liver parfait backed by Madeira, port and white wine; salmon en croûte; various salads, including a crunchy French bean with bacon; a juicy sirloin of Scotch beef cooked to a rosy rareness; and pecan nut & chocolate pie. There are various breads, including triple-grain baguettes; onion; walnut & sultana; ciabatta; and bagels; as well as a range of own-made pickles, including vegetables in vinegar, spiced apricot & raisin, chow-chow; and dark marmalades made with black treacle, with or without whisky. They also sell a few cheeses, such as Isle of Mull Cheddar see page 321 and Mrs Appleby's Cheshire see page 229.*

Elizabeth Botham & Sons
35-39 *Skinner Street, Whitby, Yorkshire* YO21 3AH

☎ 01947 602823 **FAX** 01947 820269 **CONTACT** *Mike Jarman* **HOURS** *Mon-Sat 8.30-17.30 (October to May: closed Mons)* **CARDS** *Access, Visa* **DIRECTIONS** *In town centre.*

Established in 1865, Elizabeth Botham & Sons still dispenses morning coffees and afternoon teas with light luncheons in between, served by suitably starched waitresses in a chandelier-lit upstairs dining room. Downstairs is the spacious wooden-panelled shop, stocked with 200 lines baked at a central bakery which also supplies branches in downtown Baxtergate and Sleight. In all the shops you will find a range of the more usual breads, made with flour milled at Grewelthorpe *see page* 306. There are hand-raised pork pies; various cakes, including fruit, rice and – at Easter – Simnel; biscuits; and a well-spiced buttery Yorkshire curd tart and Whitby gingerbread. A local speciality which, unlike most British gingerbreads, is baked as a firm loaf, this is closely textured, with a mild whiff of ginger. It is dry rather than treacly and is traditionally eaten cut into thin slices, spread liberally with butter and a slice of one of the Dale cheeses. Originally it was made in 1.8-kg (4-lb) blocks, then cut into four or sold by weight; now it is made in 450-g (1-lb) loaves, but is still baked in January and matured on until Christmas to allow the sugars to break down. Plum Bread, a relatively new product to them, is made in the best Lincolnshire tradition *see Derek Myers & Sons, page* 174 with lard and oodles of fruit. It has a spicy bloom, a dense texture and, in spite of the lard, a clean aftertaste. They also sell crisp crunchy biscuits: Shah features Jamaican ginger, as does chocolate chip & ginger, and there is also a plain tea.

Stockists
Cumbria: E. H. Booth & Co

Northumb: The Corbridge Larder

Oxon: Milletts Farm Shop

Suffolk: E. W. King & Sons

Yorks: Lewis & Cooper Ltd

Ainsleys of Leeds, Victor House, 14 Manor Street, LEEDS LS7 1PZ ☎ **0113 245 1561 fax 0113 243 9760** *was founded by Mr Ainsley, grandson of Elizabeth Botham. There appears to be some rivalry as to who makes the original (and best) Whitby Lemon Buns. Reports please.*

WHITBY
Kippers

Fortunes
22 Henrietta Street, Whitby, Yorkshire YO22 4DW

☎ 01947 601659 **CONTACT** Barry & Derek Brown **HOURS** Mon-Fri 9.00-16.00 Sat 9.00-15.30 (June to end-Sept: also Sun 9.00-12.00) **DIRECTIONS** *East of town centre, past the 199 steps.*

At the far end of Whitby up through the narrow cobbled streets is Fortunes, a ramshackle set of buildings – smokehouses blackened with smoke and tar – with old signs dating to who knows when hanging up in the front shed that serves as a shop. When I originally visited, nothing looked as if it had changed over the five generations of Fortunes that have smoked kippers here. Since then Bill Fortune has retired and his nephews Barry and Derek Brown have taken over the business. You may be relieved to hear that they have written, assuring me of their intention to run it without any changes.

The curing of herrings for kippers has been passed down from generation to generation. The only possible change is that the herrings now come from Iceland, 'it's 20 years since we caught herring here' and the boats lying idle in Whitby harbour can probably testify to that. Salted for 40 minutes and smoked over a mixture of hard and soft woods for anything from 16 to 30 hours, depending on the weather ('it can get right windy up here'), the kippers are sold in pairs as 'we've always sold them in pairs' and they were certainly the cheapest I've bought yet. Mildly cured but evenly and strongly smoked, they had a pleasant but not over-strong sharpness.

WOMERSLEY
Fruit and Herb Vinegars

Womersley Crafts & Herbs
Womersley Hall, Womersley, nr Doncaster, Yorkshire DN6 9BH

☎ 01977 620294 **FAX** 01977 620200 **CONTACT** Martin Parsons **HOURS** *Available any time by telephone or fax. Shop open at weekends or by appointment. Telephone ahead for times.* **CARDS** Access, Eurocard, Mastercard, Visa **DIRECTIONS** *In village centre.*

Sometimes I despair at this country. Take our labelling standards: small food producers seem beset by petty regulations on one hand, while the larger manufacturers get away with murder. It is perfectly all right for ice-cream manufacturers to label a product 'no artificial ingredients' even if they have added nature-identical but laboratory-made flavourings, but Martin Parsons of Womersley Hall who makes fruit vinegars of the finest vintage now has to call them 'condiments' on the grounds that the base is a non-brewed condiment. I ask you, where is the sense in that? These are vinegars as we know and love them and as they have been made for centuries.

You should know that there are fruit vinegars and there are Womersley fruit vinegars; and the difference is like trying to compare an industrially made balsamic vinegar with a traditionally made one. Basically you can't – they are as different as chalk and cheese. Most of our fruit vinegars are really no more than fruit infused in a vinegar; Martin, however, prepares his using the proper time-honoured process. First he soaks the fruit for a few days in a non-brewed condiment, leaves it to strain overnight through a sieve 'the finer the better, but no way should you force it through or you'd have problems', then cooks it gently with sugar, leaves it to cool and finally sieves it time after time. The result is like a bitter-sweet cordial, mellow and full-bodied, with all the richness and the ripe sweetness of the fruit balanced with mildest hint of acidity.

Using mostly own-grown fruit for blackberry, loganberry, mulberry, raspberry and golden raspberry (for a particularly limpid clear golden liquid), Martin succeeds in giving each one its own true flavour. These are serious vinegars; cook with them, use them in soups, stews or for deglazing a pan or transform a salad with them, I honestly cannot praise them highly enough. He also makes French tarragon and Opal basil herb vinegars, with Cinnamon Basil and Spice Basil just introduced. Using a different – but equally time-consuming – process, he first makes a herb mash or – as, he calls it, 'pesto' – soaks it in a little scalded vinegar, then strains and strains it to a clear concentrate. This is added drop by drop to a bottle of non-brewed condiment give the deep intensity of the herb.

Loosely-set herb and flower jellies are also touched with the same intensity; a heady flowery lavender, a mild fragrant geranium, a startling lemon verbena, a fiery Apache and, new this year, golden crab apple, cinnamon basil and lemon basil are just some of the 16 flavours he produces. Last, but by no means least, are the mellow meaty pickled walnuts. Most everything is made from produce grown in Womersley's enchanting walled garden.

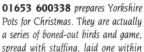

Butcher **Derek Fox, 25 Market Place**, MALTON YO17 0LP ☎ **01653 600338** *prepares Yorkshire Pots for Christmas. They are actually a series of boned-out birds and game, spread with stuffing, laid one within the other and then rolled up. Starting from the outside and working in, the pot is made from duck, chicken, pheasant, partridge and venison wrapped around the birds' livers. In fact, he will make more or less any combination a customer requests. Boning and assembling is done by his daughter Melanie and the Pots are prepared in advance and frozen. For mail order they are packed in ice and sent while still frozen, although he will prepare them to arrive fresh for Christmas as a special order.*

Stockists

Ches: Mooreland Foods

Lancs: Ramsbottom Victuallers

Oxon: The Burford Garden Co

Surrey: Vivian's

Appletons of Ripon, 6 Market Place, RIPON HG4 1BP ☎ **01765 603198** *is 'for cooked meats and table dainties'. Look out for their peppery pork pies with crisp hot-water crust; bready savoury duck, also with a distinctive peppery flavour; and roast belly of pork sliced while you wait, with chunks of crisp succulent crackling.*

While you're in the area...

The Smithy Farm Shop, BALDERSBY, Thirsk YO7 4PN ☎ **01765 640676** keep a freezer cabinet stocked with beef from Helen Ellis's Dexter herd, pork from Berkshire pigs, local corn-fed chickens, local game which is fresh in season, and Slack's sausages *see page 59*. They also sell bacon from Richard Woodall *see page 62*, Pepper Arden pies,

Brymoor ice-cream, Rosebud Preserves *see page* 304, The Toffee Shop fudge *see page* 58, local vegetables, and a whole range of cakes, tarts and savoury dishes baked by a local caterer.

Sneaton Dale Honey Farm, 1 Race Course Road, EAST AYTON, Scarborough YO13 9HT ☎ 01723 864001 fax 01723 862455 produce from their 900-odd hives a mild fruity, relatively thin, borage honey with a tang that sharpens its flavour, and a ling heather honey that is gelatinous in texture and has a deep dark flavour.

Cocketts, Main Street, HAWES DL8 3QL ☎ 01969 667251 double up as butchers and bakers. Worth seeking out are their sticky shiny parkin, a densely textured fiery ginger cake which goes down a treat with a chunk of Wensleydale cheese.

For **Mrs Atkins, Chapel House, NORWOOD, Otley LS21 2RA** jam-making is no more than a hobby. Her job is to look after the Methodist chapel attached to the house. Working on a hobby scale, she makes jam throughout the year, using fresh fruit or frozen in season for stocks to draw on. There are around 43 lines ('but never all at the same time'), including 5 marmalades – thick, thin, lemon, thick with honey, and three-fruit with pineapple orange & lemon; 5 different plums – Santa Rosa, Victoria, Burbanks, Earnest Rivers ('when I can get it'); rhubarb; rhubarb & ginger; damson; damson & pear and so on.

The Farmhouse Kitchen, 16 Market Place, OTLEY LS21 5AQ ☎ 01943 468270 has a small but interesting selection of Yorkshire cheeses, including Richard III Wensleydale *see page* 309, Swalesdale *see page* 310, and goats'-milk Braythorne. They also sell own-made pâtés and salads, bread from Kolos *see page* 301, and various cakes.

St Wilfrid is the patron saint of Ripon Minster, so it is right and proper that **Davill's, 24 Westgate, RIPON HG4 2BQ ☎ 01765 603544** should make Wilfra tarts. Traditionally made with a pastry base covered with slices of apples and topped with Wensleydale cheese, Kenneth Davill substitutes Cheddar on the grounds that the flavour needs 'more bite' and the tart 'more colour'. He also makes a 'good and clarty' parkin which is close-textured and sticks to the teeth.

The Good Food Shop, 9 Scarcroft Road, YORK YO2 1ND ☎ 01904 637445 make their own pâtés, cook ham on the bone and bake a whole range of cakes and puddings to order, such as treacle tart, Yorkshire curd tart, and pecan pie. They also sell various on-farm cheeses, including Wellington *see page* 23 and Richard III Wensleydale *see page* 309 and Richard Woodall's bacon *see page* 62.

Via Vecchia, 6 The Shambles, YORK YO1 2LZ ☎ 01904 627701 bake a wide range of breads, including plain white, rye with sunflower, Granary, and Italian-style breads. Using powerful flavours, such as pesto, olives, onions – even salami – mixed in with strong white flour and a vegetable oil, these breads are quite loose-textured and perhaps a touch doughy, but certainly vibrant in taste.

Scotland

Argyll &
the Islands

G. B. Shellfish
Lochnell Estate, Old Farm Court Yard, Benderloch, by Oban, Argyll, Argyll & the Islands PA37 1QU

☎ 01631 720525 **FAX** 01631 720392 **CONTACT** *George Burton – mail order only*

Shellfish farming is relatively new to the West Coast of Scotland. It includes the growing of oysters, mussels and scallops. Unlike salmon farming, shellfish farming causes virtually no pollution of the sea lochs as very few – if any – chemicals are used, the stocking densities are lower, the shellfish feed naturally and they expel little waste.

Mussels are cultivated by rope culture – hairy ropes are suspended from rafts or long lines, the spats (mussel larvae) attach themselves to the ropes, feed on plankton and are harvested when about 2 years old. According to George Burton, the advantage of a farmed as opposed to a 'wild' mussel is that it has a better meat-to-shell ratio; this happens because their mussels are submerged in water the whole time (most naturally occurring mussels are above the tide-line), so they grow quicker and only produce a light thin shell. Unlike wild mussels, with their deep purple and black shells, farmed mussels are the colour of a tiger's eye, dark-brown flecked with gold. Sold live with their bibus (beard) attached – as, George maintains, if it is pulled out if kills them off – they are in season from June to March.

Scallop farming is only marginally more complex. The scallop spats are caught in spat collectors, they attach themselves to the sides of the nets and, as their shell begins to grow, they drop off into the bottom of the collector. Again, according to George, there are several advantages of buying a farmed scallop: firstly, it has a known age – scallops are usually around 5 years when harvested, whereas a dived or dredged scallop can be anything up to 20 years old and quite tough at that; the texture of a farmed scallop's muscle (the white meat we eat) tends to be

BENDERLOCH
Shellfish

Stockists
London:
Southbank Fresh Fish

Lancs: C. & G. Neve

Hants: J. J. Fish

Kent: Rockport Fish

finer as, so the theory goes, it has not had to fight for its survival; also, because it is suspended in mid-water which is far richer in plankton and algae than the sea-bed, it has a higher meat content. Farmed scallops come as Kings with a flat top and concave bottom shell, and a muscle measuring about 5 cm (2 in) across; Queens are smaller, with both shells concave and their white meat is sweeter and about the size of a

 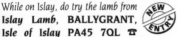

While on Islay, *do try the lamb from* **Islay Lamb, BALLYGRANT, Isle of Islay PA45 7QL** ☎ **01496 840656 fax 01496 840209**. *The pure-bred Blackface roams on the higher hills, feeding on grass, heathers and wild herbs. Smaller than most lambs, it has a fine-textured, quite dark and lean meat with a pronounced sweetness, and is in season from mid-July to February. The rest of the year, they sell Blackface-Suffolk cross lamb with both carcasses hung for at least a week.*

Although I do not rate the cheese from **Islay Creamery Co, PORT CHARLOTTE, Isle of Islay PA48 7TY** ☎ **01496 850229 fax 01496 850589** *very highly, it is worth popping in just to buy their 450-g (1-lb) blocks of whey butter.*

M. A. Mackinnons, Distillery House, PORT CHARLOTTE, Isle of Islay PA48 7TL ☎ **01496 850495** *make marmalade with Bruichladdich, a peaty single-malt whisky from the island for a surprisingly subtle finish; preserved rhubarb, this time with Invergordon single-grain whisky; and a thick and luscious rhubarb jam with no whisky at all.*

Oysters from **Islay Oysters, Craigens, GRUINART, Isle of Islay PA44 7PW** ☎/**fax 01496 850256** *are creamy and meaty and can be bought purified from the farmyard. Another treat is Islay mineral water on sale at most local shops. Bottled from the Maol Dubh spring, it is silky soft and rich amber in colour, from draining through the layers of peat. It is the water to drink with whisky.*

10p piece; and Princesses are immature Queens, with a muscle the size of a 5p piece. In season all year round, if you are particularly fond of the coral, the best time to buy is between February to April, when this is at its plumpest.

Farmed Pacific oysters *see Loch Fyne Smokehouse page 318* are available all year round. Graded by weight as 70-80 g (2½-2¾ oz), 80-95 g (2¾-3¼ oz) and 'regal', anything upwards of 95 g (3¼ oz) – and sometimes so big that it is a 'knife and fork job'. Due to EU regulations – or so they told me – all oysters are depurated (purified) by passing them through UV tanks for about 48 hours, and kept in aerated holding tanks until sold.

If you order from them, they will supply shellfish grown to the Association of Scottish Shellfish Growers standards, which take into account husbandry practice, shapes and sizes of the shellfish and the current legislation; and they guarantee to deliver to you on any weekday within 24 hours of harvesting from the sea.

 Otter Ferry Salmon, OTTER FERRY PA21 2DH ☎ **01369 860400** *farm salmon in tanks on land. With the sea water pumped through continuously, creating a constant current for the fish to swim against, they claim it makes for a fitter* *salmon which is more muscular and less fatty. Stocked at 25 kg per cubic metre (slightly higher than in cages) and fed a low-energy feed, all salmon are starved for 14 days before harvesting to empty their gut as this keeps them fresher for longer. Interestingly, they say you should never eat a salmon straight out of water, it turns to 'mush'; it needs to go through rigor and is best eaten at a couple of days old. Otter Ferry will send fresh gutted salmon from 2-2.5 kg (4½-5½ lb), packed in a sleeve on ice, anywhere in the country. They have recently started smoking, and produce a firm-textured smoked salmon with a deep fish resonance, available in 250 and 500-g (8½-oz and 1 lb 2-oz) packs, whole or sliced sides weighing 700-800 g (1⅜-1¾ lb) or 900-g-1-kg (2-2¼-lb), and 500-g (1 lb 2-oz) packs of gravadlax.*

The Island Cheese Company
Home Farm, Brodick, Isle of Arran,
Argyll & the Islands KA27 8DD

☎/FAX 01770 302788 **CONTACT** Ian McChlery **HOURS** March to end-Oct: 9.30-17.15; Nov to Dec: Tues-Sat 9.30-17.00 **CARDS** Access, Eurocard, Mastercard, Visa **DIRECTIONS** The shop and factory are 1 mile from Brodick on the road to Corrie & Loch Ranze.

There is a glass-windowed dairy next door to the shop, so you can see Ian McChlery at work. He makes three blue cheeses, using bought-in pasteurized milk. Brodick Blue, made with ewes' milk, is a seasonal cheese available from March to the end of October. A Roquefort-style cheese, it is drained for quite a short time before it is dry-salted, then left for a week before it is pierced to allow the blue veining to spread. Matured for about 8 weeks, it is at its best when quite tight and firm with a mellow sharpness; when I tried it almost at the end of its season it was quite acid which, as Ian explained, was due to the time of the year – when the sheep are almost at the end of their lactation. Glenshant, named after the area, is made by a similar process, but using goats' milk. A relatively powerful cheese, it had a stronger taste of both blue and goat. Arran blue, this time made with cow's milk, was lighter and, if left to mature, can turn soft and creamy.

Stockists
Lothian: Iain Mellis

Goatfell crottins are sold at any age from 3 days, when the curd is still young and fresh, up to 6 weeks, by which time it is dry and hard and right for grilling. I tried a 2-week old cheese which was smooth, if still quite acid, with a well-defined sense of goat. Ian also makes Crowdie which, as he says, 'is all things to all people. My mother made it with cream, but in the Western Isles they used sour milk and ate it instead of butter. The main thing is to hang it up in a cloth to drain'. Ian makes his by culturing double cream to turn it sour, and draining it for at least a couple of days. Sold as plain when it is rich and creamy, not unlike a crème fraîche only drier, or hung longer and rolled in oatmeal, crushed peppercorns or garlic, it is has a refreshing sharpness.

On the other side of the courtyard from The Island Cheese Company see above is **Arran Smoked Products, The Home Farm, BRODICK, Isle of Arran KA27 8DD** ☎/fax 01770 302797, which doubles up as a shop and Creelers fish restaurant. Tim and Fran James, the proprietors, run their own boat out of Brodick, so at various times of the year you are bound to find on the menu or in the shop, fresh monkfish, hake, skate, sea trout or grey mullet. They also catch langoustines, lobsters and crabs, which are kept fresh in the sea, and sell oysters, mussels and scallops. They smoke a lightly cured salmon, trout and hake, and prepare gravadlax and a creamy fish pâté.

Their chef, Robin Gray, runs **Kingscross Herbs, Grays Cottage, KINGSCROSS, Isle of Arran KA27 8RG** ☎ 01770 700586 and under 2 polytunnels he grows al lmanner of 'fancy lettuces', leaves and baby vegetables, such as courgettes and courgette flowers, mizuna, rocket and spinach.

Also worth a visit on the island are bakers **Wooleys, BRODICK, Isle of Arran KA8 AJ** ☎ 01770 302280 fax 01770 302715 Apart from various loaves and traditional morning rolls, soda, treacle, sultana and potato scones, they also make large and quite fat oatcakes (using oatmeal, wheat-flour and vegetable fat), which go well with Brodick blue cheese see above.

Loch Fyne Smokehouse
Clachan Farm, Ardkinglas, Cairndow, Argyll & the Islands PA26 8BH

☎ 01499 600217 **FAX** 01499 600234 **CONTACT** Andy Lane **HOURS** Easter to end-Oct: 9.00-21.00; Nov to Easter: 9.00-17.00 **CARDS** Access, Switch, Visa **DIRECTIONS** From Cairndow, take A83 towards Inveraray. Follow the road about 2 miles and shop is signposted on the right.

The waters of Loch Fyne are notoriously rich in plankton – hence the fame of the fat juicy and oily herring for Loch Fyne kippers. The advantage of growing oysters here is the feed. Loch Fyne Smokehouse buy in the spats (seeds) and lay them in sacks on racks on the loch's shore. Depending on whether the tides are spring or neap, they will survive out of the water for 4 to 8 hours: 'It does them good not to be covered as they learn to close properly and how to survive in air. We always harden off our oysters so they don't gape'. Their oysters take two summers to reach their proper size, during which time they are constantly graded out in bags, otherwise the smaller ones will suffer. The bags also have to be turned to kill off the thick racky seaweed. Harvested the day before and passed through a purification tank, Loch Fyne oysters are sent out wrapped in seaweed to keep them moist, packed in polystyrene boxes. Because they farm Pacific oysters, they are available all year round. Most weigh 80 g (2¾ oz), although Hamish – a 16-year-old veteran oyster – currently tips the scales at a massive 675 g (1 lb 8 oz) and Henrietta – no relation – is doing well at 550 g (1 lb 4 oz).

Herring catching was banned 8 years ago in the Loch as stocks were decimated. Now it is allowed again, 'but the trouble is the open season starts too soon in June, when the stocks are young and scraggy. It's far too early, as they haven't fattened up yet'. The best time is between August and November, when they are caught down-loch, heading out to sea, between Campbeltown and Tarbet. Loch Fyne cure and smoke them, supplementing their stock with Minch herring, 'But we say so, which is more than some'. As Andy Lane says rightly, because of their fine reputation, people try to pass off any old herring as a Loch Fyne.

Apart from herring, they dry-cure farmed salmon in salt and soft brown sugar for about 4-6 hours, then cold-smoke it for 4 – 8 hours. Many people, myself included, compare theirs to the famous London-smoke *see Formans, page 182* as, at its best, it does have that yielding mild texture and soft buttery flavour. They also smoke mussels, cod's roe and trout, cure gravadlax, and make Bradan (Gaelic for roast) salmon – ie hot-smoked. The smokehouse, shop and oyster bar are at the head of Loch Fyne. With a view down the loch, it is a perfect place to stop for oysters and a glass of wine or for a little shopping. As well as oysters and smoked fish, you can also buy creel-caught langoustines, velvet crabs, scallops, clams and all manner of seafood.

Stockists
Cambs: The Loch Fyne Oyster Bar
Notts: The Loch Fyne Seafood Bar

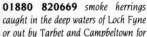

K. & G. McFall, Stanley Place, Harbour Street, TARBET PA29 6UD ☎ **01880 820669** *smoke herrings caught in the deep waters of Loch Fyne or out by Tarbet and Campbeltown for* Loch Fyne kippers, with the larger fish known locally as 'Glasgow magistrates'.

Alba Smokehouse

Kilmory, Lochgilphead, Argyll & the Islands PA31 8RR

☎ 01546 606400 **FAX** 01546 606400 **CONTACT** Michael Leng **HOURS** Mon-Fri 8.30-17.00 Sat 9.30-13.00 **DIRECTIONS** *Just outside Lochgilphead, on the main road to Glasgow.*

There are times when honestly I despair of my job. I mean, how many smokehouses are there in Scotland? And just when my heart is sinking and my stomach turning at the sight of yet another one, up pops Alba Smokehouse to make it all worth while. Yes, it is new – it has only been up and running for 2 years – and yes, it is very good.

There are so many variables to take into account when it comes to smoking food, but Mike Leng seems to have taken them all into consideration. First he places an emphasis on buying his fish, 'if you haven't got a good base raw product, you're struggling from the start,' buying as locally as possible. Then, working from a modern unit on an industrial estate using Afos kilns, Mike aims to marry traditional techniques with modern equipment. Salmon and trout are lightly sprinkled with sugar 'to take out the bitterness', then with salt, and finally wet-cured in a brine solution. Wary of over-smoking or 'kippering', Mike then pre-smokes overnight with the fans off but with the minimum of smouldering wood to dry the fish and then slowly builds up the heat over a further 12 hours to give 'depth'. This way of smoking, acquired through trial and error, would apparently have taken 3-4 days in an old-fashioned kiln. As for the result, his smoked salmon is moist and chewy, a cunning balance of a light sultry smoke and a rich fishiness.

Hot-smoked salmon, Mike's favourite, is equally successful. Smoked in whole fillets weighing 675-900 g (1½-2 lb), they too are moist and succulent with a light smoke and struck me as similar to eating poached salmon with an extra edge. He also hot- and cold-smokes trout and hot-smokes scallops and mussels for a meaty – almost roast-beef – flavour. With several ideas for new products up his sleeve, I believe Alba Smokehouse definitely has a future.

LOCHGILPHEAD
Smoked Salmon

Stockists

Argyll: The Alba Smokehouse Seafood Trailer

The Scottish Salmon and Seafood Centre

The Square Peg

Oxon: Aubrey Newman & Daughters

The Reade family seem set fair to take over Mull. Mum and Dad make the cheese see page 321, brother Joe bakes the bread and Matthew and his wife *Julia run **Calgary Farmhouse Hotel**, DERVAIG, Isle of Mull PA75 6QW ☎/fax 01688 400256 a charming hotel, restaurant and café, open from April to October. Teas are served in the gallery, surrounded by local artists' work, and include sandwiches made with Joe's bread (naturally), generously filled with fresh crab or trout, or Mum's cheese. There are also own-made scones, cakes and shortbread.*

The Original Tartan Cake Company

Lephinmore Farm, Strachur,
Argyll & the Islands PA27 8BU

STRACHUR
Fruit Cakes

☎ 01369 860625 **FAX** 01369 860400 **CONTACT** Amanda Barge – telephone ahead **CARDS** Access, Visa

Amanda Barge has only recently started baking cakes and has already

Mail Order

Fruit cakes, mincemeat & Christmas puddings only

Stockists

Argyll: Loch Fyne Oyster Bar

The Scottish Salmon and Seafood Centre

Strath: Peckhams

acquired a deserved reputation. She works on a small scale, using 'proper' ingredients, and all her produce has a delightfully fresh moist own-made feel about it. The cakes she makes fall into two categories: pound cakes, which actually weigh 400-450 g (14-16 oz) and fruit cakes. Pound cakes are fresh loaf cakes. Flavours include a moist lush passion cake, made with bananas, cream cheese and chopped walnuts for texture; ginger, which is dark and sultry and made with treacle and golden syrup for a mild spicy glow; and a farmhouse loaf, plump with fruit and with a pleasant buttery crumb. Amanda's fruit cakes weigh 1.25 kg (2½ lb) and come gleaming with a Drambuie-and-apricot glaze and neatly decorated with nibbed almonds. 'Loosely based on a Dundee recipe, but far moister,' is how she describes them and she makes with raw cane and caster sugar, butter, eggs, unbleached white flour, vine fruits steeped in rum and whisky, cherries, ground almonds and orange peel. Light and open-crumbed, again there is a moistness that strikes me as one of the hallmarks of her cakes. Although, as she says, she may be 'light on the orange peel', she certainly is heavier-handed with the alcohol as its taste shines through. Tied up in tartan ribbon and packed in a tin printed with the same blue-and-green Colquhoun tartan, her fruit cakes are usually sent out freshly baked, but will keep for months.

Amanda also makes a bright yellow runny lemon curd from eggs, butter, sugar and lemon, with a sharp lemon tang. Particularly smooth, Amanda sieves it by hand. For Christmas she makes mincemeat from chopped apples, vegetable suet, vine fruits, nutmeg and mixed spices, flavoured with a local sweet stout and packed in 450 and 900-g (1 and 2-lb) polythene buckets; and a bready 1.25-kg (2½-lb) Christmas pudding from chopped vine fruits and nuts, flour, breadcrumbs and rum – but no suet.

Black of Dunoon, 144 Argyll Street, DUNOON PA23 7NA ☎ 01369 702311 fax 01369 703778 *bake a whole range of breads, biscuits and rolls. Weekends only, they bake various 'Continental' and rye breads. The rest of the week you will find plain white and wholemeal; morning and sweeter afternoon rolls made with more fat and sugar; various scones, including treacle, sultana, potato, cream with a delicate sweetness, and lightly soured soda; pancakes (called crumpets down South); textured shortbread made with butter, sugar, eggs, plain and rice flour; and own-made crisp oatcakes.*

TAYNUILT

Trout Caviar

Inverawe Smokehouses
Taynuilt, Argyll & the Islands PA35 1HU

☎ 01866 822446 **FAX** 01866 822247 **CONTACT** Rosie Campbell-Preston **HOURS** 9.00-18.30 **CARDS** Access, Eurocard, Mastercard, Switch, Visa **DIRECTIONS** From Crianlarich, take A85 towards Oban. Drive through Dalmally and, after about 10 miles just before Taynuilt, turn right at the signpost for the smokery.

In a series of brick smokehouses using an ingenious system of fire boxes on wheels filled with oak logs, Inverawe Smokehouses smoke various fish, including trout, wild and fresh salmon, eel from Loch Awe, halibut, Icelandic cod's roe and herring from the North Sea for Inverawe kippers. They also sell venison, Argyll ham, beef and duck smoked by Roy Forsyth at Spean Bridge.

It is, however, for their trout caviar that I single them out. Robert Campbell-Preston extracts the roe from the trout between October and December, just before the fish start breeding. If you leave it later, when they are breeding between January and March, the roe is hard and tastes 'foul and bitter'. Once the roe is removed, some are frozen in their membrane for use during the rest of the year and the rest are prepared immediately. First he griddles the eggs out from the membrane, cleans them, matures them overnight in salt, then pots them in 55-g (2-oz) glass jars ready for sale. It may sound simple enough, but it took Robert three years to get the technique right and he reckons he is still learning.

> **An Tairbeart Heritage Centre, Campbeltown Road, TARBET PA29 6SX ☎ 01880 820190 fax 01880 820042** *opened over a year ago. There are walks through woodlands and farmland, and exhibits on all aspects of West Highland life. The centre's shop stocks a selection of local produce, including own-made jams, jellies and shortbread; own-farmed oysters and mussels; and own-farmed venison; the range from Alba Smokehouse see page 319; smoked salmon from Arran Smoked Products see page 317; and smoked lamb from Tombuie Smokehouse see page 376. In the restaurant, they serve fortifying high teas which include a scone, pancake and cake, as well as a choice of herring in oatmeal, haggis, neeps and tatties and an awesome mixed grill of sausage, bacon, black pudding, fried bread, tomato, mushroom and fried egg.*

I love these little (smaller than salmon eggs) bright orange balls that pop in your mouth with a mild saltiness and a delicate taste of fish. I use them for canapés, such as baby new potatoes stuffed with sour cream or spooned on top of dill-flavoured scrambled eggs. Interestingly, it is illegal in Scotland to handle salmon eggs on the grounds that they make the best bait ever. A curious anomaly, as we can import them but not cure them ourselves; hence Robert's device of using trout eggs. Perhaps, when the Ministry sees the ridiculousness of the situation, they may do something about changing it.

Isle of Mull Traditional Farmhouse Cheese

Sgriob-ruadh Farm, Tobermory, Isle of Mull,
Argyll & the Islands PA75 6QD

TOBERMORY
Cheese

☎ 01688 302235 **FAX** 01688 302546 **CONTACT** Jeff Reade **HOURS** Sun-Fri 10.00-16.00 **CARDS** Access, Visa **DIRECTIONS** *From Tobermory, take either one of the roads signposted Calgary and Dervaig. After about ¼ mile, at the crossroads, follow the signs to Glengorm. Farm is 350 yards along on the left.*

The Reades of Sgriob-ruadh (pronounced skibrooah, Gaelic for 'red furrow') Farm are the only dairy farmers on Mull. They run a mixed herd of Friesians, Holsteins, Jerseys, Ayrshires and one Ling, a Highland Shorthorn cross who 'milks like a drain and gets her forage where the more refined dairy cows wouldn't dare to go'. Cheese is made most days in the 400-gallon vat, using the unpasteurized evening and morning meal (milk) and working to a Cheddar-style recipe. They press for 2 days

While on the Isle of Mull, there are a few producers worth a visit. **Tobermory Fish Farm, Main Street, TOBERMORY PA75 6NU ☎ 01688 302120 fax 01688 302140** warm and cold-smoke salmon and trout and hot-smoke trout only for quite a salty finish, which is how the 'West coast folk like it'.

On the other side of the island is **Gremlins, 2 Acharonich Cottages, ULVA FERRY PA73 6LY ☎ 016885 262**, where Mrs Napier makes jams, jellies and marmalades. Particularly worth trying are the raw-edged green tomato chutney and the vibrantly fruited raspberry jam made with equal quantities of same-day picked fruit and sugar boiled for just one minute.

Isle of Ulva Oysters, ISLE OF ULVA, PA73 6LZ ☎ 01688 500264 are reached by driving down to Ulva Ferry and waving the red flag as a signal for the ferry to come and collect you. Once on the island (the channel is only 150 metres wide) there are walks of astounding beauty and farmed Pacific or wild Native oysters plucked straight out of the sea. On sale by the dozen at the café by the ferry, buy them for a picnic or sit down for a leisurely feast. Sweet and peaty, they serve them plain or baked with garlic & parsley butter or grilled with Parmesan & cream. Who could ask for more?

and mature for anything between 6 and 12 months, in 22.5 and 4.5-kg (50 and 10-lb) clothbound or 450-g (1-lb) wax-finished truckles.

As nothing much happens on Mull during the winter, 'One of our prime concerns, Chris Reade explains, 'is to make in the winter and be able to sell in the summer'. Winter, do not forget, lasts longer up here – from October through to March – and the winter cheeses tend to be much paler in comparison to the buttercup-yellow of the summer ones. I tried a 10-month-old winter cheese; on first bite it warmed the mouth with a sweet grassy resonance which lingered on most pleasurably. It is a very good cheese indeed.

Since my very first visit nearly 8 years ago, there have been several changes and improvements. The sheep no longer clamber upstairs, as the stone house has been lovingly and comfortably restored. The cheese is now turned and stored in an underground cellar buried under a field, and tacked on to the house is a huge plant-filled greenhouse reconstructed from Salen village hall. Here visitors can buy cheese and occasionally own-made butter, or sit enjoying the view while trying own-made bread, chutney and a hunk of cheese.

Incidentally, I feel honour-bound to mention the Tobermory 'Flavells'. Described as having added mixed herbs or black peppercorns or caraway seeds or mustard, they are actually made by milling Isle of Mull Cheddar, mixing in the flavourings, then reconstituting it for a smooth paste-like texture. Several cheese-makers are resorting to this (in some cases using creamery-made block cheeses) and it worries me, primarily because they create a false impression. I bracket them along with processed cheese slices, spreads et al, in that they have very little to do with real cheese. Why anyone should want to buy them when they can have a slice of superb well-textured Isle of Mull Cheddar, beats me? Apparently, though, they are very popular.

Stockists

Fife: St Andrews Delicatessen

London: C. Lidgate Ltd
Jeroboams

Lothian: Iain Mellis

Strath: The Cheese and Wine Shop

The Island Bakery, Dervaig Road, TOBERMORY PA75 6PY ☎ 01688 302223 produces an original range of breads, including an unbleached white made with a long fermentation for a good firm texture and nicely developed flavour; malted grain with black treacle; a fiery spiced bread streaked with coriander, paprika, cinnamon and ginger; a plaited caraway and green peppercorn; and a boldly flavoured cheese bread, made with baker Joe Reade's parents' Isle of Mull cheese see page 321 and it is at their establishment that you can actually buy the breads.

While you're in the area...

Fyne Game of Inveraray, Unit 3-4, Upper Riochan, INVERARAY PA32 8UR ☎ 01499 302055 fax 01499 302415 deal in local game – anything from wild venison from Red or Sika deer to pheasant, pigeon, rabbits, wild duck, partridge, snipe or hares. They also smoke venison and make venison sausages, burgers and venison salami with juniper, garlic and rum – an interesting idea but one, I think, that still needs a little work.

The Cheese & Wine Shop, 112 George Street, OBAN PA34 5NT ☎ 01631 564409 prides itself on its collection of over 100 malt whiskies. They also stock lots of Scottish cheeses, including Bonchester *see page* 324 and a creamy Cara made by Inverloch Creamery using Jersey milk. You will also find plenty of smoked produce, including the inevitable salmon, venison and trout.

Andrew Abrahams runs **Isle of Colonsay Oysters** and **Isle of Colonsay Apiaries, POLL GOURM, Isle of Colonsay PA61 7YR ☎/fax 01951 200365**. Oysters are farmed Pacific and honey is collected from hives scattered around the island. It comes as a thick butterscotch-coloured wildflower with a light almost lemon fragrance; and heather is thicker and darker, with a powerful lingering flavour.

Butchers **James McIntyre, 74 Montague Street, ROTHESAY, Isle of Bute PA20 0HL ☎ 01700 503672** make their own haggis; white mealie pudding, with oatmeal, suet, onions and seasoning; black pudding, with ox blood; and fruit pudding heavily laden with suet. They sell Isle of Bute beef and lamb butchered into such useful cuts as flank, hough and shanks, and sell among other things dried marrowfat peas.

Ritchies of Rothesay, 111 Montague Street, ROTHESAY, Isle of Bute PA20 9OJ ☎ 01700 505414 smoke a fine pair of kippers, 'you feel the tail, when there's a wee crick on them, you know they're ready', a sweet meltingly textured smoked salmon, haddock fillets, and a pleasantly earthy cold-smoked trout. They also sell a good selection of fresh fish and make up salmon fish-cakes.

Inver Cottage, STRATHLACHLAN, Strachur PA27 8BU ☎ 0136986 396/377 fax 0136986 559 is a restaurant decked out in check (but not tartan), with views over Loch Fyne and Lachlan Castle. Stop here for a bowl of soup, feuilletée of wild mushrooms or locally smoked salmon, and to buy jars of own-made jams, chutneys, treacly butterscotch pouring sauce and piquant lemon curd.

Square sausagemeat is a Scottish curiosity. Cut from an oblong block into slices, it is a stiff mixture of either beef or pork, rusk and seasonings. Locals, including Mrs McRae, recommend **Robert Coulter, Main Street, TAYNUILT, ☎ 01866 822275**; his is finely spiced, suitably stiff and has a meat content of 70 per cent.

Easter Weens Enterprises
Bonchester Bridge, Hawick, Borders TD9 8JQ

☎/FAX 01450 860635 **CONTACT** John Curtis **HOURS** Apr to Christmas Eve: 8.00-18.00 **DIRECTIONS** From Hawick, take A6088 towards Bonchester Bridge. Follow the road about 7 miles down the hill to the village. At the war memorial T-junction, turn left on to B6357, towards Jedburgh. After about 1 mile, farm is signposted on the right.

Bonchester cheese was the *Food Lovers' Guide* 1993 rosette-winner for best cheese. It is every bit as good as it ever was and the fact that it has not won this year is no reflection on John Curtis's cheese-making; it is just that others are meeting his impeccable standards.

Using the unpasteurized milk from his Jersey herd, John makes cheese every morning. First he adds the mould, *penicillium candidum*, and a starter, leaves the milk to stand for about 1½ hours, adds the rennet, leaves it for another hour, then he cuts the curds with a curd knife, tips them into moulds and, after lunch, the moulds are turned. The following day the cheeses are moved out of the dairy into the brining room; here they are brined briefly, left to stand and drain, turned and so remain for about 4 days. Then they are moved into the maturing room to develop a flossy white coat and their flowery creamy flavour.

When John sends them out, either as 100 or 285-g (3½ or 10-oz) rounds, the interior is still firm. The cheese is best eaten when soft and creamy, with the centre oozing in a run of custard yellow cream. If you keep a Bonchester at room temperature it runs within a couple of days; in a cold fridge it can take up to 2 months. It is a sublime cheese, deep and rich and as good as any French mould-ripened cheeses but with a flavour of its own. John also makes Teviotdale, which he describes as 'a larger cheese, the equivalent of four Bonchesters in one, weighing about 2½ pounds'. Made in the same way as a Bonchester, the only difference is that it is lightly pressed: 'This changes its character as it's a

MAP 8   BORDERS   **325**

drier cheese, it remains harder and won't run when it's ripe'. None the less, it still has that flowery creaminess – a hallmark of John's cheeses – if a more intense and deeper flavour. Belle d'Ecosse is a smaller and more lightly pressed version; similar to a Vignotte, it does soften but it too will not run. 'It's a question of pressing; the more pressure you apply, the more moisture you take out and the harder the cheese is. If you press too dry, it won't ripen. If it's not dry enough, it ripens too quickly.'

Making cheese is an exacting craft and John is the first to admit he's made a lot of mistakes on the way. As Randolph Hodgson of Neal's Yard Dairy *see page* 180 says, however, 'John is one of the best. It's the care and attention he pays to every detail, from the management of his herd to the making of his cheese. And it's reflected in the quality'.

Stockists

Fife: St Andrews Delicatessen

London: Neal's Yard Dairy

Paxton & Whitfield

Lothian: Iain Mellis

Surrey: Vivian's

With Jethart Snails from Jedburgh, Hawick Balls from Hawick, Berwick Cockles from Berwick and Gala Soor Plums from Galashiels, the Borders are strong on sweets. **Millers at 10 High Street, JEDBURGH, TD8 6AG** ☎/fax **01835 862252** have been making Jethart Snails ever since they were shown how by a French Napoleonic prisoner of war. Sugar boiled with mint essence is hand-pulled into long thin strands and twisted round until it looks like a brown snail.

Hills of Hawick, 16 Commercial Road, HAWICK TD9 7AQ ☎ **01450 373869 fax 01450 371139** first made Hawick Balls, brittle buttery mint sweets, at the turn of the century. Now they also produce the startling green sharp-tasting Soor Plums and red-and-white striped Berwick Cockles, which may look like humbugs but have a softer chewier texture achieved by 'knocking' the heated sugar to introduce air then leaving the finished sweets to 'grain' for a creamy texture.

The Teviot Game Fare Smokery
Kirkbank House, Eckford, Kelso, Borders TD5 8LE

ECKFORD
Smoked Fish

☎ 01835 850253 **FAX** 01835 850293 **CONTACT** Dennis Wilson **HOURS** Apr to Sept: Mon-Sat 10.00-16.30 Sun 11.00-16.00; Oct to Mar: Mon-Sat 10.00-16.30 **DIRECTIONS** From Kelso, take A698 towards Jedburgh. Follow the road for about 4 miles and smokery is signposted on the right.

Housed in an 18th-century coaching house, Teviot Game Fare Smokery is a small family business which concentrates on smoking the local produce. Eel is a speciality and the Wilson's son is the officially recommended eel-catcher for the river Tweed. He catches them there when in their prime, in the late summer or autumn when plump and silver as they move downstream preparing for their long hard slog back to the Sargasso Sea to breed. Because the river waters are colder this far north, the eels take comparatively longer to grow. For a good size for smoking, they are usually about 12 years upwards. Once caught, they are 'starved' in the river for a couple of weeks to cleanse them, then lightly brined, cold-smoked over oak chips for between 6-7 hours, then hot-smoked for about 3 hours to 'cook' them right through. A whole

Tweed Valley Smokehouse, Tweed Valley Hotel, WALKER-BURN EH43 6AA ☎ 01896 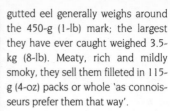 **870636 fax 01896 870639** *smokes a whole range of food, primarily for the hotel, but they will sell to passers-by. They also run week-end courses on learning how to smoke, covering the subtleties of which wood to use, how to dry-cure or brine, right through to hot- and cold-smoking or roast-smoking – and even how to go about building your own smoker.*

gutted eel generally weighs around the 450-g (1-lb) mark; the largest they have ever caught weighed 3.5-kg (8-lb). Meaty, rich and mildly smoky, they sell them filleted in 115-g (4-oz) packs or whole 'as connoisseurs prefer them that way'.

Trout comes from a local trout farm and is smoked in the same way as the eels. As a rule I try to avoid it, as either fresh or smoked it is an insipid fish. Theirs was a delight: moist with a good body and texture, and a light smoke which served to heighten the flavour of the fish. Dennis Wilson's approach is 'to smoke for a long time – very slowly. It's the essence of a good flavour'.

New this year are the succulent hot-smoked salmon steaks. I am also pleased to say their smoked salmon is much improved, far less harshly salty so the taste of fish comes through. Pheasants from local shoots are hung for about 4 days to develop a flavour, then brined for a good day, cold-smoked for 24 hours and finally briefly hot-smoked. Wood pigeon is subjected to a similar treatment. In summer they cure gravadlax but, interestingly, use fennel from the garden rather than the more usual dill; and also make 115-g (¼-lb) pots of pâtés, using their smoked produce and mixing it with cream and yoghurt. When visiting, take time to inspect the Teviot Water Gardens and to stroll along the riverside walk. They also run a restaurant where you can tuck into – among other things – smoked salmon or chicken sandwiches made with their own produce.

Stockists

Borders: Teviot Fish

GALASHIELS

Selkirk Bannock

Alex Dalgetty & Sons
21 Island Street, Galashiels, Borders TD1 1NZ

☎ 01896 752508 **FAX** 01896 750452 **CONTACT** Bill Murray **HOURS** Mon-Sat 7.30-17.00 **DIRECTIONS** In town centre.

The *Concise Oxford Dictionary* describes a bannock as 'Sc. & N. Engl. a round flat loaf usu. unleavened'. The Selkirk bannock, however, is a different beast; it is a rich yeasted fruit-loaf shaped like a round cob. History has it first made by a Robbie Douglas in his bakery in Selkirk Market Place in 1859. Queen Victoria, on visiting Sir Walter Scott's granddaughter at Abbotsford in 1867, refused the sumptuous spread in favour of a slice of Selkirk bannock – no producer could hope for a better endorsement. Alexander Dalgetty, a canny Scot, worked for the bakery in Selkirk and, on leaving to start his own business in Galashiels, took the recipe with him. Today his great-grandchildren run the bakery and still make the Selkirk bannock following the original recipe.

Mail Order

Selkirk bannock only

Heavily fruited with sultanas and only sultanas – some recipes call for mixed peel but Bill Murray claims they are no more than a recent addition – the yeast-based dough is made with strong unbleached flour, sugar, salt enriched with butter and a little vegetable fat that originally would have been lard. Its secret lies in a long fermentation and Bill starts the process with a sponge (flour, water and yeast). This is left to ferment for 7-8 hours, then is mixed in with the

Houstons Bakers, 16 Bourtree Place, **HAWICK TD9 9HW** ☎ **01450 370075** *fax* **01450 370343** *with branches at* **17 High Street,** JEDBURGH ☎ **01835 862373** *and* **33 Market Place,** SELKIRK ☎ **01750 20244** *also make a Selkirk bannock. Theirs is a little dry and salty for my taste, but several Scots say that is exactly how it is meant to be.*

dough and lies for another 3 hours; then the fats and sugar are added and the dough rests for 1 hour. Finally the sultanas are folded in and there is another 3-hour fermentation until it is ready to be hand-shaped, glazed with an egg for a light shiny crust and baked off. Dalgetty's bannock comes packed with fruit and is markedly firm with a pleasant yeastiness.

They also make Black Bun *see page* 367, fruit girdle scones baked on hot-plates; Border and rhubarb tarts; hand-cut oatcakes from pinhead (fine) oatmeal, lard and a touch of salt; and a variety of breads, including Bavarian dark rye, Bavarian fruit bread and mixed grain.

Stockists

Cumbria: E. H. Booth & Co

Lothian: Baxters of Edinburgh

Norfolk: Larner's of Holt

Lindsay Grieve
29 *High Street, Hawick, Borders* TD9 9BU

☎ 01450 372109 **CONTACT** Lindsay Grieve **HOURS** *Mon–Sat* 8.00–17.30 (–13.30 *Tues*) **DIRECTIONS** *In town centre.*

There is no getting away from the fact that haggis is made from an animal's pluck – lung, liver and heart – and either you like it or, if you are squeamish, you don't. If you don't, you probably will not appreciate the subtle differences between one haggis and another but, according to butcher Lindsay Grieve, they do exist. Having worked in different butchers picking up their particular ways en route, he now runs his own shop making his haggis in his way.

The choice of animal for the pluck is all-important: 'Some butchers use whatever they can get, as there is no set rule. I only use mutton pluck as it's sweeter and not so strong'. Mutton, I should add, encompasses a spring lamb through to a 2-year-old, but 'that doesn't matter,' Lindsay assured me, 'it's using lamb and Border lamb at that, that counts'. For a good texture, he uses a mixture of medium and pinhead (fine) oatmeal, 'so it's not too rough, not too smooth'; for moistness he adds suet and for flavour, onions, herbs and spices – such as a touch of cinnamon, nutmeg and ginger. Earthy, with a well-defined texture and a pronounced pepperiness, his haggises are meaty and sweet, pungent but not unacceptably so – even for the fainter-hearted. Packed into a choice of plastic or natural skins, they range in size from 675 g (1½ lb) to as large as 13.5 kg (30 lb), although obviously these have to be ordered. As a haggis enthusiast, he also makes haggis pudding, a mini 115-g (4-

oz) haggis which restaurants snap up to serve as a starter; haggis suprêmes, dollops of haggis with Scottish Cheddar wrapped in lattice pastry; and haggis olives, haggis rolled up in pork escalopes.

 Kailzie Gardens Restaurant, KAILZIE, Peebles EH45 9HT ☎ 01721 722807 *is open when the gardens are open – from mid-March to mid-October,* *when the clocks change. The gardens are relatively new, but delightfully planted; with a formal rose garden, a laburnum alley and 15 acres of wild garden with sweeps of bulbs and ambling wood- and burn-side walks. The restaurant is in the converted stables, with particularly bold chaffinches and arrogant peacocks wandering around outside. One of the latter fanned out his tail especially for Violet's benefit and she was scared witless. The only possible way to calm her down was a slice of Grace Innes's cake – naturally.*

Everything served for tea – with the possible exception of the jam – is own-made by Grace and her husband Ewen (he bakes the wholemeal bread). 'Proper' tea consists of sandwiches, scones with butter, jam and cream, and cake. As Grace's cakes and tarts are so glorious, however, you may be tempted to try just them – and several slices. She rings the changes pretty regularly, but her repertoire includes rhubarb pie, apple cake, a three-layered strawberry sponge, nutty meringues, mincemeat tart and Ecclefechan tart. For the uninitiated, this is a buttery treacly open tart filled with dried fruit and peel.

INNERLEITHEN

**Traquair
Spice Cake**

Traquair House
Innerleithen, Borders EH44 6PW

☎ 01896 830323 **FAX** 01896 830639 **CONTACT** *Catherine Maxwell Stuart* **HOURS** *Easter to end-Oct: 12.00-17.30 (July and Aug: 10.30-17.30)* **CARDS** *Access, Mastercard, Visa* **DIRECTIONS** *From Peebles, take A72 to Innerleithen. House is signposted, about 1 mile along*

Traquair is the oldest inhabited house in Scotland. Built as a royal hunting lodge, its massive grey walls lay claim to having sheltered 27 Scottish and English kings. When Mary Queen of Scots visited in 1566, a brewery was working there; but it was not until 1739 that a 200-gallon copper was installed in the brewhouse underneath the chapel. The brewery fell into disuse for about 150 years, but was re-opened several years ago by Catherine Maxwell Stuart's father. Catherine has carried on the tradition and now they brew a full-bodied Traquair House Ale, similar to a rich stout. The family are fervent Stuarts; the main gates stay firmly shut waiting for a Stuart once more to ascend the throne. This year, to celebrate the 250th anniversary of the Jacobite Uprising, they have brewed an 8 per cent proof Jacobite Ale, spiced with corian-der – an old trick – to give it a full, heady and spicy flavour.

Stockists

Derbys:
Chatsworth
Farmshop

London:
Selfridges

Lothian: Baxters
of Edinburgh

The Wine Society

The 1745 cottage restaurant in the grounds serves lunches and own-baked teas. There are scones with butter and jams, various sand-wiches and tray bakes, all baked in the cottage kitchen. From here you can also buy the ale and Traquair Spice cake made with their ale. Using an old Jacobite recipe developed by Catherine in tandem with Hos-sacks *see opposite*, it is more like a bread in texture and indeed was developed to be eaten with butter and/or cheese. Made with light treacle to give 'more rise', a mixture of spices that includes ginger, nutmeg, cloves, cinnamon, coriander and dill, and of course Traquair House Ale, it is a moist warm cake, succulent but not too dense and with a well-balanced whiff of hoppy spices.

Floors Castle Coffee Shop, Floors Castle, KELSO TD5 7SF ☎ 01573 225714 *has acquired a certain contemporary fame as, apart from being the setting of the* Tarzan of Greystokes *film, it is also where Andrew proposed to Fergie. The walled kitchen garden where this momentous event took place are open to the public; do have a wander there as the vegetables and fruit trees, even figs and peaches this far north, are to be wondered at.*

The Coffee Shop sells a small selection of produce made in the Duke of Roxburghe's own kitchens (I have been down there and they are gargantuan) and prepared by his own private chef, Ian Collingborne. He makes a 'house' (i.e. what the Duke has for breakfast) marmalade with Seville oranges and lemons; sharp and pithy it is very fruity. There also is a three-fruit made this time with orange, lemon and lime. At various times of the year, there are locally made jams 'when there's a glut of fruit in the garden', such as rhubarb, apple, apple & bramble, and gooseberry. Ian also bakes for the shop, producing various fruit pies and tarts; a rich smooth all-butter shortbread with cornflour; a dark nicely spiced gingerbread; and Border tart. Salmon fish-cakes are a speciality, made to a 'house' recipe of wild salmon, cream and 'one or two bits and pieces', rolled in breadcrumbs and sold in packs of 5. In season you can also buy dressed game from the estate, anything from wild duck to grouse.

R. T. Hossack
50 Horse Market, Kelso, Borders TD5 7AE

KELSO
**Selkirk
Bannock**

☎/FAX 01573 224139 **CONTACT** Mr Jack **HOURS** Mon-Sat 6.00-17.00 (-13.30 Winter Weds) **DIRECTIONS** In town centre.

R. T. Hossack bake a very nice Selkirk bannock *see also Alex Dalgetty, page* 326. Theirs has a well-glazed top, is heavily fruited, buttery and quite lightly salted. Not content with one local product, Mr Jack is now developing others using local produce.

For a start there is the Tweed bannock made with stone-ground flour milled in the Borders. This he makes along similar lines to a Selkirk bannock, mixing the dough and leaving it to rest for about 45 minutes before adding the fruit, then resting it for a further 20 minutes, cutting it and moulding it and finally proving it for about 1 hour before glazing and baking it. Although it is made with a 100 per cent wholemeal flour, the result is surprisingly light and it has a pleasant wheatiness. Mr Jack also makes the Traquair Spice cake *see opposite* and, new last year, beer bread. For this he uses Greenmantle, a hoppy ale

---

Shirra Bakery, 14 Market Place, SELKIRK TD7 4BT ☎ 01750 20690 *produce a rich crunchy shortbread that crumbles in the mouth on first bite. Made with plain flour, salted butter and caster sugar, it comes as 400-g (14-oz) blocks of 16 fingers, 200-g (7-oz) blocks of 8 fingers, and – my favourite – 375-g (13-oz) rounds marked up into 8 petticoat tails neatly forked around the edges. As well as plain, shortbread comes in a variety of flavours; apart from brown sugar, however, I think these are best avoided as essences (brandy or almond) or a poor-quality chocolate are used and inevitably these detract from the shortbread.*

brewed by the local Broughton Brewery and mixes it with white and wholewheat flour. Again it has a light – if slightly floppy – texture, but the flavour is very lingering; nutty and flowery I can imagine enjoying it with a chunk of well-matured Cheddar.

While you're in the area...

St Ronan's Wells, Wells Brae, INNERLEITHEN claims to be the oldest spa in Scotland. The waters, rich in minerals and salts and with a mildly sulphuric flavour, were once thought to be good for aches and pains, stomach upsets, skin disorders and – interestingly enough – sterility ('regular partaking enhancing fertility in married life'). The mineral water from Ronan's spring is now piped direct to the pavilion, where from April to October you can take a sulphur bath and buy bottles of the water. The water from the artesian well is aerated, bottled and sold specifically recommended for drinking with whisky.

Butchers **James R. Mitchell, 40/44 Bridge Street, KELSO TD5 7JD ☎ 01573 224109** make their own haggis, potted meat, and white mealie (oatmeal) puddings. They sell Border lamb in various cuts and joints, including the much undervalued lamb shanks, pork shanks and smoked ham shanks, as well as Floors Castle gingerbread and fruit tarts *see page 329*.

Fanny's, Briarbank, Tweedside Road, NEWTOWN ST BOSWELLS TD6 0PB ☎ 01835 822400 comes highly recommended by Scottish food writer Sue Lawrence for their Eymouth slice, which is similar to a Border tart except that it has added nuts, cherries and coconut for texture. Fanny also bakes various scones, sponges, loaves and cakes, including a popular carrot, and fruit tea.

The fish from fishmonger **Dan Ross, 19 Northgate, PEEBLES EH45 8RX ☎ 01721 720108** comes from Aberdeen's fish market. Here you will find Aberdeen 'pales' or Finnan haddock; fresh haddock; and, when in season from 24 May to September, North Sea herring. Dan Ross told me 'the harder the sun, the better the herring'. He also sells wild salmon from the river Tay and he prefers to buy it further down the river as, 'up here, far away from the salt, the fish is soft in texture,' and salmon smoked by John Ross of Aberdeen.

The Olive Tree, 7 High Street, PEEBLES EH45 8AG ☎ 01721 723461 is packed with Scottish produce. This includes smoked salmon from Mermaid Fish Supplies *see page* 351, preserves and wines from Moniack Castle *see page 358*, Galloway oatcakes *see page 335*, Edinburgh House and Shirra shortbread *see page 329*, local honey, Pettigrew's jams and jellies, various cheeses and breads baked in Edinburgh.

Loch Arthur Creamery

Camphill Village Trust, Beeswing, Dumfries,
Dumfries & Galloway DG2 8JQ

☎ 01387 760296 **CONTACT** *Barry Graham* **HOURS** *Mon-Fri 9.00-17.30
Sat & Sun – telephone ahead* **DIRECTIONS** *From Dumfries, take A711 towards
Beeswing. Follow the road about 4 miles into the village and take the first turning
on the left past the church. After about 30 yards, Camphill Trust is signposted on
the left.*

Loch Arthur Creamery is part of Loch Arthur Community, which
belongs to the Camphill Village Trust *see Botton Village Foods, page 302.*
The 500-acre estate is farmed to organic (Soil Association) and
Demeter (Biodynamic) standards. As well as the dairy, they run a small
bakery and weavery, keep sheep and grow vegetables. The dairy
started several years ago, partly because of the problems with milk
quota and partly because, as Barry Graham who now runs the dairy
explained, 'we had one community member crippled from the waist
down. He needed work and he could sit and churn butter'. Since then
the Ayrshire herd has grown to 18, there is a new purpose-built creamery (in the throes of building when I visited) and they process 50,000
gallons of milk a year into Loch Arthur Farmhouse cheese.

'It is' Barry told me, 'a cheese that has grown out of our circumstances. Every day – come hell or high water – we stop for lunch at
12.30. So we needed a cheese with a long pitch (settling time for the
curds). It had to fit in, balancing with the working as well as with the
cultural and social lives. But whatever we make here, it must stand up
on its own right. Actually, a dairy suits many of our members as it's
important that everything is the same – every day. Rhythm and routine
are their structure. That's one of the reasons we must break for lunch.
And routine is exactly what you find in any dairy'. The net result, for
anyone who actually calls, is to find the rewarding sight of community

There are two other on-farm cheeses that I like. Cairnsmore by **Galloway Farmhouse Cheese, Millairies, SORBIE, Newton Stewart DG8 8AL ☎ 01988 850224** is a hard-pressed cheese made with unpasteurized ewes' milk. It

is matured for around 7 months and sold in 170 g (6 oz) waxed wedges or truckles weighing up to 2.3 kg (5 lb). Pale straw in colour, it has a sweet toffee flavour with a sharpish note on first bite that opens up in the mouth.

California Dairy Goats, California Farm, WHITEHORN, Newton Stewart DG8 8DY ☎ 01988 500732 produce, as the name suggests, pasteurized goats'-milk hard and soft cheeses. Matured for 2-3 months, the hard

cheese has a light saltiness and a slightly grainy texture with the mildest of hints of goat and is sold in 150-g (5½-oz) waxed wedges or 1.25-kg (2½-lb) truckles. The creamy, smooth and delicate Coulommiers-style fresh cheeses come as plain, rolled in herbs, flavoured with whisky and rolled in oatmeal, and flavoured with garlic in olive oil with fresh herbs.

members working within their abilities alongside Barry and his co-worker. But Barry is right; his cheese must stand up on its own so it is bought because it is a good cheese rather than because of the circumstances under which it is made.

Believe me, it is a very fine cheese. Often described as a Cheddar, 'although, because of its acidity and moisture, it may be more of a Dunlop', says Barry, it is made 3 times a week using unpasteurized milk and matured for around 7 months. 'Powerful, tangy, with lots of bite', is how Michael Bateman of The Independent on Sunday describes it. It has a creamy finish, rich nuttiness and a length of flavour that meanders on – which probably makes it one of our best cheeses. Made in 9-kg (20-lb) moulds, it comes as plain or flavoured with mixed herbs, cumin seed or caraway. The dairy also makes a 'live' yoghurt; a smooth and creamy quark; a full-fat lactic curd cheese; and Crannog, a soft cheese simply made from 'scooping off the Cheddar curds early on', straining them and coating the finished cheese (either as plain or mixed with fresh herbs).

Mail Order

Loch Arthur Farmhouse cheese only

Stockists

Highland: The Island Cheese Company

London: Neal's Yard Dairy

Lothian: Dam Head Holdings

Iain Mellis

Valvona & Crolla

CARSLUITH

Smoked Salmon

The Galloway Smokehouse
Carsluith, Newton Stewart, Dumfries & Galloway DG8 7DN

☎ 01671 820354 **FAX** 01671 820545 **CONTACT** Allan Watson **HOURS** 9.00-17.30 **CARDS** Access, Eurocard, Visa **DIRECTIONS** From Newton Stewart, take A75 towards Dumfries. Smokery is 8 miles from Newton Stewart on the left, signposted on the left.

The view from Galloway Smokehouse over Wigtown Bay and beyond is just one of the pleasures of a trip here; a chat with Allan Watson is another. Forthright and with decided views, he has opted for a particular style of curing. As he says without even flinching, 'I cure and smoke for my taste. If customers don't like it, they can go somewhere else'.

He sees curing and smoking as 'all about a balance between sugar, salt and smoke. The more salt you use, the more sugar it needs. If you don't use sugar, then you have to cut down on salt and smoke, and it turns out very bland'. Salmon is dry-cured in straight salt for 6-12 hours, dark syrup (molasses) mixed with rum is ladled on top and left for a further 12 hours, then it is smoked over whisky-impregnated oak sawdust from Grant's Distillery for 24-36 hours. Let me tell you, this customer does like it; moist, with a good firm texture and an obvious – but not overly so – sweetness balanced with smoke, this is a distinctive salmon. Allan also cures sea and freshwater

Loch Ryan Seafoods and Smokehouse, Market Street, STRANRAER DG9 7RF ☎/fax 01776 706661 *favour a brine-cure of salt, water, rum, sugar and a 'secret' mixture of herbs for all their curing. Using oak chips to smoke with, they produce whole or sliced sides of salmon with a firm texture and a marked saltiness, weighing 900 g-1.25 kg (2-2½ lb), and 115, 225 and 450-g (¼, ½ and 1-lb) sliced packs. They also smoke scallops, mussels, meaty and succulent trout, the finer textured sea-trout, and hot-smoke salmon with dill and peppercorns.*

trout in exactly the same way; chicken eggs on the grounds that 'quails eggs are so tiny, I felt sorry for them. Anyway they tend to be a bit dry'. He hot-smokes wild venison with herbs and black pepper; cold-smokes 'probably Norwegian' herrings for kippers; bacon; venison sausages prepared by Grierson Brothers *see page 336*; cheeses from Galloway Farmhouse Cheese *see opposite* and California Farm *see opposite* which were surprisingly mild and subtle (usually I loathe smoked cheeses); and a meaty dry eel. In fact, he is always trying things, 'but I can't always sell them. Like goat, I thought it tasted OK, but no one would buy it'. So you can also expect smoked mussels, duck breasts, chicken, pollack, cod and cod's roe, and most everything is cured using the same brine.

He also deals in game and sells a variety of locally landed fish, such as monkfish, plaice, both wild (in season) and farmed salmon, as well as the occasional conger eel.

Galloway Lodge Preserves
Gatehouse-of-Fleet, Dumfries & Galloway DG7 2HP

GATEHOUSE-OF-FLEET
Preserves

☎ /FAX 01557 814357 **CONTACT** *Fiona & Nigel Hesketh* **HOURS** *Jan and Feb: Mon-Sat 9.30-13.00; rest of year: 9.30-17.00* **CARDS** *Access, Visa* **DIRECTIONS** *In town centre.*

Highly recommended by Food Lovers Mrs Evelyn McGibbon of Church Broughton and Joanna Allison of Kirkcudbright, Nigel Hesketh of Galloway Lodge Preserves – helped by his 'girls' – makes the jams, mustards and preserves in a small dedicated jam 'factory' just off the High Street, converted from the fire station; while his wife Fiona runs the gift/preserve shop on the High Street.

The range is comparatively small, but features no less than 11 marmalades. Nigel uses the recipe he learnt from his mother's cook, cooking in open pans which have to be stirred the whole time (even if there is the 'odd bit of caramelization – it adds to the home-made feel'). Three-fruits, sold only in the shop, is made with sweet oranges, lemons and grapefruit, first passed through the mincer 'as some

Mail Order

12 or more jars
only

Stockists

Dorset:
Trenchermans of
Dorset

Dumfries: Moffat
Toffee Shop

Lothian: Jenners

Lowe's Country
Stores
- - - - - - - -
Royal Mile
Whiskies

people don't like chunks of peel'. Vivid and sharp, it was very tangy. Other marmalades are made with bought-in pulp and include demerara, whisky, and orange & lemon. Jams and jellies feature a bright green apple & mint which Nigel promises contains 'absolutely no colouring', but is made with apples strained through a jelly bag then flavoured with dried mint; the inevitable (for Scotland) rhubarb & ginger jam, using crystallized ginger; and lemon cheese that traditionally he has always made with lemons and margarine. Fruits of Autumn chutney, Nigel disarmingly told me is 'just a fancy name for apples and raisins'; and everyone's favourite is Poacher's Pickle. Usually made by number-one cook Gwen, it contains raisins, tomatoes, apples, sugar, brewed vinegar, salt, sugar and spices and has a good texture and a nice mature balance of spice. Do not leave without trying Fiona's tablet: super-sweet, with a sugar crunch, she uses an Orcadian recipe that calls for sugar, butter, milk, cream and condensed milk.

Ancient Recipes Ltd, Empire Way, GRETNA DG16 5BN ☎ 01461 338117 fax 01461 338436 use old English recipes to produce a range of jams, pickles and chutneys. The pity is they remain unwilling – or unable – to give chapter and verse of their sources. Not that it makes any difference to the taste, but seeing how they make such a thing of it – saying they are 'preserving the past with ancient recipes' – I think it is only reasonable to be told. Using a brewed malt vinegar for all their pickles, the results are quite strong and harsh; in fact rather old-fashioned. They include pungent but crisp Olde English pickled onions; Chow-Chow, a chopped piccalilli; Cumberland pickle; a gentle, quite sweet and nicely crunchy mixture of sliced cucumber and onions known as a 'bread and butter pickle' (presumably because it was once eaten spread on a slice of bread); pickled red cabbage and pickled beetroot. In the jam and marmalade line, there is Jamaican Lime, Tudor and Appledore Jam, a blend of Bramley apples and sweet oranges.

Mail Order

☎ 01229 433433

GATEHOUSE-
OF-FLEET

Ice-cream

Cream o' Galloway

Rainton Farm, Gatehouse-of-Fleet, Castle Douglas,
Dumfries & Galloway DG7 2DR

☎/FAX 01557 814040   **CONTACT** Wilma Dunbar   **HOURS** Easter to end-Sept: 11.00-18.00   **DIRECTIONS** Take Sand Green exit from A75 immediately after Gatehouse-of-Fleet exit, then follow Cream o' Galloway signs.

The 800-acre Rainton Farm has been in the Finlay family since 1927. They have always kept a dairy herd of Ayrshires. Once the milk was used for cheese, now it is ice-cream. Made in a converted threshing barn, visitors can look down into the dairy and watch the ice-cream being made – incidentally tourism is something positively encouraged. There are two nature trails, covering 80 acres of rugged countryside (stout walking shoes recommended), where you might spot herons, buzzards or yellowhammers. Although it was pouring when I visited and far too grey a day even to think of venturing out, Evelyn McGibbon of Church Broughton wrote assuring me '(the trails) make an excellent outing for a family'.

Friesian milk has a 3.8-4 per cent butterfat content, Jersey milk is nearer to 5 per cent and Ayrshire milk falls somewhere in between, at about 4.1 per cent. It follows then that Cream o' Galloway ice-cream should have a high fat content – and indeed it does, 16 per cent. My only criticism is that it has a relatively high over-run (added air), so although it makes for a smooth airy ice-cream, it also means that it is a touch insubstantial – you lack the density of flavour and sheer delight of its creaminess.

> **Carsegowan Ice-Cream, Carsegowan Farm**, NEWTON STEWART DG8 6BG
> ☎ **01988 402259** *make a rich smooth ice-cream from the milk of their Ayrshire herd, using 1 litre of double cream for every 7 litres of milk. There are various flavours, including vanilla actually made with vanilla pods, bananas made with the fresh fruit and, best of all, treacle toffee with slithers of own-made dark toffee.*

Their recipe uses milk, cream, cane sugar, egg yolk and skimmed milk powder. There are 8 flavours in the basic range: Luxury vanilla, made with an essence but nicely clean-flavoured and pleasantly sweet; Real Strawberry, with frozen fruit so there were plenty of pips and a good fruitiness; Real Raspberry, also using frozen fruit, tasted a little 'thin'; Whisky, Honey & Oatmeal bounced with flavour and reminded me of a creamy Atholl Brose; Banoffee, a mixture of fresh bananas and toffee chips, was very lush and sticky sweet; Chocolate & Orange comes textured with orange zest, but weak on chocolatiness; Millionaire's Shortbread, with chunks of caramel shortcake, was seriously sweet; and Elderflower, using own-made cordial, was flowery and refreshing. They also sell 'specials' from the coffee shop which can be flavours they are experimenting with and these nearly all have chocolate and/or alcohol.

Stockists

Fife: Galloway Country Style

Lothian: Nastiuks

Strath: Peckhams

Galloway Oatcakes
22-24 Albert Street, Newton Stewart,
Dumfries & Galloway DG8 6EJ

NEWTON STEWART
Oatcakes

☎ 01671 402678 **CONTACT** James MacGregor **HOURS** Mon-Sat 7.30-16.30 (-13.30 Wed) **DIRECTIONS** In town centre.

From the front of the shop, Jas. A. MacGregor looks like an ordinary enough bakers, with its loaves of Pan Fleurie (bloomers), fruit bread, scones, pancakes, etc. stacked on the shelves. Out back is another story, for every day they mix and hand-cut at least 50 dozen round oatcakes, about 6 cm (2½ in) in diameter.

The ingredients are simple enough: stone-ground pinhead oatmeal, vegetable oil, baking powder, bicarbonate of soda, a touch of sugar and even less salt. These are mixed together to form quite a sticky mass which cannot possibly go through a machine. 'Anyway,' avows James MacGregor, 'you cannae mass-produce through a machine'. He considers machine-cut oatcakes far too dry and inferior in texture to his hand-cut ones. Rolling out and cutting by hand obviously means different thicknesses of biscuits, but that surely is part of their charm. Dusted in flour, lightly baked, then packed in packets of 12, they have a rich nuttiness and a good crisp texture, and – according to James – a shelf-life of 12 months, although I have never been able to keep a packet that long. One thing to remember, should you ever cook them at home, never let them burn; James tells me this is a sure sign that 'your mother and father a' nae married'.

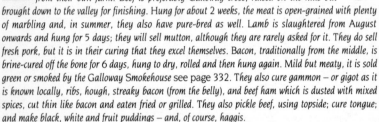

Grierson Brothers, 148 King Street, CASTLE DOUGLAS DG7 1LU ☎ **01556 502637** *is an old-fashioned butchers who obtain their meat straight from their own farm. Beef is preferably Galloway cross, raised on the hills but brought down to the valley for finishing. Hung for about 2 weeks, the meat is open-grained with plenty of marbling and, in summer, they also have pure-bred as well. Lamb is slaughtered from August onwards and hung for 5 days; they will sell mutton, although they are rarely asked for it. They do sell fresh pork, but it is in their curing that they excel themselves. Bacon, traditionally from the middle, is brine-cured off the bone for 6 days, hung to dry, rolled and then hung again. Mild but meaty, it is sold green or smoked by the Galloway Smokehouse see page 332. They also cure gammon – or gigot as it is known locally, ribs, hough, streaky bacon (from the belly), and beef ham which is dusted with mixed spices, cut thin like bacon and eaten fried or grilled. They also pickle beef, using topside; cure tongue; and make black, white and fruit puddings – and, of course, haggis.*

While you're in the area...

Bakers **M. Corson, 160 King Street, CASTLE DOUGLAS DG1 7DA** ☎ **01556 502489 fax 01556 504147** bake various breads, scones, pancakes, and old-fashioned brown and white farls. Particularly good are the coffee buns, which are really more of a biscuit; brittle with a good crunch, they had a satisfyingly coffee taste.

Locals say that **William Lindsay, 66 St John Street, CREE-TOWN, Newton Stewart, DG8 7JG** ☎ **01671 820248** has the best haggis for miles, because of its balanced blend of seasonings. They also sell Galloway beef hung for at least 14 days, and black-face lamb in season.

Alex Hepburn & Son, 25 Well Street, MOFFAT DG10 9DP ☎ **01683 220068** sell fingers of a buttery own-made short-bread, made with butter, flour and sugar.

The Moffat Toffee Shop, High Street, MOFFAT DG10 9DW ☎ **01683 220032** is full of gloriously garish sweeties, the sort that are ruination for your teeth. Best of all is the Moffat toffee round; curled up to look like a Danish pastry, it is chewy with a good treacly flavour and is sold individually or in a black-and-white houndstooth check – the local shepherds' tartan.

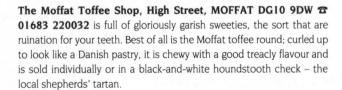

Fife

Fletchers of Auchtermuchty
Reediehill Deer Farm, Auchtermuchty, Fife KY14 7HS

☎ 01337 828369 **FAX** 01337 827001 **CONTACT** Nichola Fletcher **HOURS** 9.00-18.00 **CARDS** Access, Eurocard, Mastercard, Visa **DIRECTIONS** From Auchtermuchty, take B936 towards Newburgh and Perth. At the small 'venison 2 miles' sign on the gabled end of the white house on the left, bear left. Go to top of hill and down other side and farm entrance is signposted.

Fletchers is a founder-member of the quality assurance scheme British Prime Venison, run by the British Deer Farmers Association. If you buy venison with the BPV mark it is a guarantee it comes from farmed deer less than 27 months old that is fed on natural feedstuffs with no growth promoters, and is slaughtered, hung and butchered in approved premises. As far as Nichola Fletcher is concerned the obvious advantages of farmed over wild venison are, 'reliability and consistency – it's not variable. As it's under 27 months, you know for certain the meat is going to be tender, as opposed to wild venison which can be any age. Also our deer are clean shot, we take a rifle to them in the field – so there's no stress. And we all know just how much stress can affect the texture of meat. Farmed deer are better fed and sheltered, we even house them in winter because of our ghastly weather – they can go out but they never do. It's infinitely preferable to the lot of the wild deer that can starve or die of exposure when the

---

Reilly, The Harbour, Shoregate, CRAIL KY10 3SU ☎ **01333 450476** sell live lobsters and crabs caught by Wilma's two sons, and dressed crab or morning rolls stuffed full of crab-meat. On a sunny day, sit outside the shop at the bare wooden table with a view of the harbour and an old cottage with its dormer roof decorated with a crab, lobster and langoustine made out of pebbles, and Wilma will boil up a lobster. Regulars know to bring a bottle of wine and a slab of butter which Wilma will melt on top of the boiler. It may be basic, but could you ask for anything more?

Fisher & Donaldson, 21 Crossgate, CUPAR KY15 5HA ☎ 01334 652551 *fax* **01334 653729** *also have branches at* **13 Church Street, ST ANDREWS KY16 9NW ☎ 01334 473870** *and* **12 Whitehall Street, DUNDEE DD1 9GR ☎ 01382 223488**. *They bake a wide variety of breads, including the seven-grain Dr Floyd's (named after the current owner, Eric Milne's grandfather), the usual Scottish selection of pancakes, crumpets, scones (including treacle and potato), girdle scones and pikelets, and some interesting biscuits. These include paving stones, a hard ginger 'dunking' biscuit with currants; Abernathy biscuits, traditionally made with ammonium carbonate instead of baking powder, which should 'honk until it is baked'; and raggy biscuits. An old fashioned biscuit, these are like a rich tea, but ragged around the edges and were often eaten with cheese. Made with flour, butter and sugar, they were considered a 'cheap' shortbread as they contain far less butter. They also bake a suspiciously yellow Dundee cake, but for all that it was moist and fruity and contains orange peel, and make their own moulded chocolates, such as Grand Marnier, whisky and champagne truffles and golf balls filled with a milky praline centre.*

weather gets rough'.

But what about taste? A tricky one that as we all probably want to believe that a wild deer roaming with all of Nature's glorious bounty to feed on will have a better flavour. Nichola was quick to dispel that illusion. 'There are many things that affect taste and texture – age, how and where it's shot and for how long it's been hung. Strangely, its diet doesn't affect the flavour of its meat. This is because in ruminants with many stomachs – such as a deer – flavour only goes into fatty tissue and venison is almost completely fat-free.

Nichola's deer are red deer; the other species farmed in this country are the roe, which are about a quarter of the size of the red, and the fallow that come halfway between the two. The only difference in their respective eating qualities, as far as Nichola is concerned, is the tighter grain of the meat of the smaller species. All her meat is hung for between 2 and 3 weeks as a carcass, a point she wishes to stress as she is very dismissive of dealers who hang their meat jointed and vacuum-packed as it does not have the desired effect. Butchered into shoulder on or off the bone, haunch (leg) on or off the bone, saddle, escalope (knuckle steaks), topside or silverside steaks, medallions (sirloin steaks), whole fillets, chops (cutlets), casserole (chopped shoulder), stew (chopped shin) and veniburgers, she also makes 8 different venison sausages, a firm rich venison haggis from meat mixed with the lights and oatmeal, spiced venison parcels, venison olives and a smooth venison liver pâté.

She also makes venison carpaccio using a single muscle butchered from the haunch; it is dry-cured in salt, sugar, pepper and spices for about 5 days, then thinly sliced. With a rich resonance, it is superb drizzled with olive oil and lemon juice and scattered with finely chopped flat-leaf parsley. She also cures other cuts for about 7 days in a salt, sugar, beer, juniper and root ginger brine, then sends them off for hot- or cold-smoking. When cold-smoked, it has a mildly gamy mellow flavour with a soft pliable texture. From the shop you can also buy Nichola's strongly flavoured Wild Rowan Jelly – splendid with venison –

Stockists

Borders: Jed Forest Deer & Farm Park

Lothian: Lowe's Country Store

Tays: The House of Bruar

as well as copies of her two cookery books which, not surprisingly, are about venison and game. For details of other members of the quality assurance scheme British Prime Venison run by the British Deer Farmers Association, contact Anne Dymond, Holly Lodge, Spencers Lane, Berkswell, Coventry CV7 7BZ ☎ 01203 465957.

Isobel Steven's Farmhouse Kitchen

Ardchoille Farmhouse, Dunshalt, nr Auchtermuchty, Fife KY14 7EY

DUNSHALT
Shortbread

☎/FAX 01337 828414   **CONTACT** *Isobel Steven – telephone ahead*

For the Scots, the exact recipe for shortbread is every bit as controversial as that for cassoulet is for the French. Should it be gritty and made with rice flour, velvety smooth and made with cornflour or mixed just with wheat-flour? Isobel Steven's shortbread is of the latter school; she makes it in her kitchen from where she also cooks up dinners and substantial breakfasts (they even include pancakes) for guests staying at the farmhouse. The ingredients she uses are butter, sugar, flour and salt, and it is well and truly handmade and hand-finished.

Isobel was somewhat reticent to give me chapter and verse about proportions and methods, but it is all 'finger-mixed – and I know with my eyes when it's ready'. Apparently if you over-mix, it turns solid and hard and that, as any Scot will tell, is not a good thing as shortbread is as much about lightness as it is butteriness. Equally, you should never roll out shortbread as it will compact it, squashing out the air. Isobel actually pats it out into 23-cm (9-in) rounds, which are, relatively speaking, quite thick, but then husband Donald is such a fan of Aero chocolate that he likes the shortbread to have a similar thick bubbliness. They are then pricked to stop the mixture from bubbling up, shaped into eights and the edges twisted or nicked, or as she would rather I described it 'finger-fluted to represent petticoat tails', as her trademark.

According to Isobel, you should never judge a shortbread until you swallow, then you wait for a buttery glow to come up and through. Hers passes the test with flying colours; it is smooth to the bite and glows with a rich moist creaminess. Neither too sweet nor too dry, it is how I imagine the best should be. Sold in tartan envelope packs as whole rounds, she also produces packs of two 5-7.5-cm (2-3-in) round biscuits.

Stockists

Fife:
Auchtermuchty
Post Office

Ellery Deli

Icicles Delicatessen

With the historic town of Falkland awash with tea-shops, **Kind Kyttock's Kitchen, Cross Wynd, FALKLAND KY15 7BE ☎ 01337 857477** is generally acknowledged as the best. Here you can comfortably tuck into afternoon tea consisting of a pot of tea, a choice of 2 own-made scones or 2 own-made pancakes (or 1 of each) with butter and own-made jam and 2 own-made cakes. Produce really is own-made: both scones and pancakes are light and airy, shortbread crumbly and meltingly rich, ginger-cake has a nice spicy bite; and the jams – a choice of apricot, raspberry or strawberry – bursting with fruit. Portions are generous, I was given a second slice of cake as the waitress thought my original one had been cut too thinly. On the way out you can buy both own-made jams and chutneys.

The Garden
Burnside of Letham, Leven, Fife KY8 5NP

☎ 01333 351811   **CONTACT** *Judy Bennett – telephone ahead*

Judy Bennett is Scotland's answer to Frances Smith *see page* 143. With no more than 1 acre under cultivation, she grows an exciting range of herbs, salads, leaves and unusual vegetables, supplying such top restaurants as The Peat Inn, and Martins and The Atrium in Edinburgh, with several others on a waiting list eager for her crops.

Apart from a wide range of culinary herbs, Judy grows such edible flowers as borage, buckwheat (a new one to me but it is, she assures me, decorative and edible), cornflowers, sage and yarrow. Then there are her salads in which she includes not only the (comparatively) common Greek or curled cress, purslane and rocket but also radish pods which are 'crunchy and fiery', ryokusai with a small dark biting leaf and vegetable amaranth, which looks interesting with its red-and-green leaves and has a distinctive flavour. Lettuces include lumina, red fire, Thai salad, mizuna and mibuna, and these she can sell in mixed bags to order. 'A bit different' varies from year to year, but this year you will find: strawberry spinach, with its tiny spinach-tasting leaves and small sweet nutty berries; horny cucumbers; alpine strawberries, with both red and yellow fruit; Barbabietola di Chioggia, an old Italian variety of beetroot which produces small pink heads about 5 cm (2 in) in diameter with a milder than usual flavour; red Brussels sprouts and tiny tomatoes the size of a grape.

From her wild garden, Judy cuts such 'weeds' as chickweed, with its large juicy leaves and white flowers which you can use as a vegetable or in a salad; delicately flavoured hawthorn leaves; young shoots from hogweed that are not unlike asparagus; and nettle tops for soups. The season is relatively short, from April to October, and inevitably her crops are at least a couple of weeks behind those grown further south, but Judy does have two poly-tunnels for her 'tender plants'. Busy though she is, she 'loves people coming around to buy from the door'; the only proviso is that you phone first to discuss your order, then Judy can harvest it especially for you.

While you're in the area...

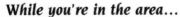

Herbs and Preserves, 61 Watt's Gardens, CUPAR KY15 4UG ☎ 01334 656804 make a range of jams and preserves, including a bitter Seville marmalade with ginger and Grandpa Maxwell's Jellied Beetroot, with well-textured chopped beetroot set in a loose sharp jelly.

With a window filled with a glorious display of lamb and Aberdeen Angus carcasses and trays of haggis, mealie and black puddings, butchers **Murray Mitchell, 110 Market Street, ST**

ANDREWS KY16 9PB ☎ 01334 474465 have a good reputation for the quality of their meat. They also sell all sorts of useful 'bits and pieces', including ham houghs and lambs' sweetbreads.

St Andrew's Delicatessen, Unit 1, Mercat Wynd, Market Street, ST ANDREWS KY16 9BE ☎ 01334 476444 boasts at least 26 different Scottish cheeses. The pity is that the day I called, no one serving seemed able to answer any questions let alone tell me by whom or where the cheeses were made. If small delis are to flourish, it is not enough to stock different produce; they must provide good service and information on the products.

Grampian

Map No. 8

Chalmers of Bucksburn Ltd
13-15 Auchmill Road, Bucksburn, Aberdeen,
Grampian AB2 9LB

ABERDEEN
Butteries

☎ 01224 712631 **FAX** 01224 712464 **CONTACT** Mrs Chalmers **HOURS** Mon-Fri 5.30-17.30 Sat 5.30-17.00 **DIRECTIONS** On main A96 Inverness road, going to Aberdeen, follow signs to airport. Continue past airport and Chalmers is on left.

Rowies or butteries, one of the specialities of the area, are similar in texture to a croissant and eaten for breakfast. Most fans say that originally they were made with lard, although butter and/or vegetable shortening is also used nowadays, but Mr Chalmers ventures to suggest that once it was fish oil. The fishermen would take them on fishing trips and they were so rich in oil they would keep for a fortnight, ending up as croûtons in a soup. How they tasted was another matter.

I spent a morning making rowies with Mr Chalmers and it is serious work. You start with quite a yeasty dough and then chop the fat in (he

George A. Robertson, 68-72 Allardice Street, STONEHAVEN AB3 2AA ☎ **01569 762734** *make rowies by chopping the fat in by hand for a particularly light flaky texture. They also bake Stonehaven spiced slab, a mixture of cake crumbs, syrup and spices baked in a case of shortcrust.*

uses vegetable shortening), tearing and pulling at the dough until all the fat is absorbed. Working in the fat is quite an art and apparently one of the secrets to a good rowie. Most bakers, including Mr Chalmers, mix it in by machine nowadays; but if you do work it in by hand, the result is a freer lighter rowie.

Now I am no expert, but I found them awesomely filling, far more so than a croissant. Crisp on the outside, doughy inside and soft-textured with a certain richness. You have to try a rowie at least once in your life.

ALFORD
Oatmeal

A. MacDonald & Son
Montgarrie Mill, Alford, Aberdeenshire, Grampian AB33 8AP

☎ 01975 562209 **FAX** 01975 562295 **CONTACT** *Mr Donald MacDonald* **HOURS** *Mon-Fri 7.00-17.00 Sat 8.00-12.00* **DIRECTIONS** *From Tillyfourie, take A944 towards Alford. Follow the road about 4 miles into the centre of Alford and turn right just before the Spar shop. Follow the road about 1 mile to the Montgarrie Post Office on the right. Turn left opposite the post office and, after about 100 yards, mill is on the left.*

The MacDonalds have owned and run Montgarrie Mill since 1894. Four generations on, Donald MacDonald is still producing his oatmeal in exactly the same traditional way, running a mill powered by water from the Essett burn, which turns the huge mill wheel – 7.5 m (25 ft) in diameter and weighing 21 tons.

To explain the process briefly; Donald buys his oats as locally as possible, ideally choosing the matra variety for its light shell and substantial kernel but, he told me, 'even with the same variety there's a localized difference in taste'. First they are dried (conditioned) down to a 15 per cent moisture to ensure they keep fresh and 'sweet', then they are laid out to dry on the flat kiln floor made of perforated mild steel sheets with a furnace fired by smokeless anthracite coal 7.2 m (24 ft) below. The oats are turned by hand shovel so they dry evenly, and slowly the temperature is increased until after four hours, it has reached 88°C (190°F) and the oats are toasted to give them that rich nutty flavour. Donald dries the oats down to moisture content of 4.5 per cent, which is far lower than most producers, but essential for an intense flavour.

Meal Mill of Towie, DRUMMUIR, by Keith AB55 3HX ☎ **01542 810274**, *while a traditional working mill – with, incidentally, a woman miller – is open to the public. You can wander around and see the various stages, from toasting the oats to grinding. Then you can buy packets graded into fine, medium and rough oatmeal, and oatcakes baked by a local baker.*

Cooled down and stored until needed, the dried oats are screened to remove any extraneous matter and put through the shelling stones to remove the husk from the kernel. Then they are ground into 4 different cuts (grades): fine (no. 3½), medium (no. 4), rough (no. 5) and pinhead which is the kernel cut in half with any floury meal sifted out. Sold from the mill door in 0.5, 1, 1.5, 3, and 6-kg (1, 2¼, 3½, 6½ and 13-lb) polythene packs, these are the real thing – with a fresh nutty fragrance and a wholesome richness. Try making oatmeal biscuits with MacDonald's oatmeal and you will realize just how good they can be.

Stockists

London:
Selfridges

Tesco

Ken Watmough, 29 Thistle Street, ABERDEEN AB1 1UY ☎ 01224 640321 *is a first-rate fishmonger and one of the few who keeps a shelf piled high with cookery books in case you are stuck for a recipe. Fresh fish comes from Aberdeen fish market every day (he is closed Mondays) and you will see a sparklingly fresh selection of cod, monkfish, turbot, halibut, Dover sole, rock fish and so on. He also has some interesting shellfish, such as clams, sand gapers and long thin razor shells from Orkney Seafayre see page 355, as well as crabs, lobsters from the Moray Firth, and dived scallops from the Northern Isles. For his Spanish and Portuguese customers he salts cod, curing it in salt 'to remove as much water as possible', then hanging it up to dry in the wind. He also sells smoked salmon, monkfish, Arbroath smokies from D. & A. Spink see page 369 and undyed Aberdeen pales. For the uninitiated, these are smoked haddock fillets which, as Ken took great pains to explain to me, unlike a Finnan have no secondary cut to slash and raise the flesh. If the bone is on the left it is a London pale, but if it is on the right it is an Aberdeen pale – so now you know.*

Highland Goat Products
Corglass Farm, Ballindalloch, Grampian AB37 9BS

☎ 01807 500269   **CONTACT** Mrs Jane Heape – *telephone ahead*

Jane Heape lives miles from anywhere – but what a drive, through rolling hills and lush pastures, to her valley on the edge of the Highlands. Jean keeps a small herd of heather-fed British Saanen and Cashmere goats which she milks throughout the year, except for between December and January when she lets them run dry. Letting them rest, she feels, contributes to a higher milk yield during the rest of the year. The butterfat content does vary, it is higher in the spring and autumn, which in turn affects the cheese. But then, who ever suggested that a cheese does not vary according to the seasons?

Ballindalloch is made on a small scale, no more than twice a week, using unpasteurized milk. Made in 2.3-2.7-kg (5-6-lb) rounds 'to fit my ripening cupboard', it is pressed then brine-washed every day for 2 weeks, then washed and turned every 2 weeks until matured. In summer Jane sells the cheeses younger, at about 2 months, by which time they have developed a nice clear tang – surprising for a cheese so young – that will intensify as its ages. She also makes Corglass, an unpressed cheese.

BALLINDAL-LOCH

Goats' Cheese

Mail Order
Only through Scottish Gourmet *see page 365*

Stockists
Grampian: Gordon & MacPhail

London: Jeroboams

Lothian: Iain Mellis

Strath: Scottish Gourmet

Surrey: Vivian's

DINNET
Smoked Salmon

Deeside Smoked Salmon
Headinch House, Dinnet, Aboyne, Grampian AB34 5NY

☎ 01339 885304   **CONTACT** Fergus Cumming – telephone ahead

What makes Fergus Cumming's smoked salmon unique is his deep and serious understanding of the nature of the fish. He knows when the wild salmon are in peak condition or when they are softer, and so – operating on a tiny scale – he is able to adjust and tailor his curing and smoking to suit each and every fish. 'You should always leave a salmon at least a day or two – depending on the weather', he told me, 'to go through rigor mortis. They are stiff when caught, but as the muscles relax they loosen up. Then you can start to cure.'

He smokes both farmed and wild salmon; the latter is either netted at sea and bought in Aberdeen or caught in the river and bought wherever possible. Sea-caught fish, Fergus notices, can sometimes be softer than river fish, which tend to have harder tougher muscles 'no doubt from fighting the currents as it swims upstream'. A wild salmon can be richer in oil ('sometimes it just oozes oil in the kiln'), whereas a farmed fish is drier but fatter, with reserves of fat around its belly. Then again, it is so variable; but, as Fergus says, 'one thing is certain, if you start with a good fish, you will end up with a good smoked one'.

The fish are salted in a vacuum-dried salt – similar to a table salt – which, he feels, is best for curing. Interestingly, he notices that frozen fish take a cure far more quickly 'possibly because they've lost some moisture in the freezing'. The whole sides are washed down, then put in the cold kiln, which is then fired up using oak sawdust and chippings as fuel so that it smoulders gently, 'if it goes to flame, I'm in trouble'. Whole sides will stay there for anything between 9 and 10 hours; then he turns off the kiln and the fish are left for a 'drying period', leaving them there until – going by feel – he

---

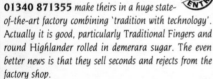

The region is awash with makers of shortbread. Of course a good shortbread must be made with butter and only butter, whether you then add eggs is up to the individual as is whether you use plain flour and/or cornflour and/or rice flour – it is all a matter of texture and finish. Now, although I have not tried every single example, I am pretty confident this is a selection of the best.

Walkers Shortbread, ABERLOUR-ON-SPEY AB38 9PD ☎ 01340 871555 fax 01340 871355 *make theirs in a huge state-of-the-art factory combining 'tradition with technology'. Actually it is good, particularly Traditional Fingers and round Highlander rolled in demerara sugar. The even better news is that they sell seconds and rejects from the factory shop.*

 In comparison, **Maclean's Bakery 61 High Street, FORRES IV 36 0PB ☎ 01309 672859** *bake on a tiny scale. Their shortbread is not only attractively finished in thistle-stamped rounds but – made with plain and rice flour, butter, sugar and eggs – is soft and lush with an interesting catch of grittiness.*

 George Leith, 8 Golf Road, BALLATER AB35 5RE ☎ 01339 755474 *is baker and confectioner to HM The Queen when she is staying at Balmoral. Sadly she never shops as she has 'nae money', but the royal connection runs true. They were asked to make Princess Anne's (second) wedding cake for no charge and no advertising, so perhaps I should not be mentioning it. Their shortbread was crisp to bite, then dissolved in a warm buttery crumbliness. They also bake butter puffs and biscuits, whisky cake and a terrific black bun sent to 'that place' for the New Year. Rich and fruity, it was suitably thick and moist, surrounded by a coating of dryish pastry. Go early in the morning to catch their butteries.*

Ghillie & Glen, Burghmuir Drive, INVERURIE AB51 4FS ☎ 01467 625700 fax 01467 624209 *smoke conservation-grade salmon which, to put it at its simplest, is salmon farmed to a lower stocking density, sited in stronger currents, with the use of chemicals, pesticides, and drugs kept to a minimum. The result is a fish with a better textured, leaner flesh, farmed at a reduced cost to the environment.*
On the other hand **Gourmet's Choice Smoked Salmon, Harbour Head, Shore Street, PORTSOY AB45 2RX ☎ 01261 843255 fax 01261 842884** *use Shetland farmed fish, which they think has 'the edge'. Cured in dry salt and demerara sugar for about 48 hours, they then leave it to dry before smoking over oak shavings from whisky barrels for 8 hours to obtain a firm but buttery texture and a good balance of salt and sweet. From their shop they also sell various wet fish and own-smoked finnan haddock and kippers.*

knows they are ready.

Fergus smokes to order, selling his smoked salmon as whole or sliced sides. By choice, he would always buy wild salmon provided, of course, that the fish was in good condition to start with, but such fish are becoming more 'elusive'. 'Farmed is improving in quality, but there is still a difference in texture. Farmed is generally much softer, but the wild salmon has had to work for a living'.

Macbeth's
20 Tolbooth Street, Forres, Moray, Grampian IV36 0PH

FORRES
Beef

☎/FAX 01309 672254 **CONTACT** Susan Gibson **HOURS** Mon & Wed 9.00-13.00 Tues, Thurs, Fri & Sat 9.00-17.00 **CARDS** Access, Visa **DIRECTIONS** In town centre, near the floral gardens.

Lovers of good beef know and respect Aberdeen Angus but, according to Michael Gibson, 'Highland beef from pure-bred Highland cattle has the slight advantage It's leaner with a little more flavour'. Not that you or I or, as Michael politely puts it, 'over 90 per cent of the population could probably tell the difference. But just like connoisseurs can tell their malt whiskies, I'd like to think I can tell my beefs apart'.

Michael specializes in Scottish native breeds of cattle, he has a 500-strong herd of pure-bred Aberdeen Angus, pure-bred Beef Shorthorn, Aberdeen Angus-Shorthorn cross and pure-bred Highland Cattle. Not for him the Continental Limousin or Charolais, which have a lot to

Butchers **A. E. Brown & Son, 14 Main Street, TURRIFF AB53 7AD ☎ 01888 563379** *butcher and sell on pure-bred certified Aberdeen Angus beef*   *hung for 14 days upwards, which means that not only are the specific cuts and joints from Aberdeen Angus but also all their beef products.*
A. W. Herd & Sons, *with shops at* **277 Rosemount Place, ABERDEEN AB2 4YB ☎ 01224 638293** *and* **481A Great Western Road, ABERDEEN AB1 6NN ☎ 01224 314981** *also only sells pure-bred certified Aberdeen Angus hung for about 14 days* *and he uses it in such prepared dishes as beef stroganoff. He cooks his own hams; makes haggis; mealie stuffing with oatmeal, suet and spices; and various pies, including minced mutton with a crisp lard pastry.*

D. F. Campbell, 15 Low Street, BUCKIE AB56 1UX ☎ 01542 **831385** *smokes from an old-fashioned smokehouse, lighting a fire on the floor using wood shavings from the shipyard. Smoked salmon is cured in salt for a day, then in brown sugar and rum for another 2 days and finally smoked for about 15 hours. The result is markedly sweet, with a medium smoke. He will also smoke kippers, haddock and cod's roe, and smokies to order (as it means getting the pit going).*

 At the other end of town, *past the old fishing village, is* **John Thompson Seafoods, 28 Harbour Head, Buckpool, BUCKIE AB56 1XR ☎ 01542 835413,** *who also works from a wooden slatted smokehouse only he processes crabs by their hundreds, selling them live, boiled and/or dressed.*

answer for when it comes to comparison with the flavour of most home-bred beef. He unashamedly concentrates on 100 per cent beef breeds and rears them for slaughtering at the right weight for butchering and at the right maturity for eating. Finishing an animal is a skilled business; for Michael the aim is to get the right degree of marbling through the meat which is essential for the flavour. 'Marbling is a function of maturity. Until an animal reaches a certain age, it won't lay any significant marbling down unless you are grossly overfeeding it. And if you have pushed it, the meat will be lighter in colour, it may be tender but it will be bland like processed cardboard. But a properly reared animal will have close-textured firm meat with a fine marbling for flavour.'

Only steers (castrated males) are sent for slaughter, for two good reasons: the first is practical, his heifers are sold for breeding stock; the second has more to do with eating quality 'as, dare I say, like most females, they put fat on in the wrong places and their meat tends to be flabbier and looser'. His steers are slaughtered at a minimum of 24 months; once taken to the slaughterhouse, he insists they are rested for 18 hours prior to slaughter to reduce 'dark cutting'. This, as Michael explains, comes when the animal is stressed, as it releases adrenaline into the muscles to tense them. The net result is tougher darkened meat which, no matter how long you hang it, will never tenderize. All his beef is hung for 7 days at the slaughterhouse, then transferred to his shop in the small village of Forres. The fore-quarters for mince, sausages and the like is processed immediately, prime cuts from the hind sirloin are hung for another 10 days and 'it is hung on the bone, essential to draw out the flavour of the bone'.

You can go in and buy from his shop – and they also sell lamb from black-faced sheep, game, sausages, black pudding and haggis – but you will not see meat on display. Everything, even the mince, is cut to order

Every Saturday and Sunday in the months of May to September from 14.00-17.00, **The Village Hall, CLATT ☎ 01464 831465** *is open for teas. Started 10 years ago as an initiative of the Rural Forum Villages in Action, everyone in the village contributes. Baking is done on a rota by all the farmers' wives. The young – dressed primly in black-and-white pinnies, with nose-rings and Doc Martins to liven them up – serve at the tables, and you are seated by Jimmy Lumsden who at 85 must be the oldest maître d' in the business. For all that, you get a jolly traditional tea: filled rolls, airy plain, fruit, treacle or cheese scones, pancakes, cream scones, currant loaf, and various cakes and shortbread. There is a shop that sells village-made produce, including jams, marmalades, fruit tarts, ducks' eggs – even a farmhouse cheese that, sadly, no one seemed to know from whence it came.*

by his staff, or 'technicians' as he likes to call them. 'We butcher every which way, in traditional cuts or Continental seaming and we'll send whatever you want. If you just want a fillet, we'll send you a fillet.' As for which of the breeds you should choose, in fact most of his customers do not specify; but, if you want to, Michael will be delighted to accommodate provided you are prepared to wait if necessary. As he has already said, the difference is minimal but, when pushed, he describes Highland as bigger with more flavour,

Candycraig Mushrooms, Cairnquheen Cottage, Crathie, BALLATER AB35 5TD ☎ 01339 742342 *pick wild mushrooms 'around the Royal Deeside area'. These include chanterelles, orange birch bolete, brown birch bolete and – best of all for flavour – the Penny bun. Some are sold fresh to* **A. & B. Flowers, Bridge Street, BALLATER AB35 5QD** *or private customers; the rest are dried on wooden boards up in the attic and sold in 25 and 50-g (1 and 2-oz) packets. They also grow various vegetables, including such Oriental greens as five varieties of pak-choi and pe-tsai.*

Aberdeen Angus as richer and slightly fattier 'with not quite the edge' and Shorthorn as somewhere between the two. As far as I'm concerned they were all superb – deep, rich and with the resonance of properly reared and hung beef.

Thistle Confectionery, New Leeds, LONMAY, Peterhead AB4 28HX ☎/*fax* **01346 532673** *make a range of Scottish sweets sold in 1.35-kg (3-lb) trays or 95 and 175-g (3½ and 6½-oz) packets. My favourite is Special Toffee, made with sugar, black treacle, golden syrup butter, condensed milk and a touch of liquid glucose, boiled at a high temperature as quickly as possible until it turns a deep rich dark brown. Set in trays, it is broken by a hammer into lumps, for a gloriously sticky confection with a thick treacle glow. They also make tablet – similar to fudge but harder and grainier in texture – using evaporated and condensed milk, butter and sugar, in plain and various flavours; and such old-fashioned 'boilings' as butterscotch, fruit drops and clove balls.*

While you're in the area...

Grocers **George Strachan, Station Square, ABOYNE AB34 5HX** ☎ **01339 886121** boasts three royal warrants, the Queen, the Queen Mum and Prince Charles – but then it is only a couple of miles from Balmoral. A proper grocers, with wooden shelves and bags of character, it has over 750 whiskies, including malts, blends and varieties, and nearly – or so it seemed – as many mustards and jams. Go to soak up the atmosphere, if not the food.

Butchers **H. M. Sheridan, 11 Bridge Street, BALLATER AB35 5QP** ☎ **01339 755218** have a game licence and in season sell grouse, mallard, rabbit, hare and venison from the Balmoral estate, and own-made game pies with sage stuffing. They also smoke game and poultry, make haggis, white pudding and fruit suet pudding (with raisins, sultanas, milk, spices and breadcrumbs), which was surprisingly light and airy, and a Christmas pudding for Christmas. Beef is Aberdeen Angus-Highland cross, hung for 3 weeks, and they make their own sausages and steak pies.

Pauline Mackinnon, Wester Lochagan, BANFF AB45 3BS ☎ **01261 843244** makes Balhagan, a hard-pressed cheese, from unpasteurized Jersey milk. Sold very young, from 1-4 weeks' old, it has a pleasant open texture and a rich butteriness.

Speyside Cooperage, Dufftown Road, CRAIGELLACHIE AB38 9RS ☎ **01340 871108 fax 01340 881303** is where the oak casks for maturing whisky are made. Food lovers may be interested to know that they sell bags of oak shavings, useful for home-smoking or barbecuing.

Beaton's, 4 Union Road, MACDUFF AB44 1UJ ☎ **01261 832638 fax 01261 833272** sell exceptionally fresh fish landed at Macduff, Frazerburgh or Whitehill from the small shop attached to the processing plant. Expect to find turbot, halibut, cod, scallops and herring, as well as live lobsters and langoustines. They also smoke salmon, herring for kippers and haddock in their own smokehouse.

Smith's, 104 High Street, NEW PITSLIGO AB4 4NN ☎ **01771 653207** bake extraordinarily good butter biscuits. Quite how or why they were not letting on, but reading from the label I could see they are made with flour, vegetable and animal fat, butter, sugar, salt and baking powder. If you are passing through, do stop and buy some.

Butcher **Charles McHardy, 11 Market Square, STONE-HAVEN AB3 2BT** ☎ **01569 762693** has a gleaming modern shop overlooking the town square. He sells a mixture of Continental cuts, prepared meat such as beef olives or pork loin gourmet, as well as such traditional cheaper cuts as hough (shin) cut through the bone for soups and stews. He also sweet-cures bacon, makes meat pies and haggis using barley and a mixture of fine and rough oatmeal from A. MacDonald *see page* 342 wrapped in natural skins.

Highlands & Islands

Map No. 8

Summer Isles Foods
Achiltibuie, Ullapool, Highlands & Islands IV26 2YG

☎ 01854 622353 **FAX** 01854 622335 **CONTACT** *Keith Dunbar* **HOURS**
Mon-Fri 9.30-17.00 **CARDS** *Access, Visa* **DIRECTIONS** *From Ullapool, take
A835 towards Ledmore. Follow the road about 10 miles and turn left, signposted
Achiltibuie, on to a single-track road. Follow the road about 12 miles to the second
junction and turn right, signposted Summer Isles Smokehouse. Smokehouse is on
the left after about 2 miles, just before The Fuaran Bar.*

From what must be the smokehouse with one of the best views in
Britain, overlooking the humpbacks of the Summer Isles scattered in
the sea, Keith Dunbar smokes a range of fish. One of his specialities is
salmon; he uses mainly farmed fish and cures them in a sweet brine of
salt, rum, molasses and boiled-up juniper berries for about 8 hours.
Opinions seem to be divided as to whether a dry-salt or brine cure is
the more effective. Keith prefers a brine, as he feels it offers him more
control and a greater subtlety of flavours. The salmon is smoked up to
20 hours, over oak shavings from the sherry casks supplied by a local
whisky distillery and the result is a mellow rich fish with that melt-in-
the-mouth texture. Wild salmon and farmed sea trout are prepared in
the same way, but he has recently developed a new whisky salmon.
Plainly cured, after smoking it is sprayed with Glen Moray whisky and
left to stand for 24 hours to mature, 'It is more a sensation on the
nose, you can smell it as you lift your fork to your mouth, but the
actual taste of whisky is minimal'. Then there are his hot-smoked
salmon steaks, cut across a boned-out fish for a 115-140-g (4-5-oz)
slice, they are brined and hot-smoked 'to cook them through', then
lightly dusted with tarragon.

Another speciality is kippers, which have proved so popular that he
now runs a kipper club. A subscription secures you 900 g (2 lb) of fine
plump kippers – a pair weighs around 450 g (1 lb) – every month. Keith

buys Scottish herrings landed at the Ayrshire ports or Loch Fyne 'when the quality is right and the fat content is high enough'. With a catching season between June and September, he freezes stock to draw on, but he does also use Norwegian or Icelandic herring and defies 'anyone to spot the difference. What is critical is the oil content of the fish and the size'. Brined for about 30 minutes, then smoked for between 18 to 24 hours 'a good bit longer than most', his kippers are particularly plump and juicy, with plenty of punch. He also smokes eel, queen scallops and mussels, cures gravadlax and sells smoked chicken and duck breasts smoked especially for him in the Borders.

Scottish Crannog Seafoods, Blar Mhor, FORT WILLIAM PH33 7NG ☎ 01397 703919 fax 01397 705026 *sell smoked salmon, gravadlax, hot- and cold-smoked trout, pots of smoked trout pâté, and smoked mussels smoked in their smokehouse. They will also send fresh cooked langoustine in 2.3, 4.5 and 9-kg (5, 10, and 20-lb) boxes. Set up by a catch of fishermen, they also run* **Crannog Seafood Restaurant, Town Pier, FORT WILLIAM ☎ 01397 705589,** *from a converted bait shed where you can tuck in to such seafood delights as bouillabaisse, their own smoked fish, or langoustines in garlic butter – with most of the fish caught from their own boats. Recently they have opened branches at* **28 Cheapside, GLASGOW G3 8BH ☎ 0141 221 1727** *and* **14 South St Andrew Street, EDINBURGH EH2 2AZ ☎ 0131 557 5589.**

Sargasso Ltd

Units 1-3, Alness, Alness, Highlands & Islands IV17 0XS

☎ 01349 883954 **FAX** 01349 883015 **CONTACT** *Dr Andrew Seymour – telephone ahead* **CARDS** *Access, Mastercard, Visa*

Dr Andrew Seymour either buys eels in as elvers or catches them himself from rivers in Scotland, and it can take from between 1 and 3 years to grow them on in his tanks. This involves some very sophisticated currents pumped through their tanks so they get plenty of exercise; separation of solids in the water and then cleaning the water; and a constant flow of clean water from the loch. Eels are apparently 'great escape artists' and they are constantly wriggling out of one tank into another. A great deal of time is spent grading the tanks, sorting the eels out for size, as apparently no two eels grow at the same rate. If stressed, eels are aggressive, even cannibalistic; Andrew seems to have cracked this problem by creating a dark quiet stress-free environment which better suits the eel, with its nocturnal feeding habits. His eels swim peacefully enough, all facing in the same direction.

Harvested when they weigh 150-350 g (5½-12 oz), Andrew will send them out live, but in large quantities only. He also cures them in salt and smokes them over a mixture of oak and beech (oak by itself is too strongly flavoured) and sells them in 50-g (2-oz) portions or whole in any size, from 'pencil' eels 30 cm (1 ft) long upwards. He also produces Kabayaki, a Japanese speciality of broiled eel marinated in soy sauce

Stockists

Highlands: The Cook's Cupboard

London: Harvey Nichols

Yaohan UK Ltd

Surrey: Miura Foods

Tays: Keracher

Waitrose

MAP 8　　　　　HIGHLANDS & ISLANDS　　　　　351

mixed with sweetened sake. Sold in 60, 124 and 260-g (2¼, 4½ and 9-oz) packets, with sachets of additional sauce, it has a particular taste that is sweet, rich and full-bodied. The Japanese eat it either warm with sticky rice or in a sushi roll wrapped up in seaweed.

Strathspey Mushrooms

Kila, Grampian Road, Aviemore,
Highlands & Islands PH22 1RH

AVIEMORE
Dried Mushrooms

☎ 01479 810573　**FAX** 01479 811465　**CONTACT** *Duncan Riley – telephone ahead*

It was Duncan Riley's mother who suggested he should start dealing in mushrooms. A keen cook, she would 'go out now and again to collect for the pot'. Duncan runs a far larger crew, somewhere between 50 and 100 pickers, who scour the silver birch woods and coniferous forests in the Highlands on his behalf, collecting ceps, chanterelles, pieds de mouton and – a new one to me – orange birch bolete. Similar to a cep with an orange cap and white stem spotted with black, they 'come and go' between July to September and you may be interested to know that Roger Phillips in his great book *Mushrooms* pronounces them as good for eating.

　　All Duncan's mushrooms are sold fresh or dried in his insulated drying room. The secret is to get the temperature high enough, while extracting the humidity in the air, otherwise you are in danger of steaming the mushrooms, allowing them to toughen, discolour and lose their intensity of flavour. It takes Duncan about 24 hours to dry his mushrooms and for every fresh 100 kilos he gets 10 kilos dried weight.

Mail Order
Dried mushrooms only

Mermaid Fish Supplies

Clachan, Lochmaddy, North Uist, Outer Hebrides, Highlands &
Islands H56 5FG

CLACHAN
Smoked Salmon

☎ 01876 580209　**FAX** 01876 580323　**CONTACT** *George Jackson* **HOURS** *Mon-Sat 8.00-18.00* **CARDS** *Access, Mastercard, Switch, Visa* **DIRECTIONS** *On the west side of the island, near Clachan Corner.*

What makes George Jackson's salmon unique is how he smokes it. On North Uist, wood is in short supply, so he uses peat instead. Using farmed salmon from the smaller local farms, which, according to George, 'produce good fish, unlike the larger farms', he dry-cures then smokes it in his kiln, which is really 'more of a box with drawers underneath for the burning peat and a fan at the back to circulate the smoke. And as it's so damp here, humidity is a problem'. Peat burns hot and, unlike wood, does not smoulder, so cold-smoking could prove difficult. Somehow George manages it – but that is his secret.

Once every fisher-house had a smoke-hole attached, now **Stewarts Smokehouse, The Harbour, NAIRN 1V12 4PH ☎ 01667 453750** *is the only smokehouse left. Salmon, either farmed or wild in season, is lightly cured, then lightly smoked by laying it flat, skin side down, on sticks suspended over a lit fire on the floor. Sold as whole or sliced sides, weighing about 900 g (2 lb) or 225 g (½ lb) sliced in packs, it is succulent and very moist with a pronounced flavour of smoke.*

The result is quite distinctive; the salmon acquires a gentle smoky haze unlike any other, as it is soft and gentle with none of the fierceness often associated with a strong smoke. Sold as whole or sliced sides or as sliced packets, George also smokes fillets of cod, whiting and haddock.

CONON BRIDGE

Honey

Struan Apiaries
Burnside Lane, Conon Bridge, Ross-shire, Highlands & Islands IV7 8EX

☎/FAX 01349 861427   **CONTACT** Hamish Robertson   **HOURS** Mon-Fri 9.00-18.00   **CARDS** Access, Visa   **DIRECTIONS** In the village centre, opposite the post office.

Struan Honey produce a range of monofloral honey in 45-g (1½-oz) jars. They run about 400 hives themselves, with a few local bee-keepers working with them. They shift their hives several times during the season, to be near the different blossoms and flowers; even then, beekeepers can be thwarted, as bees in theory can buzz off as far as three miles in any direction. In practice, Hamish Robertson told me, 'Nature sorts itself out rather well. It produces a high density of flowers from particular crops at particular times of the year and the bees work the flowers to a maximum of one crop'. To further emphasize the flavour from that particular flower, Hamish extracts the honey from the combs each time he moves the hives and changes the combs.

Weather permitting, from the woods of two local estates (Foulis and Castle Leod) comes a sycamore, horse & Spanish chestnut honey with a good nutty flavour in May; June sees a raspberry honey from around the Black Isle, which is delicately fruity and pale-white. A rich deep lime comes from the trees from between mid-July to mid-August; a pert clover is collected in July; a flowery, almost port-wine-coloured bell heather from mid-July to the beginning of August; and finally a powerful thixotropic (jelly-like) ling heather honey from the beginning of August through to the middle of September. At certain times of the year their Scottish Blossom contains a large proportion of willowherb, as well as other wild flowers, for a particularly delicate aroma; and then there is the ubiquitous (and rather disappointing) rape.

For ease of extraction, Hamish shaves off the face of his combs and the honey drips out, helped by spinning them in a centrifuge. He did show me around and explain the process in minute detail, but I am still

Stockists

Highlands: The Tomatin Distillery Co. Ltd

W. A. Baxter & Sons

London: Fortnum & Mason

Lothian: Jenners

Worcs: Egertons

not a lot the wiser. What I did grasp is the importance of seeding honey to stop it from turning granular; the tongue-test is all-important for, as he says, 'rub a little on your tongue, it should be as smooth as butter'. His are delightful honeys with highly individual characteristics, their only drawback is the irritating ordering system. At the moment, apart from heather and blossom, they sell their honeys as random selections; this means that you cannot choose your flavours, nor will you be guaranteed to receive every flavour even if you order all the selections. Try as I have, I cannot convince them to change this, which is a great pity.

Tod Holdings Ltd, 18 Bridge Street, Kirkwall, ORKNEY KW15 1HT ☎ 01856 873288 fax 01856 873655 *still bake old-fashioned round ships'* *biscuits that, as part of a ship's store, were made to last for months. An interesting alternative to the ubiquitous Carr's water biscuit, the basic mix is flour, water, salt, sugar and a little fat. Varieties include a crisp and slightly gritty Rice, made with rice flour; slightly sweeter Carvie, with carvie (caraway) seed; a crisp puffed-up Water; Flakey, which is smaller, even puffier and contains vegetable fat; Butter, made with butter for a richer taste; and Blacks Water, made to an old Shetland recipe which in texture is halfway between a Flakey and a Water biscuit.*
Tods of Orkney Limited, 25 Northend Road, STROMNESS, Orkney KW16 3AG ☎ 01856 850873 *make a range of oatcakes from oatmeal, salt, vegetable oils, a tiny amount of sugar and, occasionally, wheat flour. These include: thin (about 3 mm / ⅛ in); thick (about 7-8 mm / ¼ in); wholemeal & honey; cheese, flavoured with a dried cheese powder; large rounds and small cocktail-size oatcakes.*

Golspie Mill
Golspie, Highlands & Islands KW10 6RA

GOLSPIE
Beremeal

☎ 01408 633278   **CONTACT** *Fergus Morrison – telephone ahead*

'Beremeal', Fergus Morrison told me, 'is Neolithic barley from Mesopotamia. And if you think we can trace farming back 6,000 years, that's how long it has been around'. Beremeal (pronounced bearmeal) has a reputation for its earthy taste and, as Fergus says, 'it's much better than ordinary barley and far less bland'. It was widely grown in Scotland and used for bere bannocks until about the mid-19th century when 'it started to fade out', although it still remains popular in Orkney. In fact, before wheat was grown, barley was one of the main bread flours in Europe.

Fergus has beremeal grown under contract in Caithness, 'As it's genetically pure, it behaves like wild grass. We use untreated seed, never spray the grain. It grows quickly and just bosses out the weed'. After harvesting, it has to be dried in the mill's kiln, fired by the chaff from the previous load; the moisture content is taken down to around 8 per cent for a 'nutty, smoky taste'. It then is ground between three pairs of stones, driven by water. The first set removes the awn or 'spiky bit' and the grain is cleaned and aspirated; then it is coarsely ground, and finally ground to a fine consistency by the last set of stones, then bagged into 1.5-kg (3½-lb) packs.

Baking with it is very easy. Traditionally beremeal bannocks were made with heated milk or soured milk and a little fat but no yeast. The beremeal was stirred in until it made a stiff but pliable dough, then it was baked on a griddle or baking stone for a distinctive, richly nutty and earthy bread.

Fergus also buys in Lincolnshire peas from down South, which he roasts and grinds for peasemeal, and packs into 650-g (1½-lb) tubs. It can be used for brose, thickening soups or even in breads.

Stockists

Highland:
Highland
Wholefoods

Strath: Green City
Wholefoods

Mace

Argo's Bakery, 50 Victoria Street, Stromness, ORKNEY KW16 3BS ☎ 01856 850245 fax 01856 851264 *is a good old-fashioned bakery which makes just about everything you see on the shelves. Breads include rye, based on a Nordic recipe; oatmeal ruchie; bran quarters, with an open texture and a light nuttiness; tea loaf; flour bannock, similar to a soda bread but aerated with baking soda and cream of tartar; and crumbly beremeal bannocks, made with beremeal from Golspie Mill see page 353. Doughnuts are light and yeasty, with a white rim running around the centre 'always the mark of a good 'un. It shows they aren't so heavy, they sink in the fat'. There are various ships' biscuits (a tradition that started in 18th century, when the ships of the Hudson Bay Company stocked up in Orkney see also Tod Holdings, page 353); thin Syrup biscuits, made with golden syrup and treacle that 'fizz' in the mouth; plain, treacle cheese, wholemeal and fruit scones; crumpets; pancakes; muffins; and butteries.*

GRIMBISTER
**Orkney
Cheese**

Grimbister Farm Cheese
*Grimbister Farm, Grimbister, Kirkwall, Orkney,
Highlands & Islands KW15 1TT*

☎ 01856 761318   **CONTACT** Hilda Seator – telephone ahead

There are still a few farms on Orkney and the surrounding islands making an Orkney cheese, with the recipes varying slightly from farm to farm. Do not, for one moment, allow yourself to confuse it with the creamery-made Orkney cheese; this is an animal of an altogether different breed, made along similar lines to a Cheddar. The 'real' thing is generally eaten quite young and quite moist; some are known as 'squeaky' for the obvious reason that they squeak against your teeth when you bite in. You still hear tales about how they are put out on the dikes to dry, with hens walking over them or the cat sleeping on them in the sun (yes, it can be sunny in Orkney), but these versions I failed to track down.

Hilda Seator makes her cheese in the manner taught to her by her

Stockists

Highland:
Cumming &
Spence

Scott's Fish Shop

London: Neal's
Yard Dairy

Lothian: Iain
Mellis

A visit to **Scott's Fish Shop, Bridge Street, KIRKWALL, Orkney KW15 1HR ☎ 01856 873170** *will reveal a creamy farmhouse butter made on Shapinsay, Mrs Seator's Orkney cheese above and a very squeaky Orkney cheese from Swannay Farm at Birsay, as well as salted ling hanging up to dry, a traditional Orkney speciality.*

mother. Using the unpasteurized milk of her Friesian herd, she regards it 'as similar to a Wensleydale, best eaten young and always made without a starter. That's what a real Orkney cheese was. A farming cheese made for the family without a starter'. It is simple and quick to make: the milk is renneted, the curds

Lairobell Goats, East Lairo, SHAPIN-SAY KW17 2DZ ☎ 01856 71341 *is but a 25-minute ferry ride from Kirkwall. If you telephone and make arrangements, the Bells will fetch you from the harbour. With 15 milking goats, they make a soft curd cheese 'with a bit of a kick' and a delightfully fresh and mild hard cheese with a crumbly texture.*

are broken up, then left to settle for several hours, drained, left to stand, then milled very fine and pressed. It is ready the next day although, like a Dale cheese, it can be matured on. It is very surprising how much flavour comes from such a young cheese; light and fresh, crumbly with a slightly sour aftertaste, it is just one of the pleasures of visiting the Isles.

Orkney Seafayre

Marsdene, Grimbister, Kirkwall, Orkney, Highlands & Islands KW15 1TU

GRIMBISTER
Shellfish

☎/FAX 01856 761544 **CONTACT** *Duncan Geddes* **HOURS** Mon-Fri 8.00-17.00 *(mail order or telephone ahead)*

Orkney has an abundance of shellfish, both farmed and wild. Of all the farmers/dealers I met, none has as unusual a selection as Duncan Geddes in his holding/packing shed right down on the seashore.

Duncan farms Pacific oysters – which prove fat and juicy, with a salty breeziness – and, occasionally, the odd Native. Cockles are hand-raked and gathered; Dog cockles (*amande de mer* in France) and various other clams (which Duncan disarmingly told me 'taste good although I don't necessarily know their name') are suction-dredged from the shallow sandy banks, as are meaty large mussels from Dornoch Firth. Long thin Razor shells – or 'spoots' as they are known up here – are

Stockists

Grampian: Ken Whatmough

Northumb: Lindsay Brothers

another speciality; some are dredged, others 'so big and fat you only get 8-9 to a kilo' are dived for. The secret of a tender juicy spoot is never to overcook it; if it is left too long it will look like – and have the texture of – an inner tube of a bicycle tyre, not an enticing prospect. Duncan also has dredged sandgapers. Now if you have never seen one, you have a shock in store. They look – I suppose the word is –

Orkney Fishermen's Society, Garson Industrial Estate, STROMNESS, Orkney KW16 3JU ☎ 01856 850375 fax 01856 850332 *works as a co-operative for live and processed shellfish. For a minimum order of £50.00 value, they will send such shellfish as king or queen scallops, spoots (razor clams), lobsters, langoustines or velvet crabs, packed in ice anywhere in the country.*

William Jolly, Scott's Road, Hatston, KIRK-WALL KW15 1RE ☎ 01856 872417 fax 01856 8774960 *sell a good selection of both wet fish and shellfish, including megrim, squid, monkfish, packs of spoots steamed open then vacuum-packed and frozen, and also smoke various fish, including hot-roast salmon for a smoky finish, and cheese.*

Orkney Meat, Hatston Industrial Estate, KIRK-WALL, Orkney KW15
1RE ☎ 01856 874326 *is responsible for culling the North Ronaldsay lamb which graze on seaweed on the isle of Lingaholm. Culling takes place in August and supplies are limited, perhaps no more than 100 carcasses, weighing about 16 kg (35 lb). I have yet to try it but hear the meat has a fine texture and a sweet-salt earthy flavour. More reports please.*

suggestive, with more than a passing resemblance to a gentleman's private parts popping out of his shell (pants). They are sweet and succulent to eat, with a faintly chewy texture. Then there are dived king and queen scallops, green (shore) crabs for soups, velvet crabs which apparently none of us in Britain are remotely interested in so they get whizzed off to Spain, brown crabs and, of course, lobsters. Duncan deals mainly with the trade and smarter hotels around the country. He will supply privately by two-day chilled delivery but, be warned, the cost of transporting a small domestic order from Orkney can be prohibitive.

SKELD
Smoked Salmon

The Shetland Smokehouse
Skeld, Shetland, Highlands & Islands ZE2 9NS

☎ 01595 860251 **FAX** 0159586 203 **CONTACT** *Dave Hammond* **HOURS** *Mon-Fri 7.30-16.30* **CARDS** *Access, Visa* **DIRECTIONS** *On west mainland, take the road from Lerwick to Walls. ½ mile past village of Bixter, turn left at sign for Skeld. In Skeld, follow road past church round the head of the vole (sea inlet) and up the hill turn right, past the village hall on the left and the smokehouse is a large building with a green roof 100 yards along on right.*

Stockists

Borders: The Teviot Game Fare Smokery

Edinburgh: Cambells of Edinburgh

Strath: Scottish Gourmet

Yorks: Peter Meyers

The Shetland Smokehouse smoke salmon farmed to the Shetland Salmon Farmer's Association specifications. Their fish has a good reputation; the cages are generally well-sited in open seas, their stocking densities are (relatively) low and they go well beyond the Government's requirements with regard to the use of chemicals, lengthening the statutory period before fish can be harvested. If antibiotics have been used, fish must be tested by Shetland Seafood Quality Control and passed as residue-free and suitable for harvesting.

The smokehouse itself is in the centre of the salmon farming area, 'so we are well placed for fresh fish,' Dave Hammond told me. 'On the other hand, if you start to process salmon when it is too fresh, it will gape.' The days have long since gone when, as Dave remembers, 'salmon was like jerky. Over-cured and over-smoked, so you could

 J. & M. Fraser, Universal Fish Shop, Esplanade, LERWICK, Shetland ZE1
0LL ☎ 01595 69230 *sell herrings landed in Lerwick as round (whole) or split, smoked for kippers and salted in brine. They also sell salt ling and cod still in their brine, cod roes, crabs, live lobsters to order and langoustine, in season from September to May.*

almost lay it down for the winter'. He aims for a 'less-is-more' style and to this end dry-salts his fish for 6-12 hours, depending on size and smokes over oak sawdust (ground from barrels obtained from Burgundy) for about 8 hours. Whole sides, once vacuum-packed, will keep for about 1 month; but, if they are sliced and laid back, they keep only for 21 days and then only when chilled. His salmon is buttery in texture, but with a good bite and a nice fishy balance; it was also a rather startling orange, but Dave assured me this was due to the clarity of the light on Shetland.

He also cures for gravadlax using, interestingly enough, cloves, cognac and coriander, as well as the usual dill, salt and pepper. For gravadlax 'it's the fresher the better as far as the fish are concerned'. Whole sides are left to cure for about 36 hours and the result is briskly salty, with a pleasant crunch of pepper and the merest hint of coriander.

While on Shetland, you might be tempted to try a local speciality, reestit (salted and cured mutton) from **Peter Anderson, Globe, 49 Commercial Road,** *LERWICK ZE1 ONJ* ☎ **01595 692819** *or* **Smith & Co, 61 Commercial Street,** *LERWICK ZE1 0AB* ☎ **01595 693306**. *I did and was pleasantly surprised by its meaty sweetness. Incidentally, Peter Anderson also sells another Shetland speciality, saucermeat – which is described as 'special Shetland sausage meat' – this one I confess I did not try.*

Highland Fine Cheeses
Knockbreck, Tain, Ross & Cromarty,
Highlands & Islands IV19 1LZ

☎ 01862 892034 **FAX** 01862 894289 **CONTACT** Mrs Susannah Stone **HOURS** Mon-Fri 9.30-16.30 **DIRECTIONS** *Follow Tain high street north, past the Royal Hotel, and take the second right at the St Duthus Hotel into Shore road. Follow the road and turn left at the bottom of the hill, opposite the tractor garage. Follow the road along the high wall until you come to sign for farm.*

Susannah Stone makes Caboc – sublimely rich, unctuous and buttery, it is a delicate yellow cheese enriched with double cream and rolled in toasted pinhead oatmeal. A chieftain's cheese, it comes from the Western Isles and lays claim to being one of Scotland's oldest cheeses. As far as I know Susannah is the only person to make it, from a recipe handed down from her illustrious ancestors. Crowdie (*gruth* in Gaelic) is an old Highland and Island cheese 'and only made in the Highlands and Islands and it's so darn simple – only cooked curd that's citrusy tasting'. In the old days, Susannah told me, it was made by the crofters; they left a bowl of whole fresh milk to sour by the windowsill or near the stove, at some point skimming it to remove the cream. Once the milk had thickened, it was heated on the stove 'until scrambled, tipped in muslin, drained, mashed with a fork with – if they could afford it – a little cream. Mostly it was eaten fresh, but it was also pressed to make a hard cheese, which was rolled in straw in the stack or hung up under the eaves until it grew a grey rind. And, don't ask me why, the curds were hung up in the rowan tree'. Susannah makes her Highland Crowdie more or less the same way – minus the cream as hers is a low-fat cheese, and minus the rowan tree.

Gruth Dhu (black Crowdie) is Crowdie mixed with double cream and rolled in toasted pinhead oats and black pepper; Hramsa, sold in pots,

Stockists
Highland:
Farmers Dairy
- - - - - - - - - -
The Co-op

London: Fortnum & Mason
- - - - - - - - - -
Selfridges
- - - - - - - - - -
Sainsbury's

West Highland Dairy, Dailfearn, ACHMORE, Stromeferry IV53 8UW ☎ **01599 577203** *makes a range of pasteurized cheeses, using bought-in cows' and goats' milk and their own sheep's milk. Cheeses include a creamy smooth cows'-milk Coulommiers and an even creamier one made with sheep's milk which hints of dark chocolate; a fresh curd cheese from any of the three milks; Craig Mhaol, a close-textured cheese matured for 3-6 months, described as a cross between a Double Gloucester and a Wensleydale and again made with any of the three milks; and a sharp, quite acidic Crowdie, made by hanging cows' milk in cloths to drain for a couple of days. In season it is mixed with cream, oatmeal, whisky and honey and laid on a bed of raspberries for Cranachan.*

is Crowdie mixed with double cream and the 'all-healing herb', wild garlic; Galic is Hramsa rolled in toasted and crumbled and flaked hazelnuts, which by Susannah's admission, 'are not very authentic'; Highland soft, in spite of its name, is a soft full-fat Lowland cheese from Ayrshire. All her cheeses are made with pasteurized milk from selected farms and all are made with a natural lactic acid rather than rennet: 'It's the key to their flavour, their fresh, sharp, lemony taste – rennet would kill that off. And they never used to use it'.

 Fish merchants **Andy Race, The Harbour, PORT-OF-MALLAIG PH41 4PX** ☎ **01687 462626 fax 01687 462060** *sell a range of both fresh and own-smoked fish, with about 99 per cent landed in the port. There seems no end to the fish they smoke, over a mixture of oak, peat, pine and beech. The range includes peat-smoked salmon; Mallaig kippers slowly smoked for about 24 hours; Dublin Bay Prawns (aka Norwegian lobsters or langoustines); turbot; halibut; cod; monkfish; prawns; sprats; huss; whelks and Finnan haddies.*

While you're in the area...

  Butcher **Geo Cockburns, 19 Mill Street, DINGWALL, IV15 9PZ** ☎ **01349 862315** proclaims it is Scotland's Champion Haggis Makers. Sadly it was shut when I arrived, but I have heard they are every bit as good as they ever were. More reports please.

   Highland Wineries, MONIACK CASTLE, Kirkhill, Inverness IV5 7PQ ☎ **01463 831283 fax 01463 831419** make a range of wines from 'wild things'. These include still and sparkling Silver birch, described by wine-writer Andrew Jefford as 'haunting but mildly oppressive'; elderflower; meadowsweet, reputedly a cure for headaches; bramble; sloe gin; and black cherry. They also produce mead from five different honeys; peppermint liqueur; and various preserves, such as sloe, hawthorn and rowanberry jelly.

   Letterfinlay Game Services, The Boathouse, LETTERFINLAY, Spean Bridge PH34 4DZ ☎ **01397 712626 fax 01397 712510** is worth a trip if only for the view over Loch Lochy. Here you can buy oven-ready game, such as hare, rabbit, grey- and red-legged partridge, pheasant and grouse. They also smoke game, chicken, turkey and Scottish topside or silverside, which is then air-dried for several months. In season they also sell locally gathered chanterelles and ceps.

Lothian

Map No. 8

Balfour's Dulce de Leche
Buteland Farm, Balerno, Lothian EH14 7JJ

☎ 0131 449 5202 **CONTACT** Silvia Balfour – telephone ahead

Until I met the Balfours, I had never tried *dulce de leche* which, as they explained, is 'a jam or preserve made of milk and sugar'. Apparently it is very popular in South America, particularly Argentina where they come from. You could eat it on its own if you were feeling very self-indulgent, but they suggest using it in all manner of ways – from an ingredient in crème caramel and cakes or as a spread with toast and pancakes to a sauce for ice-cream.

The basic principle is to boil milk until its water evaporates and the natural sugars in the milk and the added sugar caramelize. The Balfours make theirs by boiling milk with sugar and dextrose for between 2-3 hours, then adding bicarbonate of soda. The result is particularly moreish, a sweet sticky but spoonable mass packed in 200 and 300-g (7 and 10½-oz) jars or 2.5-kg (5½-lb) containers. It could easily catch on here.

BALERNO
Dulce de Leche

Stockists

Highland: Kessock Post Office

London: La Tienda Delicatessen

Lothian: Iain Mellis

Jenners

Northumb: Ford and Etal

About 90 per cent of the produce is own-grown or own-made at **Knowes Farm Shop, by East Linton, DUNBAR EH42 1XJ** ☎ **01620 860221**. *Cauliflower, calabrese and main-crop potatoes – Maris Piper, Pentland Squire and Kerr – are grown on a field scale, but on a smaller scale they grow unsprayed vegetables especially for the shop, which customers can ask to have picked at baby-size should they want. These include carrots, parsnips, courgettes, various cabbages, dwarf French beans, broad beans, sugar-snaps, beetroot, the ideal chipper Golden Wonder, Pink Fir Apple and Scotland's favourite roaster Kerr's Pink potatoes. There are about 15 different fresh herbs, 'none of them too obscure', radicchio, oak leaf, frisée and iceberg lettuce; and customers can pick-their-own from the small herb and salad garden next to the shop. They also make marmalade, a range of Hedgerow Harvest jams, jellies and chutneys, herb vinegars and salad dressings, mayonnaise, ready-meals, eight different frozen soups and, for Christmas, cranberry sauce and brandy and whisky butter. In season they sell local soft fruit and asparagus, with own-made cartons of hollandaise sauce; and all year there are cakes and biscuits locally baked for the shop and bread delivered from two local bakers.*

Edinburgh

Breads

Mail Order

Sour-dough only

Sausages

Fish and Game

Mail Order

Smoked salmon only

Bread and Pâtés

Pasta

■ **The Auld Alliance, 4-8 Murieston Lane, EDINBURGH EH11 2LX ☎ 0131 220 0874** is named in honour of the  special relationship between the French and the Scots. Baker Bertrand Espoui bakes an earthy and powerful 100 per cent rye sour-dough and a relatively lighter version from a mixture of strong Canadian wheat, rye flours and rye meal to give it texture in 800-g (1¾-lb) and 2-2½-kg (4½-5½-lb) loaves. All his breads start with a poolish or sponge and the results are breads of character and interest; look out for 'proper' baguettes', various flavoured breads and an interesting Granary made with 4 different flours.

■ Butchers **A. Crombie & Son, 97-101 Broughton Street, Edinburgh EH1 3RZ ☎ 0131 557 0111** produce a range of over 20 sausages from pork classed as 'welfare pigs'. Varieties include Italian-style with an 80-90 per cent meat content, which is coarsely cut and flavoured with aniseed and fennel; 90 per cent meat Sicilian hot is made with pork marinated in white wine mixed with chilli, fennel and flat-leaf parsley; Northumbrian leek is made with fresh leeks; and wild venison comes from the Balmoral Estate, with Stilton & pork 'for a bit of moistness', is also turned into sausages. They are also well-known for own-made haggis.

■ **George Campbell & Sons, The Smokehouse, West Harbour Road, Granton, EDINBURGH EH5 1RF ☎ 0131 552 0376 fax 0131 551 1149** sell a wide range of whole and filleted fresh fish, with varieties differing according to the season. They also smoke Scottish farmed salmon over oak chips for a rich smoky flavour, which come as whole, trimmed or pre-sliced sides weighing between 675 g and 1.5 kg (1½ and 3½ lb) or sliced 115-450-g (¼-1-lb) packs. In season they also sell game, including grouse, ptarmigan and capercaillie (these last two both members of the grouse family), snipe and woodcock.

■ Recently opened **Glass & Thompson, 2 Dundas Street, EDINBURGH EH3 6HZ ☎ 0131 557 0909** is a well- 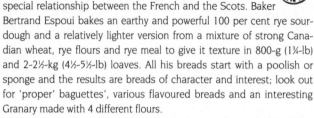 designed food shop/café, but then you would hope for nothing less from a couple of architect owners. Own-made food includes chocolate brownies, wood-roasted peppers and various pâtés, with *falafel* and *dolmati* made specially for them by an Iraqi cook. There are some interesting breads, such as focaccia with rosemary, a earthy sour-dough, and 100 per cent wholemeal baked by the Garveld Institute. Cheeses include St Andrews *see page* 372 and Bonchester *see page* 324, and they stock James White apple juices *see page* 248, The Village Bakery organic oatcakes *see page* 57, Rosebud preserves *see page* 304 and Womersley jellies and pickled walnuts *see page* 312.

■ **Gourmet Pasta, 54-56 Morningside Road, EDINBURGH EH10 4BZ ☎ 0131 447 4750 fax 0131 447 4756** make fresh pasta every day using an exceptionally hard semolina imported from Canada. Subscribing to the belief that 'pasta should be pasta – then you add the sauce you like' they make only plain (egg) or pasta flavoured with tomato or spinach in a variety of shapes and widths. Ravioli is a speciality and their range of fillings knows no bounds: wild goose & chestnut, venison, pheasant, artichoke or haggis are just a few of their possibilities. They also make pasta sauces, such as milanese with tomato; and ham, mushroom & cream. They bake pizzas too, as well as preparing lasagne, gnocchi and cannelloni.

Cheeses

■ **Iain Mellis, 30a Victoria Street, EDINBURGH EH1 2JW** ☎ **0131 226 6215** is one of the very few cheesemongers who really understands the nature of cheese. Fourteen years' experience in cheese-making has taught him, if nothing else, 'how modern production methods can ruin the delicate flavours of many cheeses'. As you might expect, he concentrates on farmhouse (on-farm) cheeses – ideally from Scotland, although this is a bit of a struggle. In his opinion, few measure up to his high standards, so his 60-odd cheeses come from all over Britain. What also singles out his cheeses is their condition; he knows how to look after them, bringing them on or maturing them in his cellar down the road. His shop is also air-conditioned and humidity-controlled, and is a joy to visit; cheeses are simply displayed in plain cool surroundings. Look out for Hilda Seator's Orkney Farmhouse *see page* 354, Bonchester in peak condition ready to run *see page* 324, and a tangy Loch Arthur *see page* 331. This autumn sees the opening of a second shop at **492 Great Western Road, GLASGOW G12 8EN ☎/fax 0141 339 8998** where there will be an even bigger cellar – a prospect that really pleases Iain.

Fish and Shellfish

■ **Longa Fish Ltd, 23 Leven Street, EDINBURGH EH3 9LH ☎ 0131 229 2160** sell an interesting range of wet fish and shellfish, including fresh tuna, sea-cat, dabs, queen and princess scallops and wild sea trout. There is also a good choice of smoked and cured fish, such as Finnan haddies, Arbroath smokies and a tub of salt herrings soaked in salt for 24 hours.

Haggis

■ **Macsweens of Edinburgh, 130 Bruntsfield Place, EDIN-BURGH EH10 4ES ☎ 0131 229 1216 fax 0131 229 9102** make haggis from sheep's pluck – the lung, heart and liver – using only a small proportion of liver 'so it's not too livery'. The pluck is cooked and minced and is mixed with beef fat (body back fat) which in Mr Macsween's view is infinitely preferable to the more normal suet, as 'it doesn't cook out and keeps the meat moist and gives a much cleaner taste'. Next comes oatmeal from the Borders in two grists (cuts): pinhead and medium, dried onions and seasoning of salt, black and white pepper, nutmeg, mace and coriander and finally a little of the gravy from the meat.

Everything is mixed together, put into a hopper with the 'bung' (the bovine equivalent of an appendix) fixed around the nozzle. Using only natural casings, for haggis between 450 g and 2.3 kg (1 and 5 lb) they use bungs and for the sizes upwards to 8 kg (18 lb), they use the stomach to make the traditional kidney-shaped haggis known as the Chieftain or Ceremonial. Smaller haggises are filled in a long link and clipped with a metal clip, 'in the old days we used string and I can honestly say that is the only difference in how we make them now'. The links of haggis are put back in the hot water and gently cooked for about 45 minutes, or until the required inner temperature is reached and the skins contract to form a tight round ball. Left to cool they are ready for dispatch. All you need to do is to wrap them in foil (in case you allow it to boil and the skin bursts) and gently simmer for about 45 minutes per 450 g (1 lb). Moist, crumbly and spoonable – if you can slice a hot haggis there is something badly wrong with its texture – it has a mild meatiness and a rich nuttiness and a noticeably clean aftertaste (so many I've tried cloy the mouth).

Incidentally, as Mr Macsween believes that eating haggis is a ritual, he caters for vegetarians with a haggis containing black kidney beans, lentils, swedes, onions, carrots and mushrooms, in case they should feel left out on Burn's Night.

Breads and Pastries

■ **Pâtisserie Florentin, 8 St Giles Street, EDINBURGH EH1 1PT ☎ 0131 225 6267**, just off the Royal Mile, sell pâtisserie and breads in the Continental style. As well as a nicely textured plain, breads include a generously studded walnut, a fruity raisin, anchovy & olive for a salty cut, and a rich sun-dried tomato. Croissants are French-textured (by that I mean neither too doughy nor too bready, but with an interior that pulls away in long buttery shards), and their Danish pastries are well-yeasted and generously filled with raisins. They also bake fruit tartlets filled with fresh fruit, *religieuse* (choux pastries filled with a deep chocolate *crème pâtissière*) and an airy *millefeuille*.

Grains

■ **Real Foods, 37 Broughton Street, EDINBURGH EH1 3JU ☎ 0131 557 1911 fax 0131 558 3530** is a very well stocked health-food store and a good source for beremeal and peasemeal from Golspie Mill *see page* 353, oatmeal in a range of grists, and spelt flour *see Doves Farm Foods, page* 21.

Italian Specialities, Cheeses and Wild Mushrooms

■ **Valvona & Crolla, 19 Elm Row, EDINBURGH EH7 4AA ☎ 0131 556 6066 fax 0131 556 1668** is *the* Italian deli of the North. As well as Parmesan, salamis, fresh pasta and one of the best selection of Italian wines and olive oils, expect to find good indigenous produce. British on-farm cheeses include Bonchester *see page* 324, Isle of Mull Cheddar *see page* 321, Cornish Yarg *see page* 50, and Innes *see page* 246. There is Bresaola-style Aberdeen Angus beef from Linlithgow, fresh herbs and Luca's of Musselburgh vanilla and strawberry ice-cream. Very much a family shop, all the relations go out on tutored mushroom forays and bring back chanterelles and porcini to sell in the shop, and they organize wine tastings and cookery demonstrations throughout the year.

Meat

■ Thanks to food writer Grace Mulligan for pointing out that from the butcher's counter at **T. G. Willis, 135 George Street, EDINBURGH EH2 4JS ☎ 0131 225 2101** you can buy proper tripe with a firm good texture, pickled tongues and beef.

While you're in the area...

My thanks to Clarissa Dickson-Wright, cookbook-seller-extraordinary for introducing me to fishmonger **Clark Bros, The Harbour, MUSSELBURGH EH21 69J ☎ 0131 665 6181**. He sells a wide and interesting range of fish and shellfish, keeping several lobsters in his tanks for appreciative customers.

Strathclyde

Map No. 8

Ramsay of Carluke
22 Mount Stewart Street, Carluke, Lanarkshire,
Strathclyde ML8 5ED

CARLUKE
Ayrshire
Bacon

☎ 01555 772277 **FAX** 01555 750686 **CONTACT** *Andrew Ramsay* **HOURS**
Mon-Fri 8.00-16.30 Sat 8.00-12.30 **DIRECTIONS** *From Bogside, take A73 into the centre of Carluke. Take the first turning on the right after The Crown Hotel, into Mount Stewart Street. After about 100 yards, shop is on the right.*

Ramsay of Carluke are members of the National Q Guild of Butchers, the group of Britain's top butchers. Their meat is perfectly good, but it is perhaps for their Ayrshire-cure bacon that they are best known. Ayrshire is similar to a Wiltshire cure in that both are brine-cures but – and this is the significant difference – for an Ayrshire cure the pig is skinned, the fat trimmed to a layer about 1 cm (½ in) thick and the side boned before curing.

Using Large White-Landrace cross farm pigs with 'no hormones, no injections and no boars because of possible taint – but not free range' (as Andrew Ramsay thinks they are tasteless) – Ramsay slaughter and skin the pigs themselves, split them down the middle into full sides of the gigot (leg) middle and fore, bone them out and trim them. The sides are pickled (cured) for about 2 days in a solution of salt, water, saltpetre and sodium nitrate, then stacked to drain for up to 2 weeks. Andrew's family have been curing for the last 150 years and, as he stresses, 'the water content of our bacon when we sell it is 0 per cent'.

The bacon sides are either smoked by them over hardwood chips for about 6 hours for a mild finish or left green. Then they are cut up into Ayrshire gigot, sold mostly as gammon steaks; Ayrshire fore, sliced as bacon; and Ayrshire middle, rolled up whole and sold in the round surrounded by a circle of gleaming fat, or separated into back and streaky rashers. It may have slightly more fat than mass-processed bacon, but its full-bodied taste cannot be compared. With the resilient texture of proper 'old-fashioned' bacon, cooking it is a pleasure; it does not spit or shrink, nor does it leave an unfortunate pool of scum in the pan – always a sign of a badly cured bacon or one that has been pumped up with polyphosphates.

Mail Order

Only through Scottish Gourmet *see opposite*

Stockists

Grampian: Alfred Kane

Lothian: Ian Proudfoot

Strath: D. W. Ferguson
- - - - - - - -
W. Watson & Son

FAIRLIE
Smoked Fish

Fencebay Fisheries
Fencefoot Farm, Fairlie, Largs, Strathclyde KA29 0EG

☎ 01475 568918 **FAX** 01475 568921 **CONTACT** Bernard Thain **HOURS** 8.30-17.30 **CARDS** Access, Diners, Eurocard, Mastercard, Visa **DIRECTIONS** About 2 miles from Largs and just after Fairlie, shop is in between the 2 round-abouts just before Hunterston Power Station.

Fencebay Fisheries is a compact concern. They rear trout, smoke it along with salmon and herring, and sell them in their farm-shop or serve them in their seafood restaurant, Fins. Salmon curing is done with rock salt over 3-4 days, in the chill at a temperature of -2°C (28°F) to avoid deterioration; and smoking is carried out over beech logs in their traditional brick kilns. They hot-smoke salmon supremes and trout, cold-smoke sides of salmon and herrings for Fairlie kippers, which are sold in half stone or stone boxes of 18 pairs. They also marinate herring in various sauces, prepare an interesting range of fish-based cooked dishes, such as seafood lasagne and salmon fish-cakes, and make fish pâtés with a low-fat cheese. From the shop they also sell fresh fish caught locally, such as plaice, turbot, hake, lemon sole and sea bass, and keep lobsters, squat lobsters and crabs in their vivier.

Stockists

Strath: Cairns Fish Shop

OGSCASTLE
Lanark Blue Cheese

H. J. Errington & Co
Braehead Farm, Walston, Ogscastle, Carnwath, Strathclyde ML11 8NF

☎ 0189 981257 **FAX** 0189 981257 **CONTACT** Humphrey Errington **HOURS** Mon-Fri 7.00-16.00 **DIRECTIONS** From Carnwath, take A721 towards Peebles. After about 3 miles, turn left signposted Walston. After about ¼ mile, go straight over the crossroads and farm is signposted about 300 yards along on the right.

MAP 8 STRATHCLYDE 365

The Scottish Gourmet, Thistle Mill, Station Road, BIGGAR ML12 6LP ☎
01899 221268, freephone 0500 340640 fax 01899 220456 *is a subscription mail-order food club, with an emphasis on Scottish recipes and produce. Anyone can join for one or five years or as a lifetime member. Each year you receive 12 monthly newsletters, recipes and an order form. Food divides into three categories: ready-dishes, cooked by chef Bernard Alessi and delivered chilled for re-heating and assembling; raw ingredients for you to cook; and Scottish-made products, such as cheese, jams, smoked meats or fish and so on. They ring the changes every month, but typical dishes are Tobermory Mushrooms 'border mushrooms are prepared with a rich Cheddar-like cheese from Tobermory on the Isle of Mull... into the sauce go tomatoes, onions, garlic and a dash of elderberry wine' or Aberdeen Angus Braise 'top-quality Aberdeen Angus steak sliced thinly and braised in oatmeal stout from the little Broughton Brewery. The braising beef (two 85-g / 3-oz slices per person) is cooked slowly and gently with celery and carrots, mushrooms and onions in a thickened gravy'. On the ingredients/produce front you can order Ramsays of Carluke Ayrshire-cure bacon see page 363, Black Mount grouse supplied with bacon, heather and a traditional stuffing of skirlie (oatmeal, onions and dripping), marinated wild venison from Johnny Rutherford of Burnside, Border or Ecclefechan tarts, shortbread from Shirra see page 329, or cheese from Ann Dorward see page 366.*

At the time of going to press, the future of Lanark Blue Cheese hangs in the balance. You may well have seen such terrifying headlines as 'Killer Cheese' in the *Sun* (natch) and read about the torturous story of how Humphrey Errington was taken to court because of the 'health risk' of his cheese. His local Environmental Health Officer (EHO) found the presence of *Listeria monocytogenes* and condemned the entire stock on the grounds that it was contaminated. This was in February and the story grinds on, with Humphrey rushing from one appeal to another stoutly defending his cheese on the grounds that there are several strains of *L. monocytogenes*, not all of which are virulent, the sampling methodology is not reliable and eating Lanark Blue presents no possible danger to anyone.

A principle is at stake here; listeria is ubiquitous and not necessarily harmful, but still many small producers have been forced to close down when it has been found on their premises. Several years ago, Professor Richard Lacey wrote complaining about the Food Police aka EHOs; today producers still have to deal with their lack of knowledge and high-handedness. Seemingly, they have no interest or understanding of food, particularly the smaller craft food-producer, and yet they

Stockists

London: Harrods

Paxton & Whitfield

Real Cheese Shop

Lothian: Iain Mellis

Sussex: Horsham Cheese Shop

Braidwoods, Drumastle Mill Cottage, DALRY KA2 44LN ☎ 01294 833544 *is a cottage restaurant in the middle of the country, run by the talented husband-and-wife team of Nicola and Keith Braidwood. Using plenty of local produce, their food has great intensity of flavour – a timbale of Arbroath smokies was wonderfully pitched. Puddings are a speciality, and coffee is served with own-made truffles, again marked by a certain vigorousness. Made with a ganache of chocolate, double cream, butter and a drop of liquid glucose, whipped when cool to give it an airy texture, they are hand-dipped in chocolate. Flavours are white chocolate & crème de menthe; milk chocolate brandy & coffee: dark chocolate & Grand Marnier or Glayva whisky. Sold in 225-g (8-oz) boxes, they are mostly snapped up by the diners but anyone can pop in to buy them, provided they call during restaurant hours. As they are freshly made to order, however, it is probably wise to ring first.*

wield immense power. Humphrey, crippled by debt, is fighting his corner and he feels he owes it not only to himself and his much-beloved cheese, but also to all the producers who have been unnecessarily closed down. Let us wish him the best of luck.

Bradfords, 245 Sauchiehall Street, GLASGOW G2 3EZ ☎ 0141 3325071 fax 0141 3532671 *is food writer Catherine Brown's favourite bakers for Scotch pies. A Scotch pie is a tricky thing to get right: first the pastry has to be relatively thin – the pastry-to-meat ratio is all-important – but not too thin, otherwise it will collapse under the weight of the filling, and it has to be crisp. The filling should have plenty of lean meat, flavoured fat (preferably suet) and good seasoning. Bradfords' version qualifies on all fronts. They also bake batch, tea and milk breads; potato scones; crumpets; Scotch pancakes; soda, treacle and wheaten scones; Glasgow (as opposed to Forfar) bridies; morning, afternoon and hard Glasgow rolls; shortbread; oatcakes; and all sorts of fruit-filled pies.*

STEWARTON

Dunloppe Cheese

Mail Order
Only through Scottish Gourmet *page 365*

Stockists
London: Barstow & Barr

Lothian: Valvona & Crolla

Strath: Peckhams
The Cheese and Wine Shop

Ann Dorward
West Clerkland Farm, Stewarton, Strathclyde KA3 5LP

☎ 01560 482494   **CONTACT** *Ann Dorward – telephone ahead*

Dunloppe – spelt with one or two 'p's – has always been known as a sweet-milk cheese. It was once made by several on-farm cheese-makers on the East coast, from Ayrshire (the actual village Dunlop is only a few miles away) to as far south as Wigtonshire. Now, however, apart from Ann Dorward, none remain. Often compared with Cheddar, it is made to a very similar recipe, but it has a higher moisture content, is softer textured and generally milder.

Ann has been making her Dunloppe with bought-in pasteurized Friesian milk for about 6 years now. Until recently, she was maturing it for about 6 months, vacuum-wrapped. However, she has just started following the 'old way' of bandaging (wrapping in cheesecloth) and leaving it to mature open in the cheese store. There are problems, the cheese can turn out a little dry, so she is sorting out the cheese-store and adjusting the humidity. None the less, the bandaged cheese shows promise; nuttier and with a good tang, it compares favourably to its vacuum-wrapped cousin, which tends to a pastier finish and a more acidic flavour.

Two bakers in Glasgow produce good Continental breads. **Das Brot, 51 Hyndland Street, Partick, GLASGOW G11 5QF ☎ 0141 334 8234** *bake an interesting range of rye breads, including a dense 100 per cent rye; a heavy Russian, a mixture of 65 per cent rye and wholemeal; 50 per cent Bavarian; 40 per cent rye with caraway seeds; Kassler with 30 per cent rye and wheat; and rye with sunflower seeds. They also make chewy bagels, rye rolls, crisp Bavarian salt sticks, egg loaf, and a proper baked cheesecake with a hint of vanilla and lemon.* **Star Continental Bakery, 158 Fore Street, Scotstoun, GLASGOW G14 0AE ☎/fax 0141 959 7307** *also produce a Polish 60 per cent rye, Russian 80 per cent rye, as well as egg loaf, banaura, a 100 per cent wholemeal, Scottish oatmeal and ciabatta.*

MAP 8 STRATHCLYDE 367

Using more or less the same recipe, she also makes Swinzie, named after a nearby burn (stream), with the pasteurized milk from her Friesland flock for a mild milkiness. Bonnet, also the local name for Stewarton, is made with pasteurized milk from her own goat herd and eaten younger, at about 3-4 months, by which time it already has a sharp goatiness. If asked, she is more than happy to bandage all her cheeses, maturing them in the traditional way or, as she puts it, 'making cheese as it should be'.

Alexander Taylor of Waterside Bakery

10-11 *Waterside Street, Strathaven, Strathclyde* ML10 6AW

☎ 01357 21260 **FAX** 01357 22774 **CONTACT** *Barry Taylor* **HOURS** *Mon-Fri 8.30-17.30 Sat 7.30-17.30* **DIRECTIONS** *In the Conservation areas, near the Castle.*

STRATHAVEN
**Traditional
Scottish
Breads,
Cakes and
Biscuits**

Alexander Taylor of Waterside Bakery bakes an interesting range of thoroughly traditional Scottish cakes, biscuits, breads and scones, which in some cases have been 'improved' by Barry Taylor's trips abroad. Happily an 'if it needs butter, it has butter' attitude prevails; there is no scrimping on the quality of ingredients or cutting of corners and inevitably this shines through in the end products.

Dealing with the traditional first, there is a rich but soft shortbread made with plain flour, butter and sugar, baked in whole farls (circles), neatly stamped with a thistle or cut into quarters. Black bun is robust and tangy and made traditionally with fermented dough chopped up into a mixture of heavily spiced dried fruits, then wrapped in a thin sheet of dough and baked. Fruit bread, improved by a visit to Holland where Barry picked up a tip to pre-soak the fruit in water to improve its moistness, is moist and plump on fruit but light on spice. Gingerbread is firm and sticky; round oatcakes made with medium oatmeal, butter, water and salt are luxuriously nutty; and, borrowed from Holland, are crisp biscuits blocked out in shapes spiced with cardamom.

From the hot plate – and here I must admit that I may get a little confused between Scottish and English terminology, so forgive me if I have got it wrong – there are drop scones; thin triangular potato scones made with mashed potato; crumpets (or pancakes in England), including treacle which is superb with an unctuous bitter-sweet taste that hits just the right level of sweetness; and clear melting butter rowies made with a lavish 225 g (½ lb) butter for every 36. Breads are both traditional and fashionable; white bread is fermented overnight to give it a creamy earthiness, such as the round white crusty cut into four peaks which were supposed to be four church spires to frighten away the Devil; cheese bread is firmly textured and highly flavoured right through with Scottish Cheddar; ciabatta is less impressive, but there is an interesting sun-dried tomato & herb loaf which also includes olive oil, fresh onion, garlic and black olives. With a coffee shop across the

Mail Order
Shortbread and
black bun only

road for cakes, crumpets, scones and light meals, customers who drive all the way from Glasgow for their weekly loaf testify that this is a very good bakery.

Would that every city had a fishmongers as good as **MacCallums of Troon, 944 Argyle Street, GLASGOW G3 8YJ ☎ 0141 204 4456 fax 0141 423 9294***. Apart from a wide range of wet fish, including silver hake and Solway turbot, you will find such interesting shellfish as tiny bright-red velvet crabs which are best eaten by sucking the shells, long thin razor shells, and squat lobsters. These tiny weeny lobsters have a sweet flesh but a bitter shell and should be cooked by tearing off their heads, squeezing out their bodies and either steaming or sautéing them. They also cure and sell salt ling, Scotland's answer to salt cod, which is cooked in exactly the same way. At weekends they often have fish parfaits and terrines cooked by Scotland's finest chefs and, in season, a good selection of wild mushrooms.*

While you're in the area...

Fishmongers **Alex S. Walker, 7 Park Place, BIGGAR ML12 6TD ☎ 01899 20243** buy their wet fish every day from the market at Newhaven on the Forth. Salmon cured in brown sugar and Drambuie is smoked for 3 nights – and only the nights – for a sweet finish. They also produce a traditional undyed Finnan haddock with a burst of salt.

Butchers **James Allan, 85 Lauderdale Gardens, Hyndland GLASGOW G12 9QU ☎ 0141 334 8973** buys his Aberdeen Angus straight from the farm and hangs his beef for anything up to 21 days. He makes an interesting range of sausages with an 80 per cent meat content, including venison with claret, lamb with cumin, beef & horseradish, and pork provençal with white wine, garlic, peppers, coriander and mace. He pickles tongues; pots hough; and makes various meat pies, including hand-raised pork and beef & carrot; bridies; ready-to-cook dishes; and white, black and fruit puddings.

Peckham's, 100 Byres Road, GLASGOW G51 4TQ ☎ 0141 357 1454 fax 0141 445 5511 sell various on-farm Scottish cheeses, including Bonchester *see page* 324, Howgate Brie *see page* 372 and Bonnet *see page* 367. They stock bread from Star Continental Bakery *see page* 366 and preserves from Moniack Castle *see page* 358 and Baxters.

Tayside

Map No. 8

R. R. *Spink & Sons*
33-35 Seagate, Arbroath, Tayside DD11 1BJ

ARBROATH
Arbroath
Smokies

☎ 01241 872023 **FAX** 01241 875663 **CONTACT** *Bob Spink – telephone ahead* **DIRECTIONS** *In town centre, near the harbour.*

Smokies come from the haddock 'with its distinctive "thumb-print" behind each gill', writes H. V. Morton in *In search of Scotland*. 'It is gutted at sea, washed and boxed ready for auction on its arrival at the fish market. After auction, it is "headed and sounded" – sounding being the local name given to the thorough cleaning of the fish. It is then salted and brined in tubs for a given period, depending on the size of the fish and the method adopted by each curer. Usually the period is 1-2 hours, after which they are tied by the tail in "pairs". Following a final wash, the "pairs" are hung on poles to dry (or drouth). The pit barrel will vary in construction, but the most commonly used is of brick – about 2 metres square. The poles are set over the pit and a lingering fire of beech or hardwood. A hessian cover over the pit allows the fire to breathe and maintain the required heat. How long does it take? The exact method and time scale is something of a family secret … usually a minimum of 30 minutes is necessary however'. Hot-smoked to lock in the flavour while – the theory is – the bone running up the centre retains their moisture, Arbroath smokies are pale gold in colour with a

---

A visit to Arbroath will reveal a few traditional smokers working in their yards. **D. & A. Spink, 51-3 High Street, ARBROATH DD11 1AN** ☎/*fax* 01241 430753 *still use a huge brick pit, smoking the fish over the heat from the embers of oak chips, once the fire has been 'suffocated'.*
E. D. & J. Scott, 5 Seagate, ARBROATH DD11 1BJ ☎ 01241 872331 *will burn 'any hardwood' and favour quite a high smoke. Subtly different, frankly I find it impossible to recommend one against the other – if you are smokie fan you ought to come up here and try for yourself.*

juicy meaty flesh sharpened by a good cut of salt.

Spink, in these parts, is one of the fisher-names; others are Beattie, Buchan, Cargill and Milne, and the families originally came from Auchmithie, a small fishing village up the coast, to settle here in Arbroath. R. R. Spink are probably the largest producers of Arbroath smokies, and they have recently moved to a new factory 'tidied up', as Bob Spink puts it, 'by food technologists'. Wooden speats have been replaced by non-stick coated ones; the hessian cloth has been removed and the fire is now controlled by stainless steel plates. With a fully indoor unit, 'we are not subjected to the vagaries of the weather. If it's rainy, muggy or brisk and windy, it doesn't affect us', fish are now blast-chilled on arrival and they are even planning to freeze the fish during May to late summer, when they are at their fattest and juiciest, to last them through the year. Bob maintains that these hi-tech improvements have enhanced the eating qualities of his smokies; all that has happened is that 'generations of knowledge have been harnessed to modify the processes'. I must admit his smokies tasted as moist and juicy as ever.

Stockists

Safeway

Scotmid Co-ops

Tesco

William Morrison Supermarkets

From their farm-shop, **Gowrie Growers, Kingswell, Castle Huntly, LONGFORGAN DD2 5HJ ☎ 01382 360620 fax 01382 360637** sell own-grown soft fruit and vegetables in season, such as pumpkins and, this year, trials of Italian cavallo nero (black cabbage). The shop also sells Scottish asparagus from the Carse of Gowrie; shallots; fresh chanterelles picked for them near Aberfeldy; own-baked cakes; and a good selection of freshly cut or pot-grown culinary herbs, such as buckler-leaf sorrel, garlic chives and rockette (sic), as well as bags of edible flowers and cardoon plants all grown by Scotherbs from their nursery down the road.

BROUGHTY FERRY

Dundee Cake

Goodfellow & Steven
81-83 Gray Street, Broughty Ferry, Dundee, Tayside DD5 2BQ

☎ 01382 730181 **FAX** 01382 736041 **CONTACT** David Goodfellow **HOURS** Mon-Sat 8.00-17.00 **DIRECTIONS** From Dundee, take A930 towards Broughty Ferry. Follow the road about 3 miles to the crossroads, with The Occidental pub on the left. Turn right at the crossroads into Church Street. Take the first turning on the left into Brook Street. Follow the road to the centre of Broughty Ferry and turn right just before The Royal Arch pub into Gray Street. Shop is on the right.

No two people seem able to agree on what is a true Dundee cake – should it contain sultanas and/or currants, glacé cherries, treacle, spices, whole or nibbed almonds, candied mixed peel or just candied orange peel or even freshly grated orange peel, sherry, brandy or no alcohol at all, or any combination of the above? Even its origin is under dispute. It has been suggested that it is a descendant of Dundee gingerbread cake rather than, as I had always thought, an invention by Keillers because they needed some way of using up the excess orange peel from their marmalade-making. The original Mr Goodfellow, David

Goodfellow's grandfather, knew the Keillers and he believed the recipe did come from them.

That recipe is still used 'more or less'. There are various 'adjustments', such as the fat used is now vegetable margarine rather than butter. Their Dundee cake is made with plain white flour, eggs (pasteurized not fresh), vegetable margarine and golden shortening, Primrose sugar (a golden brown baker's sugar halfway between demerara and white, which apparently has the advantage of 'not clagging'), sultanas, candied orange peel and 'black jack' (burnt sugar) to give it its deep gingerbread colour. Apparently a Dundee cake should not be too heavily fruited 'if it is, it's not a proper Dundee', so the Goodfellows mix in one-third fruit in proportion to the rest of the ingredients. On top there must be split almonds turned to a golden brown as they are placed before the cake is baked. The Goodfellows bake theirs straight in 750-g (1¾-lb) in tins and seal them while still hot to create a vacuum; that way, unopened it can last up to 2 years, although the Dundee is a cake that does not benefit from ageing and is best eaten fresh, straight out of the oven. As for its taste, it is lighter and plainer than a fruit cake, quite crumbly, with the barest hint of orange. They also bake whisky cake, flavoured with Tobermory malt whisky from the Island of Mull, and cherry & ginger cake.

Stockists

National Trust for Scotland

Aberfeldy Water Mill, Mill Street, **ABERFELDY PH15 2BG** ☎ **01887 820803 fax 01887 829485** *was restored by Tom Rodger in 1987. He buys in oats locally and only from suppliers growing to organic (to Soil Association) standards because he thinks, 'the flavour is slightly better and it gives me peace of mind'. Dried in the kiln to take their moisture level down to around 5 per cent and cracked by one set of mill-stones to remove their shells or husks, finally the oats are ground in the other set of milling stones into three grades: fine, 'a bit coarser than wheat flour for a gruel or bannocks; medium for oatcakes, parkins and porridge; and coarse for a chewier porridge'. Sold in 500-g, 1 and 1.5-kg (1-lb 2-oz, 2¼ and 3½-lb) bags, his oats are rich and nutty and so dry that Tom claims they will keep up to 12 months if stored properly.*

A. H. & H. A. *Pattullo*
Eassie Farm, by Glamis, Tayside DD8 1SG

NEW ENTRY

GLAMIS Seakale

☎ 01307 840303   **CONTACT** *Sandy Pattullo – telephone ahead*

Sandy Pattullo is an arable farmer who 'indulges in two hobby crops – asparagus and seakale'. Asparagus is more or less straightforward; he has about 14 acres under cultivation and the only drawback is that, growing as far north as he does, his season is slightly shorter than in the south, so cutting does not start here until the first week of May.

Seakale is another matter; currently he has only 3½ acres and last year picked a mere ¾ ton. In spite of the fact that 'most people up here wouldn't give it the time of day', he persists – encouraged, in particular, by David Wilson of The Peat Inn restaurant who introduced us in the first place. Seakale is one of those old-fashioned vegetables that for some inexplicable reason has fallen out of favour. It is quite labour-intensive, the crowns have to be dug up 'as soon as the first frosts have knocked off their leaves, but not much later than that or the ground will have frozen solid'. Then the thongs (roots) are cut off and put aside for the following year, while the crowns are laid in trays filled with peat in a dark insulated forcing shed. By the first week of January they are sprouting their blanched shoots, and these are picked at between 15 and 22.5 cm (6 and 9 in). A good crown will carry on shooting until March, by which time the thongs can be planted out to produce more crowns, and so the cycle continues.

If you have never tried seakale – please do. It is delicate in flavour, similar to asparagus but sharper in flavour and crisper in texture. Sandy will send you a 225-g (½-lb) bunch and once you have eaten it, you will probably be hooked for life.

Stockists

London: Wild Harvest Ltd

Dunkeld Smoked Salmon, Springwells Smokehouse, Brae Street, DUNKELD PH8 0BA ☎ 01350 727639 fax 01350 728760 is on a brae (hill), but a short distance from the river Tay. Not surprisingly they smoke wild Tay salmon as well as farmed. Opinions differ as to which is superior. Most people like to think wild is better, but it is not as simple as that – it depends on the fish's condition when caught and how soon it is gutted. Indeed, in the company of Rachciel Allenby Wilcox of Watterbutts Lodge (my landlady for that night), I compared samples of Dunkeld wild and farmed. We both thought the farmed preferable – juicier and more moist than the wild, which was quite dry with a stronger smoke and had noticeable blood spots. Both fish are available as unsliced sides, hand-sliced sides and packs, and machine-sliced packs. Dunkeld also offer a comprehensive service for smoking anglers' own fish, even offering to collect them if they are too absorbed in fishing to leave the river banks. Since my visit, they have come under new management, so I would welcome any reports on their current standards.

DUNDEE
Strathkinnes
Cheese

Howgate Cheese
Camperdown Creamery, Faraday Street, Dundee,
Tayside DD2 3QQ

☎ 01382 811622 **FAX** 01382 811722 **CONTACT** Graeme Webster **DIRECTIONS** In Dryburgh Industrial Estate on King's Way road towards Aberdeen.

Working from a dairy based on a trading estate on the north side of Dundee and using mainly pasteurized milk from three local farms, Graeme Webster produces some very satisfying cheeses. Apart from Howgate cream cheese, a soft cheese made using 'top of the milk' in the Highland tradition, his cheeses follow a determinedly Continental approach, with a pasteurized and unpasteurized Brie, a pasteurized Camembert and, best of all, three rind-washed cheeses.

St Andrews, made in 450-g (1-lb) minis and 2.3-kg (5-lb) cheeses, is 'modelled on Reblochon and similar to a Chaume'; it is matured over 6-8 weeks and develops into a densely textured cheese with a salty fruitiness. Bishop Kennedy is also rind-washed, but this time Graeme uses whisky; as you cut into the orange-crusted cheese there is a dis-

MAP 8 | TAYSIDE | 373

tinctive aroma which runs through the cheese on first bite. Best of all is the just-on-the-market Strathkinness, made in 18-kg (40-lb) rounds. A large flat cheese modelled on Beaufort, as Graeme says, it is the first 'mountain' cheese in the UK. Rind-washed and matured over 6 months, it develops a springy denseness, with some cheeses forming natural holes. I tried it quite young at 3 months and already its flavour was well under way; sweet and clean with a glorious rich sugariness and plenty of follow-through, I reckon this is a cheese with a future and certainly deserved the prize it won at the 1995 London International Cheese Show.

Stockists

Ches: The Cheese Shop

Fife: Ellery Deli

St Andrews Delicatessen

London: Neal's Yard Dairy

Lothian: Glass & Thompson

Thanks to Margaret Hickey, Food Editor of Country Living *for telling me about* **Denrosa, Victoria Street,** COUPAR ANGUS PH13 9AE ☎ 01828 627721 *fax* 01828 628262 *who collect raspberry flower honey from Tayside's raspberry fields. Pale and gloriously soft and fruity, it is packed in 225 and 450-g (½ and 1-lb) jars and 450-g (1-lb) beehive jars. In these larger beehive jars only they also have a lush-textured heather honey from Royal Deeside with an intense floweriness. They also produce a range of preserves and jellies, including Rhubarb & Ginger extra jam; this is green in colour and thick in texture, with a hint of ginger on first taste which opens out to reveal a lingering shock of rhubarb. Their elderberry jelly is darker and richer, with a dense meaty fruitiness. They have also started making intensely flavoured vinegars using French white wine vinegar as the base, these are infused with lime & rosemary, mixed herbs including borage and heartsease flowers, elderflower, and summer berries. Not only do they look pretty in the 250-ml (8-fl oz) bottles, but they really do have flavour.*

James McLaren & Son
22-26 Market Street, Forfar, Angus, Tayside DD8 3EW

FORFAR
Forfar
Bridies

☎ 01307 463315 **FAX** 01307 461806 **CONTACT** Bill McLaren **HOURS** Mon-Sat 7.45-16.45 (-13.00 Thurs) **DIRECTIONS** In town centre.

Saturday is the day to eat bridies for lunch in Forfar, although, as far as I could see from the brisk trade, everyone here eats one every day. A virtually unintelligible description of what a bridie actually is comes from Jeems Stark 'a one-time local character and frequenter of bakehouses… '(it is) just a brodie – a big roond slap o'dough wi' the tap hauf' spread wi' steak cut sma' an' chapp't ingins. Syne th' boodom hauf's lufit an' laid ower the tap an sculpit ee aidge'. None the wiser? Quite so. Bill McLaren, great-grandson of James, did explain what a bridie is – Scotland's answer to a Cornish pasty, but made for wedding meals – the bride's meal, hence the name and horseshoe shape – for luck.

Enter Bill's old-fashioned shop and you will be hit by a very tempting smell of cooking; bridies keep coming out of the oven at all times of the day. If you want to eat one hot, it must be fresh; cold ones are best a day-old. With several bridie shops in town, what makes his the best? For a start he makes his own short pastry with vegetable fat, flour, salt and water, cuts it in pieces, chaffs it (rolls in the palms of his hand), then pins it (rolls it out) into a round. It is passed through a dough-brake for an oval shape, one half is painted with water and then it is ready for the filling.

James uses only Aberdeen Angus beef; it may be expensive, but 'you get out what you put in'. At least 115 g (4 oz) of coarsely chopped shoulder steak goes into each one. The other ingredients are suet (the quantities vary according to how lean the beef is), salt and pepper – and, for some only, onions. The pastry is folded over, the edges are 'heeled' and nicked and the top pierced with one hole for meat and onions, two if without 'so I can tell which is which'; the bridie is rested 'a wee while' then baked off. Catch one straight out of the oven and it is the meal for the day. Crisp pastry surrounds meaty chunks with a pungent pepperiness. Watch out as you take your first bite, otherwise you will not be prepared for the meaty gravy that oozes out. I wasn't and it dribbled all over the pavement – luckily Violet was quick to lick it up.

<table>
<tr><td>KINLOCH
RANNOCH
Smoked
Wild
Venison</td></tr>
</table>

Rannoch Smokery
Kinloch Rannoch, Pitlochry, Tayside PH16 5QD

☎ 01882 632344 **FAX** 01882 632441 **CONTACT** *Leo Barclay – mail order only* **CARDS** *Visa*

In November 1993, Rannoch Smokery was gutted by fire. The good news is that by May 1994 it was completely rebuilt and Leo and Sarah Barclay are back in business, with state-of-the-art premises. Here Leo Barclay concentrates on smoking local produce. Wild red deer shot on the surrounding estates is hung for about a week to develop its flavour; if he let it go for longer, he found some customers would complain about a 'really gamy taste'. Leo butchers the haunch (leg) into the three main cuts – silverside, topside and thick flank for 'decent slices of meat from the three main muscles'. These he brines in a mixture of muscovado sugar, salt and 'three secret ingredients' for about three days, then hangs them to dry for about 48 hours. Both of these processes are done at a controlled temperature, which Leo considers 'really counts for the flavour and texture'.

Next comes the smoking, which takes about 3 days. He favours a heavy cold-smoke and uses oak chips from whisky barrels. Finally, the venison is thinly sliced and vacuum-packed in 100 or 250-g (¼ or ½-lb)

Ellery's, 2 Mill Street, PERTH PH1 5HZ ☎ 01738 633362 *is a particularly pretty delicatessen. Here you will find a good selection of local cheeses, including the range from Howgate Cheese see page 372, Isle of Mull Cheddar see page 321 and Swinzie see page 367; Herbs and Preserves marmalades see page 340, Isobel Steven's shortbread see page 339, and chanterelles in season. They cook hams and rib of beef, roulades, quiches, three-cheese torte, lasagne and a range of pâtés, including a meaty pheasant, mackerel sharpened with grapefruit, and Arbroath made with smokies and cream.*

packs, either as plain or marinated in oil and herbs or, new this year, oil and chanterelles. Leo picks these himself, dries them slightly if they are a little wet as they sometimes can be, then marinates them in an Italian olive oil, 'extra-virgin is too heavy and pervasive. It drowns the delicate flavour of the chanterelles'. The chanterelle-infused oil, complete with tiny bits of the mushrooms, is poured over the meat; the result is delightfully delicate, a mix of gentle woodiness with mild gaminess. Also new are Leo's boned venison hams; sold as whole joints weighing 2-3 kg (4½-6½ lb), they come from the haunch and are cured then smoked and cooked through for a moist finish with a deeper gamier flavour. In season he hot-smokes pheasant and sells them vacuum-packed as whole birds or as two drumsticks or two breasts; and between August and January he also hot-smokes grouse.

Stockists

London: Harrods

Harvey Nichols

Selfridges

Lothian: Jenners

Tays: Keracher

The raspberries of Blairgowrie have a reputation for their fine taste, but whether it is because of the climate or the limy soil no one seems to sure. Within the area you can still pick-your-own at **Bankhead of Kinloch**, MEIGLE PH12 8QY ☎ 01828 640265 fax 01828 640687 who have 6 acres of Glen Moy and Glen Prosen raspberries as well as Elsanta and Pegasus strawberries, redcurrants, blackcurrants and white currants and gooseberries. At **Stiellsmuir Farm, Woodland Road, Rosemount**, BLAIRGOWRIE PH10 6LE ☎ 01250 872237 picking starts around the second week of July, but it is wise to telephone to check.

McIntyre's
2 Main Street, Perth, Tayside PH2 7HB

PERTH
Morning Rolls

☎ 01738 626962   **FAX** 01738 628211   **CONTACT** Arthur McIntyre   **HOURS** Mon-Fri 8.00-17.00 Sat 8.00-14.00   **DIRECTIONS** By old Perth bridge on road to Scone Palace, on corner.

I make no claims to being an expert myself, but I am reliably informed that McIntyre's make the best morning rolls in Scotland. Morning rolls, for the uninitiated, are creamy, squidgy and soft to bite – not unlike a bap down South – and must be freshly baked every morning. Arthur McIntyre makes his with white Canadian flour (for the high protein level), lard, water, malt, sugar, salt and live fresh yeast. The dough has two risings: one on the table, the other in a steam press. The secret, so he tells me, lies in hand-mixing and a complete fermentation. He also puts the dough through flour at each stage he handles it, to give his rolls that floury crust finish essential for the best of morning rolls.

    If you have never tried one, be warned, morning rolls are eaten in the morning. Like a true French *baguette*, they do not last through a day. Anyway, McIntyre's is usually sold out by mid-morning .

While you're in the area...

Tombuie Smokehouse, ABERFELDY PH15 2JS ☎ 01887 820127 fax 01828 820038 cold-smoke among other things Perthshire lamb. Sold as either whole legs weighing 1.8-2.3 kg (4-5 lb) or mini-roasts, boned joints from the leg weighing 350-400 g (12-14 oz), they are brined then smoked 'for a number of days', leaving 'hostesses or chefs to cook them in imaginative ways'. More reports please.

North Street Dairy, North Street, FORFAR DD8 3BJ ☎ 01307 463796 must be one of the few milk-bottling plants left in Britain that churns butter. Using the surplus cream from skimming the milk, it is actually made in a food-mixer rather than a churn. Bright yellow, lusciously rich and slightly salted, buy it from Mrs McLeod who presides at her desk next to the freezer which also houses the milk.

Star Rock Shop, 25 Roods, KIRRIEMIUR DD8 4EZ ☎ 01575 572579 make a number of old-fashioned boilings (boiled sweets), including humbugs, horehounds, barley sugar and star rock. A mixture of sugar, syrup, water and lemon essence, this is boiled, cooled down then pulled into long thin brittle sticks that taste of lemon. As far as I know, they are the only shop still producing it.

Fishmongers **Andrew Keracher, 168 South Street, PERTH PH2 8NY ☎ 01738 638374** with branches at **5-6 Whitefriars Street, PERTH PH1 1PP ☎ 01738 38454, 64 King Street, CRIEFF PH7 3AX ☎ 01764 652025** and **108 Market Street, ST ANDREWS KY16 9PB ☎ 01334 72541** have a good range of fresh fish and shellfish, including monkfish tails, netted sea trout, oysters, winkles and live lobsters in a vivier. In season they sell samphire and game, and they also smoke a wide range of fish.

Scone Palace, PERTH PH2 6BD ☎ 01738 552300 fax 01738 552588 now runs a produce shop in the basement. Nicola Robinson bakes in the glass-walled kitchen attached to the shop, so you can see her at work. She makes an all-butter shortbread with rice flour for a gritty texture; black bun; marmalade cake with satisfying chunks of peel; scones and soda bread. She also makes various chutneys using produce from the garden and Seville Orange marmalade.

The Cheese Shop, Westfields, Blairgowrie, RATTRAY PH10 7HY ☎ 01250 872493 is run single-handedly by Mrs McDonald, who describes herself as 'a little old lady who never rests'. She is also good for a gossip and will sell you more cheese than you probably ever intended to buy. Her Scottish range is perhaps limited, but she is so charming that no one minds. While you are there, stock up on crisp oatcakes from a local baker, packets of dried ceps gathered nearby and, in season, pop over the road to buy punnets of ready-picked raspberries from Thompsons Fruit Farm.

Wales
Clwyd
Map No. 7

Alwyn Thomas Bakery
124 Vale Street, Denbigh, Clwyd LL16 3BS

☎ 01745 812068 **CONTACT** *Alwyn Thomas* **HOURS** Mon-Sat 8.30-17.00
Thurs 8.30-13.30 **DIRECTIONS** *In town centre.*

Alywn Thomas is what I like to call a 'proper' baker, with everything for
both this shop and 'up top' at 47 High Street, Denbigh ☎ 01745
814080 baked on the premises. White bread is made with untreated
flour, milk powder, salt, water and yeast by the bulk fermentation
process. First he makes a sponge and leaves it for about 20 hours to
develop; this is, as Alwyn puts it 'the source of flavour to my bread'.
Then he mixes it in the proportions of one-third sponge to two-thirds
flour, leaves it to rise, knocks it back, cuts it or hand-moulds it into
loaves, and leaves it to rise again before baking. Of course, this is how
all our white bread was once made, but sadly it is all too rare to find a
baker who still indulges in the time-consuming practice.

Brown bread is made from flour from Pentrefoelas Mill *see below*, and
organic from Pimhill in Shropshire. Alwyn also bakes a dark and light
rye with a nicely developed sour tinge; multigrain; soda bran; and his
version of the current 'trendies', such as focaccia and ciabatta. In the
more traditional line, there are griddle scones and Welsh cakes to
order; bara brith is made to an old recipe, which includes spices, cherries and mixed peel, butter, lard, fresh eggs, and brown sugar. Heavily
spiced and quite bready in texture, it is a satisfying, if heavy, example.
Christmas pudding is made with just a small amount of flour but, not

Stockists

Clwyd: Forge
Stores
- - - - - - - - -
Gellifor Post Office
- - - - - - - - -
Jan's
- - - - - - - - -
Llandyrnog Post
Office

**The Watermill, PENTREFOELAS, Betws-y-Coed LL24 0HU ☎
01690 770201** *stone-grinds a 100 per cent strong flour made from 70 per
cent Canadian and 30 per cent English wheat, especially suited for bread-
making. The water-powered mill stands in the post office gardens and here you can always buy the
flour and stop for a cup of tea.*

surprisingly, lots of breadcrumbs, suet, eggs, vine fruits and Irish stout, rum, brandy and sherry. These are to be found in the shop from September onwards. Just to prove how many egg yolks he uses in his baking, Alwyn is a good source for meringues and meringue flats, with or without hazelnuts.

While you're in the area...

As the setting of *The Flopsy Bunnies*, Beatrix Potter fans probably already know about **Gwaynynog Country World, Pentrefoelas Road, DENBIGH LL16 5NU ☎ 01745 812991**. They also make their own ice-cream and sell a selection of Welsh produce.

Ty Newydd Farm Shop, The Green, DENBIGH ☎ 01745 812882 is a good source of organic (to Soil Association) vegetables. Here you can find various lettuces, peas, spinach, courgettes, cherry tomatoes and a good choice of potatoes, including Maris Bard, Pentland Javelin, Cara and Romano.

Dyfed

Map No. 7

Wendy Brandon
Felin Wen, Boncath, Dyfed SA37 OJR

☎ 01239 841568 **FAX** *01239 841746* **CONTACT** *Wendy Brandon* **HOURS** *Mon-Fri 9.00-17.00* **CARDS** *Access, Mastercard, Visa* **DIRECTIONS** *From Newcastle Emlyn, take A484 towards Cenarth. Follow the road about 2½ miles and turn left on to the B4332, signposted Boncath. Follow the road into Boncath and turn right at the crossroads, signposted Bwlch-y-groes. Jam factory is on the right at the bottom of the hill.*

Wendy Brandon makes excessively good preserves. Visit her in her kitchen unit attached to a picture-postcard stone mill deep in the heart

MAP 7   DYFED   **379**

of rural Wales and you will find a true preserve-maker at work. Everything is done 'properly', using fresh (or frozen out-of-season) fruit and vegetables, fresh spices and good cider vinegars. Commercial pectin is banned, 'we don't need it. If I'm making an apricot jam I'll put stones in and kernels or

> To keep them busy during the quieter winter months, in their hotel kitchen **Welsh Rarebit Products, Penbontbren Farm Hotel, GLYNARTHEN, Cardigan SA44 6PE** ☎ **01239 810248** fax **01239 811129** make a loose-set fruity raspberry jam with kirsch, three-fruit marmalade with ginger brandy and a honey mustard.

apple cores or I'll make my own apple pectin'. Wendy also works in small batches, so textures and vibrant flavours are retained.

Wendy makes four distinctive ranges of jams, chutneys and marmalades: 'Green-label' for no salt and no added sugar (but concentrated apple juice instead); 'Orange-label' (marmalades only), made with a mixture of cane sugar and concentrated apple juice; 'Red-label' for traditional preserves (meaning with sugar); and 'Blue-label' for her international range. Although I must mention the clear clean tang of her Red-label Lemon & Lime Marmalade and the gentle Italian-style Pickled Onions in Oil, it is her Blue-label range that is so unusual and exciting. Here Wendy's inventiveness and expertise come to the fore.

Try the Pineapple Pickle, made with dried pineapple, apples, vegetable oil, cane sugar, cider vinegar, spices, garlic, ginger, chillies and salt. She recommends using it with ham, pork or fish, but when chef Stephen Bull was cooking at my home, he used it in a salad dressing poured over mixed leaves and it was a sensation. Her Green Bean Chutney, made with sliced and lightly spiced green beans lightly thickened with cornflour, has a texture and gentle sweetness that is incredibly satisfying. As for Aubergine Pickle, it is a superb combination of spices underscoring the (again) firm texture of the vegetable. All too often pickles and chutneys are an amorphous mass lacking in texture and clear flavours; not so with Wendy's, each one retains the intrinsic character and flavour of the main ingredient, while setting it against a background of subtle spices. That having been said, Lemon & Chilli is violent; 'seriously hot' would be understating its power but, even as I reached out for a glass of water, I could recognize an interesting balance of fieriness sharpened by a citrus tang.

There are also her cloudy but definitely fruity fruit vinegars; sweet and crunchy pickled radishes, subtly flavoured with honey, ginger, soy sauce and star anise; and Green Label fruit sauces, including a rich smooth buttery Spiced Apple. Wendy's style is to create flavour and interest and in her hands even the more mundane of jams or pickles packs an interesting punch.

Stockists

Ches: Mooreland Foods

Lancs: Ramsbottom Victuallers

London: Villandry

Lothian: Iain Mellis

Notts: Smiths Deli

Oneida Fish, Oneida Viviers, Brunel Quay, NEYLAND SA73 1PY ☎ **01646 600220** fax **01646 602240** are happy to let you choose your own shellfish from the seemingly miles and miles of filtered sea-water holding tanks. Here you will find lobsters, velvet and spider crabs, crawfish, cockles, winkles, and a few Native oysters. Remember, however, as they are strictly speaking wholesalers, everything is sold live.

CASTLE MORRIS
Cheese

Llangloffan Farmhouse Cheese

Llangloffan Farm, Castle Morris, Haverfordwest,
Dyfed SA62 5ET

☎/FAX 01348 891241 **CONTACT** Leon Downey **HOURS** Mon-Sat 9.00-17.00 **DIRECTIONS** From Fishguard, take A487 towards St David's. Follow the road about 4 miles and turn left, signposted Llangloffan Farmhouse Cheese. Follow the road about ½ mile and farm is signposted on the left.

One-time viola player with the Hallé Orchestra, Leon Downey now performs most days on a round cheese vat. Join him any morning on a Monday, Wednesday, Thursday or Saturday in April or October or between Monday and Saturday from May to September in his dairy to see him making cheese. The audience may be smaller and the ovation quieter, but he finds it just as satisfying.

Llangloffan is a farmhouse cheese in every sense of the word, made on-farm with the unpasteurized milk from their 20-strong herd; with 10 Jersey and 10 Brown cows, they graze on permanent ley pastures for a rich milk which transforms into a rich grassy cheese with great depth. Cheese-making starts up some time in March, when the cows go, and lasts through to December, when the cows come in. Leon only makes when the cows are on grass and never when they are indoors and fed on silage as, he believes, it taints the milk. The best of all cheeses come from the September milk and these he selects for keeping until Christmas. Llangloffan, he describes as a 'creamy Cheshire' and the curds are broken down in a similar way. Pressed for 2 days, it can be eaten at 10 weeks, when still mild, or matured for up to 6 months, when it becomes far more deeply flavoured. A cheese with a good resonance, quite dry and crumbly, but with a buttery flavour, Leon makes it both plain and flavoured with chives and garlic and coloured red using anatto. You can buy it from the farm-shop, along with various Welsh cheeses and products from Rachel's Dairy *see below*.

Stockists

Gwent: Irma Fingal-Rock Food

Gwynedd: Blas Ar Fwyd

London: Neal's Yard Dairy

Oxon: Wells Stores

Sussex: Adsdean Farm Shop

DOLYBONT
Butter

Rachel's Dairy

Brynllys Farm, Dolybont, Borth, Dyfed SY24 5LZ

☎ 01970 625805 **FAX** 01970 626591 **CONTACT** Rachel Rowlands **HOURS** Mon-Fri 10.00-15.00 Sat & Sun 10.00-16.00 **DIRECTIONS** From Borth, take B4353 towards Llandre. Follow the road about 2 miles and turn right signposted Dolybont. Follow the road about ¼ mile and take the first turning on the left at farm sign.

From a small on-farm dairy processing organic milk, Rachel's Dairy has grown out of all recognition. Yoghurt and their other products are now made in a gleaming processing unit on Aberystwyth's industrial estate and distributed nationally to such multiples as Sainsbury's and Safeway. Even if the factory is out of bounds to the public, you can still visit the farm where, to this day, there are walking routes over the farm with a farm-shop selling their range. Butter and its by-product butter-milk continue to be made on-farm.

Their butter is made with Guernsey milk and is a lactic butter. This means that once the milk is separated, the cream is ripened with a lactic culture for about 3 days to give it a sharper but creamy taste with a good depth. Most butter made in Britain is, in fact, sweet cream butter, that is to say it is made with cream that is usually aged or rested but never cultured. Rachel, however, has chosen to follow the French style of butter-making and the result is a fine example. Tart, creamy and delicate, it is far more gentle than a farmhouse whey butter. Like all good butter-makers, she always churns it in a wooden churn; according to Rachel this is vital, 'other materials will just not do – only wood won't taint the butter'. Once the butter granules are formed and have come together like clusters of grapes, the butter is washed again and again until the water runs clean; then, if required, salt is added. Finally it is patted by hand into neat blocks with wooden butter-pats and wrapped in butter paper.

Stockists

London: Harrods

Selfridges

Sainsbury's

Leo Stores

Safeway

Teifi Cheese
Glynhynod Farm, Ffostrasol, Llandysul, Dyfed SA44 5JY

FFOSTRASOL
Cheese

☎ 01239 851528 **CONTACT** *John Savage* **HOURS** 9.00-18.00 (*Carmarthen Market Wed, Fri & Sat 9.00-16.00*) **CARDS** *Access, Eurocard, Visa* **DIRECTIONS** *From Llandysul, take A486 towards New Quay. Follow the road about 11 miles and turn left, signposted Teifi Cheese, on to a dead-end road. After about ¾ mile, farm is signposted on the left.*

Teifi, a Gouda-style cheese, is made by Patrice, whom John Savage met and married in Holland and had the good sense to bring back to Wales. She works in a round wooden vat imported from Holland and produces 450 and 900-g and 3.5-kg (1, 2 and 8-lb) truckles and 7-9 and 11.3-kg (16-20 and 25-lb) wheels. Her cheese is buttery, dense and smooth, with a light sweetness when young; the longer it is matured, the more it develops its sweet, toffee-like flavour. Patrice also makes the smaller cheeses, flavoured with garlic, garlic & onion, celery, nettle (a traditional Dutch flavouring), sweet pepper, chives, seaweed, mustard seed and cumin seed.

About 2 years ago, Patrice added Caerphilly to her repertoire. She learnt to make it under the guiding hand of the redoubtable cheese-maker Cyril Woolley who has since retired after 52 years, and Patrice's Caerphilly shows the same sure confidence. Using unpasteurized Friesian milk from the neighbouring farm, the essential differ-

Little Acorn Products, Mesen Fach Farm, BETHANIA, Llanon SY23 5NL ☎ *01974 821348 make various cheeses with the unpasteurized milk of their Friesland dairy sheep flock. My favourite is Lady Llanover: hard-pressed for a dense dry texture, then washed with saffron for about a month, it is at its best when matured for 7-8 months, as it develops the powerful tang and crisp pungency of a Manchego.*

ence in Patrice's cheese is that the curds are cut by hand to 'less than walnut-size'. Most Caerphilly-makers use a machine, usually a peg mill, and in doing so tend to extract more moisture from the curds; by cutting by hand you get a looser, crumblier texture and, obviously, a more moist one. Not only is this how traditionalists claim Caerphilly should be made but it also means that it can be matured on without drying out. Consequently you can buy it as a 2-week cheese when it is crumbly, moist but not 'wet' and still acid; also as Mild at 4 weeks, when it starts to soften out; as well as Mature at 8 months, by which time it has a salty edge and is soft with a honey sweetness

The Savages also keep a small Jersey herd exclusively for their cream, butter and soft cheese. Butter is made with the full-cream milk, which Patrice likes to age for at least 2 days before she churns it; it is surprisingly sharp but interestingly creamy.

Stockists

Derbys: Pugsons of Buxton

Devon: Ticklemore Cheese Shop

London: Neal's Yard Dairy

Lothian: Iain Mellis

Surrey: Eastside Cheese

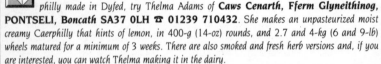

There are only a few cheese-makers still making Caerphilly on-farm. A relatively simple cheese to make, each maker tends to have his or her particular methods or foibles, but characteristically it is a crumbly, quite sharp cheese, eaten comparatively young. At its best it offers a clear clean butteriness with a hint of greenness, often described as lemon-flavoured. Out of the county – and indeed out of Wales altogether – is R. A. Duckett see page 237; for Caerphilly made in Dyfed, try Thelma Adams of **Caws Cenarth, Fferm Glyneithinog, PONTSELI, Boncath SA37 0LH ☎ 01239 710432**. She makes an unpasteurized moist creamy Caerphilly that hints of lemon, in 400-g (14-oz) rounds, and 2.7 and 4-kg (6 and 9-lb) wheels matured for a minimum of 3 weeks. There are also smoked and fresh herb versions and, if you are interested, you can watch Thelma making it in the dairy.

Caws Nantybwla is made at **Nantybwla, College Road, CARMARTHEN SA31 3QS ☎ 01267 237905** from unpasteurized Holstein milk. Matured for a minimum of 4 weeks, it is quite sharp but has a pleasant underlying richness, although it can on occasions be quite dry and crumbly. They also make it flavoured with laver bread. Last but by no means last is **Teifi Cheese** see above.

JOHNSTON
Pure-bred Meat

Neville Pugh

Hayston Hall, Johnston, Haverfordwest, Dyfed SA62 3HJ

☎ 01437 890143   **CONTACT** Neville Pugh – telephone ahead

Neville Pugh rears small quantities of the national breeds – Black Welsh Mountain sheep and Welsh Black cattle. Neville believes both have superb eating qualities, particularly when bred as pure-breeds as his are. Lamb is in season mainly from late August to the end of the year and it is bred 'naturally' on low-lying grasslands. Butchering is done by Postmaster Martin Davies, who also runs a butcher shop. With its finely grained meat and rich sweet fresh flavour, lamb is sold only as whole carcasses butchered into the various cuts and joints.

Kept in during the winter months, his cattle are hay-fed and the rest of the year they are out on grass. Neville rears bullocks (steers) for meat, taking them up to about 2 years when they are good hefty beasts. Hung for about 3 weeks, the beef is juicy with a good lingering glow and sold in packs of 1.8-2.3 kg (4-5 lb) of prime roasting joint, 1.8-2.3 kg (4-5 lb) of rolled rib or similar, 6 prime steaks, 1.35 kg (3 lb) of casserole beef and 1.35 kg (3 lb) of mince. Available as fresh meat, mainly from August through to March, quantities are limited so it is best to put your name down as soon as possible.

Llanboidy Cheesemakers
Cilowen Uchaf, Login, Whitland, Dyfed SA34 OTJ

☎ 01994 448303 **CONTACT** Sue Jones – *telephone ahead*

Sue Jones runs one of the few milking herds of rare-breed Red Poll cattle in the country. Their rich milk is ideal for cheese-making as 'the ratio of protein to fat is well-balanced and the molecules are small so that the cheese is smooth, even in texture and easy to digest'. She makes the cheese to an old Dunlop recipe, using the unpasteurized morning and evening milk from her 40-odd cows. It is heated, started, renneted, the curds are cut, milled, packed into 4.5-kg (10-lb) wheels and pressed for about 36 hours. Then it is dry-salted and matured for anything from 2 to 11 months. When fairly young it is still mild but buttery; as it matures, however, a fullness develops, revealing a warm butteriness backed by a mild fragrance of herbs. Sue also makes Llanboidy, with added laver bread from the Gower Peninsula. The laver bread hastens the maturity and gives the cheese a speckly appearance and a crisp saltiness.

Penbryn Cheese
Ty Hen Farm, Penbryn, Sarnau, Dyfed SA44 6RD

☎ 01239 810347 **CONTACT** *Andrea Degen* **HOURS** *Mon-Sat 12.00-17.00* **DIRECTIONS** *From Cardigan, take A487 towards Aberystwyth. After 8 miles, at Tan-y-groes, take second turning on left out of Tan-y-groes. Go down hill to staggered crossroads where farm is signposted.*

In a county awash with on-farm cheese-makers, it is always satisfying to find a particular cheese that started in a small way and shows every sign of developing well and improving over the years. Penbryn is one such cheese. Made by Andrea Degen using unpasteurized organic (to Soil Association standards) milk from their mainly Friesian herd, it is very similar to a Gouda – but then Andrea, like Patrice Savage with her Teifi *see page 381*, also came over from Holland.

Andrea makes her cheese in the typical Gouda fashion, pumping off the whey then adding hot water to the curds. This gives it that typical creamy, almost caramely, sweetness as the curds are, in effect, lightly cooked. Penbryn is then packed into 900-g and 2.3-kg (2 and 5-lb) moulds, pressed, turned and pressed again, making sure that (as for all

LOGIN
Cheese

Stockists

Dyfed: Deli Delights

Gwent: Irma Fingal-Rock Food

Gwynedd: Blas Ar Fwyd

Heref: The Mousetrap

London: Harrods

PENBRYN
Cheese

Stockists

Dyfed: Deli Delights

Llwynhelyg Farmshop

The Fish Plaice, Walter Davies & Sons, The Docks, MILFORD HAVEN SA73 3AE ☎ 01646 692331 fax 01646 690810 *is – as its address suggests – right down by the docks, next door to the fish market. Fish is gleamingly fresh, straight off the small trawlers fishing along the Welsh coastline and in the Irish Sea. Here you will find shining examples of brill, turbot, skate, dabs, lemon and sand soles, red and grey mullet, and sea bass. In fact, if it is caught on the boats, it will be on sale in the shop. Service is friendly and obliging, with gutting, filleting and scaling done in a flash by 'the boys'.*

Further up the coast and also renowned for the freshness of their fish is **The Fish on the Quay, Cadwgan Place, ABERAERON SA46 0BU ☎ 01545 571294**. *Sewin comes from the river Aeron (the shop overlooks its estuary), live cockles or cooked cockle meat from Penclawdd see page 387 and there are brill, cod, codling, whiting, huss, turbot and plaice caught mainly from day boats fishing in Cardigan Bay. Shellfish, such as crabs, lobster, whelks and rock prawns (big shrimps), is mostly local and freshly cooked in the shop. Everything is displayed whole and filleted to order, so you can see exactly how fresh it is.*

good Goudas) 'it is never thicker than one-third of its width; otherwise it will never ripen evenly'. It is briefly brined and left to mature, turned every day for the first 2 weeks, then every other day until it is 2 months and from then on, twice a week.

In Holland, Andrea told me, most cheese-makers put a plastic coating around their cheese after brining, but then 'The Dutch are so clean and tidy. For them a natural mould is something of the past'. Disregarding the practices of her countrymen, she does allow her cheeses to develop their natural moulds in the proven belief that it 'adds to the flavour and keeps the flavour in'. She has a point: if you compare Penbryn to a mass-produced Gouda there is no contest. Andrea's reveals a complexity and interest which bears no comparison. Mild, a 2-month cheese, is moist with a delicate sweet nuttiness; Mature, a 7-8-month cheese, is firmer and drier with a cracking edge that reverberates in the mouth.

WEST WILLIAMSTON Oysters

Carew Oysters

Tything Barn, West Williamston, Cresselly, Kilgetty, Dyfed SA68 0TN

☎ 01646 651452 **FAX** 01646 651307 **CONTACT** Joe Folder **HOURS** Mon-Sat 8.00-18.00 Sun 9.00-13.00 **CARDS** Mastercard, Visa **DIRECTIONS** From Carew, take A4075 towards Canaston Bridge. Cross the old bridge in Carew and take the first turning on the left, at sign for the picnic site. Follow the road about 1 mile and oystery is on the left.

When Joe and June Folder first saw Tything Barn, they fell in love with the place – and you can see why. They are surrounded by little meadows and ancient limestone quarries, the river Carew flows past just a few yards away from their doorstep and low tide reveals the salt marsh that is a feeding ground for ducks and waders, and on its opposite bank stand the impressive ruins of the Norman Carew Castle.

Joe farms his Pacific oysters fairly high up in the estuary of the river Carew, about 20 miles from the sea. As a result they tend to be sweeter and less salty than most. The water is brackish and rich in plankton, and the big tidal range that deposits silt right where the oysters are sited causes them to 'feed well'. For these reasons his oysters are plump and with larger than usual frilly shells, often splashed with colour. Sold in one size, the equivalent to 3s, they are purified and pressure-washed inside and out to ensure they reach the customer clean.

Visitors to the oyster farm are welcome to picnic in the specially provided area – oysters will be opened for you, but you must bring everything else – with the breathtaking view over the river down to where the oysters are farmed. There is an 'explanation centre', where you can find out about the oyster's life cycle. Otherwise, Joe operates a 24-hour mail-order service and, by special arrangement, 'Deliver and Open' and 'Manage and Man' (oyster bar) services.

Stockists
Glam: Ashtons Fishmongers

Glos: J. W. Rigby

Gwent: Vin Sullivan

Humber: Superior Seafoods

W. Mids: George Smith

Now under new management, **The Treehouse, 2 Pier Street, ABERYSTWYTH SY23 2LJ ☎ 01970 615791** *has kept the same policy of selling salads made freshly each day or lettuces, salad leaves and vegetables grown to organic (Soil Association) standards at Borth, on land adjoining Rachel's Dairy see page 380. Most of what is grown are outdoor crops, so it follows that most of what is sold is anything that can be grown outdoors in Wales. These include Little Gem, lollo rosso and biondo, Four Seasons lettuces, mixed Japanese greens, radicchio and different endives, healthy bunches of beetroots with their tops on, various herbs, potatoes, and courgettes with their flowers. They also sell various Welsh cheeses, Graig Farm meat see pàge 398, bread baked upstairs in their tea-room, and own-made herb-flavoured vinegars from elder-flower, tarragon, borage, raspberry, green and purple basil, and sage.*

While you're in the area...

Coed Cwm Wyre, Old Mill Gardens, LLANRHYSTUD SY23 5DN ☎ 01974 202922 grow a wide and interesting range of vegetables, including such baby vegetables as carrots, leeks, cauliflowers, cucumbers and turnips, a wide range of lettuces, aubergines, various herbs and, as they have one vine in a poly-tunnel, even grapes.

Andrew Malein, Penpant, NINE WELLS, Solva SA62 6UH ☎ 01437 721369 comes highly recommended by Neville Pugh *see page 382* for his vegetables. These include various lettuces, scorzonera, mangetout, broad beans, various lettuces, and soft fruit.

Quail World, Glenydd, PENRHIWLLAN, Llandysul SA44 5NR ☎ 01559 370105 sells oven-ready quail, cold-smoked quail, fresh quails' eggs and jars of quails' eggs pickled in a sharp Champagne vinegar.

Tucked away in a little back street with a stream running through the back garden is **Y Felin** (The Mill), **Mill Street, ST DOGMAELS, Cardigan SA43 3DY ☎ 01239 613999**. From here you can buy stone-ground flours, including a 100 per cent wholemeal, unbleached white, rye and occasionally barley. Miller, Michael Hall also runs a kiln where he malts wheat for a nutty 'Granary-type' flour with a wholemeal base, with rye flour, malted wheat, malted grain and malt flour. He also blends a seed-and-herb flour, again with a wholemeal base with sunflower, poppy, sesame and millet seeds and sage and thyme; and makes up an Irish soda bread mix. He sells bread baked in Cardigan with his own flour.

Glamorgan

Map No. 7

Gorno's Charcuterie,
30 Tudor Street, Grangetown, Cardiff, Glamorgan CF1 8RH

☎ 01222 372782 **CONTACT** *Franco Gorno* **HOURS** Mon-Sat: 8.00-17.30
DIRECTIONS In *city centre, near the Empire Pool.*

Wales boasts a large Italian community, many having come over – as did Franco Gorno – to work in the steel industry. When employment in that sector declined, they were mostly drawn to making ice-cream or running pizza parlours. As far as I know Franco is the only Italian to run a proper Italian *salumeria* here in the centre of Cardiff. Franco hails from the Po Valley in Lombardy and it follows that his repertoire should include their regional specialities.

His range can be divided into fresh products for cooking (*salumi freschi da cuocere*), matured products ready to eat (*salumi stragionati*), and cooked pork products (*salumi cotti*). For everything, he uses free-range pork. He makes Milano or *luganica*, a single coil of thin, fresh and lightly spiced sausages; *pancetta affumicata*, dry-salted matured and smoked belly of pork. In winter only, Franco produces *cotechino*, the fat boiling sausage; and *Rosetta Lombarda*, Lombardy rosette made with coarsely chopped shoulder of lightly cured pork, pistachios, spices, herbs, garlic and white wine, wrapped in caul.

Franco makes authentic salamis by salting the various cuts of pork, chopping or mincing it to the required texture, then adding the spices and stuffing the skins for curing. Lombardo is spiked with black pepper, Calabrese a fiery mix of chilli and fennel seed, Napoli comes lightly smoked and the finer textured Milano is suitably mild. He prepares his own *prosciutto crudo*, a cured raw ham that is succulent with a well-defined flavour, *coppa* cured from the loin, and Lonza *piccante* or *al pepe nero* where the centre of the pork loin is cured in wine, brandy, spices and either hot capsicums or black pepper for biting slices of tender meat. Smoked pepperoni is very popular on pizzas and he also makes pork *rillettes*, black and white puddings and an excellent dry-cured bacon.

Stockists

Glam: Glyn T. Jenkins

Munchies

Shelley's Delicatessen

Gwent: William Baldock Cooked Meat Delicatessen

Powys: Top Drawer

Cwm Tawe Cheese

Cwm Cyrnach Farm, Glais, Swansea, Glamorgan SA9 2NH

☎ 01792 844637   **CONTACT** *Giovanni Irranca – telephone ahead*

It may be difficult to find a more Welsh-sounding cheese than Cwm Tawe (*cwm*, meaning hill, by the river Tawe), but do not be fooled, the cheese is Pecorino and its maker, Giovanni Irranca, is about as Italian as you can get, with an accent as thick as a bowl of minestrone. In fact Giovanni has lived here for several years, but came to cheese-making late in life, on retiring. He did help his grandfather though, when a child in Italy, and no doubt harboured fond memories.

Surprisingly, Giovanni thinks that making Pecorino in Wales has advantages. 'It's made mostly in Southern Italy and on the islands. It's hot there and by early summer there's no grass left. That makes for a rich strong cheese. Here it's greener and grassier, so the cheese is lighter, not so condensed'. He keeps a flock of 120 Friesland ewes, tended by a shepherd, while he preoccupies himself with the cheese-making. As with all ewes'-milk cheeses, making is a seasonal business, as ewe's milk only flows from April to mid-November. Giovanni produces his Pecorino in 450-g and 2.3-kg (1 and 5-lb) rounds, selling 2-month cheeses 'for the cheese-board' while they are moist with a light pleasant floweriness. The harder, drier and more intense 6-7-month cheeses, he specifies, are for grating. In Giovanni's opinion, 'the older the cheeses get, the better they are … like women'. Spoken like a true Italian.

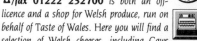

Recently opened **The Old Brewery Shop, St Mary's Street, CARDIFF CF1 1SP** ☎/fax **01222 232700** is both an off-licence and a shop for Welsh produce, run on behalf of Taste of Wales. Here you will find a selection of Welsh cheeses, including Caws Cenarth see page 382, Lady Llanover see page 381 and Llanboidy see page 383; jams, pickles and preserves from Wendy Brandon see page 378 and Welsh Mountain Garden see page 395; flour from Y felin see page 385; jars of cockles and the inevitable tins of laver bread; and chocolates from Pembertons.

Sidebar

GLAIS
Pecorino

Stockists

Derbys: Chatsworth Farmshop

Gwent: Abergavenny Fine Foods

London: Barstow & Barr

Neal's Yard Dairy

Lothian: Iain Mellis

Lynch Cockle Factory

Marsh Road, Gwernfrwdd, Penclawdd, Glamorgan SA4 3TN

☎ 01792 850033   **CONTACT** *Brian Jones – telephone ahead*

All along the wide open expanses of sand flats that hug the coast of the Gower Peninsula is where you will find cockles, buried deep in the sands. They are gathered daily by cockle collectors who are limited in number by licence to 46; each collector has to gather by rake and, in order to protect the harvest, cannot collect more than 500 cwt a day.

Cockle gathering is immensely hard work as it is still done by hand, using a rake to turn up the sands. If you do see a tractor on the beach, it is there only to transport the gatherers down to the sea's edge or to bring their haul up to the shore-line. Raking for the full day's weight usually takes a good 4 hours 'from tide to tide' and in the winter

GWERN-FRWYDD
Cockles

Pencoed Organic Growers, Felindre Nurseries, Felindre, PENCOED CF35 5HU ☎ 01656 861956 *grow organically (to Soil Association standards) such vegetables as curly kale, cabbages, runner beans, broccoli, courgettes, cherry tomatoes, as well as various herbs, salads and salad leaves, including green and red lollo, green and red oak-leaf, Four Seasons and a red-tinged butterhead. In winter, there are at least ten different leaves, such as mizuna; the spoon-shaped leaves of tatsoi with their gelatinous texture; crisp komatsuna with a clear sharp bite; a seriously mustardy amsoi; and the milder gai-cho which would give any salad a 'bit of pep'. In the European line, they grow rocket, radicchio, claytonia and corn salad.*

months the wind can blow chillingly. Collected throughout the year, cockles are at their plumpest from May to December, as once the frosts come they 'shrink back in their shells'.

The peninsula is dotted with cockle factories where the cockles are boiled in huge cauldrons, separated from their shells and washed clean of sand. Some will sell to you if you are passing by, other refuse. There have been attempts to bring them together into larger units, but cockle gatherers are notoriously independent and have worked in family units for generations. Brian Jones has a large (certainly by comparison to the others) cockle unit and is one of the more go-ahead cockle collectors. He is more than happy to sell cockle meat from the door. Although he does not collect it himself, he also has supplies of laver bread boiled up into a deep dark green dense mass and potted in 225-g (8-oz) tubs. Although available throughout the year, this is considered to be at its peak of flavour during the winter months; the exact opposite of the cockle.

PENDOLYN
Elderflower
Cordial

Llanerch Vineyards
Hensol, Pendolyn, Pendolyn, Glamorgan CF7 8JU

☎ 01443 225877 **FAX** 01443 225546 **CONTACT** Mr Peter Andrews **HOURS** Visitor Centre 10.00- 17.00 **DIRECTIONS** *From Junction 34 of M4, follow signposts to vineyard, which is 1 mile south.*

With a Welsh 'Oscar' awarded for tourism, Llanerch Vineyards not only produces elderflower drinks and 4 wines (3 white and a rosé) but also runs a guest house, wine bar, coffee shop and guided tours, and rents out cottages.

The elderflower cordial is called Cariad, a Welsh term of endearment like 'dear' or 'sweetheart' and rather an appropriate name for this drink. It is made by Peter Andrews who, having trained as a pharmacist, understands its true nature. First he advertises in the local papers for freshly picked elderflower heads that must be picked and delivered on the same day; then he infuses them in a sugar solution with citric acid and fresh lemon juice, turning and immersing them using, of all things, an artexing paddle to push the flowerheads right down into the huge barrels so the 'liquid oozes through'. The point is to extract as much of their muscat flavour as possible. They can stay in to the syrup for months, but this has to be finely judged as the last thing he wants is for them to start fermenting. The flowerheads are strained off and the liquid is then filtered as for a wine. Stored as a concentrate, it is sent off for bottling. The cordial, sold in 37.5-cl (about ½-pint) bottles, is diluted with a sucrose solution for a pert flowery drink; and the spritz 'a sort of non-alcoholic Champagne, only no one is allowed to call it that' is further diluted with carbonated spring water and bottled into 25 and 75-cl bottles. Refreshing, with a flavour which Peter points out 'is not unlike a Riesling wine', it makes for a fine summer drink when chilled.

Stockists

Glam: Howells
The Old Brewery Shop

Ices from the Fruit Garden
Groes Faen Road, Peterston-super-Ely, Cardiff, Glamorgan CF5 6NE

PETERSTON-SUPER-ELY
Ice-cream and Fruit

☎ 01446 760358 **CONTACT** *Linda George* **HOURS** *May to end-Aug: 9.00-20.00* **DIRECTIONS** *From Cardiff, take A48 towards Swansea. After 5 miles, at main road junction turn right for Peterston. Farm is signposted 'PYO Fruit Farm'.*

Linda George and her husband Charles run about 5½ acres of pick-your-own and ready-picked fruit and asparagus. Grown in half an acre, the asparagus kicks off the season. Sold as ready-picked and graded into sprue, cooking and mixed, it lasts through to mid-June. Describing the land as 'top grade loam on a south-facing well-drained site and well suited to soft fruit', they grow Elsanta strawberries and other varieties that 'vary enormously from year to year', such as Red Lake redcurrants; a green cooking gooseberry that 'ripens to dessert quality' and the red Whinham's Industry; and a big juicy cultivated blackberry. There are also various hybrid berries, including tayberries, tummelberries (a raspberry-blackberry cross that is bigger than a tayberry but perhaps lacks its flavour) and jostaberries, a blackcurrant-gooseberry cross that 'makes gorgeous jam'.

Ice-cream started as an extra, purely for the visitors, then it was just 'strawberries and cream'. That side of the business grew, Linda built an ice-cream parlour and began supplying delis and restaurants. The pity is that the product changed; whereas once it was just fruit and cream now she adds emulsifier E471 and sodium alginate as a stabilizer, presumably for commercial considerations. I am not suggesting that there is anything inherently wrong with that and, believe me, I do have sympathy with the reasoning behind it; it is just that these additions detract from the goodness of the products, they so to speak 'gum up the works'. I also cannot believe that their inclusion is inevitable. Where once there

Swansea Market, Oxford Street, **SWANSEA** ☎ **01792 301301** *is set in a light airy and utterly charmless market hall, but the food you will find here is interesting. Unlike any other market I visited, room is made for 'casuals' – growers, mostly from the Gower Peninsula, who come to town and set up on wooden benches or tables to sell their wares. There are freshly cut cauliflowers, bunches of carrots, beetroots dug up that day still with their tops on, earthy potatoes and bunches of herbs. Nearby are the bakery stalls, where cosy ladies cook up Welsh cakes and pancakes on griddles, and fish stalls piled high with Penclawdd cockles see page 387, gooey green-brown fresh laver bread and the inevitable crab sticks. You can buy Thayer's clotted cream, inspect* **Nancy Morgan's** *stack of freshly baked breads and cakes and, from* **Tuckers** *in the corner, buy a leg of Welsh lamb wrapped in caul fat. As markets go in Britain, it is one of the best.* **Cardiff's Central Market, St Mary's Street,** **CARDIFF** ☎ **01222 822670**, *on the other hand, may look more picturesque but the food is perhaps not as varied.* **J. T. Morgan** *sells mountain lamb and some lean-looking, well-trimmed lamb shanks, lamb & mint sausages and freshly cooked pressed chitterlings.* **J. T. Evans** *does a good line in dry-salt bacon and* **Ashtons** *the fishmonger sells a varied range of wet fish, all sort of clams, freshly boiled crabs and, naturally, fresh laver bread.*

was an ice-cream with a clean pure and vibrant flavour made with own-grown fruit, it now has a marginally muddied taste.

Sold in ½ litres (16 fl oz) – in the chicest packaging I've seen – the basic mix contains whole milk, double cream, skimmed milk powder, pasteurized egg yolks and the above mentioned emulsifier and stabilizer. The fat content is around 14 per cent and the over-run (added air) varies from 50 per cent upwards. Flavours include strawberry, gooseberry fool made with her own gooseberries cooked in sugar, and crème brûlée made with the vanilla mixed with caramel. She also makes three fruit sorbets, again using her own fruit: strawberry, blackcurrant and summer fruits – a mixture of tayberries, redcurrants and blackcurrants with blackberry liqueur. Here the fruit flavours were far fresher, if a little sweet for my taste.

Stockists

Glam: Glyn T. Jenkins

- - - - - - - -

Shelley's Delicatessen

ST FAGANS
Bara Brith

Dderwen Bakehouse,
Welsh Folk Museum, St Fagans, Cardiff, Glamorgan CF5 6XB

☎ 01222 569441   **CONTACT** *Chris Gough*   **HOURS** *10.00-17.00 (18.00 July to Sept)*   **DIRECTIONS** *Turn off the M4 at Junction 33 and follow signposts for the Welsh Folk Museum.*

The Welsh Folk Museum is a huge open-air museum with the stated aim 'to show how many of the people of Wales lived, worked and spent their leisure time over the last 400 years'. To this end they have moved 30 original buildings from all over the country and carefully re-erected and furnished them in the period. There is a 1610 farmhouse from Gower, painted red as it was thought the colour protected the house against evil spirits; a working corn-mill with flour for sale; a circular pig-sty, complete with pig; a toll-house; a cock-pit; a saddler's workshop; a smithy; a pottery; and a tannery – all with the appropriate working craftsmen.

The Dderwen Bakehouse built in 1900 comes from Thespian Street in Aberystwyth, where it was the main bake-house or 'commune' (after 'communal oven'). In those days, housewives would prepare the dough at home, bring it to the wood-fired ovens for baking and pay the baker for cooking it. Chris Gough has been installed as the baker and runs it as a shop, using the original brick wall-oven that she fires with silver birch and ash 'as whatever wood you put in makes a difference'. In the tiny cramped shop you can watch her at work, mixing the dough using all the old equipment – wooden dough bins and paddles – and working to traditional recipes, and then buy the bread. It is an imaginative operation which other museums would do well to copy.

Chris makes a nutty dense wholemeal bread; apple bread puffs (slices of apple baked like a turnover in slices of bread for a crisp finish and an interesting contrast of textures); light and cheesy cheese puffs; and bara brith, literally translated, it means 'speckled bread'. Using a yeast-based rich dough, Chris makes hers with eggs, demerara sugar and oil (instead of the more traditional lard), liberally scattered with mixed peel, currants, and raisins. Rich, with a mild fragrance of honey, moist and chewy, it was wonderfully fresh as, if you time your visit right, you can buy it straight out of the oven. At different times, she bakes the range of traditional Welsh cakes and breads. It is worth checking out when she will be there as these are as authentic as you can hope to get.

Gwent

Map No. 7

Abergavenny Fine Foods
4-6 Castle Meadows Park, Abergavenny, Gwent NP7 7RZ

☎ 01873 850001 **FAX** 01873 850002 **CONTACT** Melanie Bowman **HOURS** Mon-Fri 10.00-18.00 **CARDS** Access, Mastercard, Visa **DIRECTIONS** *From Abergavenny, take A40 towards Brecon. At the first roundabout outside Abergavenny, take the first exit and unit is 400 yards on the right.*

Pantysgawn, a soft goats'-milk cheese, was once made on-farm in the Brecon Beacons National Park by Tony Craske using milk from his own herd; now it is made with bought-in pasteurized milk on an industrial unit outside Abergavenny and comes as natural, herb, garlic with chives, and black pepper. It is what I think of as a 'safe' cheese: smooth, mild, bland and very consistent, it is always perfectly acceptable but could never be described as 'great'. The unit is also home to several other cheeses you may have seen in the supermarkets: such as St David's, a mildly flavoured washed-rind cheese made with bought-in pasteurized cows' milk to a Chaume-style recipe; or Chevelles, which is Pantysgawn rolled in breadcrumbs and is suitable for grilling, baking or frying.

What I probably find more interesting than the actual cheeses is the whole operation run by Tony himself. Production has mushroomed over the years and he now runs one of the very few dairy-units in Britain that operates on a medium scale. It is neither a huge and anonymous creamery nor a small on-farm craft operation – it comes somewhere in between, where some attempt is made to introduce character into a cheese while making on a relatively large scale. France boasts several operations on a similar scale, while we – as I have already said – have but very few.

Stockists
London: Harrods

Harvey Nichols

Jeroboams

Paxton & Whitfield

Upper Pant Farm Traditional Meats, Upper Pant Farm, LLANDEWI, Rhydderch **NP7 9TL** ☎ **01873 858091** *do not run a mail-order service as such but organize group deliveries as far afield as London, Cardiff, Bristol and Oxford. Beef is organically reared (to Soil Association standards) from traditional British breeds, either Aberdeen Angus or Hereford, crossed with Continental Limousin and Blonde d'Aquitaine 'for flavour and size'. Slaughtered at 2-3 years and hung for at least 2 weeks, you can order anything from a butchered whole carcass to one-eighth of a carcass (which apparently includes 'roasts, steaks, stewing steaks and mince'). Organic lamb is sold as a whole or half carcass, as is free-range pork.*

Park Farm Natural Meats, Park Farm, LLANTILIO CROSSENNY, Aber- **gavenny NP7 8TD** ☎ **01600 85218** *will not deliver but will sell as butchered joints and cuts from the farm. They are 'recommended strongly' by Food Lover Lloyd Davies, who has 'bought meat there on several occasions and it has always been superb'. They farm on traditional lines, with new season's lamb starting in April and Hereford-cross beef slaughtered at between 15 and 18 months available all year.*

While you're in the area...

Mail Order

laver bread only

Downstairs in **Vin Sullivan Stores, 4 Frogmore Street, ABER-GAVENNY NP7 5AE** ☎ **01873 856989** is an impressive array of ethnic tins and preparations; upstairs is an equally impressive choice of fresh fish. Here you will find brill, fresh laver bread from Swansea, turbot, lemon sole, pollack, plaice, flounder, mackerel and a regular supply of sewin in season. They also sell game from local shoots.

Berryhill Farm, COEDKERNEW, Newport NP1 9UD ☎ **01633 680827 fax 01633 680907** sells both ready-picked and pick-your-own soft fruit: plums including Sanctus Hubertus, a black early that crops in July with a luscious sweetness, and apples. Vegetables include ready-picked asparagus, broad, French and runner beans, Vanessa tomatoes, sweetcorn and such winter squashes as butternut ponca, table ace, sweet dumpling and butternut. There are own-made jams, chutneys and marmalades, as well as Wendy Brandon's *see page* 378; and cakes, such as a traditional fruit cake for Christmas which can be ordered in advance. The rest of the year there are fruit pies, tarte Normande, coffee, chocolate, lemon and vanilla sponges with butter cream, cider and fruit wholemeal cake, Bramley apple or blackcurrant cake and runny honey cake.

Irma Fingal-Rock, 64 Monnow Street, MONMOUTH NP5 3EN ☎ **01600 712372** sells a selection of Welsh cheeses, including Llangloffan *see page* 380, Penbryn *see page* 383 and Llanboidy *see page* 383, as well as the superb Tyn Grug, an organic (to Soil Association standards) Cheddar-style cheese made by Dougal Campbell; Welsh wine made near Monmouth; a glorious rich farmhouse butter made with Jersey cream ripened over 4 days; and organic vegetables to order.

G. & P. Roser, Coleford Road, TUTSHILL, nr Chepstow NP6 7BN ☎ **01291 622063** is more than a mere butchers. Apart from making their pies and dry-curing bacon, they also bake their own bread, sell local game, wild salmon from the rivers Severn and Wye, lamb from their own flock of Jacob sheep and a full-cream farmhouse butter from Netherend Dairy in Woolaston, near Lydney.

Gwynedd

Map No. 7

Capel Garmon Bakery & Post Office
Capel Garmon, Llanrwst, Gwynedd LL26 0RW

☎ 01690 710223 **CONTACT** Roger Cavey **HOURS** Mon-Wed & Fri 8.30-17.30 (closed 13.00-14.00) Thurs & Sat 8.30-12.30 **DIRECTIONS** In village centre.

Bara brith – the fruit or speckled bread of Wales – is ubiquitous around these parts. Of course, I make no claims to having tried a loaf from every single baker but, believe me, I – and Violet occasionally – have tried an awful lot of them, you only have to glance at our hips to know it is true. From our extensive – if not comprehensive – experience, as far as I am concerned the loaves from Capel Garmon Bakery & Post Office rate very highly indeed.

At first glance the bakery/post office perched on the side of Capel Garmon's steep hill does not look too promising. It was taken over about 6 years ago by Roger Cavey, an 'incomer' from Kent whose baking experience until then had been non-existent. With the business came the recipe for bara brith and he has stuck with it – more or less – ever since.

The secret lies in the ingredients: Roger uses flour, yeast, fresh eggs (which he thinks improves its keeping qualities), spices, raisins, sultanas, mixed peel, black treacle and lard. The use of lard is quite controversial, as most bakers have dispensed with it. At one time most bread was made

Gwynedd has a certain reputation for baked goods. **Siwgr a Sbeis** ('Sugar and Spice') **25 Watling Street, LLANRWST LL26 OLS** ☎ 01492 641775, with a branch at **Pen y Bryn, GROESFFORDD, nr Llanrwst** ☎ 01492 641940, bakes

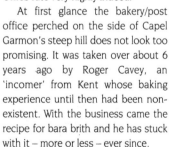

cakes, puddings, pastries and desserts (but no bread). Worth seeking out if you have thrown the diet to the wind is the bread & butter pudding (actually they use marg, but it is good).

Castle Bakery, Castle Street, BEAU-MARIS ANGLESEY OL48 8AN ☎ 01248 810400 have branches all over the county at **212** and **293 High Street** ☎ 01248 351721 and 01248 364000 respectively and **High Street, MENAI BRIDGE** ☎ 01248 712265 and also make a superbly stodgy pudding cake, Welsh pancakes and inevitably, bara brith.

with lard, indeed when Roger came to Capel Garmon lard was included in all the recipes but he removed it for reasons of health from all but the bara brith on the grounds that it is both a traditional and a luxury item and not eaten all the time. So he kept in the lard, and quite right too. All too often you come across bara brith that is dry, crumbly and rather 'short', it obviously cries out for lard to give moisture. Mixed in small batches to allow the dough to rise evenly and at its own pace, he adds treacle for richness and lard for the right texture and moisture. His 450 and 900-g (1 and 2-lb) loaves are dense, moderately spiced and moderately sweet, with a succulence which I assure you has no taint of lard. Locals eat it liberally spread with Welsh salted butter and, according to Roger, prefer the darker loaves from the back of the oven; whereas 'tourists' like them lighter from the front.

Stockists

Gwynedd: Llys Caradog Stores

Farm and Dairy

Siopbach

PENRHOS
Bacon

Cig Moch Pen Llyn (Llyn Peninsula Bacon)
Penyberth, Penrhos, Pwllheli, Gwynedd LL53 7HG

☎ 01758 701737　**CONTACT** George Lovering – telephone ahead

It is not every day that you find a bacon-curing unit on a caravan site next door to a Polish settlement camp but that, dear readers, is where you will find George Lovering at work. Quite how and why he has ended up there is far too convoluted a story, but it takes in rearing bacon pig for Wall's somewhere along the route. Now, at the tender age of 73, he dry-salts whole middles for bacon to a 'closely guarded secret', using Welsh pigs whenever possible.

Curing takes between 14 and 21 days, during which time he drains the sides every day, as 'you can only complete the process by taking off the liquid – otherwise osmosis won't happen'. Once cured the sides are hung to dry for 7-21 days, again depending on the conditions of both the meat and climate; this is a crucial part of the process as it enables the bacon to dry out and mature, thus enhancing its texture and flavour. Cut into rashers right across the belly and back into horse-shoe shaped slices, this is fine bacon – it is dry, with a good bite and a clean marked flavour with a pleasing layer of fat and it certainly does not shrink or splutter in the pan.

Stockists

Gwynedd: Brian Hughes

Spar

Talafon Stores

Not a million miles away is **Dafydd Evans, Dolwgan, GARNDOL-BENMAEN LL51 9AJ** ☎ **01766 530639** who also dry-cures bacon. He uses a mixture of sea salt and ordinary salt and saltpetre, cures for about 6 days, then hangs for no more than a day on the grounds his customers like it wet. His bacon is softer in texture but saltier in flavour – and certainly better than most.

The Fridge at PORT PENRHYN, Bangor LL57 4HN ☎ **01248 351814 fax 01248 351651**, down by the quay overlooking Anglesey, has a good choice of fresh fish from local boats. At the time of my visit in summer, there was skate, sea bream, sea bass, sea trout, brill, herrings and lemon sole. Lobsters and crabs are kept in the vivier, with 'a bit of seaweed to keep them company', and dressed crab is usually available. Mussels and oysters are farmed in the Menai Straits, scallops come from the Irish Sea by the Isle of Man and wild salmon is caught by hook and line locally.

Popty'r Dref, Upper Smithfield Street, DOLGELLAU LL40 1ET ☎ 01341 422507 means 'the village oven' in Welsh. From their two ovens – one original and the other modern – they bake most everything you could hope for from a village bakery. The 100 per cent stone-ground bread has a pleasant nutty flavour with a crumbly moist texture not unlike soda bread; white is well crusted and tightly textured; and they also bake mixed herb rolls with poppy & sesame seeds. Bara brith comes heavily spiced, with an abundance of vine fruits and – perhaps controversially – cherries; and a whole range of cakes, biscuits and slices, such as Apricot crewi with Felin Crewi flour, apricots and sultanas. Honey buns are sticky sweet and similar to a doughnut but, in spite of their name, are made from a sweet yeast dough batter, brown sugar and no honey. There are fat Chelsea buns studded with currants; scones; comforting slices of bread pudding; apple turnovers; squidgy eclairs, macaroons and, in summer, fresh strawberry tarts.

Welsh Mountain Garden

Hotel Maes-y-Neuadd, Talsarnau, Harlech,
Gwynedd LL47 6YA

☎ 01766 780319 **FAX** 01766 780211 **CONTACT** June Slater **HOURS** 8.30–23.00 **CARDS** Access, Visa **DIRECTIONS** From Porthmadog, take A487 towards Penrhyn Deudraeth. Take toll-bridge signposted Harlech on A496 and follow Harlech signs (road becomes B4573). Just before a stone bridge, turn left up lane. Hotel is ½ mile along.

Like several of the 'smarter' country house hotels, Maes-y-Neuadd has its own vegetable garden to supply its kitchen. Chef Peter Jackson, obviously a thrifty sort of chap, was concerned about wasting the surplus and so a range of jams, dressings, flavoured oils and vinegars under the label 'Welsh Mountain Garden' was started. At first it was a question of 'recycling mineral bottle and jam jars' but since the produce did well everything now comes prettily packaged in spanking new bottles and glass jars.

Preparation still takes place in the hotel's kitchens, and batches are kept to a manageable size. There are 200 and 250-ml (7 and 8-fl oz) bottles of herb oils, made with an extra-virgin olive oil imported directly from Spain, infused with fresh basil, oregano, rosemary, salad herbs & seeds, and garlic. The white wine vinegar is infused with garlic, oregano, salad herbs & seeds, wild fruits, and thyme & citrus. In both cases the flavourings are macerated for a good 3-6 months, the liquid is strained, bottled and topped up with fresh flavourings 'for eye appeal'. The result is a definitely flavoured oil or vinegar with some, inevitably, more successful than others. I particularly liked the pungency of the basil and the woody sharpness of the thyme & citrus vinegar. Peter does mix salad dressings in such curious combinations as

> Possibly the tea with the most spectacular view in Wales is to be had at **Hotel Maes-y-Neuadd**. The only caveat is the weather must be good enough to have it out on the terrace, where you overlook Tremadoc Bay and the distant Llyn Peninsula with Snowdonia National Park behind you. You do not have to be staying in the hotel to enjoy generous quantities of scones with cream and, of course, their own jams, biscuits baked in their kitchen and thinly cut slices of bara brith.

blackberry and carrot & cardamom. To be perfectly honest, as I think that a salad dressing is such an easy thing to make and is best made to order, I ignored them.

Where I think his inventiveness is put to far better use is in the preserves. The onion & thyme confit had a pleasing crunchy texture of onion with a laid back sweetness and a hint of the herb; plum, walnut & raisin jam was earthy and rich, with a nibble of nuts to give it texture; apple & rosemary jelly was tart and refreshing; ginger marmalade with treacle was dense and dark, whereas breakfast marmalade was lighter and sharper, with its tiny shards of peel. Peter also makes various chutneys, chocolate pouring sauces and an intriguing-sounding apple, peach & carrot conserve.

As bread is baked in the kitchens, you can also buy it if you pop in, although it is probably a good idea to ring first to find out the 'flavour of the day'. This can be anything from leek, with bite-size pieces of the vegetable, tomato & herb, poppy seed, brioche, and bara brith, to mushroom – where the level of pungency just hit the mark.

Stockists

Ches: Tatton Park

Dyfed: Solva Post Office

Glam: Howells

Welsh Food Promotions

Gwynedd: Maes Artro Enterprises

Surprisingly – and I am only surprised because of where it is, a tiny village in mid-Wales – **Blas Ar Fwyd, 25 Heol yr Orsaf, LLANRWST LL26 0BT** ☎/fax **01492 640215** is an exciting food shop. The name is adapted from a Welsh saying which roughly translates as 'enjoying good food and a good life' and that is owner Deiniol ap Dafydd's philosophy. Brought up in Llanrwst, he returned after a few years 'abroad' (London, actually working in the food trade). The shop is packed with an amazing selection of basic ingredients ('people around here still know how to cook') as well as on-farm Welsh cheeses which are 'held back to age them'. Most everything else is own-made, including jams, pickles and chutneys; pâtés such as a smooth chicken liver which jumped with Cointreau and orange; glorious sides of hams and other cooked meats; and salads, such as plain or prawn & cranberry coleslaw, mint or chive potatoes, and Madras butter beans with a spicy mayonnaise. There are quiches with various fillings, crumbly French onion tarts, spiced vegetable or turkey & leek pasties, and even own-made dolmades. Locals bring in wild mushrooms and he prepares croustades, preserves them in oil or dries them to sell in packets. There are also various cakes, cheesecakes, puddings and – more often than not – their own tart and cakey bara brith, which Deiniol makes with a little whey rather than all milk 'so important for its depth and moisture'. If you give him a bit of warning, he will make almost anything for you and even provide picnic plates and glasses which you can return unwashed.

Butchers **Brian Hughes, 5 Market Square, PWLLHELLI LL53 5RU** ☎ **01758 612195** has two shops: one for fresh meat and the other, diagonally opposite, for cooked meats. The latter is a small narrow shop which looks as if it has been untouched for generations; indeed it is one of the last of its kind, cooked meat shops being almost a thing of the past. Most everything here is roasted and you will find ham and ham hocks; belly of pork, complete with crackling; breast of lamb; juicy faggots and a rich and gelatinous brawn that for once is a natural dusty grey rather than a chemically induced pink. Everything is sliced by hand, so you may have to wait; but do pop in, there are not many shops like this – if any – left in Britain.

MAP 7 GWYNEDD 397

While you're in the area...

Gwydryn Hir Pick Your Own Farm, Gwydryn Hir, BRYN-SIENCYN, Anglesey Ll61 6HQ ☎ 01248 430344 sells either pick-your-own or ready-picked from a stall at the top of the road. They grow asparagus sold in mixed bunches, artichokes, broad beans, dwarf French and runner beans, peas, courgettes 'en fleur'; various soft fruit, such as raspberries, tayberries, and gooseberries, as well as lettuces and herbs also sold ready-picked.

Butcher **Edwards of Conwy, 18 High Street, CONWY LL32 8DE ☎ 01492 592443** has recently moved to smart new premises, a converted bank. Here you can buy beef from 2 year-old Welsh Black heifers hung for up to 3 weeks; local lamb; various sausages, including pork & apple and lamb & mint with a 65 per cent meat content; cooked ham shanks; and tripe. They make a Penrhyn pie from Welsh lamb, leeks and herbs topped with potato, various 'kitchen-ready' meat dishes and sell various cheeses.

Locals consider the faggots made by **Roberts Bros, Eldon Square, DOLGELLAU LL40 1PY ☎ 01341 422619** to be the best for miles around. His Welsh lamb and pork & leek sausages also have much to recommend them.

The Fish Shop, Unit 4, The Old Abattoir, Builder Street, LLANDUDNO LL30 1DR ☎ 01492 870430 fax 01492 **870327** sell locally caught fish whenever possible, even monkfish complete with their ugly heads – a rare sight. They also process local game, plucking as many as 2,000 birds a week at the height of the season; and oak-smoke a variety of fish, poultry, meat and game including lamb, pigeon, beef, bacon and salmon.

Emrys Roberts, Parc, Station Road, LLANRWST LL26 0DB ☎ 01492 640328 has 'proper' Welsh lamb from the Conwy Valley, hung for a good 5 days. Here you can also buy sweetbreads and lambs' fry (which are apparently opened-out testicles).

DOLAU
Chicken and Meat

Graig Farm Meat

Graig Farm, Dolau, Llandrindod Wells, Powys LD1 5TL

☎ 01597 851655 **FAX** 01597 851991 **CONTACT** *Bob Kennard* **HOURS** *Mon-Sat 9.00-18.00 Sun – telephone ahead* **DIRECTIONS** *From Knighton, take A488 towards Llandrindod Wells. Follow the road about 10 miles and farm is signposted on the left.*

Since my first visit there have been changes at Graig Farm. The poultry-slaughtering unit has been upgraded to full EU approval and they now employ two full-time butchers, so carcasses are delivered from the slaughterhouse for hanging and butchering on-farm. With only 22 acres of land, they are easing out of farming – apart from poultry – concentrating more on marketing meat (mainly organic) along similar lines to Swaddles Green *see page 233*. My only concern is how do you maintain a consistency of finish, particularly if you buy in from differing sources? That having been said, reports on Graig Farm are complementary.

Dealing with their own-reared 'additive-free' chickens first, these are bought in as day-old and kept in small groups of 300, otherwise – as Bob Kennard explains – 'in larger groups they can develop and maintain a "pecking" order'. They cannot be classified as free-range as they do not have constant access to the outdoors; but in good weather the barn doors are opened and the birds are free to roam outdoors. Whereas most broiler birds are slaughtered at around 50 days, Bob slaughters his at 63-77 days to allow them to mature, then wet-plucks them before hanging them uneviscerated for about 8 days. Up until now I had always thought, indeed always been told, that you cannot hang an uneviscerated wet-plucked bird for fear of infection. 'Not so,' Bob's wife Carolyn assured me, 'Actually we had always thought so too, it surprised us. But our experience has proved it safe'.

They do buy in organic (to Soil Association standards) chickens reared by a farmer at nearby Leominster. The difference in price currently runs at about 30p a pound (organic being the more expensive, of course). Both birds have a good deep flavour and I admit I could not discern any pronounced difference between the two; but the texture of the organic bird is more resilient, giving a firmer bite. At Christmas they rear a modern hybrid turkey to similar standards and are currently expanding their guinea fowl flock.

Beef, lamb, pork and mutton (from any sheep over 2 years old), are bought in from various local farmers within the Welsh borders and Hereford who are all registered members of the Soil Association and there is additive-free wild boar farmed in Radnorshire. Slaughtered at Lentwardine, the carcasses are then hung on-farm and butchered into cuts and joints. They produce an intensely flavoured dry-cured smoked bacon, which incidentally won an Organic Food Award; sausages; and a new range of pies, pâtés and prepared dishes, such as chicken breast Kiev, all of which I have yet to sample. They also sell wild rabbit shot on their land and other local farms, and wild fallow and roe deer culled in local forests.

Stockists

Dyfed: Treehouse

Heref: Organic Options

Salop: Pimhill

Warks: Ryton Organic Gardens

Worcs: Greenlink

Little Cefn Smokehouse

Little Cefn Farm, Hyssington, Church Stoke, Powys SY15 6EQ

HYSSINGTON
Megan Lamb

☎ 01588 620603   **CONTACT** Peter Gray   **HOURS** 7 days' notice

Peter Gray and his wife Mary set up a small smokery in a bothy (outbuilding), with the avowed intent of producing as traditional a product of the area as possible. Hampered, I have to say, by what strikes me as a particularly fastidious Environmental Health Officer, they smoke only to order (their EHO will not allow them to hold stock). Their problem proves to be our gain, however, as everything comes sparklingly fresh.

Peter only cold-smokes and then only meat and game, using oak chippings and sawdust. In his research he discovered evidence that oak leaves were once used in Montgomeryshire but, as he says, 'obviously they knew something we don't. Try as I did, I couldn't get them to work'. With an obvious tradition of smoking lamb in the area, to preserve the meat for the winter months, Peter produces a self-styled Megan, a boned rolled leg weighing from about 1.5 to 2.7 kg (3½ to 6 lb), 'depending on the time of year and size of the lamb'. This is first brined in a pickle made with various spices, including ginger, and mustard seed ('a Tudor mixture'), then hung up on sticks over the fire and cold-smoked for no more than a few hours, although times will vary again depending on size and layer of fat. The effect is to give the lamb no more than a mild woody finish, and it has to

The Welsh Venison Centre, Middlewood Farm, BWLCH, nr Brecon LD3 7HQ   **☎ 01874 730929 fax 01874 730566** *farm red deer. Sold butchered into various cuts or in slices cut from the haunch, marinated with orange and juniper and hot-smoked over oak, they also make-up hampers for the serious enthusiast. Hamper no. 2 consists of 'venison casserole 3 x 1-lb packs, venison haunch joint x 2 lb, venison T-bone 2 x 8-10 oz each, venison sausages x 2 lb' and to go with '8 oz redcurrant jelly'.*

be subsequently cooked. I tried grilling a couple of lamb steaks; the flavour was interesting, offering no more than the faintest hint of smoke and almost undetectable spicing. A slight complaint was that the standard of butchery left a little to be desired; my steaks were boned-out from the leg and, although they arrived tied up neatly enough, they fell apart in the cooking. Peter will also supply smoked lamb steaks, chicken, duck, wood pigeon, pheasant, ham and loin of pork.

LLANBISTER ROAD

Sheep's-milk Yoghurt

Yan-tan-tethera,
Llugwy Farm, Llanbister Road, Powys LD1 5UT

☎ 01547 550641   **CONTACT** *Belinda Scadding – telephone ahead*

Belinda Scadding uses the milk from her 36-strong Friesland dairy sheep herd to make a first-rate yoghurt. Rich and creamy, with a refreshing but nicely rounded tang, it is named after the Celtic shepherd's way of counting sheep – *yan-tan-tethera*, meaning 'one-two-three'. Brenda makes her yoghurt twice a week in 12.5-litre batches: a starter is added to milk, it is incubated for between 2½ and 4 hours and then ladled into pots and left to set – with a satisfyingly thick crust forming on the top. Her milk, Brenda claims, 'is naturally rich. In the spring the fat content is around 6 per cent but it can go as high as 8.5 per cent and we ride on the back of its flavour'. Perhaps that is the secret.

She also makes a fresh soft cheese in 115-g (4-oz) rounds either plain, with garlic & parsley or chives. The same cheese she hangs up in cheesecloth to drain, then salts and rolls out in little balls by hand, and puts them in glass jars with extra-virgin olive oil and sea salt. With a firm texture and a light creamy flavour, like the yoghurt, it had all of the sheep's milk's richness and was clear and clean-tasting. As soon as the cheese store is finished, Brenda promises a hard cheese, 'halfway between a Caerphilly and Cheddar' called Radnorshire. She has been developing it for a while and, if it is as good as her yoghurt, it will not disappoint.

Stockists

Heref: Barbour & Manuel

- - - - - - - - - -

Fodder Wholefoods

- - - - - - - - - -

Hay Wholefoods

Powys: G. M. Hall

Worcs: Greenlink

From June to Christmas she sells her Friesland wether (male) lambs when they are about 18 months old, which is, Brenda told me, 'the traditional, but rarely practised way of rearing wethers in the uplands. It ensures a terrific flavour and, because these are dairy sheep, they carry little fat, so the meat is lean and tender'. Sold as either whole carcasses or in butchered joints, frozen or fresh to order, 'if you hit the right time', the meat is a deep dark red, similar in colour to venison.

While you're in the area...
Look out for honey by **P. L. & G. Jennings, Beekeepers, CWM-BRAIN, Llandrindod Wells LD1 6UE ☎ 01597 840294**. Flavours can vary from year to year, but you may well find a dark rich hawthorn, a delicate willowherb or a flowery mixed blossom.

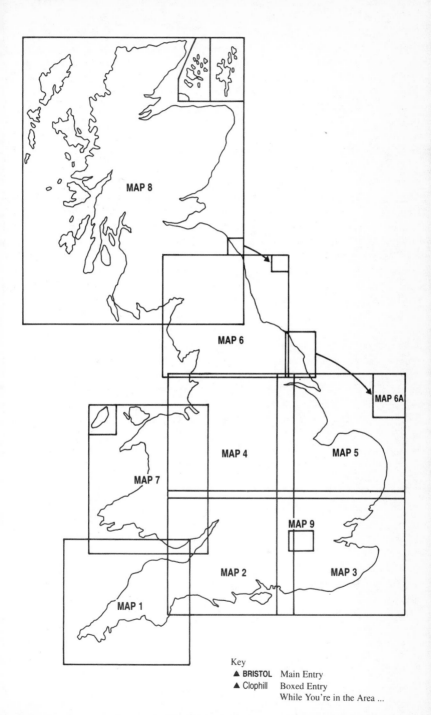

Key
▲ **BRISTOL**   Main Entry
▲ Clophill   Boxed Entry
       While You're in the Area ...

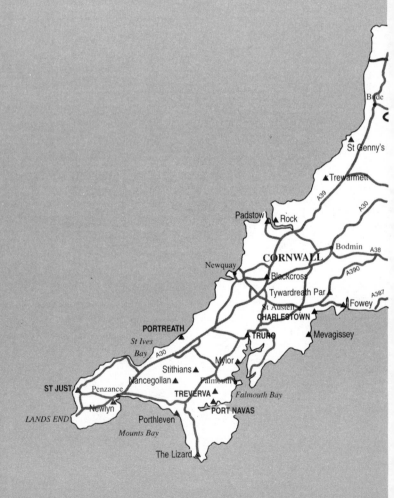

Bude

St Genny's

▲ Trewarmett

Padstow ▲ Rock

Bodmin A38

CORNWALL

Newquay ▲ Blackcross

Tywardreath Par ▲ A387

St Austell ▲ Fowey

CHARLESTOWN

PORTREATH ▲

TRURO ▲ Mevagissey

St Ives Bay A30

Mylor ▲

Stithians ▲

Nancegollan ▲ Falmouth

ST JUST Penzance **TREVERVA** ▲ *Falmouth Bay*

Newlyn **PORT NAVAS** ▲

LANDS END

Porthleven

Mounts Bay

The Lizard ▲

Map 1
England –
Devon &
Cornwall

Cornwall
pages 42-53

Devon
pages 70-87

4
7
1
Cwmbrain
Leominster
Cotheridge
WORCESTER
M50
Alcester
PEMBRIDGE
SUCKLEY
WORCESTERSHIRE
ALMELEY
WEOBLEY
Bretforton
Builth Wells
HEREFORDSHIRE
Kempsey
Bengeworth
Great Malvern
Evesham
Hay-on-Wye
HEREFORD
TUPSLEY
Upton-upon-Severn
Childs Wickham
A470
Sugwas Pool
LEDBURY
BROADWAY
POWYS
Tewkesbury
Ross-on-Wye
WORMBRIDGE
M5
Brecon
Cheltenham
St Owens Cross
Bwlch
A40
GLOUCESTER
Llantilo Crossenny
Birdwood
CHURCHAM
A429
ABERGAVENNY
MINSTERWORTH
Monmouth
NORTH CERNEY
Llandewi
GLOUCESTERSHIRE
South Woodchester
Stroud
A419
CIRENCESTER
Merthyr Tydfil
GWENT
A449
NAILSWORTH
Pontypool
Ozleworth
LONG NEWNTON
Tutshill
Chepstow
Tetbury
Leigh
ALVESTON
Pontypridd
Newport
M4
Tockington
Malmesbury
River Severn
A46
SHERSTON
GLAMORGAN
Coedkernew
CHIPPING SODBURY
WROUGHTON
Cardiff
Avonmouth
AVON
ST PAGANS
A350
BRISTOL
Corsham
Chippenham
A4
PETERSTON-SUPER-ELY
GRANGETOWN
KELSTON
Gastard
Barrow Gurney
COMPTON DANDO
Lower Weston
BROMHAM
Bishops Cannings
A38
BATH
Bradford-on-Avon
Weston-Super-Mare
TIMSBURY
Norton St Philip
WILTSHIRE
Chewton Mendip
A37
Kilmersdon
Frome
A360
WARMINSTER
A361
Wells
HEYTESBURY
HEATH HOUSE
A36
A303
Pawlett
PILTON
Shepton Mallet
SOMERSET
Glastonbury
MERE
A358
Bridgwater
North Newton
Castle Cary
West Monkton
MILTON-ON-STOUR
Wilton
Lydeard St Lawrence
CREECH ST MICHAEL
SOUTH BARROW
A30
NORTH CADBURY
Holton
WINCANTON
Taunton
Sandford Orcas
Shaftesbury
CURRY RIVEL
Wellington
Childe Okeford
HAMBRIDGE
KINGSBURY EPISCOPI
Iwerne Minster
Compton Park
Yeovil
Cranborne
CLAYHIDON
A303
Shillingstone
BUCKLAND ST MARY
STOCK GAYLAND
A357
Crewkerne
LEIGH
Tarrant Keynston
CULLOMPTON
Blandford
PEVERSTONE
A356
DORSET
A354
WIMBORNE
A35
HAMPRESTON
A31
MORCOMBELAKE
Bournemouth
DEVON
BRIDPORT
Poole
West Knighton
Otterton
A352
Corfe Castle
Swanage
WEYMOUTH
FERRY BRIDGE

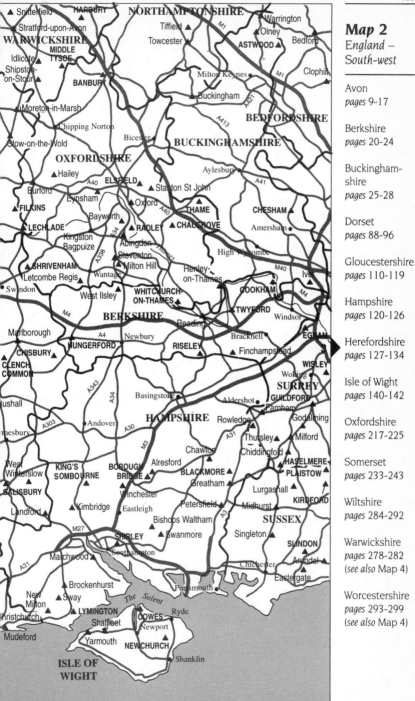

Map 2
England –
South-west

Avon
pages 9-17

Berkshire
pages 20-24

Buckingham-
shire
pages 25-28

Dorset
pages 88-96

Gloucestershire
pages 110-119

Hampshire
pages 120-126

Herefordshire
pages 127-134

Isle of Wight
pages 140-142

Oxfordshire
pages 217-225

Somerset
pages 233-243

Wiltshire
pages 284-292

Warwickshire
pages 278-282
(*see also* Map 4)

Worcestershire
pages 293-299
(*see also* Map 4)

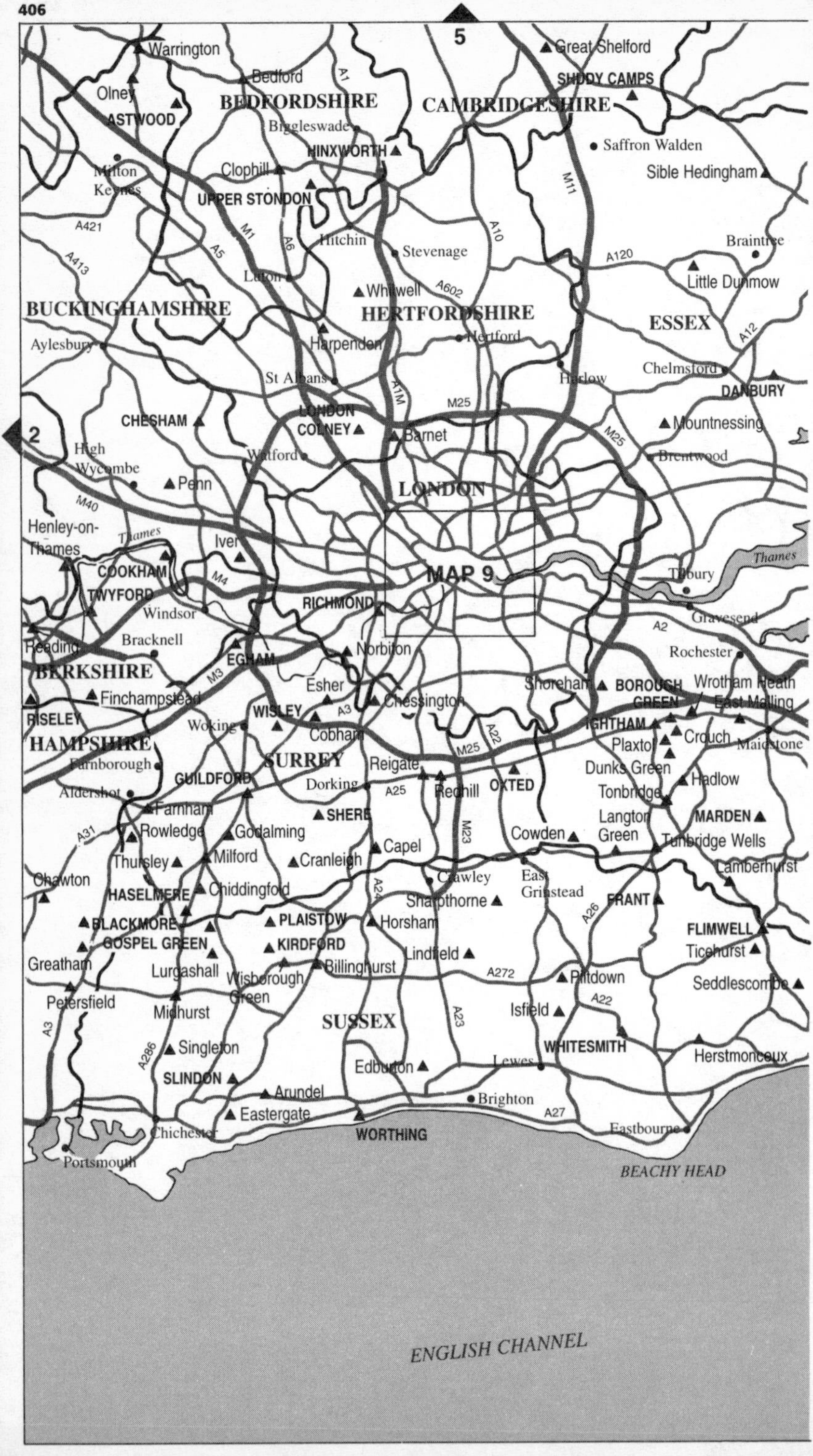

▲ 5

▲ Great Shelford

SHUDY CAMPS ▲

▲ Warrington

Olney ●
ASTWOOD ▲

● Bedford

BEDFORDSHIRE

Biggleswade ●

CAMBRIDGESHIRE

● Saffron Walden

Milton
Keynes ●

HINXWORTH ▲

Clophill ●

Sible Hedingham ▲

UPPER STONDON ▲

A421

A413

Hitchin ●

Luton ●

Stevenage ●

A602

▲ Whitwell

HERTFORDSHIRE

Braintree ●

A120

● Little Dunmow

ESSEX

A12

BUCKINGHAMSHIRE

Aylesbury ●

Harpenden ●

St Albans ●

● Hertford

DANBURY

Chelmsford ●

CHESHAM ▲

**LONDON
COLNEY** ▲

Watford ●

▲ Barnet

M25

Hadlow

▲ Mountnessing

● Brentwood

M25

High
Wycombe ●

▲ Penn

LONDON

MAP 9

Thames

Tilbury ●

Gravesend

A2

Rochester ●

Henley-on-
Thames ●

Thames

Iver ▲

COOKHAM ▲

TWYFORD ▲

Windsor ●

RICHMOND ▲

Reading ●

Bracknell ●

BERKSHIRE

EGHAM ▲

● Norbiton

RISELEY ▲

▲ Finchampstead

Esher ●

WISLEY ▲

A3

▲ Chessington

Shoreham ▲

**BOROUGH
GREEN**

Wrotham Heath

East Malling

HAMPSHIRE

Farnborough ●

Woking ●

Cobham ●

SURREY

Reigate

M25

A22

IGHTHAM ▲

Plaxtol ▲

▲ Crouch

Maidstone

Aldershot ●

GUILDFORD ▲

Farnham ●

Dorking ●

A25

Redhill ●

OXTED

Dunks Green ▲

Hadlow

Tonbridge

MARDEN ▲

▲ Rowledge

Godalming ●

SHERE ▲

Langton
Green

Tunbridge Wells

Thursley ▲

Milford ●

▲ Cranleigh

Capel ▲

Cowden ▲

Camberhurst

Chawton ●

HASELMERE ▲

Chiddingfold ●

Crawley ●

East
Grinstead

FRANT

A26

▲ **BLACKMORE**

PLAISTOW ▲

Sharpthorne ▲

FLIMWELL ▲

▲ **GOSPEL GREEN**

KIRDFORD ▲

Horsham ▲

Ticehurst ▲

Greatham ●

Lurgashall ●

Billinghurst ●

Lindfield ▲

A272

Pitdown ▲

A26

Seddlescombe ▲

Petersfield ●

Wisborough
Green

A22

A3

Midhurst ●

SUSSEX

A23

Isfield ▲

WHITESMITH

Herstmonceux

A286

▲ Singleton

Edburton ▲

Lewes ●

SLINDON ▲

▲ Arundel

● Brighton

Eastbourne

Chichester ●

▲ Eastgate

WORTHING

A27

● Portsmouth

BEACHY HEAD

ENGLISH CHANNEL

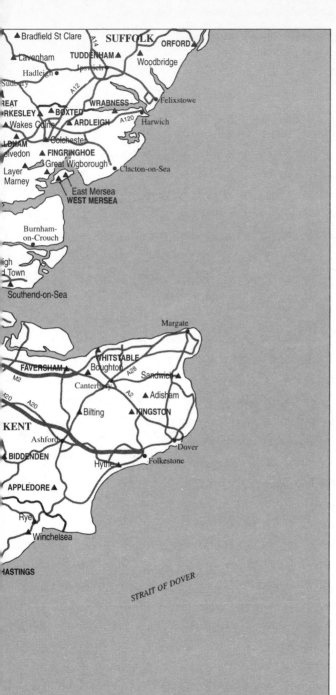

Map 3
England –
South-east

Bedfordshire
pages 18-19

Essex
pages 100-109

Hertfordshire
pages 135-137

Kent
pages 143-153

Surrey
pages 258-267

Sussex
pages 268-277

▲ Bradfield St Clare   **SUFFOLK**   **ORFORD**▲
• Lavenham   **TUDDENHAM** ▲   ▲ Woodbridge
Hadleigh •   Ipswich
Sudbury
REAT   **WRABNESS** ▲   **•** Felixstowe
RKESLEY ▲   ▲ **BOXTED**
▲ Wakes Colne   ▲ **ARDLEIGH**   A120   Harwich
LDHAM   • Colchester
elvedon   ▲ **FINGRINGHOE**
Layer   • Great Wigborough   • Clacton-on-Sea
Marney
East Mersea
WEST MERSEA
Burnham-
on-Crouch
igh
d Town
Southend-on-Sea

Margate

WHITSTABLE ▲
FAVERSHAM ▲   Boughton   A28
M2   Canterbury   Sandwich ▲
M20   A20   ▲ Bilting   ▲ Adisham
KENT   ▲ **KINGSTON**
Ashford
▲ **BIDDENDEN**   Dover
Hythe ▲   Folkestone
APPLEDORE ▲
Rye
Winchelsea

HASTINGS

STRAIT OF DOVER

0   10   20miles

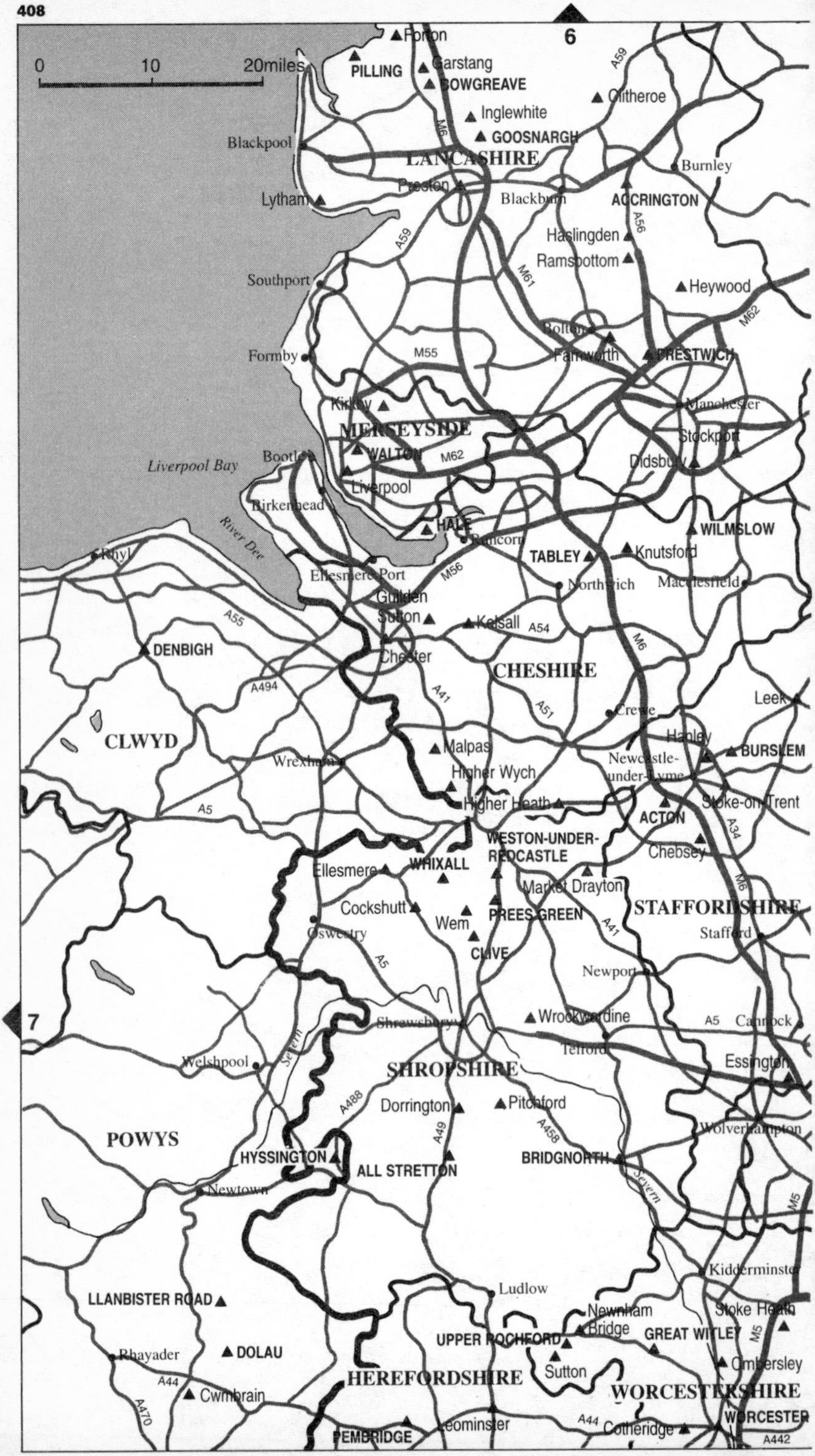
0
10
20miles
6
7
Forton
PILLING
Garstang
BOWGREAVE
Clitheroe
Inglewhite
GOOSNARGH
Blackpool
LANCASHIRE
Burnley
Preston
Blackburn
ACCRINGTON
Lytham
Haslingden
Ramsbottom
Southport
Heywood
Bolton
Farnworth
PRESTWICH
Formby
Kirkby
Manchester
MERSEYSIDE
Stockport
Bootle
WALTON
Didsbury
Liverpool Bay
Liverpool
Birkenhead
River Dee
HALE
Runcorn
WILMSLOW
Rhyl
TABLEY
Knutsford
Ellesmere Port
Northwich
Macclesfield
Guilden Sutton
Kelsall
DENBIGH
Chester
CHESHIRE
Leek
Crewe
CLWYD
Malpas
Hanley
BURSLEM
Wrexham
Newcastle-under-Lyme
Higher Wych
Higher Heath
Stoke-on-Trent
ACTON
WESTON-UNDER-REDCASTLE
WHIXALL
Chebsey
Ellesmere
Market Drayton
Cockshutt
STAFFORDSHIRE
Wem
PREES GREEN
Stafford
Oswestry
CLIVE
Newport
Wrockwardine
Shrewsbury
Cannock
Telford
Welshpool
Severn
Essington
SHROPSHIRE
Dorrington
Pitchford
Wolverhampton
POWYS
HYSSINGTON
ALL STRETTON
BRIDGNORTH
Newtown
Kidderminster
LLANBISTER ROAD
Ludlow
Newnham Bridge
Stoke Heath
UPPER ROCHFORD
GREAT WITLEY
Rhayader
DOLAU
Ombersley
Sutton
HEREFORDSHIRE
Cwmbrain
WORCESTERSHIRE
PEMBRIDGE
Leominster
Cotheridge
WORCESTER
A59
M6
A56
M61
M62
M55
M56
A55
A54
A494
A41
A51
A5
A34
A488
A49
A458
M5
A44
A470
A442

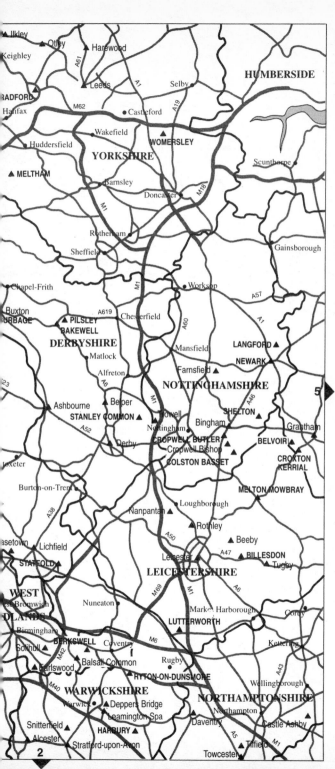

Map 4
England –
Midlands &
North-west

Cheshire
pages 35-40

Derbyshire
pages 65-69

Lancashire
pages 154-161
(*see also* Map 6)

Merseyside
pages 194-195

Northampton-
shire
pages 204-206
(*see also* Map 5)

Shropshire
pages 226-232

Staffordshire
pages 244-247

Warwickshire
pages 278-281
(*see also* Map 2)

West Midlands
pages 282-283

Worcestershire
pages 293-299
(*see also* Map 2)

Yorkshire
(south)
pages 300-314
(*see also* inset
Map 6A *on page*
411)

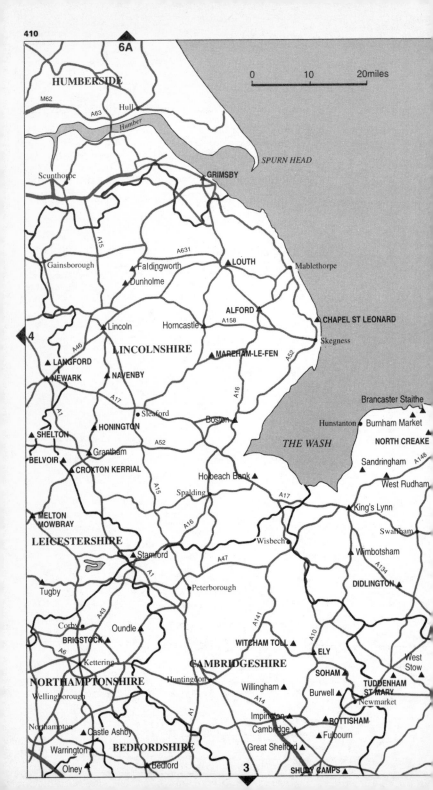

6A

0   10   20miles

HUMBERSIDE

M62

A63

Hull

Humber

SPURN HEAD

Scunthorpe

▲ GRIMSBY

A15

A631

Gainsborough

▲ Faldingworth

▲ LOUTH

Mablethorpe

▲ Dunholme

ALFORD ▲

▲ CHAPEL ST LEONARD

4

▲ Lincoln

Horncastle ▲

A158

Skegness

A46

LINCOLNSHIRE

▲ MAREHAM-LE-FEN

▲ LANGFORD

▲ NAVENBY

A16

Brancaster Staithe ▲

▲ NEWARK

A17

Hunstanton ● Burnham Market

A1

● Sleaford

Boston ▲

THE WASH

NORTH CREAKE ▲

▲ SHELTON

▲ HONINGTON

A52

A148

Sandringham ▲

● Grantham

West Rudham ▲

BELVOIR ▲

▲ CROXTON KERRIAL

A15

Holbeach Bank ▲

King's Lynn ●

▲ MELTON
MOWBRAY

Spalding ▲

A17

Swaffham

A16

LEICESTERSHIRE

Wisbech ●

Wimbotsham ▲

▲ Stamford

A134

A47

A1

DIDLINGTON ▲

Tugby ●

● Peterborough

A141

A10

A43

Corby ●

Oundle ▲

WITCHAM TOLL ▲

West
Stow

▲ BRIGSTOCK

A6

▲ ELY

Kettering ●

CAMBRIDGESHIRE

SOHAM ▲

TUDDENHAM
ST MARY ▲

NORTHAMPTONSHIRE

Huntingdon ●

Willingham ▲

Burwell ▲

● Newmarket

Wellingborough ●

A14

Northampton ●

▲ Castle Ashby

Impington ▲

▲ BOTTISHAM

Warrington ●

BEDFORDSHIRE

Cambridge ▲

▲ Fulbourn

Olney ▲

● Bedford

Great Shelford ▲

3

SHUDY CAMPS ▲

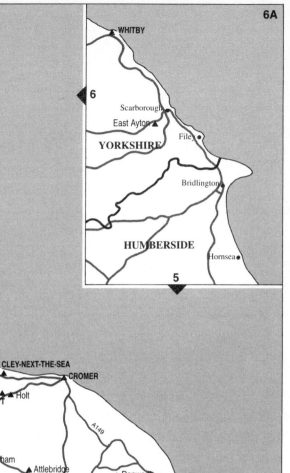

Map 5
*England –
East*

Cambridgeshire
pages 29-34

Humberside
pages 138-139

Lincolnshire
pages 166-174

Norfolk
pages 195-204

Northampton-
shire
pages 204-206
(*see also* Map 4)

Suffolk
pages 248-257

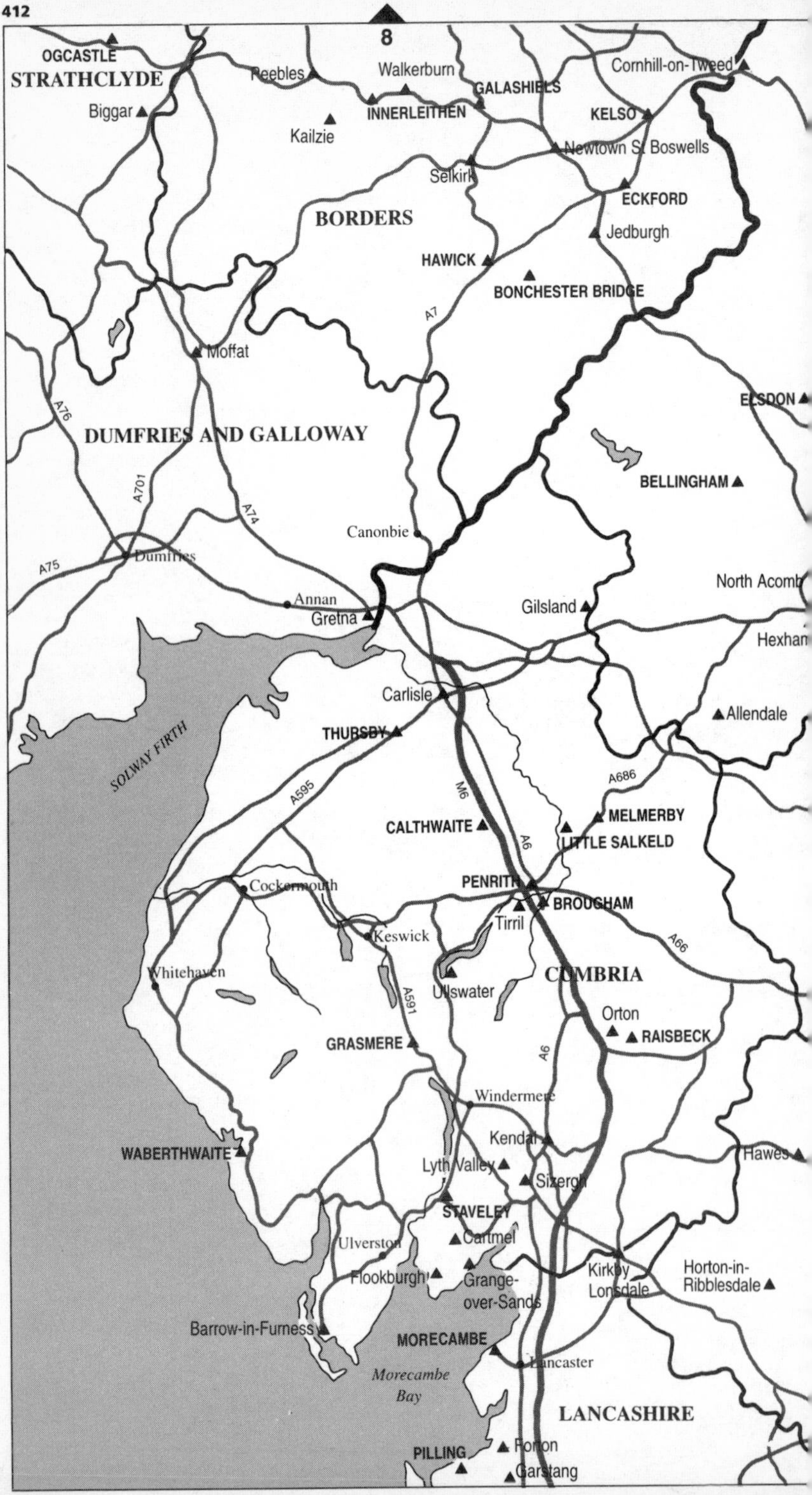

8

OGCASTLE ▲
STRATHCLYDE
Peebles
Walkerburn
GALASHIELS
Cornhill-on-Tweed
Biggar ▲
INNERLEITHEN
KELSO ▲
Kailzie ▲
Newtown S. Boswells
Selkirk
ECKFORD
BORDERS
Jedburgh ▲
HAWICK ▲
BONCHESTER BRIDGE ▲

Moffat ▲

A76

A701

A74

A75

DUMFRIES AND GALLOWAY

Canonbie ●

ELSDON ▲

BELLINGHAM ▲

North Acomb

Dumfries ●

Annan ●
Gretna

Gilsland ▲

Hexham

Carlisle ●

THURSBY ▲

A595

M6

A686

Allendale ▲

SOLWAY FIRTH

CALTHWAITE ▲

MELMERBY ▲
LITTLE SALKELD ▲

A6

Cockermouth ●

PENRITH ▲
BROUGHAM ▲

Keswick ●

Tirril

A66

Whitehaven ●

A591

Ullswater ▲

CUMBRIA

Orton ▲
RAISBECK ▲

GRASMERE ▲

Windermere

A6

WABERTHWAITE ▲

Kendal ▲

Hawes ▲

Lyth Valley ▲
Sixergh ▲

STAVELEY ▲
Cartmel ▲

Ulverston ●

Flookburgh ▲

Grange-
over-Sands

Kirkby
Lonsdale

Horton-in-
Ribblesdale ▲

Barrow-in-Furness ▲

MORECAMBE ▲

Morecambe
Bay

Lancaster ●

LANCASHIRE

PILLING ▲
Forton ▲
Garstang ▲

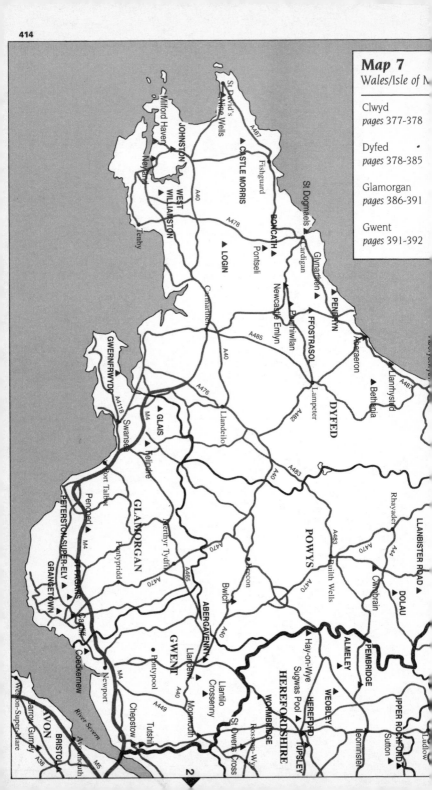

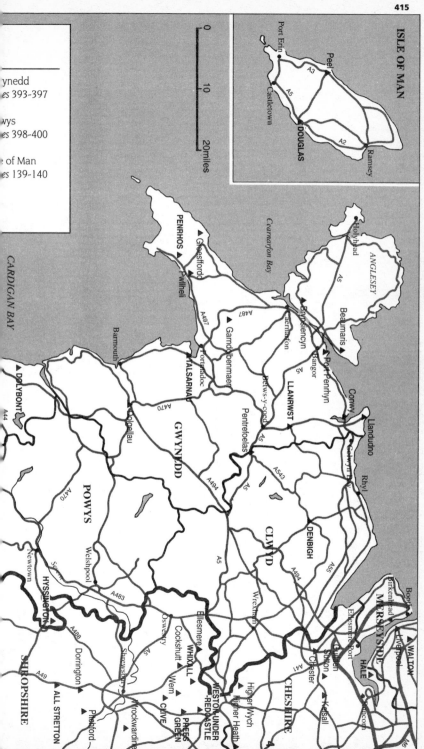

ISLE OF MAN

Port Erin
Peel
Castletown
A3
A5
DOUGLAS
Ramsey
A2

0
10
20miles

Caernarfon Bay

PENRHOS
Clynnog
Pwllheli
Holyhead
A5
ANGLESEY
Beaumaris
Caernarfon
Bangor
Blydaencyn
Port Penrhyn
Conwy
Colwyn Bay
Llandudno
Rhyl

CARDIGAN BAY

Barmouth
▲DOLYBONT
A44
A497
TALSARNAU
Portmadoc
Gamallbenmaen
▲
A487
Betws-y-coed
LLANRWST
Pentrefoelas
A5
A543

A470
Dolgellau
GWYNEDD
A470
A494
A5
DENBIGH
CLWYD
A55
A494

Newtown
POWYS
Welshpool
A483
Wrexham
A5

HYSSINGTON▲
A488
Dorrington
A49
ALL STRETTON▲
Pbslford
▲
Shrewsbury
A5
Ellesmere
Cockshutt
Wem
Wrockwardine
Oswestry
WHIXALL▲
Higher Wych
WESTON-UNDER
-REDCASTLE
CLIVE▲
PREES
GREEN
Higher Health
SHROPSHIRE

Birkenhead
MERSEYSIDE
▲WALTON
Liverpool
Boot
HALE▲
▲Kelsall
Ellesmere Port
Chester
CHESHIRE
A41
M6
Runcorn
A55

416

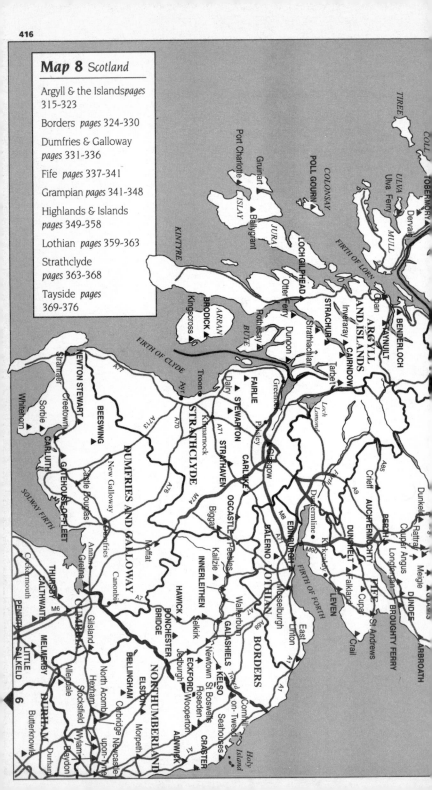

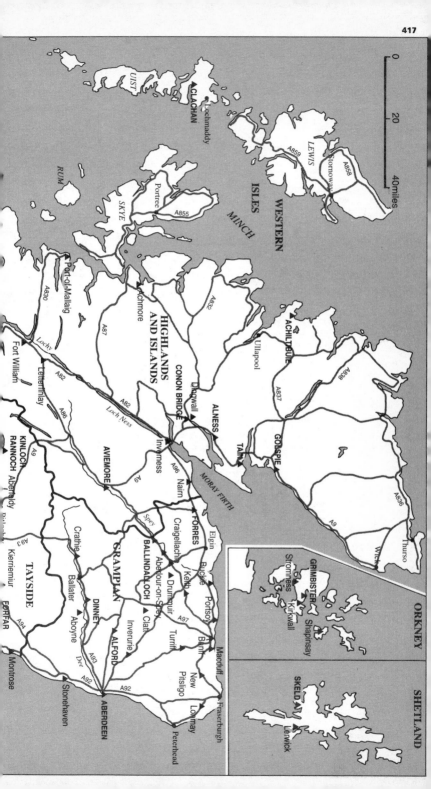

Map 9
London
pages 175-193

HIGHBURY

Holloway Rd

A503

A10

DALSTON

HACKNEY

Hackney
Marshes

ISLINGTON

Victoria
Park

SPITALFIELDS

A11 Mile End Rd

A13

Commercial Rd

COVENT
GARDEN

Thames Tower Br

Westminster Rd

BOROUGH

BUTLERS
WHARF

CANNING
TOWN

Thames

Vauxhall Br

A2

Clapham Rd

A3

Old Kent Rd

A202

GREENWICH

A2

BRIXTON

A20

A23

A205

Dulwich
Park

STREATHAM

0   1   2miles

Index of producers

Index of products

List of stockists

The following information has been supplied by the Producers and Stockists themselves, the Author and the Publishers cannot accept responsibility for any errors or ommissions.

A. Betteridge & Son, ☎ 01285 712208, London Street, Fairford, Gloucestershire GL7 4AH

A. Crombie & Son, ☎ 0131 5570111 FAX 0131 5563920, 97–101 Broughton Street, Edinburgh, Lothian EH1 3RZ

A. Dove & Son, ☎ 0171 223 5191, 71 Northcote Road, Battersea, London SW11 6JP

A. F. Huddleston, ☎ 015394 43080, 16A Crescent Road, Windermere, Cumbria LA23 1EA

A. Strand, ☎ 01772 50218, Unit 38, Market Hall, Preston, Lancashire PR1 2JD

A. Waller & Son, ☎ 01223 350972, 15 Victoria Avenue, Cambridge, Cambridgeshire CB4 1EG

A10 Farm Shop, ☎ 01920 821246 FAX 01920 821246, Hamels Park Farm, Buntingford, Hertfordshire SG9 9NA

Abergavenny Fine Foods, ☎ 01873 850001 FAX 01873 850002, Dairy 4–5, Castle Meadows Park, Abergavenny, Gwent NP7 7RZ

Adsdean Farm Shop, ☎ 01243 575212, Funtington, Chichester, Sussex PO18 9DN

Alana Wholefoods, ☎ 0171 837 1172 FAX 0171 833 8089, 56–58 Marchmont Street, London WC1N 1AB

Alex Dalgetty & Sons, ☎ 01896 752508, 6 Bank Street, Galashiels, Borders TD1 1NZ

Alex Dalgetty & Sons, ☎ 01896 822364, High Street,Melrose, Borders TD6 9PB

Alfred Kane, ☎ 01224 633 986, 205 Rosemount Place, Aberdeen, Grampian AB2 4XP

Alligator, ☎ 01904 654525, 104 Fishergate, York, Yorkshire YO1 4BB

Alwyn Thomas Bakery & Coffee Shop, ☎ 01824 703145, St Peter's Square, Ruthin, Clwyd LL15 1AA

American Museum, ☎ 01225 460503, Claverton Manor, Bath, Avon BA2 7BD

Andy Howse, ☎ 01452 525943, 70 Calton Road, Gloucester, Gloucestershire GL1 5DY

Anthony Rowcliffe & Son Ltd, ☎ 0181 853 4228 FAX 0181 293 4037, Tyrrell House, 9 Lombard Trading Estate, Anchor & Hope Lane, Charlton, London SE7 7SN

Arcimboldos, ☎ 01423 508760, 146 Kings Road, Harrogate, Yorkshire HG1 5HY

Armstrong 's Delicatessen, ☎ 01347 823434, 1 Tyler's Walk, Crabmill Lane, Easingwold, Yorkshire YO6 3QP

Army & Navy Stores, ☎ 0171 834 1234 FAX 0171 630 8822, 101 Victoria Street, London SW1E 6QX

Arthur Purchase & Son, ☎ 01243 783144 FAX 01243 533397, 31 North Street, Chichester, Sussex PO19 1LY

Arthur Rickett, ☎ 01442 832217, 35 High Street, Bovingdon, Hemel Hempstead, Hertfordshire HP3 0HG

Arvonia Bakery, ☎ 01654 702061, 14 Maengwyn Street, Machynlleth, Powys SY20 8DT

Ashburton Delicatessen, ☎ 01364 652277, 16 North Street, Ashburton, Devon TQ13 7Q0

Ashdowns, ☎ 0171 626 1949, 23–25 Leadenhall Market, London EC3V 1LR

Ashtons Fishmongers, ☎ 01222 229 201, Central Market, Cardiff, Glamorgan CF1 2AU

Aubrey Newman & Daughters, ☎ 01993 823466, 79 – 81 High Street, Burford, Oxfordshire OX18 4QS

Auchtermuchty Post Office, ☎ 01337 28201, 26 High Street, Auchtermuchty, Fife KY14 7AP

Averys, ☎ 01275 811100 FAX 01275 811101, Orchard House, Southfield Road, Nailsea, Bristol, Avon BS19 1JD

B. & M. Seafoods, ☎ 0171 485 0346, 258 Kentish Town Road, London NW5 2AA

B. Clark & Son, High Street, Wantage, Oxfordshire

B.V. Berry & Son, ☎ 01793 812262, 1 Ellendune Centre, Wroughton, Swindon, Wiltshire SN4 9LN

Bach Fruit Farm, The Bach, Chester, Cheshire

Badgers Hill Farmshop, ☎ 01227 730573, Chilham, Canterbury, Kent CT4 8BW

Bagel Express, ☎ 0171 353 0761, 62 Fleet Street, London EC4Y 1J4

Ballater Flowers, ☎ 013397 55741, 47 Bridge Street, Ballater, Grampian AB35 5QD

Banbury Fisheries, ☎ 01295 256842, 12 Parson Street, Banbury, Oxfordshire OX16 8LW

Banesberie Coffee Shop, ☎ 01295 269066, 10 Butchers Row, Banbury, Oxfordshire OX16 8JH

Barbour & Manuel, ☎ 01568 613381, Jubilee Buildings, Victoria Street, Leominster, Herefordshire HR6 8LP

Bardfield Stores , ☎ 01371 810662, 1 St John's Terrace, Great Bardfield, Braintree, Essex CM7 4RQ

Barker Bros, ☎ 01223 843292, 43 High Street, Great Shelford, Cambridgeshire CB2 5EH

Barlows, ☎ 01962 865593, 95 Oliver's Battery Road South, Winchester, Hampshire SO22 4JQ

Barstow & Barr, ☎ 0171 359 4222, 24 Liverpool Road, Islington, London N1 0PU

Bartlett & Son (Butchers), ☎ 01225 466731, 10 Green Street, Bath, Avon BA1 2JZ

Batchelors, ☎ 01494 563125, 19 Main Road, Naphill, Buckinghamshire HP14 4QD

Bats Wing , ☎ 01983 840634, Church Hollow, Godshill, Isle of Wight PO38 3HH

Battlers Green Farm Shop, ☎ 01923 856551, Common Lane, Radlett, Hertfordshire WD7 8PH

Baxters of Edinburgh, ☎ 0131 226 2022, 122–4 Rose Street, Edinburgh, Lothian EH2 3JF

Baxters of Speyside, ☎ 01343 820393, Fochabers, Moray IV32 7LD

Beards Deli & Tea Room, ☎ 01379 870383, 39 Church Street, Eye, Suffolk IP23 7BD

Benedicts Delicatessen, ☎ 01983 529596, 128 Holyrood Street, Newport, Isle of Wight PO30 5AU

Bennetts, ☎ 01332 344261, 8 Irongate, Derby, Derbyshire DE1 3AL

Bettys, ☎ 01609 775154, 188 High Street, Northallerton, Yorkshire DL7 8LF

Bettys, ☎ 01904 659142, 6–8 St Helen's Square, York, Yorkshire YO1 2QP

Bettys, ☎ 01943 608029, 32–34 The Grove, Ilkley, Yorkshire LS29 9EE

Bibury Trout Farm, ☎ 01285 740212, Bibury, Cirencester, Gloucestershire GL7 5NL

Birdwood House Farm Shop, ☎ 01452 750248, Birdwood, Huntley, Gloucestershire GL19 3EJ

Blakemans, ☎ 01782 271664, Hanley Market, Stoke-on-Trent, Staffordshire

Blas Ar Fwyd, ☎ 01492 640215, 25 Heol Yr Orsaf, Llanrwst, Gwynedd, LL26 0BT

N.L. Bonners (Butchers), ☎ 01460 52465, Silver Street, Ilminster, Somerset TA19 0DW

Booth's Supermarket, ☎ 01565 652522, Stanley Road, Knutsford, Cheshire WA16 0BS

Boucherie Lamartine, ☎ 0171 730 3037, 229 Ebury Street, London SW1 8UT

Bradwell's Country Food, 2 Church Street, Falmouth, Cornwall

Bressingham Plant Centre Shop, ☎ 01379 688133, Bressingham, Diss, Norfolk IP22 2AB

Bretts Farm Market, ☎ 01279 876571, Chelmsford Road, White Roding, Essex CM6 1RF

Brian Hughes, ☎ 01758 612195, 5 Market Square, Pwllheli, Gwynedd LL53 5 RU

Bridgemere Garden World, ☎ 01270 520239 FAX 01270 520215, Bridgemere, Nantwich, Cheshire CW5 7QB

Brighton Malt House, ☎ 01273 601060, 1 North Road, Brighton, Sussex BN1 1YA

Brimarks, ☎ 0181 449 5416, 241 East Barnet Road, Barnet, London EN4 8SS

Bristol Guild, ☎ 0117 9265548, 66–72 Park Street, Bristol, Avon BS15 5JY

Buckfast Abbey Gift Shop, ☎ 01364 42882, Buckfast Abbey, Buckfastleigh, Devon TQ110EE

Bumblebee, 30 Brecknock Road, London N7 0DD

Burden Gorlston, ☎ 01493 652640, 59 Bells Road, Gorlston, Norfolk NR32 6NN

Burdettes, ☎ 01751 433014, 14 Piercy End, Kirby Moorside, Yorkshire YO6 6DS

Bury Lane Farm Shop, ☎ 01763 260418, Melbourne By-pass, Melbourne, nr Royston, Herts SG8 6DF

Bushwacker, ☎ 0181 748 2061,32 King Street, Hammersmith, London W6 0QU

Butchers, Shandag Road, Keynsham, Avon

Byfords of Holt, ☎ 01263 711400, 3A Shirehall Plain, Holt, Norfolk NR25 6BG

C. & G. Neve, ☎ 01253 770911, Siding Road, Fleetwood, Lancs FY7 6NS

C. E. Evans & Sons, ☎ 01962 732477, 8 West Street, Alresford, Hampshire SO24 9AT

C. Harrisons, ☎ 01263 512897, 23 Church Street, Cromer, Norfolk NR27 9ES

C. Lidgate Ltd, ☎ 0171 727 8243, 110 Holland Park Avenue, London W11 4VA

C. Mundy, ☎ 01458 442845, 116 High Street, Street, Somerset BA16 0ER

C. Williams, The Square, Sandbach, Cheshire

Café Fromage, ☎ 01225 313525, 1 John Street, Bath, Avon BA1 2JL

Cairn o' Mohr Winery, ☎ 01821 642781, East Inchmichael, Errol, Perthshire PH2 7SP

Cairns Fish Shop, ☎ 01563 521639, 7 St Marnock Street, Kilmarnock, Strathclyde KA1 1DZ

Calves Lane Farm, ☎ 01753 652727, Billet Lane, Iver, Buckinghamshire SL0 0LX

Cambridge Cheese Company, ☎ 01223 328672, All Saints Passage, Cambridge, Cambridgeshire CB2 3LS

Campbells of Edinburgh, ☎ 01506 858585, East Mains Industrial Estate, Roxburn, nr Edinburgh, Lothian EH52 5NB

Carley & Co, ☎ 01872 77686, 34–36 St Austell Street, Truro, Cornwall TR1 1SE

Carnfield Hall Garden Centre, ☎ 01773 832375, Alfreton, Derbyshire

Carol Sadler, ☎ 01923 779721, 3 Copthorne Road, Croxley Green, Rickmansworth, Herts WD3 4AB

Cary Fruit and Greens, ☎ 01963 350213, The High Street, Castle Cary, Somerset BA7 7AP

Catlin & Sons, ☎ 01223 262212, 10 South Street, Comberton, Cambridgeshire CB3 7DZ

Cavendish House, ☎ 01242 521300, 32–48 The Promenade, Cheltenham, Gloucestershire GL50 1HP

Caviar House, Heathrow Airport

Cegin Cymru, ☎ 01545 570460, Unit 13, Clos Pencarreg Craft Centre, Aberaeron, Dyfed SA46 0AZ

Chagford Delicatessen, Chagford, Devon

Chalmers of Bucksburn Ltd, ☎ 01224 622049, The Granery, The Scottish Co-op, Berryden Road, Aberdeen, Grampian AB9 2XY

Chalmers of Bucksburn Ltd, ☎ 01224 626344, 14 Backwynd, Aberdeen, Grampian AB1 1JP

Chambers, ☎ 01159 267034, 31 Front Street, Arnold, Nottingham, Nottinghamshire NG5 7EA

Chandos Deli , ☎ 0117 9706 565, 121 Whiteladies Road, Clifton, Bristol, Avon BS6 2PL

Charles Barnett, ☎ 01285 652418, 1 Market Place, Cirencester, Gloucestershire GL7 2NL

Charlotte's Patisserie, ☎ 01225 466158, 14/16 The Corridor, Bath, Avon BA1 5AP

Chatsworth Farmshop, ☎ 01246 583392 FAX 01246 583464, Stud Farm, Pilsley, Bakewell, Derbyshire DE45 1UF

Cheese Cuisine, ☎ 01636 703313, 10 Saracen's Head Yard,Newark, Nottinghamshire NG24 1XA

Cheese to Please, ☎ 01235 760334, 3 Grove Street, Wantage, Oxfordshire OX12 7AB

Cheeseboard, ☎ 01225 868043, 30A Silver Street, Bradford-on-Avon, Wilts BA15 1JX

Chestnut Farm Shop, ☎ 01406 363123, Gedney, Spalding, Lincolnshire PE12 0BW

Chewton Cheese, ☎ 01761 241666, Chewton Mendip, Bath, Avon BA3 4NT

Chiddingstone Causeway Store, ☎ 01892 870327, The Post Office, Chiddingstone Causeway, Tonbridge, Kent TN11 8JP

Chivers Farm Shop, ☎ 01223 237799, Manor Farm, Impington, Cambridgeshire CB4 4PJ

Christopher's Fine Foods, ☎ 01743 365417, 73 Mardol, Shrewsbury, Shropshire SY1 1PZ

Christy's Farm Shop, ☎ 01636 1234, Hockerton, Southwell, Nottinghamshire NG25 0PT

Clark's Specialist Foods, ☎ 0131 4482993, 8/4 Borthwick View, Pentland Industrial Estate, Loanhead, Edinburgh, Lothian EH20 9QH

& Clarke's, ☎ 0171 229 2190, 122 Kensington Church Street, London W8 4B4

Claytons Butchers, ☎ 01539 432143, Compston Road, Ambleside, Cumbria LA22 9DR

Clive Ramsay, ☎ 01786 833903, 28 Henderson Street, Bridge of Allan, Stirling, Central FT9 4HR

Coco, ☎ 0181 878 4800, 361 Upper Richmond Road, Sheen, London SW14 8QN

Combe Hill Stores, Hughenden, Buckinghamshire

Comestibles, ☎ 01522 520010, 82 Bailgate, Lincoln, Lincolnshire LN1 3AR

Connoisseurs, ☎ 01629 814844, Water Lane, Bakewell, Derbyshire DE4 2LW

Constantine Stores, ☎ 01326 40226, 39 Fore Street, Falmouth, Cornwall TR11 5AB

Continental Stores, ☎ 01223 246168, 14 Market Passage, Cambridge, Cambridgeshire CB2 3HX

Cook & Carve, Market Hall, Shrewsbury, Shropshire

Corbin's, ☎ 01825 766670, 23 The High Street, Uckfield, Sussex TN22 1AG

Corbridge Larder, ☎ 01434 632948, Hill Street, Corbridge, Northumberland NE45 5AA

Corncraft, ☎ 01449 740456, Monks Eleigh, Ipswich, Suffolk IP7 7AY

Cotherstone Post Office, ☎ 01833 650255, Cotherstone, Barnard Castle, Durham DL12 9PG

Cottage Deli, ☎ 0161 766 6216, 83 Park Lane, Whitefield, Manchester M45 7HL

Cottage Foods, ☎ 0161 740 2426, 8 Bury Old Road, Union Terrace, Cheethan Hill, Salford, Manchester M7 4ZH

Country Bake, ☎ 01748 850995, 4 Trinity Church Square, Richmond, Yorkshire DL10 4HY

Country Bumpkins Delicatessen, ☎ 01926 425571, 63 Warwick Street, Leamington Spa, Warwickshire CV32 5JP

Country Cheeses, ☎ 01822 615035, Market Road, Tavistock, (Natural Life is wholesaler), Devon PL19 0BW

Country Kitchen, ☎ 01986 872000, 4 The Thoroughfare, Halesworth, Suffolk IP19 8AH

Country Maid Deli, ☎ 01752 698469, 47 Fore Street, Ivybridge, Devon PL21 9AE

Country Produce, ☎ 01403 274136, 44b Carfax , Horsham, Sussex RH12 1EQ

Country Store, Main Road, Naphill, Buckinghamshire

County Delicacies, ☎ 01734 574653, St Marys Butts, Reading, Berkshire, RG1 2LN

County Stores, ☎ 01823 272235, 52 North Street, Taunton, Somerset TA1 1ND

Cousins & Sons, ☎ 01223 352856, 36 Grantchester Street, Cambridge, Cambridgeshire, CB3 9HY

Crabapple Wholefoods, ☎ 01423 865027, 3 Market Place, Castlegates, Shrewsbury, Shropshire SY1 2AQ

Cranberrys, ☎ 01202 317091, 18/19 Criterion Arcade, Bournemouth, Dorset BH1 1BU
Crawshaws Butchers Ltd, ☎ 0141 256 8054, 11 Market Street, Meadowhall Centre, Sheffield S9 1EJ
Creelers Restaurant, ☎ 0131 2204447 FAX 0131 2204149, The Royal Mile, 3 Hunter Square, Edinburgh, Lothian EH1 1QW
Cricket Malherbie Farms Ltd, ☎ 01278 732 989, Stowey Court Farm, Nether Stowey, Bridgwater, Somerset TA5 1LL
Crops, ☎ 01983 872503, 3 Lane End Court, Lane End, Bembridge, Isle of Wight PO35 5UE
Crumbs of Comfort, ☎ 01444 416939, 1 High Street, Cuckfield, Sussex RH17 5JZ
Cumming & Spence, ☎ 01856 872034, Albert Street, Kirkwell, Orkney, Highlands & Islands KW15 1HP
Currant Affairs, ☎ 0116 2510887, 9a Loseby Lane, Leicester, Leicestershire LE1 5DR
D.& D. Dairies, ☎ 01764 654271, Crieff, Tayside PH7 3SG
D.W. Ferguson, ☎ 012367 63333, 3 Buchanan Street, Airdrie, Strathclyde ML6 6BG
D.W.Rickett, ☎ 01476 62342, 4 Welby Street, Grantham, Lincolnshire NG31 6DY
Daily Bread, ☎ 01223 423177, Unit 3, Kilmaine Close, Cambridge, Cambridgeshire CB4 2PH
Daily Bread Cooperative, ☎ 01604 21531, The Old Laundry, Bedford Road, Northampton, Northamptonshire NN4 7AD
Dam Head Holdings, ☎ 0131 4455591, 32A Dam Head, Old Pentland Road, Edinburgh, Lothian EH10 7AE
Dandie Smoked Foods, ☎ 01403 790454, Clapgate Cottage, Slinfold, Horsham, Sussex RH13 7QU
Dartington Cyder Press Centre, ☎ 01803 864171, Shinners Bridge, Dartington, Totnes, Devon TQ9 6TQ
Dartington Farm Foods, ☎ 01803 864171, Shinners Bridge, Dartington, Totnes, Devon TQ9 6TQ
Dartmouth Vintners, ☎ 01803 832602, The Butterwalk, Dartmouth, Devon TQ6 9YZ
David Bowtell, ☎ 01420 588418, Home Farm Shop,Home Farm, East Tisted, Alton, Hampshire GU34 3QP
David Cook, ☎ 0171 823 3509, 61 Chelsea Manor Street, London SW3 5RZ
David North, ☎ 0116 2302263, 289 Station Road, Rothley, Leicestershire LE7 7LD
David Puttnam Coffee & Books, Dervaig, Strathclyde
Dean Farm Shop, ☎ 01329 220343, Dean Farm, Wickham Road, Fareham, Hants PO17 5BN
Deli Delights, ☎ 01239 612657, Lion Mews, Cardigan, Dyfed SA43
Delikatesserie, ☎ 01865 510447, 239A Banbury Road, Summertown, Oxford, Oxfordshire OX2 7HN
Demeter Wholefoods, ☎ 01720 760445, Welles Street, Sandbach, Cheshire CW11 9AT
Denham Estate, ☎ 01284 810231, Denham, Barrow, Bury St Edmonds, Suffolk IP29 5EQ
Di's Dairy, ☎ 01208 863531, Rock Road, Rock, nr. Wadebridge, Cornwall PL27 6NW
Dial a Deli, ☎ 01744 29473, c/o Sheil Bros, 24A Westfield Street, St Helens, Merseyside WA10 1QF
Downingbury Farmshop, ☎ 01892 824282, Maidstone Road, Pembury, nr Tunbridge Wells, Kent TN2 4AD
D.R. Earey & Son, ☎ 01787 460278, 97 Swan Street, Sible Hedingham, Halstead, Essex CO9 3HP
Durants, ☎ 01969 623251, The Post Office, Market Place, Middleham, Yorkshire DL8 4PE
Durleighmarsh Farm, ☎ 01730 821626, Rogate Road, Petersfield, Hampshire GU31 5AL
E. Allen & Son, ☎ 01969 667219, Market Place, Hawes, Yorkshire DL8 3QZ
E. Hall, ☎ 016725 12017, 4 High Street, Marlborough, Wiltshire SN8 IAA
E. Worsley, ☎ 01204 521181, Bolton Market Hall, The Market Place, Bolton, Lancashire BL1 2AR
E.H. Booth & Co Ltd, ☎ 01539 723731, 45 Highate, Kendal, Cumbria LA9 4ED
E.H. Booth & Co Ltd, ☎ 01772 251701, 4, 5 & 6 Fishergate, Preston, Lancashire PR1 3LJ
E.H. Booth & Co Ltd, ☎ 01539 446114, The Old Station, Victoria Street, Windermere, Cumbria LA23 1QA
E.W. King & Sons, ☎ 01787 372105, 8 Market Hill, Sudbury, Suffolk CO10 6EA
Eastside Cheese, ☎ 01883 723890, 59 Station Road East, Oxted, Surrey RH8 0AX
Eastwood Butchers, ☎ 01442 865012, 15 Gravel Path, Berkhamstead, Hertfordshire HP4 2EF
Edible Options, ☎ 01434 605090, 21 Market Street, Hexham, Northumberland NE46 3NU
Edwin Wild, ☎ 01663 732180, 18 Old Road, Whaley Bridge, Derby SK1 7HR
Egertons Ltd, ☎ 01386 462745, The International Gift Service, P.O. Box 5, Pershore, Worcestershire, WR10 2LR
Ellery Deli , ☎ 01738 633362, 2 Mill Street, Perth, Fife, PH1 5HZ
Elliot, ☎ 0116 9552 832, Unit 23, Block A, St Marys Works, Burnmoor Street, Leicester, Leicestershire, LE2 7JL
Elmer & Sons, ☎ 01206 240386, 43 Chapel Road, West Bergholt, Colchester, Essex, CO6 3JB
English Wine Centre, ☎ 01323 870164, Alfriston Roundabout, Lewes, Sussex BN26 5QS
Essex Rose Tea House, ☎ 01206 323101, High Street, Dedham, Essex CO7 6DE
Evergreen, ☎ 01823 322 414, 61 Station Road, Taunton, Somerset TA1 1PA
Fannys Farm Shop, ☎ 01737 554444, Gatton Bottom, Merstham, Surrey RH1 3AN
Farm and Dairy, ☎ 01492 640482, 21 Watling Street, Llanrwst, Gwynedd LL26 0LS
Farm Dairy, ☎ 01423 865027, 3 Market Place, Knaresborough, Yorkshire HG5 8AL
Farmers Dairy, ☎ 01463 233097, 6 Lochalsh Road, Inverness, Highlands & Islands IV3 6HU
Farmfare, ☎ 01271 73908, Barnstaple & South Molton Pannier Markets, Cranmere, 1 Rumsay Close,Barnstaple, Devon EX32 9ES
Farrers Coffee Shop, ☎ 01539 731707, 13 Strickland Gate, Kendal, Cumbria LA9 4LY
Fay's Delicatessesn, ☎ 01787 277 646, Well Lane, Clare, Sudbury, Suffolk CO10 8NH
Fish & Fayre, ☎ 01502 724212, 38 Leigh Street, Southwold, Suffolk IP18 6AR
Fish & Fowl, ☎ 0171 284 4184, 145 Highgate Road, London NW5 1LJ
Fish & Game Co Ltd, ☎ 01276 29252, 22 Princess Way, Camberley, Surrey GU15 3SP
Fishers Castle Farm, ☎ 01562 700188, Harvington, nr Kidderminster, Worcestershire DY10 4NF
Fletchers Butchers, ☎ 01298 812792, 5 High Street, Chapel-en-le-Frith, Derbyshire FT12 6HD
Fodder Wholefoods, ☎ 01432 358171, 27 Church Street, Hereford, Herefordshire HR1 2LR
Food For Thought, ☎ 0181 546 7806, 38 Market Place, Kingston-on-Thames, Surrey KT1 1JQ
Ford and Etal, ☎ 01890 820224, Heatherslaw Cornmill, Cornhill-On-Tweed, Northumberland TD12 4TJ
Fordingbridge Dairy Shop, ☎ 01425 652371, Salisbury Street, Fordingbridge, Dorset SP6 1AB
Forge Stores, ☎ 01745 710213, Mold Road, Bodfari, Clwyd LL16 4DN
Fortnum & Mason, ☎ 0171 734 8040 FAX 0171 437 3278, 181 Piccadilly, London W1A 1ER
Foundation Foods, ☎ 0181 420 1010, Chantry Place, Headstone Lane, Harrow, Middlesex HA3 6NY
Fox's Delicatessen, ☎ 0181 6720987, 14 Bellevue Road, Wandsworth Common, London SW17 7EG
Francis Thomas, ☎ 01244 322968, 74 Northgate Street, Chester, Cheshire CH1 2HT &, 51 Five Ashes Road, Westminster Park, Chester, Cheshire CH1 2H7
Fratelli Camisa, ☎ 0171 235 1240, 53 Charlotte Street, London W1X 3RA
Friday Street Farm Shop, ☎ 01728 602783, Friday Street, Farnham, Saxmundham, Suffolk IP17 1JX
Frugal Food, ☎ 01235 522239, 17 West St Helen Street, Abingdon, Oxfordshire OX14 5BL
G. Bowden-Witts, ☎ 01706 365103, Church Place, Hartley Street, Heywood, Lancashire OL10 1LT
G. Machin, ☎ 01492 574377, 7 Market Place, Henley on Thames, Berkshire R6 92AA
G. Walton, ☎ 0171 267 1219, 283 Kentish Town Road, London NW5 2JS
G.G. Sparks, ☎ 0181 858 7672, 24 Old Dover Road, Blackheath, London SE3 7BT
G.M. Hall, ☎ 01544 267328, 48 High Street, Presteigne, Powys LD8 2BE
Galloway Country Style, ☎ 01557 814001, High Street, Gatehouse of Fleet, Fife DG7 2HP
Garland Farm Shop, ☎ 01491 671556, Gardeners' Lane, Upper Basildon, Reading, Berkshire RG8 8NP
Garson Farm Shop, ☎ 01372 462261, Winterdown Lane, Esher, Surrey KT10 8LS
Gastromania, ☎ 01285 644611, 3 Market Place, Cirencester, Gloucestershire GL7 2PE
Gellifor Post Office, ☎ 01824 790581, Gellifor, Ruthin, Clwyd LL15 1SF
George Smith, ☎ 0121 643 4821, Bull Ring Market Centre, Birmingham, West Midlands B5 4PG
Gerald Millhouse Butchers, ☎ 0117 9734440, The Mall, Bristol, Avon BS8 4DR
Gerrard, ☎ 0181 959 1017, 137 Hammers Lane, Mill Hill, London NW7 4DY
Glass & Thompson, ☎ 0131 5570909, 2 Dundas Street, Edinburgh, Lothian EH3 6HZ
Gluttons, ☎ 01865 53748, 110 Walton Street, Oxford, Oxfordshire OX2 6EA
Glyn T. Jenkins, ☎ 0144 6 773545, 50 High Street, Cowbridge, Glamorgan CF71 7AH
Godshill Cider Co, ☎/FAX 01983 840680, High Street, Isle of Wight PO38 3HZ
Godshill Organics, ☎ 01983 840723, Yard Parlour, Newport Road, Godshill, Isle of Wight PO37 6JU
Good Food Shop, ☎ 1488 685099, 4–5 The Courtyard, 24 High Street, Hungerford, Buckinghamshire RG17 0DN
Good Food Shop, ☎ 01625 618827, 68 Chestergate, Macclesfield, Cheshire
Good Food Shop, ☎ 01883 716173, 30 Station Road West, Oxted, Surrey RH8 9EU
Goodies Delicatessen, ☎ 01225 336033, 2A St Saviours Road, Larkhall, Bath, Avon BA1 6RT
Goodness Foods, ☎ 0116 2624859, 18 Silver Street, Leicester, Leicestershire LE1 5ET
Goose Green Delicatessen, ☎ 0161 9269895, Goose Green, Altrincham, Cheshire WH14 1DW
Gordon & MacPhail, ☎ 01343 545110, 58–60 South Street, Elgin, Grampian IV30 !JY
Gossip Gate Gallery, ☎ 01434 381806 , The Butts, Alston, Cumbria CA5 3JU
Grafton Manor, ☎ 01527 579007, Grafton Lane, Bromsgrove, Worcestershire B61 7HA
Graig Farm Meat, ☎ 01597 851655 FAX 01597 851991, Graig Farm, Dolau, Llandrindod Wells, Powys LD1 5TL
Granthams Grocers, ☎ 01625 583286, Hayes Lane, Alderley Edge, Cheshire SK9 7KB
Graves Butchers, ☎ 01252 842552, High Street, Harlney, Wintney, nr Odiham, Hampshire
Great Bardfield Stores, ☎ 01371 810662, Brook Street, Great Bardfield, Braintree, Essex CM7 4RQ
Green City Wholefoods, ☎ 0141 5547633, 13 Fleming Street, Glasgow, Strathclyde G31 1PQ
Greenlink, ☎ 016845 76266, 9 Graham Road, Malvern, Worcestershire WR14 2HR
Greens Butchers, ☎ 01734 842063, The Square, Pangbourne, Reading, Berkshire RG68 7BP
Greenwells, ☎ 0191 3848484, 2 North Road, Durham City, Durham DH1 4SH
Greg Hull, ☎ 0161 6880297, 70 Old Church Street, Newton Heath, Manchester, Lancashire N10 6JS
Guildford Cheese Shop, ☎ 01483 68912, Milkhouse Gate, 142 High Street, Guildford, Surrey GU1 3HJ
Gusto Classico, ☎ 01428 642439, 1 Causeway Side, High Street, Haselmere, Surrey GU27 2JZ
Gwalia Stores, ☎ 01443 201502, St Fagans Folk Museum, Cardiff, Glamorgan CF5 6XB
H.V. Graves (Bakery), ☎ 01263 860333, 24 Gladstone Place, Briston, Norfolk NR24 2LE
Halls Butchers, ☎ 01672 512017, 4 High Street, Marlborough, Wiltshire SN8 1AN
Hamish Johnston, ☎ 0171 738 0741, 48 Northcote Road, London SW11 1PA
Hampers, ☎ 01386 853040, Cotswold Court, The Green, Broadway, Worcestershire WR12 7AA
Hand To Mouth, ☎ 0151 258 1211, 55 Castle Street, Liverpool, Merseyside L2 9XL
Harbottle Wines, ☎ 0171 731 1972, 27 Perrymead Street, London SW6 3SN
Harrods, ☎ 0171 730 1234, Knightsbridge, London SW1X 7QX
Harveststore, ☎ 01432 268209, 47 Eign Gate, Hereford, Herefordshire HR4 0AB
Harvey Nichols, ☎ 0171 235 5000, Knightsbridge, London SW1X 7RJ
Harveys Wet Fish Shop, ☎ 01728 452145, 115 High Street, Aldeburgh, Suffolk IP15 5AR
Hawkins of Shipston-on-Stour, ☎ 01608 661207, 7 Market Place, Shipston-on-Stour, Warwickshire CV36 4AG
Hay Wholefoods, ☎ 01497 820708, 1 Lion Street, Hay on Wye, Herefordshire HR3 5AA
Hay's Caterers of Richmond, ☎ 01748 824052, 6–7 Trinity Square, Richmond, Yorkshire DL10 4HY
Heal Farm Meats, ☎ 01769 574341 FAX 01769 572839, Kings Nympton, Umberleigh, Devon EX37 9TB
Heal's, ☎ 0171 636 1666, 196 Tottenham Court Road, London W1P 9LD
Heard's of Wigston, ☎ 01162 880444, 69 Long Street, Wigston, Leicester, Leicestershire DE45 1UF
Henry Reed Butchers, ☎ 0171 223 5680, 45 Tyneham Road, Battersea, London SW11 5XH
Henry Welsh & Sons, ☎ 0161 2282575, Prescott Road, Liverpool, Merseyside L13 3AT
Heritage Foods, ☎ 01275 474707,Lakeside, Bridgwater Road, Barrow Gurney, Bristol, Avon BS19 1BA
Hick Hill Farmshop, Tenterden, Kent
Highland Fine Cheeses, ☎ 01862 892034, Tain, Highlands & Islands
Highland Supply Stores, ☎ 01520 722207, Locharron, Highlands & Islands
Highland Wholefoods, ☎ 01463 712393, 13 Harbour Road, Inverness, Highlands & Islands IV1 1UA
Hilton & Family, ☎ 0181 866 9075, 59 Bridge Street, Pinner, Middlesex HA5 3HZ
Hockeys Farm Shop, ☎ 01425 652542, South Gorley, Fordingbridge, Hampshire SP6 2PW
Hockneys, ☎ 0181 688 2899, 96/98 High Street, Croyden, London CR0 1NO
Hollanden Farmshop, ☎ 01732 833858, Hildenborough, nr Sevenoaks, Kent TN15 0SG
Hollingsworth Butchers, ☎ 01335 342002, 2 Victoria Square, Ashbourne, Derbyshire DE6 1GG
Holly Avenue Delicatessen, ☎ 0191 28 15 412, 8 Holly Avenue West, Jesmond, Newcastle, Northumberland NE2 2AR
Holyroyd's, ☎ 01252 702256, The Green, Elstead, Haselmere, Surrey GU8 6DD
Hone's, ☎ 01252 716172, 52 Downing Street, Farnham, Surrey GU9 7PH
Hopkins-Porter Ltd, ☎ 01423 771466, The Old Stable Shop , Ripley Castle, Ripley, nr Harrogate, Yorkshire HG3 3AY
Horton Park Farm, ☎ 01372743984, Horton Lane, Epsom, Surrey KT19 8PT
Hortors Nurseries and Farm Shop, ☎ 01949 81312, Grove Farm, Hickling Lane, Kinoulton,

Nottinghamshire NG12 3ED
Howells, ☎ 01222 231055 FAX 01222 390908, 14 St Mary's Street, Cardiff, Glamorgan CF1 1TT
Huge Cheese Co, ☎ 01323 844807, The Old School, Upper Dicker, Hailsham, Sussex BN27 3QA
Hungry Palate, ☎ 01752 253831, 47 Ebrington Street, Charles Cross, Plymouth, Devon PL4 9AA
Hunters of Helmsley, ☎ 01439 771307, The Market Place, Helmsley, Yorkshire YO6 5BL
Iain Mellis, ☎ 0131 266215, 30a Victoria Street,Edinburgh, Lothian EH1 2JW
Ian Johnston (Butchers), ☎ 01688 302047, 26 Main Street, Tobermory, Isle of Mull, Argyll & the Islands PA75 6NU
Ian Proudfoot, ☎ 0131 315 2056, Learnmonth Avenue, Edinburgh, Lothian EH4 1DF
Icicles Delicatessen, ☎ 01334 653377, 44 Bonnygate, Cupar, Fife KY15 4LD
Ide Hill Stores, ☎ 01732 750482, Post Office Stores, Ide Hill, nr Sevenoaks, Kent TN14 6JN
Infinity Foods, ☎ 01273 603563, 25 North Road, Brighton, Sussex BN1 1YA
Innes, ☎ 01827 830097, Highfields Farm, Statfold, nr Tamworth, Staffordshire B79 0AQ
International Cheese Shop, ☎ 0171 628 6637, 3B West Hall, Liverpool Street Station, London EC2M 7PY
Irma Fingal-Rock, ☎ 01600 712372, 64 Monnow Street, Monmouth, Gwent NP5 3EN
Isle of Mull Tradional Farmhouse Cheese, ☎ 01688 302235, Sgriob-ruadh Farm Dairy, Tobermory, Isle of Mull, Argyll & the Islands PA75 6QD
J. & J. Graham, ☎ 01768 62281, Market Square, Penrith, Cumbria CA11 7BS
J. & J. Shellfish (Agiploeg & Lyn Shrimpers Inc.), ☎ 01553 772520, Alexandra Dock, King's Lynn, Norfolk PE30 2ET
J. & M. Reah, ☎ 01765 689021, 7 Market Place, Masham, Yorkshire HG4 4DZ
J. & R.'s Place, ☎ 01493 721441, 64 High Street, Caister, Norfolk NR31 5EH
J. F. Blagden, ☎ 0171 935 8321, 64 Paddington Street, London W1M 3RR
J. Sykes & Son Ltd, ☎ 0161 2239311, New Smithfield Market, Whitworth Street East, Manchester, Lancashire M11 2WJ
J. Bennett Jnr London Ltd, ☎ 0171 987 2848, Off 47 Billingsgate Mkt, West India Dock, London E14 8ST
J. Fortieth & Son, ☎ 01631 63331, 76 George Street., Oban, Argyll PA34 5NN
J. Morris, ☎ 01858 575210, Walnut Tree House, South Kilworth, Lutterworth, Leicestershire E17 6EG
J. R. Creasey, ☎ 01728 660219, The Causeway, Peasenhall, Suffolk IP17 2HU
J. Seal Butchers, ☎ 0181 876 5118, 7 High Street, Barnes, London SW13 9LW
J. Wallace, ☎ 01204 303620, Bury Market, Bury, Lancashire
J.W. Harman, ☎ 01993 830218, High Street,Milton-under-Wychwood, Oxfordshire OX7 6EW
J.W. Rigby, ☎ 01456 522527, East Gate Market, Gloucester, Gloucestershire GL1 1PL
James McLaren & Son, ☎ 01575 572964, 9 High Street, Kirriemuir, Tayside DD8 4EY
James Mclaren & Son, ☎ 01307 462762, 8 The Cross, Forfar, Tayside DD8 1BX
James Stevenson, ☎ 01556 502712, 49 King Street, Castle Douglas, Dumfries & Galloway DG7 1AE
James's, ☎ 0181 650 1411, 188 High Street, Beckenham, Kent BR3 1EN
Jan's, ☎ 01745 584694, Arnold House, 2 Mount Road, St Asaph, Clwyd LL17 0DB
JedForest Deer & Farm Park, ☎ 01835 840364, Mervinslaw Estate, Camptown, by Jedburgh, Borders TD8 6PL
Jeffersons, ☎ 0171 266 0811, Clifton Road, Maida Vale, London W9 1SY
Jenners, ☎ 0131 2252442 FAX 0131 2200327, 48 Princes Street, Edinburgh, Lothian EH2 2YJ
Jereboams, ☎ 0171 225 2232, 24 Bute Street,South Kensington, London SW7 3EX
Jerry's, ☎ 0171 225 2246, 163/7 Fulham Road, London SW3 6SN
Jessie Smiths, ☎ 01285 653387, 14 Blackjack Street, Cirencester, Gloucestershire GL7 1AN
J.J. Fish, ☎ 01962 866103, 90 Oliver's Battery Road South, Winchester, Hampshire SO22 4EZ
Jones Fishmongers, ☎ 01892 523358, 29 Campden Road, Tunbridge Wells, Kent TN1 2PS
John Pettit & Sons Ltd, ☎ 01472 342724, 33–35 Bethlehem Street, Grimsby, Humberside, DN31 1JQ
John Sole Butchers, ☎ 01420 561121, 49 Winchester Road, Four Marks, Alton, Hampshire GU34 5HG
John's Fish Shop, ☎ 01502 724 253, 5 East Street, Southwold, Suffolk IP1A 6EH
Joshua's Harvest Store, ☎ 01404 815473, Gosford Road, Ottery St Mary, Devon EX11 1NU
K. Johnson, ☎ 01832 273522, 8 West Street, Oundle, nr Peterborough, Northamptonshire PE8 4EF
Kelseys Butchers, ☎ 01642 750078, Unit 8, 1–2 Wrightson House, In-Shops, Thornaby Town Centre, Thornaby,Stockton, Cleveland TS17 9EP
Ken Warne, ☎ 01325 462198 FAX 01325 383836, 17–19 Cleveland Terrace, Darlington, Yorkshire DL3 7HD
Ken Whatmough, ☎ 01224 640321, 29 Thistle Street, Aberdeen, Grampian AB1 1UY
Kendalls, ☎ 0161 832 3414, Deansgate, Manchester M60 3AU
Keracher, ☎ 01738 638374, 168 South Street, Perth, Tayside PH2 8NY
Kessock Post Office, ☎ 01463 731470, North Kessock, Inverness, Highlands & Islands IV1 1XN
Keynston Mill Farm Shop, ☎ 01258 452596, Tarrant Keynston, Blandford, Dorset DT11 9HZ
Killerton House, ☎ 01392 882081, The National Trust, Killerton, Exeter, Devon EX5 3LE
Kimbridge Farm Shop, ☎ 01794 340777, Kimbridge, Romsey, Hampshire SO51 0LE
Kirdford Growers, ☎ 01403 820274, Pound Common, Kirdford, Billingshurst, Sussex RH14 0NQ
Kitts End Farm Dairys Ltd, ☎ 0181 449 0885, Kitts End Road, Hadley, nr Barnet, Hertfordshire EN5 4RL
Kyle Bakery, ☎ 01599 534303, Kyle of Lochalsh, Highlands & Islands IV40 8DA
La Belle Cuisine, ☎ 015394 88200, Heart of the Country, Home Farm, Swinfen, Lichfield, Staffordshire W3 149QR
La Charcuterie, ☎ 01483 277072, The High Street, Cranleigh, Surrey GU6 8AU
La Fromagerie, ☎ 0171 359 7440, 30 Highbury Park, London N5 2AA
La Provencal, ☎ 0171 586 2574, 167 Haverstock Hill, London NW3 4QT
La Solitude, ☎ 01797 270696, Wittersham, Kent TN30 7ED
La Tienda Delicatessen, ☎ 0171 4601423, 81 Praed Street, London W2 1NS
Lakeland Plastics Ltd, ☎ 015394 88200, Alexandra Buildings, Windermere, Cumbria LA23 1BQ
Langmans, Stratford upon Avon, Warwickshire
Larner's of Holt, ☎ 01263 712323, 10 Market Place,Holt, Norfolk NR25 6BW
Lather, ☎ 0171 328 6962/6985, Broadwell Parade, Broadhurst Gardens, London NW6 2BE
Laurel Bank Dairy Co, ☎ 01749 679803, 14 Queen Street, Wells, Somerset BA5 2DP
Lavender's, ☎ 01736 62800, 6a Alverton Street, Penzance, Cornwall TR18 2QW
Le Herisson, ☎ 01722 333471, 90–92 Crane Street, Salisbury, Wiltshire SP1 2QD
Le Pont de la Tour, ☎ 0171 403 4030, 36D Shad Thames, London SE1 2YE
Leathley's Quality Fare, ☎ 01748 835252, The Walkerville Industrial Estate, Colburn, Catterick Garrison, Yorkshire DL9 4FA
Lehane & Co., ☎ 0181 993 2743, 102 Churchfield Road, London W3 6D4
Leicester Wholefood Co-operative Ltd, ☎ 0116 251 2525, Unit 3, Freehold Street, Leicester, Leicestershire LE1 2LX
Lewis & Cooper Ltd, ☎ 01609 772886, 92 High Street, Northallerton, Yorkshire DL7 8PP
Liberty, ☎ 0171 734 1234 FAX 0171 734 8323, Regent Street, London W1R 6AH
Lindsay Brothers, ☎/FAX 0191 257 2576, 6a Union Quay, Fish Quay, North Shields, Tyne & Wear, Northumberland NE30 1HJ
Lindsay of Newcastle, ☎ 0191 2612995, Unit F5, New Green Market, Eldon Square 1, Newcastle-upon-Tyne, Northumberland NE1 7JG
Llandyrnog Post Office, ☎ 01824 790310, Llandyrnog, Denbigh, Clwyd LL16 4HG
Llangloffan Farm Shop, ☎ 01348 891241, Llangloffan Farm, Castle Morris, Haverfordwest, Dyfed SA62 5ET
Llwynhelyg Farmshop, ☎ 01239 811079, Sarnau, Llandysul, Dyfed SA44 6QU
Llys Caradog Stores, ☎ 01690 760209, Llys Caradog, Penmachno, Gwynedd LL24 0YG
Loaves and Fishes, ☎ 01394 385650, Thoroughfare, Woodbridge, Suffolk IP12 1AL
Loch Fyne Oyster Bar, ☎ 01499 600217 FAX 01499 600234, Clachan Farm, Cairndow, Argyll & the Islands PA26 8BH
Loders Country Fayre, ☎ 01460 76293, 3 George Shopping Centre, Crewkerne, Somerset TA18 7JP
Lomas Foods, ☎ 01298 70480, 77–79 Spring Gardens, Buxton, Derbyshire SK17 6BP
Lovat, ☎ 0181 748 4416, 1 Eyot Gardens, Hammersmith, London W6 9TN
Lowe's Country Store, ☎ 0131 6602128, Campend Farm, Dalkeith, Lothian EH22 1RS
Lowe's Farm Shop, ☎ 0131 663 2207, Home Farm, Dalkeith, Lothian EH22 2NJ
Lucy's, ☎ 015394 32223, Church Street, Ambleside, Cumbria LA22 0BU
Ludlow Larder, ☎ 01584 877353, 4 Church Street, Ludlow, Shropshire SY8 1AP
M. Feller Son & Daughter, ☎ 01865 231164, 54/55 Oxford Covered Market, Oxford, Oxfordshire OX1 3DX
M. Newitt & Sons, ☎ 01844 212103, 10 High Street, Thame, Oxfordshire OX9 2BZ
M. H. Taylor & Sons Ltd, ☎ 01422 353255, Victoria Market, Victoria Road, Halifax , Yorkshire HX1 5QD
MacGills Deli, ☎ 01548 830860, 4 Church Street, Modbury, Devon PL21 0QW
Mackintosh of Marlborough, ☎ 01672 514069, 42A High Street, Marlborough, Wiltshire SN8 1HQ
Mackintosh's, ☎ 0181 742 3137, 134 Chiswick High Road, London W4 1PU
Macsween, ☎ 0131 229 1216 FAX 0131 229 9102, 130 Bruntsfield Place, Edinburgh, Lothian EH10 4ES
Maes Artro Enterprises, ☎ 01341 23467, Maes Artro, Llanbedr, Barmouth, Gwynedd LL45 2PZ
Magnus Fish & Game, ☎ 01473 253536, 14 Tacket Street, Ipswich, Suffolk IP4 1AY
Majestic Wine Warehouses, ☎ 01923 816999, Odhams Trading Estate, St Albans Road, Watford, Hertfordshire WD2 5RE
Mark Andrews Butchers, ☎ 01705 580443, 9 High Street, Gosport, Hampshire PO12 1BX
Maretts, ☎ 01428 652189, West Town, 93 Weyhill, Haselmere, Surrey GU27 1HS
Market Pantry, ☎ 01729 823355, Market Place, Settle, Yorkshire BD24 9EX
Marmions, ☎ 01896 822245, Buccleuch Street, Melrose, Borders TD6 9LB
Martin's Stores, ☎ 01963 350208, Market Place, Castle Cary, Somerset BA7 7AH
Masons of the Mall, ☎ 0117 9238193, 56 The Mall, Bristol, Avon BS8 4JG
Mastersons, ☎ 01493 842747, 113 Regent Road, Great Yarmouth, Norfolk NR30 2AE
Maylams, ☎ 01386 840903, High Street, Chipping Campden, Gloucestershire GL55 6AG
Mayo Bros, ☎ 01494 726357, 32 Stanley Parade, Chesham Bois, Buckinghamshire, HP6 6BP
McIntyre's, ☎ 01738 628268, 233 High Street, Perth, Tayside
McIntyre's, ☎ 01738 638861, 81 South Street, Perth, Tayside
McIntyre's, ☎ 01764 655778, Unit 1, Pennys Supermarket, Church Street, Crieff, Tayside
McLeod's, ☎ 01507 601094, 11 Bridge Street, Louth, Lincolnshire LN11 0DR
Meat Matters, ☎ 01235 762461, 2 Blandys Farm Cottages, Bassett Road, Letcombe Regis, Wantage, Oxfordshire OX12 9LJ
Meatmasters Butchers, ☎ 01483 574368, 19 Swan Lane, Guildford, Surrey
Menzies, ☎ 01350 727318, 1 Atholl Street, Dunkeld, Tayside
Merediths, ☎ 01706 822922, 34 Bridge Street, Ramsbottom, Lancashire BL0 9AQ
Merlin's Gifts, ☎ 01840 Fore Street, Tintagel, Cornwall PL34 0DA
Mettricks, ☎ 01457 852239, 20 High Street West, Glossop, Derbyshire SK13 8BH
Michael's Delicatessen, ☎ 01332 360757, Shop 27, Market Hall, Derby, Derbyshire DE1 2DB
Michael Kirk Butchers, ☎ 01902 225064, 56 Wool Rack Street, Wolverhampton, West Midlands WV1 3NA
Middle Farm Shop, ☎ 01323 811411, Firle, Lewes, Sussex BN8 6LJ
Mike Sellers, ☎ 01751 472249, Stamfield Hall Farm, Pickering, Yorkshire YO18 8LX
Milletts Farm Shop, ☎ 01865 391625, Kingston Road, Frilford Heath, Oxfordshire OX13 5NX
Mise-en-Place, ☎ 0171 2284392, 21 Battersea Rise, Battersea, London SW11 1HG
Miura Foods, ☎ 0181 5498076, 44 Coombe Road, Kingston-upon-Thames, Surrey KT2 7AE
Mole Valley Farmers, ☎ 0176 9573431, Station Road, South Molton, Devon EX36 3BH
Molly's Wholefoods, ☎ 0191 3862216, 11 Front Street, Framwell Gate Moor, Durham DH1 5EJ
Monkton Farmshop, ☎ 01432 820579, Ocle Pychard, Herefordshire HR1 3QQ
Mooreland Foods, ☎ 01625 548499, Vost Farm, Morley Green, Wilmslow, Cheshire SK9 5NU
Moorlynch Vineyard, ☎ 01458 210393, Moorlynch, Bridgwater, Somerset TA7 9DD
Moortown Deli, ☎ 0113 2682943, 410 Harrogate Road, Leeds, Yorkshire LS17 6PY
Morris & Keen Delicatessan, ☎ 01222 490358, 57 Wellfield Road, Roath Park, Cardiff, Glamorgan CF2 3PA
Mortimer & Bennett, ☎ 0181 995 4145, 33 Turnham Green Terrace, London W4 1RG
Mountstevens Ltd, ☎ 01225 312467, 36 Moorland Road, Oldfield Park, Bath, Avon BA2 3PN
Mountstevens Ltd, ☎ 01225 466158, 11 Westgate Street, Bath, Avon BA11 1EQ
Mr Christians, ☎ 0171 229 0501, 11 Elgin Crescent, London W11 2JA
Mr Soden, Banbury Market, Banbury, Oxfordshire
Mrs Bumbles, ☎ 0993 822209, 31 Lower High Street, Burford, Oxfordshire OX18 4RN
Mull Crafts, ☎ 01680 812 487, The Pierhead, Craignure, Isle of Mull, Argyll & the Islands PA65 6AY
Munchies, ☎ 01222 711618, Unit 3, Windsor Arcade, Penarth, Glamorgan EH10 3DG
Murgatroyds, ☎ 01420 477727, The Forest Centre, Bordon, Surrey GU35 0TN
Mylor Stores, ☎ 01326 373615, Mylor, Falmouth, Cornwall TR11 5NA
N.H. Creber Ltd, ☎ 01822 612266, 48 Brook Street, Tavistock, Devon PL19 0BH

1657 Chocolate House, ☎ 01539 740702, 54 Branthwaite Brow, Kendal, Cumbria LA9 9XX

The Alba Smokehouse Seafood Trailer, Inveraray Pier, Inveraray, Argyll

The Bakehouse, ☎ 01263 823132, 12 Station Road, Sherringham, Norfolk NR26 8RE

The Barn Shop, ☎ 01233 740237, Canterbury Road, Challock, Ashford, Kent TN25 4DA

The Barn Shop, ☎ 01539 560426, Lower Sizergh Farm, Sizergh, Cumbria LA8 8AE

The Beer Shop, ☎ 0171 739 3701, 8 Pitfield Street, London N1 6HA

The Big Apple, ☎ 0117 986 5824, 45 Holmoak Road, Keynsham, nr Bristol, Avon BS18 2RZ

The Burford Garden Co., ☎ 01993 823117, Shilton Road, Burford, Oxfordshire OX18 4PA

The Butler's Choice, ☎ 01225 446001, 7 Pulteney Bridge, Bath, Avon BA2 4AX

The Cheddar Valley Cheese Depot, ☎ 01364 42882/743113, The Gorge, Cheddar, Somerset BS27 3QE

The Cheese and Wine Shop, ☎ 01631 64409, 112 Geroge Street, Oban, Strathclyde PA34 5NN

The Cheese Shop, ☎ 01273 601129, 17 Kensington Gardens, Brighton, Sussex BN1 4AL

The Cheese Shop, ☎ 01244 346240, 116 Northgate Street, Chester, Cheshire CH1 2HT

The Cheese Shop, ☎ 01765 635445, Lightwater Valley Theme Park, North Stainley, nr Ripon, Yorkshire HG4 3HT

The Cheese Shop, ☎ 01250 872493, Westfield, Blairgowrie, Rattray, Tayside PH10 7HY

The Cheeseboard, ☎ 0181 305 0401, 26 Royal Hill, Greenwich, London SE10 8RT

The Chocolate Box, ☎ 01899 221167, 129 High Street, Biggar, Strathclyde ML12 6DL

The Chocolate Shop, ☎ 01536 203685, Corby Old Village, Corby, Northamptonshire NN17 1AY

The Conran Shop, ☎ 0171 589 7401, 81 Fulham Road, London SW19 3XD

The Cooks' Cupboard, ☎ 01349 854404, 86 High Street, Invergordon, Rosshire, Highlands & Islands IV19 1HP

The County Stores, ☎ 01823 272235, 52 North Street, Taunton, Somerset TA1 1ND

The Dales Kitchen Tearoom, ☎ 01756 753077, 51 Main Street, Grassington, Yorkshire BD23 5AA

The Deli, ☎ 0161 903 9330, 2 The Square, Hale Barnes, Altrincham, Cheshire WA15 8ST

The Deli, Salford, Manchester

The Delicatessen & Wine Shop, ☎ 01653 694448, 23 Wheelgate, Malton, Yorkshire YO17 0HT

The English Farm Cider Centre, ☎ 01323 811411, Middle Farm, Firle, nr Lewes, Sussex BN8 6LJ

The Farmer's Dairy, ☎ 01463 233097, 4 Lochalsh Road, Inverness, Highlands & Islands IV3 6HU

The Farmhouse Kitchen, ☎ 01943 468270, 16 Market Place, Otley, Yorkshire LS21 5AQ

The Fine Cheese Company, ☎ 01225 483407, 29/31 Walcot Street, Bath, Avon BA1 5BN

The Flourbag, ☎ 01367 252322, Burford Street, Lechlade, Gloucestershire GL7 3AP

The Game Larder, ☎ 01372 749000, Rushett Farm, Leatherhead Road, Chessington, Surrey KT9 2NQ

The General Wine Co, ☎ 01428 722201, 25 Station Road, Liphook, Hampshire GU30 7DW

The Good Cheese & Nut Bar, Unit 8, The Market Under The Clock, Shrewsbury, Shropshire

The Good Earth, ☎ 01749 678600, 4 Priory Road, Wells, Somerset BA5 1SY

The Good Food Shop, 9 Scarcroft Road, York, Yorkshire YO2 1ND

The Good Life, ☎ 01736 793938, Tregunna Hill, St Ives, Cornwall TR26 1SE

The Grain Shop, ☎ 0171 229 5571, 269a Portobello Road, London W11 1LR

The Granary Restaurant, ☎ 01295 250628, 6 Butchers Row, Banbury, Oxfordshire OX16 8JH

The Haelan Centre, ☎ 0181 340 4258, 41 The Broadway, Crouch End, London N8 8DT

The Health & Diet Centre, ☎ 0181 318 0448, 31 Tranquil Vale, Blackheath, London SE3 0TA

The Health Food Shop, ☎ 01203 315627, 59 Mill Street, Bedworth, Warwickshire CV12 8JX

The Heather Hen, Glenegedale, Isle of Islay, Argyll & the Islands

The Horsham Cheese Shop, ☎ 01403 254272, 20 Carfax , Horsham, Sussex RH12 1EB

The House of Albert Roux, ☎ 0171 730 4175, 229 Ebury Street, London SW1W 8UT

The House of Bruar, ☎ 01796 483236, by Blair Atholl, Perthshire PH18 5TW

The Island Cheese Company, ☎ 0131 2266215, Home Farm, Brodick, Isle of Arran, Highlands & Islands KA27 8DD

The Loch Fyne Oyster Bar, ☎ 01832 280298, The Old Dairy, Elton, nr Petersborough, Cambridgeshire PE8 6SH

The Loch Fyne Seafood Bar, ☎ 01159 508481, 17 King Street, Nottingham, Nottinghamshire NG1 2AY

The Master's Pantry, ☎ 01386 852155, 16 The Huntings, Church Close, Broadway, Worcestershire WR12 7AH

The Mill Shop, Lower Slaughter, Gloucestershire

The Moffat Toffee Shop, ☎ 01683 220032, High Street, Moffat, Dumfries and Galloway DG10 9QU

The Mousetrap, ☎ 01432 353423, 1 Bewell Square, Leominster, Hereford, Herefordshire HR4 0BB

The Mousetrap, ☎ 01603 614083, 2 St Gregory's Alley, Norwich Norfolk, NR2 1ER

The Nadder Catering Food Shop, ☎ 01722 744707, 4 North Street, Wilton, Salisbury, Wiltshire SP2 0HE

The National Trust Shop, ☎ 01392 881691, Killerton House, Broadclyst, Exeter, Devon EX5 3LE

The Norfolk Cake Company, ☎ 01603 34229, 173 Plumstead Road, Norwich, Norfolk NR1 4AB

The Nutmeg House, ☎ 01278 457823, 8–10 Clare Street, Bridgwater, Somerset TA6 3EN

The Old Bakehouse, ☎ 01295 262681, 48 Parsons Street, Banbury, Oxfordshire OX16 8NB

The Old Brewery Shop, ☎ 01222 395828, 47–49 St Mary's Street, Cardiff, Glamorgan CF1 1SP

The Old Farmhouse Bakery, ☎ 01235 831230, Steventon, nr Abingdon, Oxfordshire OX13 6RP

The Olive Tree, ☎ 01721 723461, 7 High Street, Peebles, Borders EH45 8AG

The Organic Shop, ☎ 01451 831004, The Square, Stow-on-the-Wold, Gloucestershire GL54 1AB

The Oxford Cheese Shop, ☎ 01865 721420, 17 The Covered Market, Oxford, Oxfordshire OX1 3DW

The Real Cheese Shop, ☎ 0181 9470564, 96A High Street, Wimbledon, London SW19 5EG

The Real Cheese Shop, ☎ 01670 505555, 6 Oldgate, Morpeth, Northumberland NE61 1LX

The Real Food Store, ☎ 0171 2661162, 14 Clifton Road, Maida Vale, London W9 1SS

The Rosslyn Hill Delicatessen, ☎ 0171 794 9210, 56 Rosslyn Hill, London NW3 1ER

The Salmon Shop, ☎ 01403 865110, The Old Post Office, West Grinstead, Sussex

The Sausage Shop, ☎ 01225 318300, 7 Green Street, Bath, Avon BA1 2JY

The Scottish Co-op, ☎ 01496 8102011, Bowmore, Isle of Islay, Argyll & the Islands PA43 7JY

The Scottish Salmon and Seafood Centre, ☎ 0185 26202 FAX 0185 26262, Kinliver, by Oban, Argyll & the Islands PA34 4QS

The Square Peg, ☎ 01546 2445, 9 Colchester Square, Lochgilphead, Argyll & the Islands PA31 8LH

The Stow Wholefood Shop, ☎ 01451 832194, The Square, Stow on the Wold, Gloucestershire

The Teviot Game Fare Smokery, ☎ 01835 850253, Kirkbank House, Eckford, Kelso, Borders TD5 8LE

The Toby Inn, ☎ 01278 722202, Chilton Polden, Bridgwater, Somerset TA7 9AH

The Tomatin Distillery Co.Ltd, ☎ 01808 511234, Tomatin, Highlands IV13 7YT

The Weald & Downland Open Air Museum, ☎ 01243 811348, Singleton, nr Chichester, Sussex PO18 0EU

The Weald Smokery, ☎ 01580 879601, Mount Farm, Hawkhurst Road, Flimwell, Sussex TN5 7QL

The Whisky Shop, ☎ 01522 53784, 87 Bailgate, Lincoln, Lincolnshire LN1 3AR

The Wine Shop, ☎ 01865 243393, 8 The Square, Westway Shopping Centre, Botley, Oxford, Oxfordshire OX2 9LH

The Wine Shop & Delicatessen, ☎ 01653 694448, Wheelgate, Malton, Yorkshire YO17 0HT

The Wine Society, ☎ 01438 741177, Gunnelswood Road, Stevenage, Hertfordshire SG1 2BG

Thorogood Butchers, ☎ 0181 567 0339, 113 Northfield Avenue, Ealing, London W13 9QR

Ticklemore Cheese Shop, ☎ 01803 865926, 1 Ticklemore Street, Totnes, Devon TQ9 5DB

Tintagel Supermarket, ☎ 01840 770323, Bossiney Road, Tintagel, Cornwall PL34 0AJ

Tobermory Fish Farm, ☎ 01688 302120, Main Street, Tobermory, Isle of Mull, Argyll & the Islands PA75 6NU

Todds Vintrey, ☎ 01892 527335, The Pantiles,Tunbridge Wells, Kent, TN2 5TD

Tom's, ☎ 0171 221 8818, 226 Westbourne Grove, London W11 2RH

Top Drawer, ☎ 01874 622601, 30 High Street, Brecon, Powys LD3 7AN

Top of the Crops, ☎ 01458 834802, 54 High street, Glastonbury, Somerset BA6 9DY

Tower Farmshop, Leland St Lawrence, Somerset

Traiteur Pagnol, ☎ 0171 483 0401, 170 Regents Park Road, Primrose Hill, London NW1 8XN

Treehouse, ☎ 01970 615791, Great Dark Gate Street, Aberystwych, Dyfed SY23 2LJ

Trenchermans Deli, ☎ 013798 52719, 22–24 The Thoroughfare, Harleston, Norfolk IP20 9AU

Trenchermans of Dorset, ☎/FAX 01935 32857 FAX 01935 32857, The Old Dairy, Compton Pack,Sherborne, Dorset DT9 4QU

Tully's Farm Shop., ☎ 01342 426789, Turner's Hill, Sussex RH10 4PE

Udale Speciality Foods, ☎ 015396 20432, 37 Main Street, Sedbergh, Cumbria LA10 5BL

University Visitors' Centre, ☎ 01224 273702, King's College, Old Aberdeen, Grampian AB9 2UB

Valvona & Crolla, ☎ 0131 556 6066 FAX 0131 556 1668, 19 Elm Row, Edinburgh, Lothian,EH7 4AA

Victoria Wine Co., ☎ 01803 862 362, 22 High Street, Totnes, Devon TQ9 5RY

Village Deli, ☎ 01872 553070, 6A Churchtown, St Agnes, Cornwall TR5 0QU

Villandry, ☎ 0171 487 3816, 89 Marylebone High Street, London W1M 3DE

Vin Sullivan, ☎ 01873 858989, 14 Frogmore Street, Abergavenny, Gwent,NP7 5AE

Vivian's, ☎ 0181 940 3600, 2 Worple Way, Richmond, Surrey TW10 6DF

W. A. Baxter & Sons, ☎ 01343 820393, Fochabers, Morayshire, Grampian IV32 7LD

W. C. Rowe (Falmouth) Ltd, ☎ 01209 713717, 65 Trelowarren Street, Camborne, Cornwall

W. C. Rowe (Falmouth) Ltd, ☎ 01326 316552, 2 The Kings Hotel, Falmouth, Cornwall

W. C. Rowe (Falmouth) Ltd, ☎ 01872 261281, 22 Victoria Square, Truro, Cornwall

W. Eaden Lilley & Co Ltd, ☎ 01223 358822, 12 Market Street, Cambridge, Cambridgeshire CB2 3PD

W. J. Morris & Sons, ☎ 01844 344025, 4 High Street, Princes Risborough, Buckinghamshire HP27 0AX

W. Stares Ltd, ☎ 01794 513113, The Cornmarket, Romsey, Hampshire

W. Watson & Son, ☎ 0141 8892691, 39 High Street, Paisley, Glasgow, Strathclyde PA1 2AF

Wainhouse Country Store, ☎ 01840 230554,St Genny's, Bude, Cornwall EX23 0AZ

Walker, ☎ 01453 835385, 15 George Street, Nailsworth, Gloucestershire GL6 1AW

Walmsleys Butchers, ☎ 01706 822269, 31 Bridge Street, Ramsbottom, Lancashire BL0 9AD

Warehouse 4, ☎ 01496 810672, Bowmore, Isle of Islay, Argyll & the Islands

Warminster Fish And Fruit, ☎ 01985 212138, 49 High Street, Warminster, Wiltshire BA12 9AQ

Watty's Delicatessen, ☎ 01392 56654, 16 Catherine Street, Exeter, Devon EX1 1EU

Wavells, ☎ 01983 760219, The Square, Yarmouth, Isle of Wight PO41 0NP

Wayne Spiers, ☎ 01332 862249, 38 Market Place, Melbourne, Derbyshire DE73 1DS

Wealden Wholefoods, ☎ 01892 783065, High Street, Wadhurst, Sussex TN5 6AA

Wells Stores, ☎ 01235 535978, 29 Stert Street, Abingdon, Oxfordshire OX14 3JF

Welsh Folk Museum, ☎ 01222 569441, St Fagans, Cardiff, Glamorgan CF5 6XB

Welsh Food Promotions, ☎ 0222 640456, CBTC, Senghennydd Road,Cardiff, Glamorgan CF2 4AY

Wensleydale Creamery, ☎ 01969 667664 FAX 01969 667638, Gayle Lane, Hawes, Yorkshire DL8 3RN

West Lea Farm Shop, ☎ 01962 732476, Alresford, Hampshire SO24 0QP

What's For Dinner?, ☎ 01491 412128, 23 Market Place, Henley-on-Thames, Oxfordshire RG9 2AA

Whibleys, ☎ 01483 893450, High Street, Bramley, Surrey GU5 0HE

White Hall Delicatessen, ☎ 01398 23090, 19 High Street, Dulverton, Somerset TA22 9HB

Whitehall Garden Centre Ltd, ☎ 01249 730204, Lacock, Chippenham, Wiltshire SN15 2LZ

Whites, ☎ 01962 840805 FAX 01962 841924, 31 The Square, Winchester, Hampshire SO23 9EX

Wholefood, ☎ 0171 935 3924, 24 Paddington Street, London W1M 4DR

Wild Harvest Ltd., ☎ 0171 498 5397, 31 The London Stone Business Estate, Broughton Street, Batttersea, London SW8 3QR

Wild Oats, ☎ 0171 229 1063, 210 Westbourne Grove, London W11 2RH

Wild Oats Wholefoods, ☎ 0117 9731 967, 11 Lower Redland Road, Bristol, Avon BS6 6TB

Willey Mill Trout Farm, ☎ 01252 715481, Alton Road, Farnham, Surrey GU10 5EL

William Baldock, Cooked Meat Delicatesen, ☎ 01633 257312, 18–21 High Street, Market Hall, Newport, Gwent NP9 1DD

William Watson

William's Kitchen Ltd., ☎ 01453 835507, 3 Fountain Street, Nailsworth, Gloucestershire GL6 0BL

Willian Farm Shop, ☎ 01462 480828, Willian, Letchworth, Hertfordshire SG6 2AH

Wiltons, ☎ 01703 282006, 67 The High Street, Lyndhurst, Hampshire SO43 7BE

With Love, ☎ 0181 876 5443, 30 Sheen Lane, London SW14 8LW

Woolea Ltd, ☎ 01458 841378, Clarks Village (Unit 5), Street, Somerset BA16 0BB

Wright Wine Co, ☎ 0176 794175, The Old Smithy, Raikes Road, Skipton, Yorkshire BD23 1NP

Wyevale Garden Centres

Yaohan UK \ d, ☎ 0181 200 0009, 399 Edware Road, Colindale, London, NW9 0JJ

Ye Olde Tuck Shoppe, 9 Market Street, Rye, Sussex RN31 7LA

York Beer Shop, ☎ 01904 647136,28 Sandringham Street, Fishergate, York, Yorkshire YO1 4BA